PEARSON ALWAYS LEARNING

Mathematical Measurement and Literacy

Custom Edition II

Taken from:
Mathematics for the Trades: A Guided Approach, Tenth Edition
by Hal M. Saunders and Robert A. Carman

Thinking Mathematically, Sixth Edition
by Robert Blitzer

Cover Art: Courtesy of Photodisc/Getty Images

Taken from:

Thinking Mathematically, Sixth Edition
by Robert Blitzer

New York, New York 10013

Mathematics for the Trades: A Guided Approach, Tenth Edition
by Hal M. Saunders and Robert A. Carman

New York, New York 10013

This special edition published in cooperation with Pearson Learning Solutions.

Pearson Learning Solutions, 501 Boylston Street, Suite 900, Boston, MA 02116
A Pearson Education Company
www.pearsoned.com

Printed in the United States of America

000200010271970709

AL

ISBN 10: 1-323-16431-6
ISBN 13: 978-1-323-16431-0

Contents

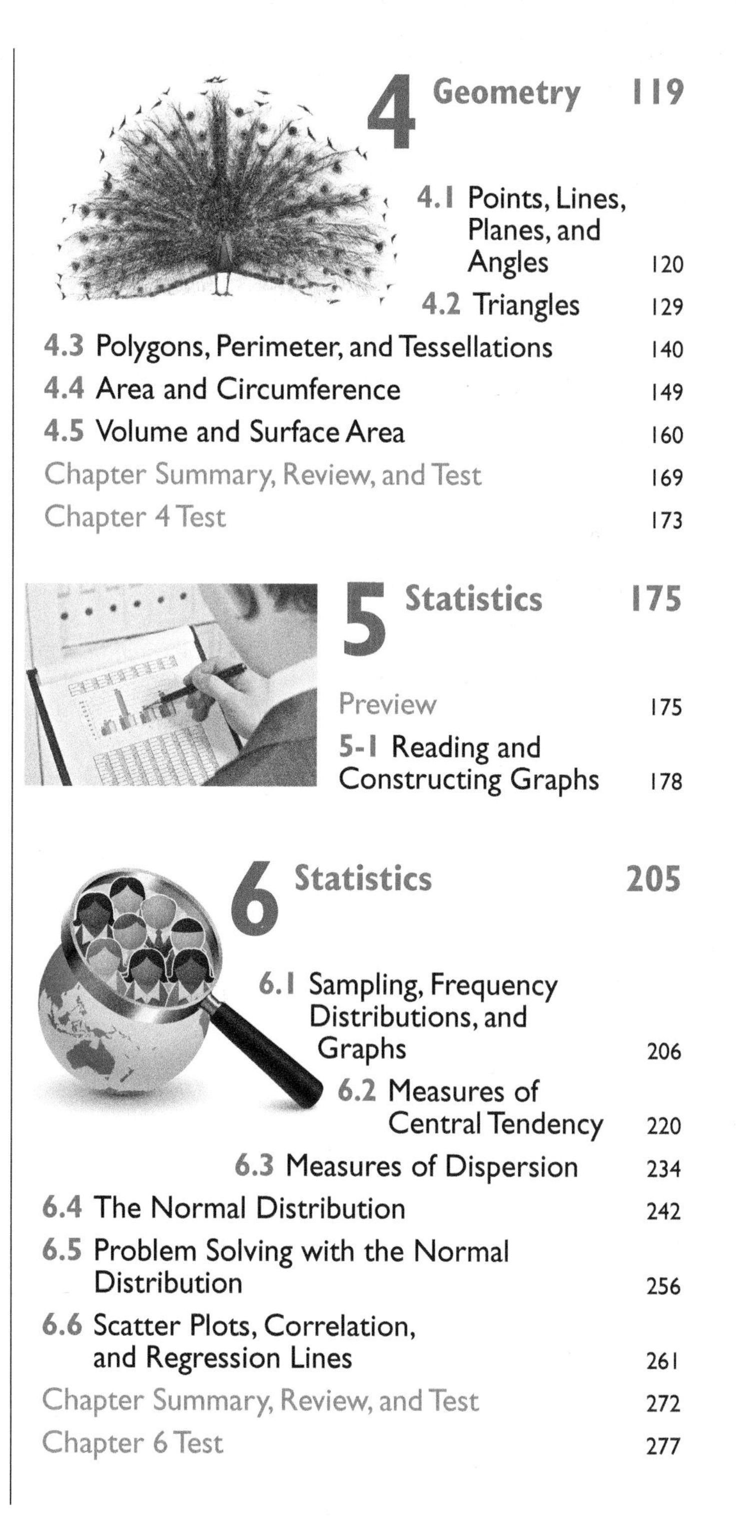

Chapters 1, 3, 4, 6, and 7 taken from *Thinking Mathematically*, Sixth Edition by Robert Blitzer

Chapters 2 and 5 taken from *Mathematics for the Trades: A Guided Approach*, Tenth Edition by Hal M. Saunders and Robert A. Carman

1

Problem Solving and Critical Thinking

HOW WOULD YOUR LIFESTYLE CHANGE IF A GALLON OF GAS COST $9.15? OR IF THE PRICE OF A staple such as milk was $15? That's how much those products would cost if their prices had increased at the same rate college tuition has increased since 1980.

TUITION AND FEES AT FOUR-YEAR COLLEGES

	School Year Ending 2000	School Year Ending 2010
Public	$3362	$7020
Private	$15,518	$26,273

Source: The College Board

If these trends continue, what can we expect for the rest of this decade and beyond? We can answer this question by using estimation techniques that allow us to represent the data mathematically. With such representations, called *mathematical models*, we can gain insights and predict what might occur in the future on a variety of issues, ranging from college costs to global warming.

Here's where you'll find these applications:

Mathematical models involving college costs are developed in Example 8 and Check Point 8 of Section 1.2. In Exercises 51 and 52 in Exercise Set 1.2, you will approach our climate crisis mathematically by developing models for data related to global warming.

1.1 Inductive and Deductive Reasoning

WHAT AM I SUPPOSED TO LEARN?

After you have read this section, you should be able to:

1 Understand and use inductive reasoning.
2 Understand and use deductive reasoning.

ONE OF THE NEWER FRONTIERS OF MATHEMATICS SUGGESTS that there is an underlying order in things that appear to be random, such as the hiss and crackle of background noises as you tune a radio. Irregularities in the heartbeat, some of them severe enough to cause a heart attack, or irregularities in our sleeping patterns, such as insomnia, are examples of chaotic behavior. Chaos in the mathematical sense does not mean a complete lack of form or arrangement. In mathematics, chaos is used to describe something that appears to be random but is not actually random. The patterns of chaos appear in images like the one shown on the left, called the Mandelbrot set. Magnified portions of this image yield repetitions of the original structure, as well as new and unexpected patterns. The Mandelbrot set transforms the hidden structure of chaotic events into a source of wonder and inspiration.

A magnification of the Mandelbrot set
Richard F. Voss

Many people associate mathematics with tedious computation, meaningless algebraic procedures, and intimidating sets of equations. The truth is that mathematics is the most powerful means we have of exploring our world and describing how it works. The word *mathematics* comes from the Greek word *mathematikos*, which means "inclined to learn." To be mathematical literally means to be inquisitive, open-minded, and interested in a lifetime of pursuing knowledge!

Mathematics and Your Life

A major goal of this book is to show you how mathematics can be applied to your life in interesting, enjoyable, and meaningful ways. The ability to think mathematically and reason with quantitative issues will help you so that you can:

- order and arrange your world by using sets to sort and classify information
- use logic to evaluate the arguments of others and become a more effective advocate for your own beliefs
- understand the relationship between cutting-edge technology and ancient systems of number representation
- put the numbers you encounter in the news, from contemplating the national debt to grasping just how colossal $1 trillion actually is, into perspective
- use mathematical models to gain insights into a variety of issues, including the positive benefits that humor and laughter can have on your life

- use basic ideas about savings, loans, and investments to achieve your financial goals (Chapter 7, Personal Finance)
- use geometry to study the shape of your world, enhancing your appreciation of nature's patterns and beauty
- develop an understanding of the fundamentals of statistics and how these numbers are used to make decisions (Chapter 6, Statistics)
- understand the mathematical paradoxes of voting in a democracy, increasing your ability to function as a more fully aware citizen
- use graph theory to examine how mathematics is used to solve problems in the business world

Mathematics and Your Career

"It is better to take what may seem to be too much math rather than too little. Career plans change, and one of the biggest roadblocks in undertaking new educational or training goals is poor preparation in mathematics. Furthermore, not only do people qualify for more jobs with more math, they are also better able to perform their jobs."

—Occupational Outlook Quarterly

Generally speaking, the income of an occupation is related to the amount of education required. This, in turn, is usually related to the skill level required in language and mathematics. With our increasing reliance on technology, the more mathematics you know, the more career choices you will have.

Mathematics and Your World

Mathematics is a science that helps us recognize, classify, and explore the hidden patterns of our universe. Focusing on areas as different as planetary motion, animal markings, shapes of viruses, aerodynamics of figure skaters, and the very origin of the universe, mathematics is the most powerful tool available for revealing the underlying structure of our world. Within the last 30 years, mathematicians have even found order in chaotic events such as the uncontrolled storm of noise in the nerve cells of the brain during an epileptic seizure.

Inductive Reasoning

1 Understand and use inductive reasoning.

Mathematics involves the study of patterns. In everyday life, we frequently rely on patterns and routines to draw conclusions. Here is an example:

> The last six times I went to the beach, the traffic was light on Wednesdays and heavy on Sundays. My conclusion is that weekdays have lighter traffic than weekends.

This type of reasoning process is referred to as *inductive reasoning*, or *induction.*

INDUCTIVE REASONING

Inductive reasoning is the process of arriving at a general conclusion based on observations of specific examples.

Although inductive reasoning is a powerful method of drawing conclusions, we can never be absolutely certain that these conclusions are true. For this reason, the conclusions are called **conjectures**, **hypotheses**, or educated guesses. A strong inductive argument does not guarantee the truth of the conclusion, but rather provides strong support for the conclusion. If there is just one case for which the conjecture does not hold, then the conjecture is false. Such a case is called a **counterexample**.

EXAMPLE 1 *Finding a Counterexample*

The ten symbols that we use to write numbers, namely 0, 1, 2, 3, 4, 5, 6, 7, 8, and 9, are called **digits**. In each example shown below, the sum of two two-digit numbers is a three-digit number.

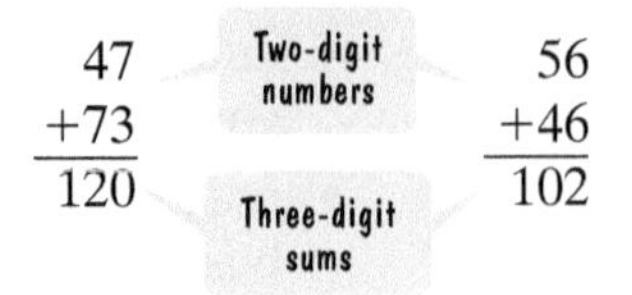

Is the sum of two two-digit numbers always a three-digit number? Find a counterexample to show that the statement

The sum of two two-digit numbers is a three-digit number

is false.

SOLUTION

There are many counterexamples, but we need to find only one. Here is an example that makes the statement false:

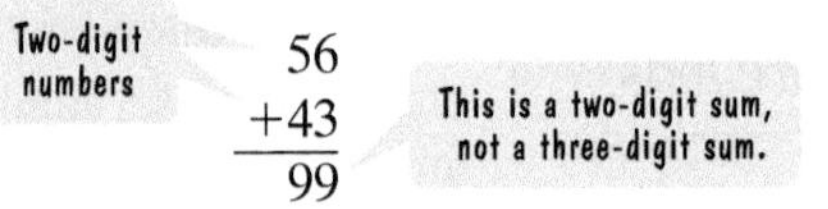

This example is a counterexample that shows the statement

The sum of two two-digit numbers is a three-digit number

is false.

CHECK POINT 1 Find a counterexample to show that the statement

The product of two two-digit numbers is a three-digit number

is false.

GREAT QUESTION!

Why is it so important to work each of the book's Check Points?

You learn best by doing. Do not simply look at the worked examples and conclude that you know how to solve them. To be sure you understand the worked examples, try each Check Point. Check your answer in the answer section before continuing your reading. Expect to read this book with pencil and paper handy to work the Check Points.

Here are two examples of inductive reasoning:

- **Strong Inductive Argument** In a random sample of 380,000 freshmen at 722 four-year colleges, 25% said they frequently came to class without completing readings or assignments (*Source*: National Survey of Student Engagement). We can conclude that there is a 95% probability that between 24.84% and 25.15% of all college freshmen frequently come to class unprepared.

  In Chapter 6, you will learn how observations from a randomly selected group, one in which each member of the population has an equal chance of being selected, can provide probabilities of what is true about an entire population.

- **Weak Inductive Argument** Neither my dad nor my boyfriend has ever cried in front of me. Therefore, men have difficulty expressing their feelings.

  When generalizing from observations about your own circumstances and experiences, avoid jumping to hasty conclusions based on a few observations. Psychologists theorize that we do this - that is, place everyone in a neat category - to feel more secure about ourselves and our relationships to others.

Inductive reasoning is extremely important to mathematicians. Discovery in mathematics often begins with an examination of individual cases to reveal patterns about numbers.

EXAMPLE 2 *Using Inductive Reasoning*

Identify a pattern in each list of numbers. Then use this pattern to find the next number.

a. 3, 12, 21, 30, 39, _____ **b.** 3, 12, 48, 192, 768, _____

c. 3, 4, 6, 9, 13, 18, _____ **d.** 3, 6, 18, 36, 108, 216, _____

"For thousands of years, people have loved numbers and found patterns and structures among them. The allure of numbers is not limited to or driven by a desire to change the world in a practical way. When we observe how numbers are connected to one another, we are seeing the inner workings of a fundamental concept."

—Edward B. Burger and Michael Starbird, *Coincidences, Chaos, and All That Math Jazz*, W.W. Norton and Company, 2005

SOLUTION

a. Because 3, 12, 21, 30, 39, _____ is increasing relatively slowly, let's use addition as the basis for our individual observations.

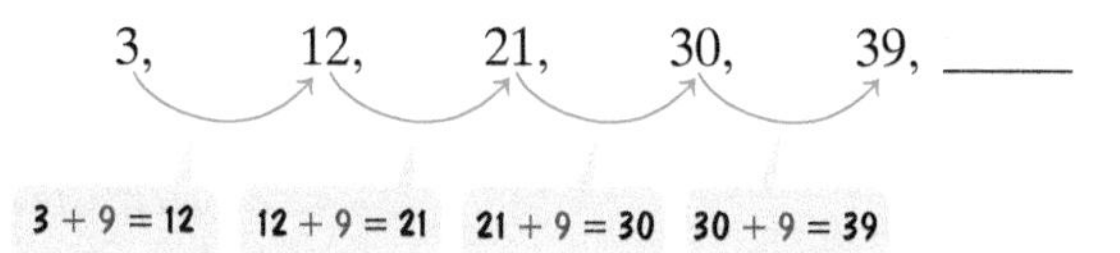

Generalizing from these observations, we conclude that each number after the first is obtained by adding 9 to the previous number. Using this pattern, the next number is $39 + 9$, or 48.

b. Because 3, 12, 48, 192, 768, _____ is increasing relatively rapidly, let's use multiplication as the basis for our individual observations.

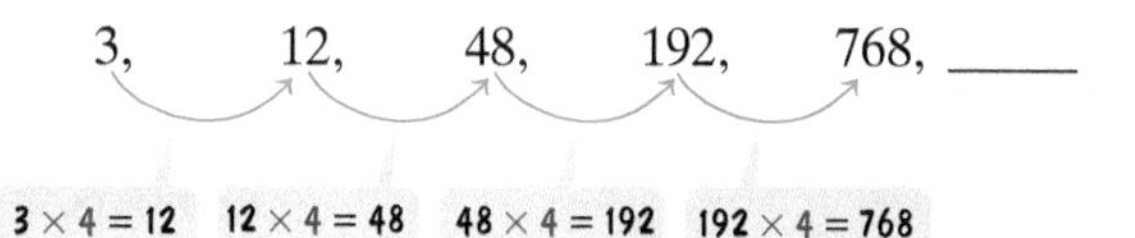

Generalizing from these observations, we conclude that each number after the first is obtained by multiplying the previous number by 4. Using this pattern, the next number is 768×4, or 3072.

c. Because 3, 4, 6, 9, 13, 18, _____ is increasing relatively slowly, let's use addition as the basis for our individual observations.

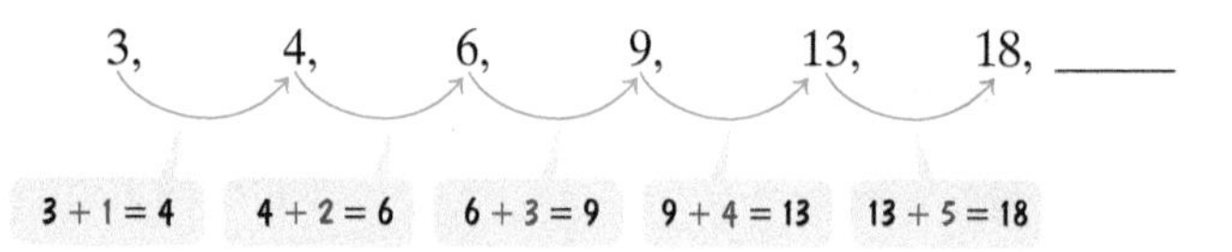

Generalizing from these observations, we conclude that each number after the first is obtained by adding a counting number to the previous number. The additions begin with 1 and continue through each successive counting number. Using this pattern, the next number is $18 + 6$, or 24.

d. Because 3, 6, 18, 36, 108, 216, _____ is increasing relatively rapidly, let's use multiplication as the basis for our individual observations.

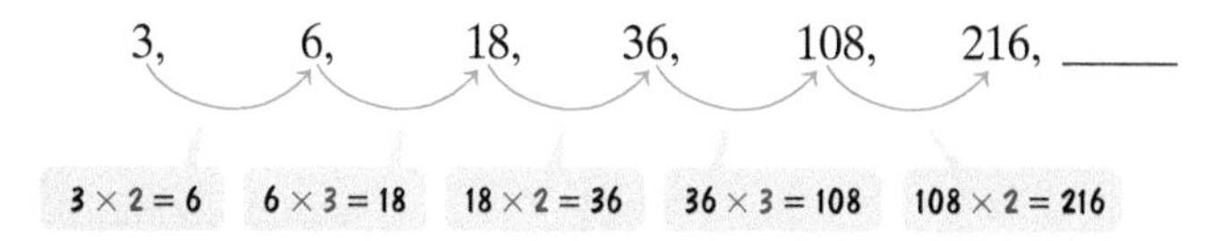

Generalizing from these observations, we conclude that each number after the first is obtained by multiplying the previous number by 2 or by 3. The multiplications begin with 2 and then alternate, multiplying by 2, then 3, then 2, then 3, and so on. Using this pattern, the next number is 216×3, or 648.

CHECK POINT 2 Identify a pattern in each list of numbers. Then use this pattern to find the next number.

a. 3, 9, 15, 21, 27, _____

b. 2, 10, 50, 250, _____

c. 3, 6, 18, 72, 144, 432, 1728, _____

d. 1, 9, 17, 3, 11, 19, 5, 13, 21, _____

In our next example, the patterns are a bit more complex than the additions and multiplications we encountered in Example 2.

EXAMPLE 3 *Using Inductive Reasoning*

Identify a pattern in each list of numbers. Then use this pattern to find the next number.

a. 1, 1, 2, 3, 5, 8, 13, 21, _____ **b.** 23, 54, 95, 146, 117, 98, _____

SOLUTION

a. We begin with 1, 1, 2, 3, 5, 8, 13, 21. Starting with the third number in the list, let's form our observations by comparing each number with the two numbers that immediately precede it.

1,	1,	2,	3,	5,	8,	13,	21, _____
		preceded by 1 and 1: $1 + 1 = 2$	preceded by 1 and 2: $1 + 2 = 3$	preceded by 2 and 3: $2 + 3 = 5$	preceded by 3 and 5: $3 + 5 = 8$	preceded by 5 and 8: $5 + 8 = 13$	preceded by 8 and 13: $8 + 13 = 21$

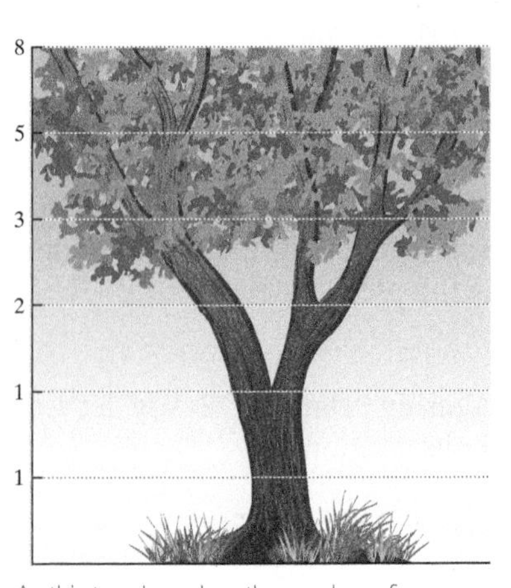

As this tree branches, the number of branches forms the Fibonacci sequence.

Generalizing from these observations, we conclude that the first two numbers are 1. Each number thereafter is the sum of the two preceding numbers. Using this pattern, the next number is $13 + 21$, or 34. (The numbers 1, 1, 2, 3, 5, 8, 13, 21, and 34 are the first nine terms of the *Fibonacci sequence.*)

b. Now, we consider 23, 54, 95, 146, 117, 98. Let's use the digits that form each number as the basis for our individual observations. Focus on the sum of the digits, as well as the final digit increased by 1.

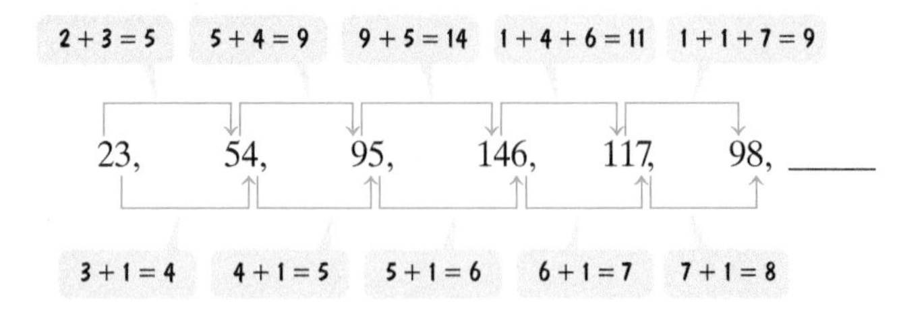

Generalizing from these observations, we conclude that for each number after the first, we obtain the first digit or the first two digits by adding the digits of the previous number. We obtain the last digit by adding 1 to the final digit of the preceding number. Applying this pattern to find the number that follows 98, the first two digits are $9 + 8$, or 17. The last digit is $8 + 1$, or 9. Thus, the next number in the list is 179.

GREAT QUESTION!

Can a list of numbers have more than one pattern?

Yes. Consider the illusion in **Figure 1.1**. This ambiguous figure contains two patterns, where it is not clear which pattern should predominate. Do you see a wine goblet or two faces looking at each other? Like this ambiguous figure, some lists of numbers can display more than one pattern, particularly if only a few numbers are given. Inductive reasoning can result in more than one probable next number in a list.

FIGURE 1.1

Example: 1, 2, 4, _____

Pattern: Each number after the first is obtained by multiplying the previous number by 2. The missing number is 4×2, or 8.

Pattern: Each number after the first is obtained by adding successive counting numbers, starting with 1, to the previous number. The second number is $1 + 1$, or 2. The third number is $2 + 2$, or 4. The missing number is $4 + 3$, or 7.

Inductive reasoning can also result in different patterns that produce the same probable next number in a list.

Example: 1, 4, 9, 16, 25, _____

Pattern: Start by adding 3 to the first number. Then add successive odd numbers, 5, 7, 9, and so on. The missing number is $25 + 11$, or 36.

Pattern: Each number is obtained by squaring its position in the list: The first number is $1^2 = 1 \times 1 = 1$, the second number is $2^2 = 2 \times 2 = 4$, the third number is $3^2 = 3 \times 3 = 9$, and so on. The missing sixth number is $6^2 = 6 \times 6$, or 36.

The numbers that we found in Examples 2 and 3 are probable numbers. Perhaps you found patterns other than the ones we pointed out that might have resulted in different answers.

CHECK POINT 3 Identify a pattern in each list of numbers. Then use this pattern to find the next number.

a. 1, 3, 4, 7, 11, 18, 29, 47, ____

b. 2, 3, 5, 9, 17, 33, 65, 129, ____

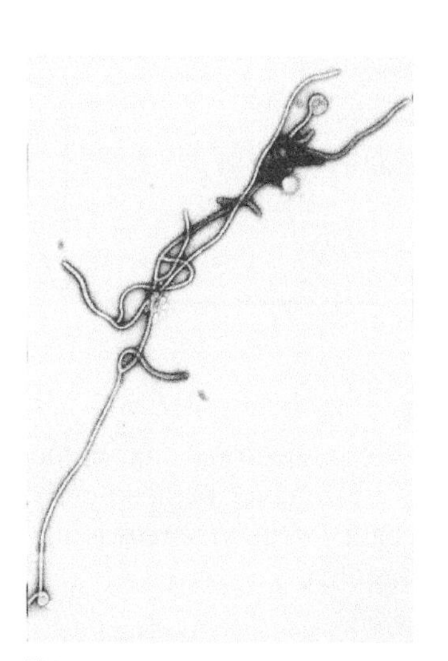

This electron microscope photograph shows the knotty shape of the Ebola virus.

Mathematics is more than recognizing number patterns. It is about the patterns that arise in the world around us. For example, by describing patterns formed by various kinds of knots, mathematicians are helping scientists investigate the knotty shapes and patterns of viruses. One of the weapons used against viruses is based on recognizing visual patterns in the possible ways that knots can be tied.

Our next example deals with recognizing visual patterns.

EXAMPLE 4 *Finding the Next Figure in a Visual Sequence*

Describe two patterns in this sequence of figures. Use the patterns to draw the next figure in the sequence.

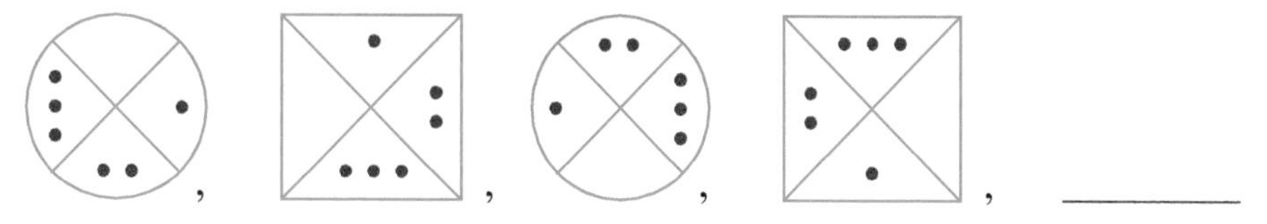

SOLUTION

The more obvious pattern is that the figures alternate between circles and squares. We conclude that the next figure will be a circle. We can identify the second pattern in the four regions containing no dots, one dot, two dots, and three dots. The dots are placed in order (no dots, one dot, two dots, three dots) in a clockwise direction. However, the entire pattern of the dots rotates counterclockwise as we follow the figures from left to right. This means that the next figure should be a circle with a single dot in the right-hand region, two dots in the bottom region, three dots in the left-hand region, and no dots in the top region.

The missing figure in the visual sequence on the previous page, a circle with a single dot in the right-hand region, two dots in the bottom region, three dots in the left-hand region, and no dots in the top region, is drawn in **Figure 1.2.**

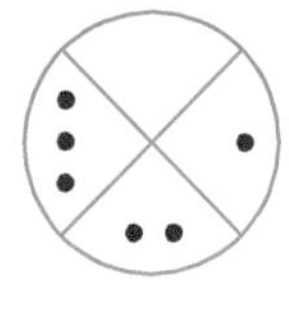

FIGURE 1.2

CHECK POINT 4 Describe two patterns in this sequence of figures. Use the patterns to draw the next figure in the sequence.

Blitzer Bonus

Are You Smart Enough to Work at Google?

In *Are You Smart Enough to Work at Google?* (Little, Brown, and Company, 2012), author William Poundstone guides readers through the surprising solutions to challenging job-interview questions. The book covers the importance of creative thinking in inductive reasoning, estimation, and problem solving. Best of all, Poundstone explains the answers.

Whether you're preparing for a job interview or simply want to increase your critical thinking skills, we highly recommend tackling the puzzles in *Are You Smart Enough to Work at Google?* Here is a sample of two of the book's problems that involve inductive reasoning. We've provided hints to help you recognize the pattern in each sequence. The answers appear in the answer section.

1. Determine the next entry in the sequence.
   SSS, SCC, C, SC, __?__
   Hint: Think of the capital letters in the English alphabet. A is made up of three straight lines. B consists of one straight line and two curved lines. C is made up of one curved line.
2. Determine the next line in this sequence of digits.

```
        1              The first row contains one 1.
      1   1            The second row contains two 1s.
      2   1            The third row contains one 2 and one 1.
    1   2   1   1
  1   1   1   2   2   1
  ?   ?   ?   ?   ?   ?
```

Deductive Reasoning

2 Understand and use deductive reasoning.

We use inductive reasoning in everyday life. Many of the conjectures that come from this kind of thinking seem highly likely, although we can never be absolutely certain that they are true. Another method of reasoning, called *deductive reasoning*, or *deduction*, can be used to prove that some conjectures are true.

DEDUCTIVE REASONING

Deductive reasoning is the process of proving a specific conclusion from one or more general statements. A conclusion that is proved to be true by deductive reasoning is called a **theorem**.

Deductive reasoning allows us to draw a specific conclusion from one or more general statements. On the next page are two examples of deductive reasoning. Notice that in both everyday situations, the general statement from which the conclusion is drawn is implied rather than directly stated.

Everyday Situation	Deductive Reasoning	
One player to another in a Scrabble game: "You have to remove those five letters. You can't use TEXAS as a word."	• All proper names are prohibited in Scrabble. TEXAS is a proper name. Therefore, TEXAS is prohibited in Scrabble.	general statement conclusion
Advice to college freshmen on choosing classes: "Never sign up for a 7 A.M. class. Yes, you did it in high school, but Mom was always there to keep waking you up, and if by some miracle you do make it to an early class, you will sleep through the lecture when you get there." (*Source*: *How to Survive Your Freshman Year*, Hundreds of Heads Books, 2004)	• All people need to sleep at 7 A.M. You sign up for a class at 7 A.M. Therefore, you'll sleep through the lecture or not even make it to class. You'll learn how to prove this conclusion from the general statement in the first line. But is the general statement really true? Can we make assumptions about the sleeping patterns of all people, or are we using deductive reasoning to reinforce an untrue reality assumption?	general statement conclusion

Our next example illustrates the difference between inductive and deductive reasoning. The first part of the example involves reasoning that moves from specific examples to a general statement, illustrating inductive reasoning. The second part of the example begins with the general case rather than specific examples and illustrates deductive reasoning. To begin the general case, we use a letter to represent any one of various numbers. A letter used to represent any number in a collection of numbers is called a **variable**.

A BRIEF REVIEW

In case you have forgotten some basic terms of arithmetic, the following list should be helpful.

Sum:	the result of addition
Difference:	the result of subtraction
Product:	the result of multiplication
Quotient:	the result of division

EXAMPLE 5 *Using Inductive and Deductive Reasoning*

Consider the following procedure:

Select a number. Multiply the number by 6. Add 8 to the product. Divide this sum by 2. Subtract 4 from the quotient.

a. Repeat this procedure for at least four different numbers. Write a conjecture that relates the result of this process to the original number selected.

b. Use the variable n to represent the original number and use deductive reasoning to prove the conjecture in part (a).

SOLUTION

a. First, let us pick our starting numbers. We will use 4, 7, 11, and 100, but we could pick any four numbers. Next we will apply the procedure given in this example to 4, 7, 11, and 100, four individual cases, in **Table 1.1**.

TABLE 1.1 Applying a Procedure to Four Individual Cases

Select a number.	4	7	11	100
Multiply the number by 6.	$4 \times 6 = 24$	$7 \times 6 = 42$	$11 \times 6 = 66$	$100 \times 6 = 600$
Add 8 to the product.	$24 + 8 = 32$	$42 + 8 = 50$	$66 + 8 = 74$	$600 + 8 = 608$
Divide this sum by 2.	$\frac{32}{2} = 16$	$\frac{50}{2} = 25$	$\frac{74}{2} = 37$	$\frac{608}{2} = 304$
Subtract 4 from the quotient.	$16 - 4 = 12$	$25 - 4 = 21$	$37 - 4 = 33$	$304 - 4 = 300$

Because we are asked to write a conjecture that relates the result of this process to the original number selected, let us focus on the result of each case.

Original number selected	4	7	11	100
Result of the process	12	21	33	300

Do you see a pattern? Our conjecture is that the result of the process is three times the original number selected. We have used inductive reasoning.

b. Now we begin with the general case rather than specific examples. We use the variable n to represent any number.

Select a number.	n
Multiply the number by 6.	$6n$ (This means 6 times n.)
Add 8 to the product.	$6n + 8$
Divide this sum by 2.	$\frac{6n + 8}{2} = \frac{6n}{2} + \frac{8}{2} = 3n + 4$
Subtract 4 from the quotient.	$3n + 4 - 4 = 3n$

Using the variable n to represent any number, the result is $3n$, or three times the number n. This proves that the result of the procedure is three times the original number selected for any number. We have used deductive reasoning. Observe how algebraic notation gives us variables to represent the general case.

CHECK POINT 5 Consider the following procedure:

Select a number. Multiply the number by 4. Add 6 to the product. Divide this sum by 2. Subtract 3 from the quotient.

a. Repeat this procedure for at least four different numbers. Write a conjecture that relates the result of this process to the original number selected.

b. Use the variable n to represent the original number and use deductive reasoning to prove the conjecture in part (a).

Concept and Vocabulary Check

GREAT QUESTION!

What am I supposed to do with the exercises in the Concept and Vocabulary Check?

An important component of thinking mathematically involves knowing the special language and notation used in mathematics. The exercises in the Concept and Vocabulary Check, mainly fill-in-the-blank and true/false items, test your understanding of the definitions and concepts presented in each section. **Work all of the exercises in the Concept and Vocabulary Check** regardless of which exercises your professor assigns in the Exercise Set that follows.

Fill in each blank so that the resulting statement is true.

1. The statement $3 + 3 = 6$ serves as a/an __________ to the conjecture that the sum of two odd numbers is an odd number.
2. Arriving at a specific conclusion from one or more general statements is called _______ reasoning.
3. Arriving at a general conclusion based on observations of specific examples is called _______ reasoning.
4. True or False: A theorem cannot have counterexamples. ____

Exercise Set 1.1

GREAT QUESTION!

Any way that I can perk up my brain before working the book's Exercise Sets?

Researchers say the mind can be strengthened, just like your muscles, with regular training and rigorous practice. Think of the book's Exercise Sets as brain calisthenics. If you're feeling a bit sluggish before any of your mental workouts, try this warmup:

In the list below, say the color the word is printed in, not the word itself. Once you can do this in 15 seconds without an error, the warmup is over and it's time to move on to the assigned exercises.

Blue Yellow Red Green Yellow Green Blue Red Yellow Red

Practice Exercises

In Exercises 1–8, find a counterexample to show that each of the statements is false.

1. No U.S. president has been younger than 65 at the time of his inauguration.

2. No singers appear in movies.

3. If a number is multiplied by itself, the result is even.

4. The sum of two three-digit numbers is a four-digit number.

5. Adding the same number to both the numerator and the denominator (top and bottom) of a fraction does not change the fraction's value.

6. If the difference between two numbers is odd, then the two numbers are both odd.

7. If a number is added to itself, the sum is greater than the original number.

8. If 1 is divided by a number, the quotient is less than that number.

In Exercises 9–38, identify a pattern in each list of numbers. Then use this pattern to find the next number. (More than one pattern might exist, so it is possible that there is more than one correct answer.)

9. 8, 12, 16, 20, 24, ____

10. 19, 24, 29, 34, 39, ____

11. 37, 32, 27, 22, 17, ____

12. 33, 29, 25, 21, 17, ____

13. 3, 9, 27, 81, 243, ____

14. 2, 8, 32, 128, 512, ____

15. 1, 2, 4, 8, 16, ____

16. 1, 5, 25, 125, ____

17. 1, 4, 1, 8, 1, 16, 1, ____

18. 1, 4, 1, 7, 1, 10, 1, ____

19. 4, 2, 0, −2, −4, ____

20. 6, 3, 0, −3, −6, ____

21. $\frac{1}{2}, \frac{1}{6}, \frac{1}{10}, \frac{1}{14}, \frac{1}{18}$, ____

22. $1, \frac{1}{2}, \frac{1}{3}, \frac{1}{4}, \frac{1}{5}$, ____

23. $1, \frac{1}{3}, \frac{1}{9}, \frac{1}{27}$, ____

24. $1, \frac{1}{2}, \frac{1}{4}, \frac{1}{8}$, ____

25. 3, 7, 12, 18, 25, 33, ____

26. 2, 5, 9, 14, 20, 27, ____

27. 3, 6, 11, 18, 27, 38, ____

28. 2, 5, 10, 17, 26, 37, ____

29. 3, 7, 10, 17, 27, 44, ____

30. 2, 5, 7, 12, 19, 31, ____

31. 2, 7, 12, 5, 10, 15, 8, 13, ____

32. 3, 9, 15, 5, 11, 17, 7, 13, ____

33. 3, 6, 5, 10, 9, 18, 17, 34, ____

34. 2, 6, 5, 15, 14, 42, 41, 123, ____

35. 64, −16, 4, −1, ____

36. 125, −25, 5, −1, ____

37. $(6, 2), (0, -4), \left(7\frac{1}{2}, 3\frac{1}{2}\right), (2, -2), (3,$ ____ $)$

38. $\left(\frac{2}{3}, \frac{4}{9}\right), \left(\frac{1}{5}, \frac{1}{25}\right), (7, 49), \left(-\frac{5}{6}, \frac{25}{36}\right), \left(-\frac{4}{7},\right.$ ____ $\left.\right)$

In Exercises 39–42, identify a pattern in each sequence of figures. Then use the pattern to find the next figure in the sequence.

39. ____

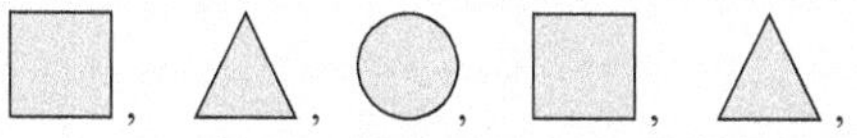

40. ____

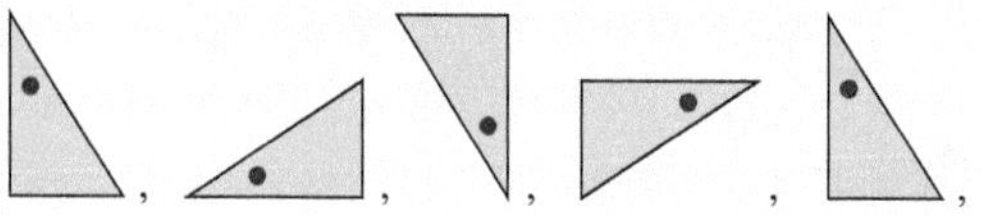

41. ____

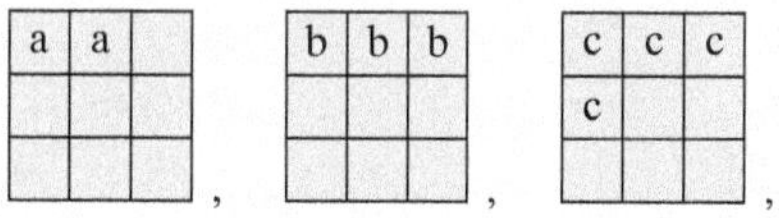

42. ____

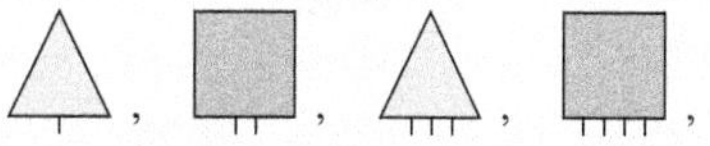

Exercises 43–46 describe procedures that are to be applied to numbers. In each exercise,

a. *Repeat the procedure for four numbers of your choice. Write a conjecture that relates the result of the process to the original number selected.*

b. *Use the variable n to represent the original number and use deductive reasoning to prove the conjecture in part (a).*

43. Select a number. Multiply the number by 4. Add 8 to the product. Divide this sum by 2. Subtract 4 from the quotient.

44. Select a number. Multiply the number by 3. Add 6 to the product. Divide this sum by 3. Subtract the original selected number from the quotient.

45. Select a number. Add 5. Double the result. Subtract 4. Divide by 2. Subtract the original selected number.

46. Select a number. Add 3. Double the result. Add 4. Divide by 2. Subtract the original selected number.

In Exercises 47–52, use inductive reasoning to predict the next line in each sequence of computations. Then use a calculator or perform the arithmetic by hand to determine whether your conjecture is correct.

47.

$$1 + 2 = \frac{2 \times 3}{2}$$

$$1 + 2 + 3 = \frac{3 \times 4}{2}$$

$$1 + 2 + 3 + 4 = \frac{4 \times 5}{2}$$

$$1 + 2 + 3 + 4 + 5 = \frac{5 \times 6}{2}$$

48.
$$3 + 6 = \frac{6 \times 3}{2}$$
$$3 + 6 + 9 = \frac{9 \times 4}{2}$$
$$3 + 6 + 9 + 12 = \frac{12 \times 5}{2}$$
$$3 + 6 + 9 + 12 + 15 = \frac{15 \times 6}{2}$$

49.
$$1 + 3 = 2 \times 2$$
$$1 + 3 + 5 = 3 \times 3$$
$$1 + 3 + 5 + 7 = 4 \times 4$$
$$1 + 3 + 5 + 7 + 9 = 5 \times 5$$

50.
$$\frac{1}{1 \times 2} + \frac{1}{2 \times 3} = \frac{2}{3}$$
$$\frac{1}{1 \times 2} + \frac{1}{2 \times 3} + \frac{1}{3 \times 4} = \frac{3}{4}$$
$$\frac{1}{1 \times 2} + \frac{1}{2 \times 3} + \frac{1}{3 \times 4} + \frac{1}{4 \times 5} = \frac{4}{5}$$

51.
$$9 \times 9 + 7 = 88$$
$$98 \times 9 + 6 = 888$$
$$987 \times 9 + 5 = 8888$$
$$9876 \times 9 + 4 = 88{,}888$$

52.
$$1 \times 9 - 1 = 8$$
$$21 \times 9 - 1 = 188$$
$$321 \times 9 - 1 = 2888$$
$$4321 \times 9 - 1 = 38{,}888$$

Practice Plus

In Exercises 53–54, use inductive reasoning to predict the next line in each sequence of computations. Then use a calculator or perform the arithmetic by hand to determine whether your conjecture is correct.

53.
$$33 \times 3367 = 111{,}111$$
$$66 \times 3367 = 222{,}222$$
$$99 \times 3367 = 333{,}333$$
$$132 \times 3367 = 444{,}444$$

54.
$$1 \times 8 + 1 = 9$$
$$12 \times 8 + 2 = 98$$
$$123 \times 8 + 3 = 987$$
$$1234 \times 8 + 4 = 9876$$
$$12{,}345 \times 8 + 5 = 98{,}765$$

55. Study the pattern in these examples:

$$a^2 \# a^4 = a^{10} \quad a^3 \# a^2 = a^7 \quad a^5 \# a^3 = a^{11}.$$

Select the equation that describes the pattern.

a. $a^x \# a^y = a^{2x+y}$

b. $a^x \# a^y = a^{x+2y}$

c. $a^x \# a^y = a^{x+y+4}$

d. $a^x \# a^y = a^{xy+2}$

56. Study the pattern in these examples:

$$a^5 * a^3 * a^2 = a^5 \quad a^3 * a^7 * a^2 = a^6 \quad a^2 * a^4 * a^8 = a^7.$$

Select the equation that describes the pattern.

a. $a^x * a^y * a^z = a^{x+y+z}$

b. $a^x * a^y * a^z = a^{\frac{xyz}{2}}$

c. $a^x * a^y * a^z = a^{\frac{x+y+z}{2}}$

d. $a^x * a^y * a^z = a^{\frac{xy}{2}+z}$

Application Exercises

In Exercises 57–60, identify the reasoning process, induction or deduction, in each example. Explain your answer.

57. It can be shown that

$$1 + 2 + 3 + \cdots + n = \frac{n(n+1)}{2}.$$

I can use this formula to conclude that the sum of the first one hundred counting numbers, $1 + 2 + 3 + \cdots + 100$, is

$$\frac{100(100+1)}{2} = \frac{100(101)}{2} = 50(101), \text{ or } 5050.$$

58. An HMO does a follow-up study on 200 randomly selected patients given a flu shot. None of these people became seriously ill with the flu. The study concludes that all HMO patients be urged to get a flu shot in order to prevent a serious case of the flu.

59. The data in the graph are from a random sample of 1200 full-time four-year undergraduate college students on 100 U.S. campuses.

The Greatest Problems on Campus

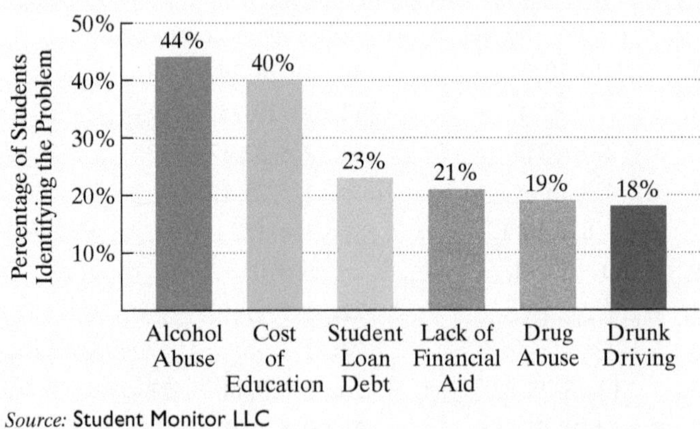

Source: Student Monitor LLC

We can conclude that there is a high probability that approximately 44% of all full-time four-year college students in the United States believe that alcohol abuse is the greatest problem on campus.

60. The course policy states that work turned in late will be marked down a grade. I turned in my report a day late, so it was marked down from B to C.

61. The ancient Greeks studied **figurate numbers**, so named because of their representations as geometric arrangements of points.

Triangular Numbers

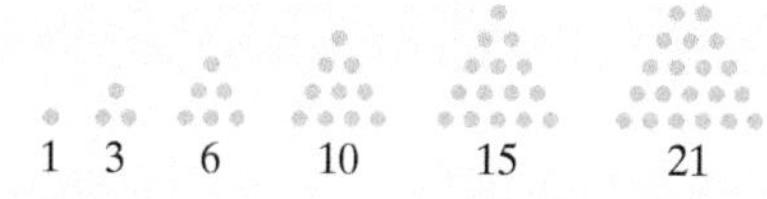

Square Numbers

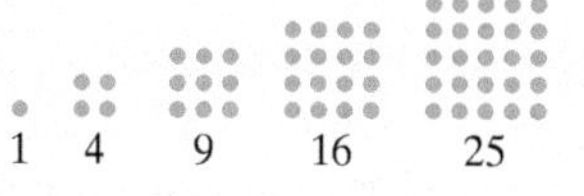

Pentagonal Numbers

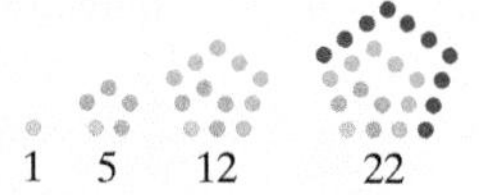

a. Use inductive reasoning to write the five triangular numbers that follow 21.

b. Use inductive reasoning to write the five square numbers that follow 25.

c. Use inductive reasoning to write the five pentagonal numbers that follow 22.

d. Use inductive reasoning to complete this statement: If a triangular number is multiplied by 8 and then 1 is added to the product, a _____ number is obtained.

62. The triangular arrangement of numbers shown below is known as **Pascal's triangle**, credited to French mathematician Blaise Pascal (1623–1662). Use inductive reasoning to find the six numbers designated by question marks.

1
1 1
1 2 1
1 3 3 1
1 4 6 4 1
? ? ? ? ? ?

Writing in Mathematics

Writing about mathematics will help you to learn mathematics. For all writing exercises in this book, use complete sentences to respond to the questions. Some writing exercises can be answered in a sentence; others require a paragraph or two. You can decide how much you need to write as long as your writing clearly and directly answers the question in the exercise. Standard references such as a dictionary and a thesaurus may be helpful.

63. The word *induce* comes from a Latin term meaning *to lead*. Explain what leading has to do with inductive reasoning.

64. Describe what is meant by deductive reasoning. Give an example.

65. Give an example of a decision that you made recently in which the method of reasoning you used to reach the decision was induction. Describe your reasoning process.

Critical Thinking Exercises

Make Sense? *In Exercises 66–69, determine whether each statement makes sense or does not make sense, and explain your reasoning.*

66. I use deductive reasoning to draw conclusions that are not certain, but likely.

67. Additional information may strengthen or weaken the probability of my inductive arguments.

68. I used the data shown in the bar graph, which summarizes a random sample of 752 college seniors, to conclude with certainty that 51% of all graduating college females expect to earn $30,000 or less after graduation.

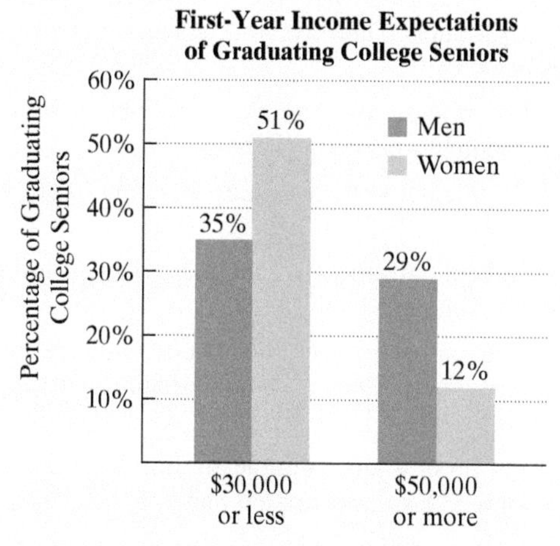

Source: Duquesne University Senior Economic Expectation research survey

69. I used the data shown in the bar graph for Exercise 68, which summarizes a random sample of 752 college seniors, to conclude inductively that a greater percentage of male graduates expect higher first-year income than female graduates.

70. If $(6 - 2)^2 = 36 - 24 + 4$ and $(8 - 5)^2 = 64 - 80 + 25$, use inductive reasoning to write a compatible expression for $(11 - 7)^2$.

71. The rectangle shows an array of nine numbers represented by combinations of the variables a, b, and c.

$a + b$	$a - b - c$	$a + c$
$a - b + c$	a	$a + b - c$
$a - c$	$a + b + c$	$a - b$

a. Determine the nine numbers in the array for $a = 10$, $b = 6$, and $c = 1$. What do you observe about the sum of the numbers in all rows, all columns, and the two diagonals?

b. Repeat part (a) for $a = 12$, $b = 5$, and $c = 2$.

c. Repeat part (a) for values of a, b, and c of your choice.

d. Use the results of parts (a) through (c) to make an inductive conjecture about the rectangular array of nine numbers represented by a, b, and c.

e. Use deductive reasoning to prove your conjecture in part (d).

72. Write a list of numbers that has two patterns so that the next number in the list can be 15 or 20.

73. a. Repeat the following procedure with at least five people. Write a conjecture that relates the result of the procedure to each person's birthday.

Take the number of the month of your birthday (January = 1, February = 2, . . . , December = 12), multiply by 5, add 6, multiply this sum by 4, add 9, multiply this new sum by 5, and add the number of the day on which you were born. Finally, subtract 165.

b. Let M represent the month number and let D represent the day number of any person's birthday. Use deductive reasoning to prove your conjecture in part (a).

Technology Exercises

74. **a.** Use a calculator to find $6 \times 6, 66 \times 66, 666 \times 666$, and 6666×6666.
    b. Describe a pattern in the numbers being multiplied and the resulting products.
    c. Use the pattern to write the next two multiplications and their products. Then use your calculator to verify these results.
    d. Is this process an example of inductive or deductive reasoning? Explain your answer.

75. **a.** Use a calculator to find $3367 \times 3, 3367 \times 6, 3367 \times 9$, and 3367×12.
    b. Describe a pattern in the numbers being multiplied and the resulting products.
    c. Use the pattern to write the next two multiplications and their products. Then use your calculator to verify these results.
    d. Is this process an example of inductive or deductive reasoning? Explain your answer.

Group Exercise

76. Stereotyping refers to classifying people, places, or things according to common traits. Prejudices and stereotypes can function as assumptions in our thinking, appearing in inductive and deductive reasoning. For example, it is not difficult to find inductive reasoning that results in generalizations such as these, as well as deductive reasoning in which these stereotypes serve as assumptions:

    School has nothing to do with life.

    Intellectuals are nerds.

    People on welfare are lazy.

    Each group member should find one example of inductive reasoning and one example of deductive reasoning in which stereotyping occurs. Upon returning to the group, present each example and then describe how the stereotyping results in faulty conjectures or prejudging situations and people.

1.2

WHAT AM I SUPPOSED TO LEARN?

After you have read this section, you should be able to:

1. Use estimation techniques to arrive at an approximate answer to a problem.
2. Apply estimation techniques to information given by graphs.
3. Develop mathematical models that estimate relationships between variables.

Estimation, Graphs, and Mathematical Models

IF PRESENT TRENDS CONTINUE, IS IT POSSIBLE THAT our descendants could live to be 200 years of age? To answer this question, we need to examine data for life expectancy and develop estimation techniques for representing the data mathematically. In this section, you will learn estimation methods that will enable you to obtain mathematical representations of data displayed by graphs, using these representations to predict what might occur in the future.

Estimation

1 Use estimation techniques to arrive at an approximate answer to a problem.

Estimation is the process of arriving at an approximate answer to a question. For example, companies estimate the amount of their products consumers are likely to use, and economists estimate financial trends. If you are about to cross a street, you may estimate the speed of oncoming cars so that you know whether or not to wait before crossing. Rounding numbers is also an estimation method. You might round a number without even being aware that you are doing so. You may say that you are 20 years old, rather than 20 years 5 months, or that you will be home in about a half-hour, rather than 25 minutes.

You will find estimation to be equally valuable in your work for this class. Making mistakes with a calculator or a computer is easy. Estimation can tell us whether the answer displayed for a computation makes sense.

In this section, we demonstrate several estimation methods. In the second part of the section, we apply these techniques to information given by graphs.

Performing computations using rounded numbers is one way to check whether an answer displayed by a calculator or a computer is reasonable. Rounding whole numbers depends on knowing the place values of the digits. (The digits that we use in base ten are 0, 1, 2, 3, 4, 5, 6, 7, 8, and 9. We'll explore other ways of representing numbers, including bases other than ten.) The place that a digit occupies in a number tells us its value in that number. Here is an example using world population at 7:49 A.M. Eastern Time on January 10, 2013.

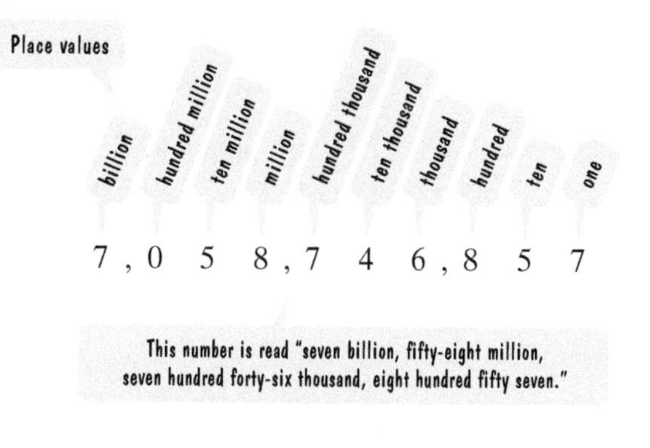

ROUNDING WHOLE NUMBERS

1. Look at the digit to the right of the digit where rounding is to occur.
2. a. If the digit to the right is 5 or greater, add 1 to the digit to be rounded. Replace all digits to the right with zeros.
   b. If the digit to the right is less than 5, do not change the digit to be rounded. Replace all digits to the right with zeros.

The symbol $\approx$ means *is approximately equal to*. We will use this symbol when rounding numbers.

EXAMPLE 1 *Rounding a Whole Number*

Round world population (7,058,746,857) as follows:

a. to the nearest hundred million

b. to the nearest million

c. to the nearest hundred thousand.

SOLUTION

a. 7,058,746,857 $\approx$ 7,100,000,000

Hundred millions digit, where rounding is to occur | Digit to the right is 5. | Add 1 to the digit to be rounded. | Replace all digits to the right with zeros.

World population to the nearest hundred million is seven billion, one-hundred million.

b. 7,058,746,857 $\approx$ 7,059,000,000

Millions digit, where rounding is to occur | Digit to the right is greater than 5. | Add 1 to the digit to be rounded. | Replace all digits to the right with zeros.

World population to the nearest million is seven billion, fifty-nine million.

c. 7,058,746,857 $\approx$ 7,058,700,000

Hundred thousands digit, where rounding is to occur | Digit to the right is less than 5. | Do not change the digit to be rounded. | Replace all digits to the right with zeros.

World population to the nearest hundred thousand is seven billion, fifty-eight million, seven-hundred thousand.

CHECK POINT 1 Round world population (7,058,746,857) as follows:

a. to the nearest billion

b. to the nearest ten thousand.

Rounding can also be applied to decimal notation, used to denote a part of a whole. Once again, the place that a digit occupies tells us its value. Here's an example using the first seven digits of the number π (pi). (We'll have more to say about π, whose digits extend endlessly with no repeating pattern.)

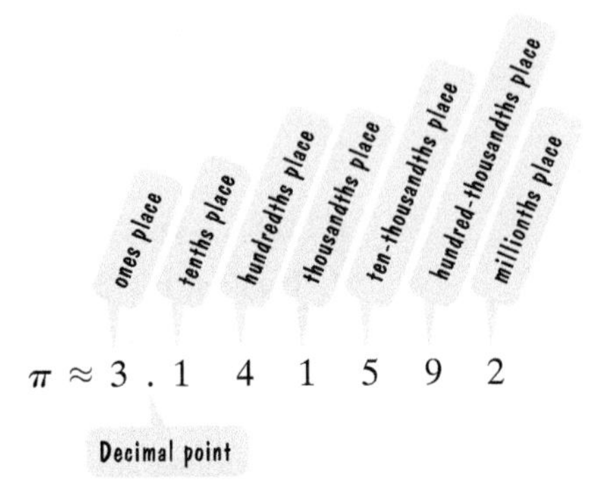

We round the decimal part of a decimal number in nearly the same way that we round whole numbers. The only difference is that we drop the digits to the right of the rounding place rather than replacing these digits with zeros.

EXAMPLE 2 *Rounding the Decimal Part of a Number*

Round 3.141592, the first seven digits of π, as follows:

a. to the nearest hundredth

b. to the nearest thousandth.

SOLUTION

a. $3.141592 \approx 3.14$

Hundredths digit, where rounding is to occur

Digit to the right is less than 5.

Do not change the digit to be rounded.

Drop all digits to the right.

The number π to the nearest hundredth is three and fourteen hundredths.

b. $3.141592 \approx 3.142$

Thousandths digit, where rounding is to occur

Digit to the right is 5.

Add 1 to the digit to be rounded.

Drop all digits to the right.

The number π to the nearest thousandth is three and one hundred forty-two thousandths.

CHECK POINT 2 Round 3.141592, the first seven digits of π, as follows:

a. to the nearest tenth

b. to the nearest ten-thousandth.

Blitzer Bonus

Estimating Support for a Cause

Police often need to estimate the size of a crowd at a political demonstration. One way to do this is to select a reasonably sized rectangle within the crowd and estimate (or count) the number of people within the rectangle. Police then estimate the number of such rectangles it would take to completely fill the area occupied by the crowd. The police estimate is obtained by multiplying the number of such rectangles by the number of demonstrators in the representative rectangle. The organizers of the demonstration might give a larger estimate than the police to emphasize the strength of their support.

EXAMPLE 3 *Estimation by Rounding*

You purchased bread for $2.59, detergent for $2.17, a sandwich for $3.65, an apple for $0.47, and coffee for $5.79. The total bill was given as $18.67. Is this amount reasonable?

SOLUTION

If you are in the habit of carrying a calculator to the store, you can answer the question by finding the exact cost of the purchase. However, estimation can be used to determine if the bill is reasonable even if you do not have a calculator. We will round the cost of each item to the nearest dollar.

Round to the nearest dollar. Use digits in the tenths place to do the rounding.

Bread	$2.59 ≈	$3.00
Detergent	$2.17 ≈	$2.00
Sandwich	$3.65 ≈	$4.00
Apple	$0.47 ≈	$0.00
Coffee	$5.79 ≈	$6.00
		$15.00

The total bill that you were given, $18.67, seems a bit high compared to the $15.00 estimate. You should check the bill before paying it. Adding the prices of all five items gives the true total bill of $14.67.

CHECK POINT 3 You and a friend ate lunch at Ye Olde Cafe. The check for the meal showed soup for $3.40, tomato juice for $2.25, a roast beef sandwich for $5.60, a chicken salad sandwich for $5.40, two coffees totaling $3.40, apple pie for $2.85, and chocolate cake for $3.95.

a. Round the cost of each item to the nearest dollar and obtain an estimate for the food bill.

b. The total bill before tax was given as $29.85. Is this amount reasonable?

EXAMPLE 4 *Estimation by Rounding*

A carpenter who works full time earns $28 per hour.

a. Estimate the carpenter's weekly salary.

b. Estimate the carpenter's annual salary.

SOLUTION

a. In order to simplify the calculation, we can round the hourly rate of $28 to $30. Be sure to write out the units for each number in the calculation. The work week is 40 hours per week, and the rounded salary is $30 per hour. We express this as

$$\frac{40 \text{ hours}}{\text{week}} \text{ and } \frac{\$30}{\text{hour}}.$$

The word *per* is represented by the division bar. We multiply these two numbers to estimate the carpenter's weekly salary. We cancel out units that are identical if they are above and below the division bar.

$$\frac{40 \text{ hours}}{\text{week}} \times \frac{\$30}{\text{hour}} = \frac{\$1200}{\text{week}}$$

Thus, the carpenter earns approximately $1200 per week, written ≈ $1200.

b. For the estimate of annual salary, we may round 52 weeks to 50 weeks. The annual salary is approximately the product of $1200 per week and 50 weeks per year:

$$\frac{\$1200}{\text{week}} \times \frac{50 \text{ weeks}}{\text{year}} = \frac{\$60{,}000}{\text{year}}.$$

Thus, the carpenter earns approximately $60,000 per year, or $60,000 annually, written ≈ $60,000.

GREAT QUESTION!

Is it OK to cancel identical units if one unit is singular and the other is plural?

Yes. It does not matter whether a unit is singular, such as *week*, or plural, such as *weeks*. *Week* and *weeks* are identical units and can be canceled out, as shown on the right.

CHECK POINT 4 A landscape architect who works full time earns $52 per hour.

a. Estimate the landscape architect's weekly salary.

b. Estimate the landscape architect's annual salary.

2 Apply estimation techniques to information given by graphs.

Estimation with Graphs

Magazines, newspapers, and websites often display information using circle, bar, and line graphs. The following examples illustrate how rounding and other estimation techniques can be applied to data displayed in each of these types of graphs.

Circle graphs, also called **pie charts**, show how a whole quantity is divided into parts. Circle graphs are divided into pieces, called **sectors**. **Figure 1.3** shows a circle graph that indicates how Americans disagree as to when "old age" begins.

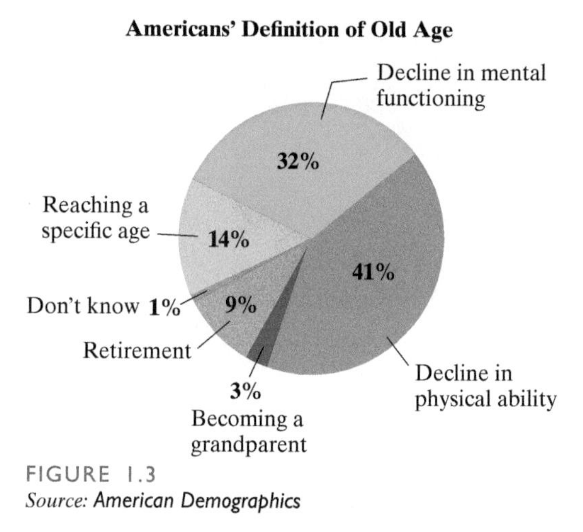

FIGURE 1.3
Source: American Demographics

A BRIEF REVIEW *Percents*

- **Percents** are the result of expressing numbers as part of 100. The word *percent* means *per hundred*. For example, the circle graph in **Figure 1.3** shows that 41% of Americans define old age by a decline in physical ability. Thus, 41 out of every 100 Americans define old age in this manner: $41\% = \frac{41}{100}$.
- To convert a number from percent form to decimal form, move the decimal point two places to the left and drop the percent sign. Example:

$$41\% = 41.\% = 0.41\%$$

Thus, 41% = 0.41.

- Many applications involving percent are based on the following formula:

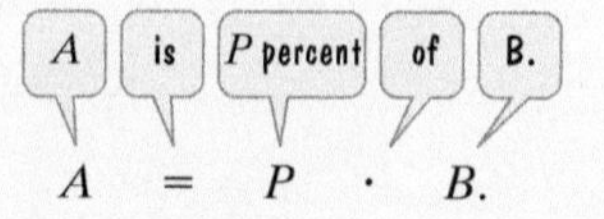

Note that the word *of* implies multiplication.

In our next example, we will use the information in the circle graph on page 18 to estimate a quantity. Although different rounding results in different estimates, the whole idea behind the rounding process is to make calculations simple.

EXAMPLE 5 *Applying Estimation Techniques to a Circle Graph*

According to the U.S. Census Bureau, in 2012, there were 229,937,770 Americans 20 years and older. Assuming the circle graph in **Figure 1.3** is representative of this age group,

a. Use the appropriate information displayed by the graph to determine a calculation that shows the number of Americans 20 years and older who define old age by a decline in physical ability.

b. Use rounding to find a reasonable estimate for this calculation.

SOLUTION

a. The circle graph in **Figure 1.3** indicates that 41% of Americans define old age by a decline in physical ability. Among the 229,937,770 Americans 20 years and older, the number who define old age in this manner is determined by finding 41% of 229,937,770.

The number of Americans 20 and older who define old age by a decline in physical ability | is | 41% | of | the number of Americans 20 and older.

$$= 0.41 \times 229{,}937{,}770$$

b. We can use rounding to obtain a reasonable estimate of $0.41 \times 229{,}937{,}770$.

Round to the nearest ten million.

$$0.41 \times 229{,}937{,}770 \approx 0.4 \times 230{,}000{,}000 = 92{,}000{,}000$$

Round to the nearest tenth.

$$\begin{array}{r} 230{,}000{,}000 \\ \times \quad 0.4 \\ \hline 92{,}000{,}000.0 \end{array}$$

Our answer indicates that approximately 92,000,000 (92 million) Americans 20 years and older define old age by a decline in physical ability.

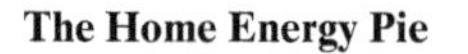
The Home Energy Pie

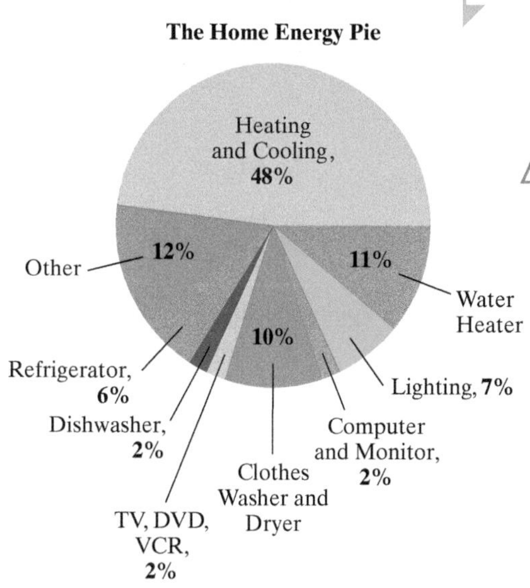

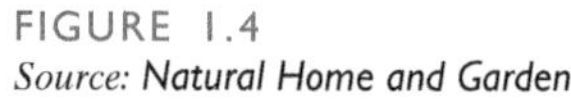
FIGURE 1.4
Source: Natural Home and Garden

CHECK POINT 5 Being aware of which appliances and activities in your home use the most energy can help you make sound decisions that allow you to decrease energy consumption and increase savings. The circle graph in **Figure 1.4** shows how energy consumption is distributed throughout a typical home.

Suppose that last year your family spent $2148.72 on natural gas and electricity. Assuming the circle graph in **Figure 1.4** is representative of your family's energy consumption,

a. Use the appropriate information displayed by the graph to determine a calculation that shows the amount your family spent on heating and cooling for the year.

b. Use rounding to find a reasonable estimate for this calculation.

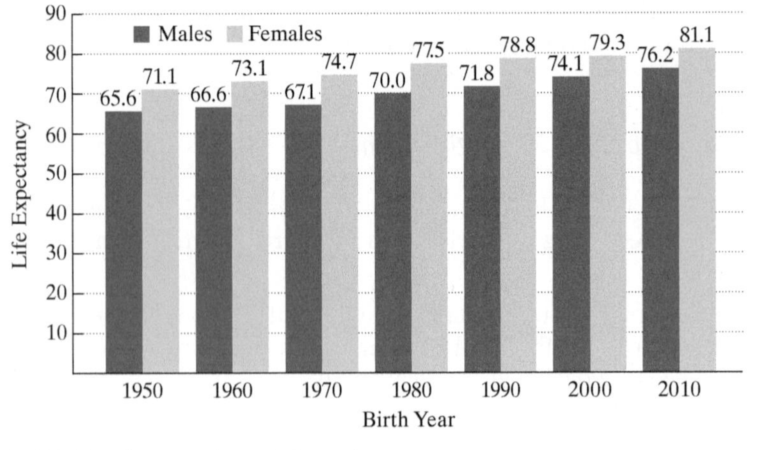

FIGURE 1.5 *Source:* National Center for Health Statistics

Bar graphs are convenient for comparing some measurable attribute of various items. The bars may be either horizontal or vertical, and their heights or lengths are used to show the amounts of different items. **Figure 1.5** is an example of a typical bar graph. The graph shows life expectancy for American men and American women born in various years from 1950 through 2010.

EXAMPLE 6 *Applying Estimation and Inductive Reasoning to Data in a Bar Graph*

Use the data for men in **Figure 1.5** to estimate each of the following:

a. a man's increased life expectancy, rounded to the nearest hundredth of a year, for each subsequent birth year

b. the life expectancy of a man born in 2020.

SOLUTION

a. One way to estimate increased life expectancy for each subsequent birth year is to generalize from the information given for 1950 (male life expectancy: 65.6 years) and for 2010 (male life expectancy: 76.2 years). The average yearly increase in life expectancy is the change in life expectancy from 1950 to 2010 divided by the change in time from 1950 to 2010.

Yearly increase in life expectancy is approximately $\frac{\text{change in life expectancy from 1950 to 2010}}{\text{change in time from 1950 to 2010}}$.

$$\approx \frac{76.2 - 65.6}{2010 - 1950}$$

life expectancy in 2010 minus life expectancy in 1950

Change in time is 2010 − 1950, or 60 years.

$$\approx 0.18$$

Use a calculator. See the Technology box below.

For each subsequent birth year, a man's life expectancy is increasing by approximately 0.18 year.

TECHNOLOGY

Here is the calculator keystroke sequence needed to perform the computation in Example 6(a).

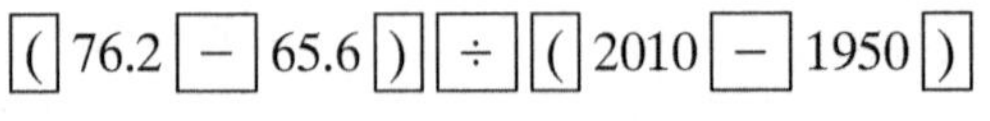

Press = on a scientific calculator or ENTER on a graphing calculator to display the answer. As specified, we round to the nearest hundredth.

The computation shown on a graphing calculator screen

(76.2-65.6)/(2010-1950)

.1766666667 ≈ 0.18

The computation rounded to the nearest hundredth

Hundredths digit, where rounding is to occur

Digit to the right is 6, so add 1 to the digit to be rounded.

b. We can use our computation in part (a) to estimate the life expectancy of an American man born in 2020. The bar graph indicates that men born in 1950 had a life expectancy of 65.6 years. The year 2020 is 70 years after 1950, and life expectancy is increasing by approximately 0.18 year for each subsequent birth year.

Life expectancy for a man born in 2020	is approximately	life expectancy for a man born in 1950	plus	yearly increase in life expectancy	times	the number of years from 1950 to 2020.

$$\approx 65.6 \quad + \quad 0.18 \quad \times \quad 70$$

$$= 65.6 + 12.6 = 78.2$$

An American man born in 2020 will have a life expectancy of approximately 78.2 years.

CHECK POINT 6 Use the data for women in **Figure 1.5** to estimate each of the following:

a. a woman's increased life expectancy, rounded to the nearest hundredth of a year, for each subsequent birth year

b. the life expectancy, to the nearest tenth of a year, of a woman born in 2050.

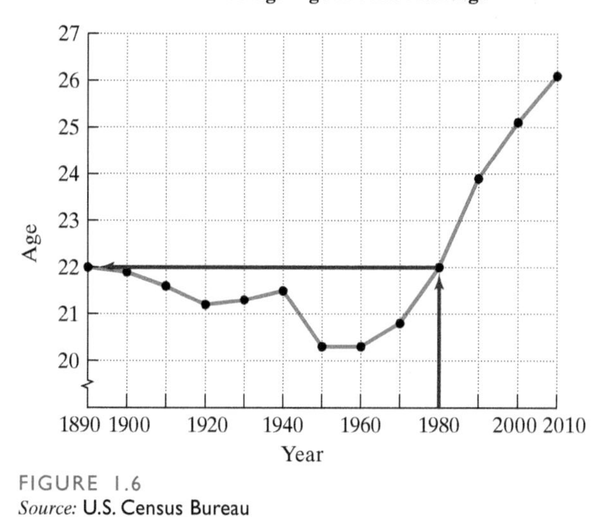

FIGURE 1.6
Source: U.S. Census Bureau

Line graphs are often used to illustrate trends over time. Some measure of time, such as months or years, frequently appears on the horizontal axis. Amounts are generally listed on the vertical axis. Points are drawn to represent the given information. The graph is formed by connecting the points with line segments.

Figure 1.6 is an example of a typical line graph. The graph shows the average age at which women in the United States married for the first time from 1890 through 2010. The years are listed on the horizontal axis, and the ages are listed on the vertical axis. The symbol ⩘ on the vertical axis shows that there is a break in values between 0 and 20. Thus, the first tick mark on the vertical axis represents an average age of 20.

Figure 1.6 shows how to find the average age at which women married for the first time in 1980.

Step 1 Locate 1980 on the horizontal axis.

Step 2 Locate the point on the line graph above 1980.

Step 3 Read across to the corresponding age on the vertical axis.

The age is 22. Thus, in 1980, women in the United States married for the first time at an average age of 22.

Using a Line Graph

The line graph in **Figure 1.7** shows the percentage of U.S. college students who smoked cigarettes from 1982 through 2010.

a. Find an estimate for the percentage of college students who smoked cigarettes in 2010.

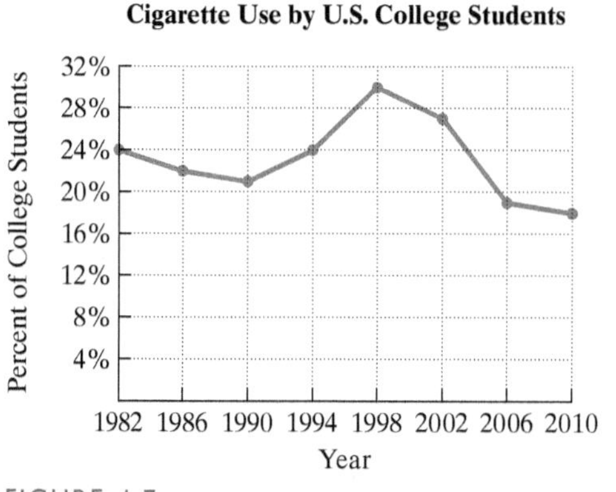

FIGURE 1.7
Source: Rebecca Donatelle, *Health The Basics*, 10th Edition, Pearson, 2013.

b. In which four-year period did the percentage of college students who smoked cigarettes decrease at the greatest rate?

c. In which year did 30% of college students smoke cigarettes?

SOLUTION

a. Estimating the Percentage Smoking Cigarettes in 2010

b. Identifying the Period of the Greatest Rate of Decreasing Cigarette Smoking

c. Identifying the Year when 30% of College Students Smoked Cigarettes

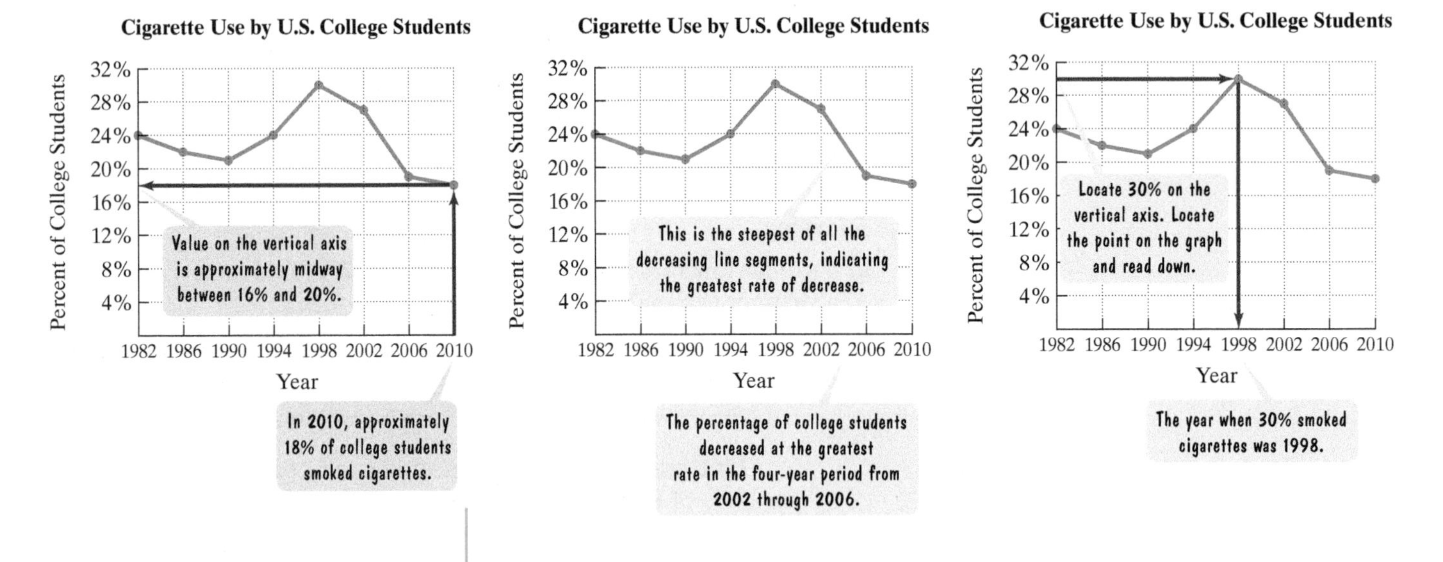

CHECK POINT 7 Use the line graph in **Figure 1.7** at the bottom of the previous page to solve this exercise.

a. Find an estimate for the percentage of college students who smoked cigarettes in 1986.

b. In which four-year period did the percentage of college students who smoked cigarettes increase at the greatest rate?

c. In which years labeled on the horizontal axis did 24% of college students smoke cigarettes?

3 Develop mathematical models that estimate relationships between variables.

Mathematical Models

We have seen that American men born in 1950 have a life expectancy of 65.6 years, increasing by approximately 0.18 year for each subsequent birth year. We can use variables to express the life expectancy, E, for American men born x years after 1950.

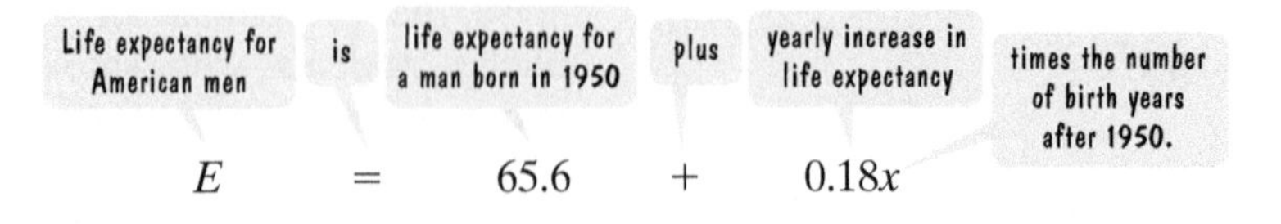

$$E = 65.6 + 0.18x$$

A **formula** is a statement of equality that uses letters to express a relationship between two or more variables. Thus, $E = 65.6 + 0.18x$ is a formula describing life expectancy, E, for American men born x years after 1950. Be aware that this formula provides *estimates* of life expectancy, as shown in **Table 1.2**.

TABLE 1.2 Comparing Given Data with Estimates Determined by a Formula

Birth Year	Life Expectancy: Given Data	Life Expectancy: Formula Estimate $E = 65.6 + 0.18x$
1950	65.6	$E = 65.6 + 0.18(0) = 65.6 + 0 = 65.6$
1960	66.6	$E = 65.6 + 0.18(10) = 65.6 + 1.8 = 67.4$
1970	67.1	$E = 65.6 + 0.18(20) = 65.6 + 3.6 = 69.2$
1980	70.0	$E = 65.6 + 0.18(30) = 65.6 + 5.4 = 71.0$
1990	71.8	$E = 65.6 + 0.18(40) = 65.6 + 7.2 = 72.8$
2000	74.1	$E = 65.6 + 0.18(50) = 65.6 + 9.0 = 74.6$
2010	76.2	$E = 65.6 + 0.18(60) = 65.6 + 10.8 = 76.4$

In each row, we substitute the number of years after 1950 for x. The better estimates occur in 1950, 2000, and 2010.

The process of finding formulas to describe real-world phenomena is called **mathematical modeling**. Such formulas, together with the meaning assigned to the variables, are called **mathematical models**. We often say that these formulas model, or describe, the relationships among the variables.

EXAMPLE 8 *Modeling the Cost of Attending a Public College*

The bar graph in **Figure 1.8** shows the average cost of tuition and fees for public four-year colleges, adjusted for inflation.

a. Estimate the yearly increase in tuition and fees. Round to the nearest dollar.

b. Write a mathematical model that estimates the average cost of tuition and fees, T, at public four-year colleges for the school year ending x years after 2000.

c. Use the mathematical model from part (b) to project the average cost of tuition and fees at public four-year colleges for the school year ending in 2016.

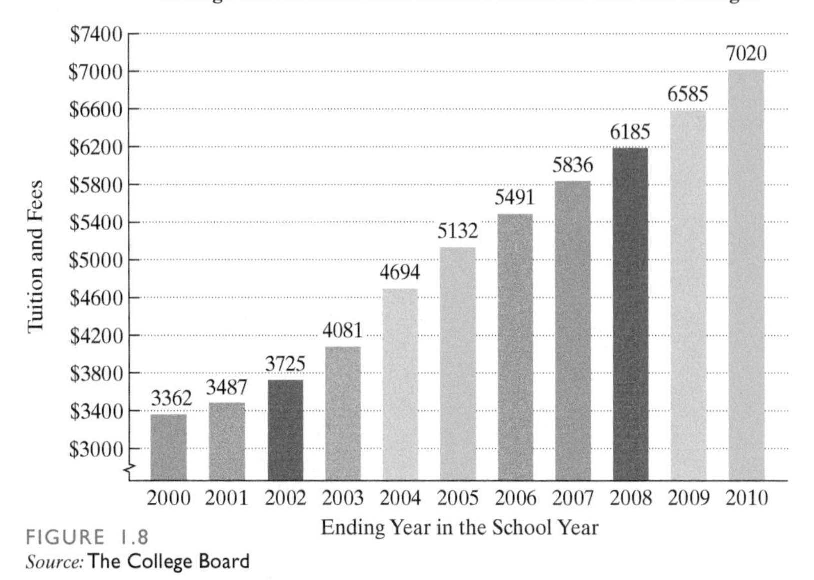

FIGURE 1.8
Source: The College Board

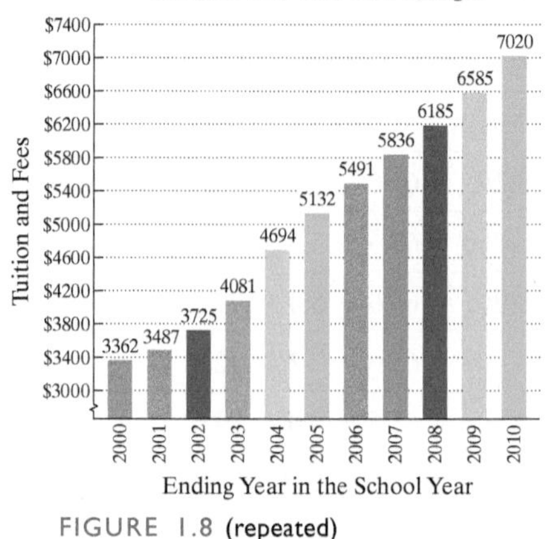

FIGURE 1.8 (repeated)
Source: The College Board

SOLUTION

a. We can use the data in **Figure 1.8** from 2000 and 2010 to estimate the yearly increase in tuition and fees.

Yearly increase in tuition and fees is approximately $\dfrac{\text{change in tuition and fees from 2000 to 2010}}{\text{change in time from 2000 to 2010}}$.

$$\approx \frac{7020 - 3362}{2010 - 2000}$$

$$= \frac{3658}{10} = 365.8 \approx 366$$

Each year the average cost of tuition and fees for public four-year colleges is increasing by approximately \$366.

b. Now we can use variables to obtain a mathematical model that estimates the average cost of tuition and fees, T, for the school year ending x years after 2000.

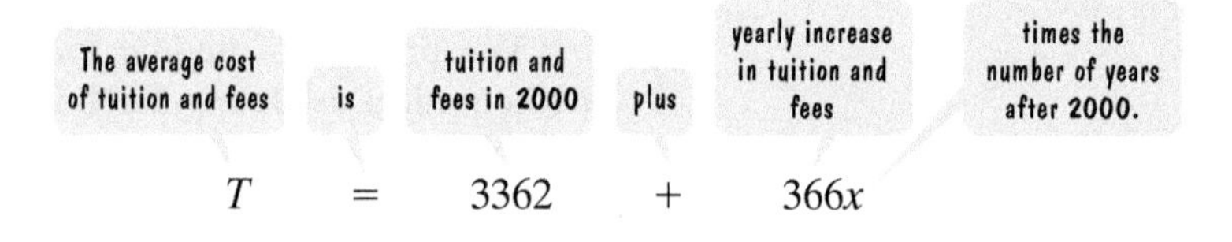

$$T = 3362 + 366x$$

The mathematical model $T = 3362 + 366x$ estimates the average cost of tuition and fees, T, at public four-year colleges for the school year ending x years after 2000.

c. Now let's use the mathematical model to project the average cost of tuition and fees for the school year ending in 2016. Because 2016 is 16 years after 2000, we substitute 16 for x.

$T = 3362 + 366x$ — This is the mathematical model from part (b).

$T = 3362 + 366(16)$ — Substitute 16 for x.

$= 3362 + 5856$ — Multiply: $366(16) = 5856$.

$= 9218$ — Add. On a calculator, enter 3362 [+] 366 [×] 16 and press [=] or [ENTER].

Our model projects that the average cost of tuition and fees at public four-year colleges for the school year ending in 2016 will be \$9218.

CHECK POINT 8 The bar graph in **Figure 1.9** on the next page shows the average cost of tuition and fees for private four-year colleges, adjusted for inflation.

a. Estimate the yearly increase in tuition and fees. Round to the nearest dollar.

b. Write a mathematical model that estimates the average cost of tuition and fees, T, at private four-year colleges for the school year ending x years after 2000.

c. Use the mathematical model from part (b) to project the average cost of tuition and fees at private four-year colleges for the school year ending in 2014.

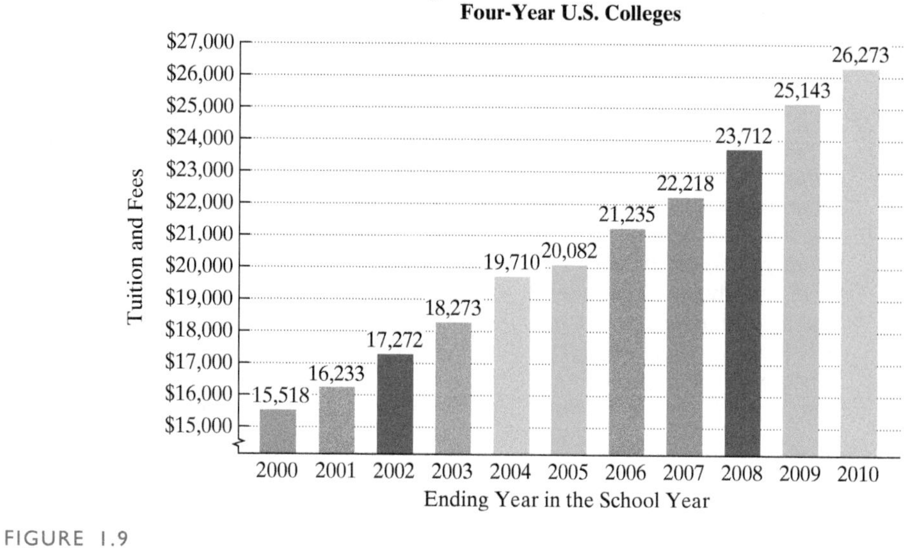

FIGURE 1.9
Source: The College Board

Sometimes a mathematical model gives an estimate that is not a good approximation or is extended to include values of the variable that do not make sense. In these cases, we say that **model breakdown** has occurred. Models that accurately describe data for the past 10 years might not serve as reliable predictions for what can reasonably be expected to occur in the future. Model breakdown can occur when formulas are extended too far into the future.

Concept and Vocabulary Check

Fill in each blank so that the resulting statement is true.

1. The process of arriving at an approximate answer to a computation such as 0.79×403 is called ________.
2. A graph that shows how a whole quantity is divided into parts is called a/an ________.
3. A formula that approximates real-world phenomena is called a/an ______________.
4. True or False: Decimal numbers are rounded by using the digit to the right of the digit where rounding is to occur. _____
5. True or False: Line graphs are often used to illustrate trends over time. _____
6. True or False: Mathematical modeling results in formulas that give exact values of real-world phenomena over time. _____

Exercise Set 1.2

Practice Exercises

The bar graph gives the 2011 populations of the ten most populous states in the United States. Use the appropriate information displayed by the graph to solve Exercises 1–2.

1. Round the population of New York to the nearest **a.** hundred, **b.** thousand, **c.** ten thousand, **d.** hundred thousand, **e.** million, **f.** ten million.

2. Select any state other than New York. For the state selected, round the population to the nearest **a.** hundred, **b.** thousand, **c.** ten thousand, **d.** hundred thousand, **e.** million, **f.** ten million.

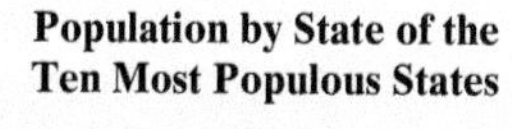

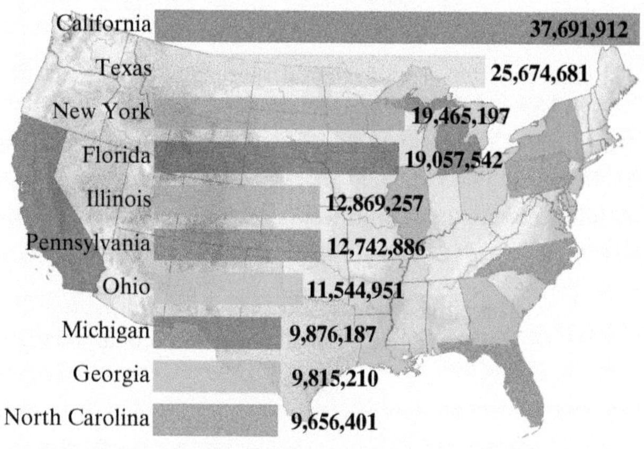

Source: U.S. Census Bureau

Pi goes on and on and on ...
And e is just as cursed.
I wonder: Which is larger
When their digits are reversed?

Martin Gardner

Although most people are familiar with π, the number e is more significant in mathematics, showing up in problems involving population growth and compound interest, and at the heart of the statistical bell curve. One way to think of e is the dollar amount you would have in a savings account at the end of the year if you invested $1 at the beginning of the year and the bank paid an annual interest rate of 100% compounded continuously (compounding interest every trillionth of a second, every quadrillionth of a second, etc.). Although continuous compounding sounds terrific, at the end of the year your $1 would have grown to a mere $e, or $2.72, rounded to the nearest cent. Here is a better approximation for e.

$$e \approx 2.718281828459045$$

In Exercises 3–8, use this approximation to round e as specified.

3. to the nearest thousandth

4. to the nearest ten-thousandth

5. to the nearest hundred-thousandth

6. to the nearest millionth

7. to nine decimal places

8. to ten decimal places

In Exercises 9–34, because different rounding results in different estimates, there is not one single, correct answer to each exercise.

In Exercises 9–22, obtain an estimate for each computation by rounding the numbers so that the resulting arithmetic can easily be performed by hand or in your head. Then use a calculator to perform the computation. How reasonable is your estimate when compared to the actual answer?

9. $359 + 596$

10. $248 + 797$

11. $8.93 + 1.04 + 19.26$

12. $7.92 + 3.06 + 24.36$

13. $32.15 - 11.239$

14. $46.13 - 15.237$

15. 39.67×5.5

16. 78.92×6.5

17. 0.79×414

18. 0.67×211

19. $47.83 \div 2.9$

20. $54.63 \div 4.7$

21. 32% of 187,253

22. 42% of 291,506

In Exercises 23–34, determine each estimate without using a calculator. Then use a calculator to perform the computation necessary to obtain an exact answer. How reasonable is your estimate when compared to the actual answer?

23. Estimate the total cost of six grocery items if their prices are $3.47, $5.89, $19.98, $2.03, $11.85, and $0.23.

24. Estimate the total cost of six grocery items if their prices are $4.23, $7.79, $28.97, $4.06, $13.43, and $0.74.

25. A full-time employee who works 40 hours per week earns $19.50 per hour. Estimate that person's annual income.

26. A full-time employee who works 40 hours per week earns $29.85 per hour. Estimate that person's annual income.

27. You lease a car at $605 per month for 3 years. Estimate the total cost of the lease.

28. You lease a car at $415 per month for 4 years. Estimate the total cost of the lease.

29. A raise of $310,000 is evenly distributed among 294 professors. Estimate the amount each professor receives.

30. A raise of $310,000 is evenly distributed among 196 professors. Estimate the amount each professor receives.

31. If a person who works 40 hours per week earns $61,500 per year, estimate that person's hourly wage.

32. If a person who works 40 hours per week earns $38,950 per year, estimate that person's hourly wage.

33. The average life expectancy in Canada is 80.1 years. Estimate the country's life expectancy in hours.

34. The average life expectancy in Mozambique is 40.3 years. Estimate the country's life expectancy in hours.

Practice Plus

In Exercises 35–36, obtain an estimate for each computation without using a calculator. Then use a calculator to perform the computation. How reasonable is your estimate when compared to the actual answer?

35. $\dfrac{0.19996 \times 107}{0.509}$

36. $\dfrac{0.47996 \times 88}{0.249}$

37. Ten people ordered calculators. The least expensive was $19.95 and the most expensive was $39.95. Half ordered a $29.95 calculator. Select the best estimate of the amount spent on calculators.

a. $240 **b.** $310 **c.** $345 **d.** $355

38. Ten people ordered calculators. The least expensive was $4.95 and the most expensive was $12.95. Half ordered a $6.95 calculator. Select the best estimate of the amount spent on calculators.

a. $160 **b.** $105 **c.** $75 **d.** $55

39. Traveling at an average rate of between 60 and 70 miles per hour for 3 to 4 hours, select the best estimate for the distance traveled.

a. 90 miles **b.** 190 miles
c. 225 miles **d.** 275 miles

40. Traveling at an average rate of between 40 and 50 miles per hour for 3 to 4 hours, select the best estimate for the distance traveled.

a. 120 miles **b.** 160 miles
c. 195 miles **d.** 210 miles

41. Imagine that you counted 60 numbers per minute and continued to count nonstop until you reached 10,000. Determine a reasonable estimate of the number of hours it would take you to complete the counting.

42. Imagine that you counted 60 numbers per minute and continued to count nonstop until you reached one million. Determine a reasonable estimate of the number of days it would take you to complete the counting.

Application Exercises

The circle graph shows the most important problems for the 16,503,611 high school teenagers in the United States. Use this information to solve Exercises 43–44.

Most Important Problems for High School Teenagers

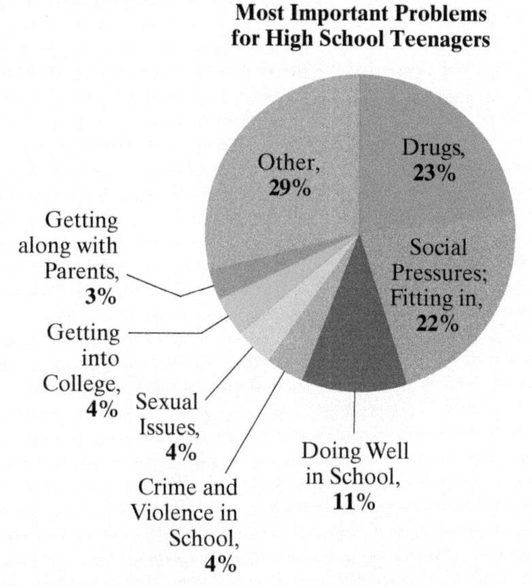

Source: Columbia University

43. Without using a calculator, estimate the number of high school teenagers for whom doing well in school is the most important problem.

44. Without using a calculator, estimate the number of high school teenagers for whom social pressures and fitting in is the most important problem.

An online test of English spelling looked at how well people spelled difficult words. The bar graph shows how many people per 100 spelled each word correctly. Use this information to solve Exercises 45–46.

Number of People per 100 Spelling Various Words Correctly

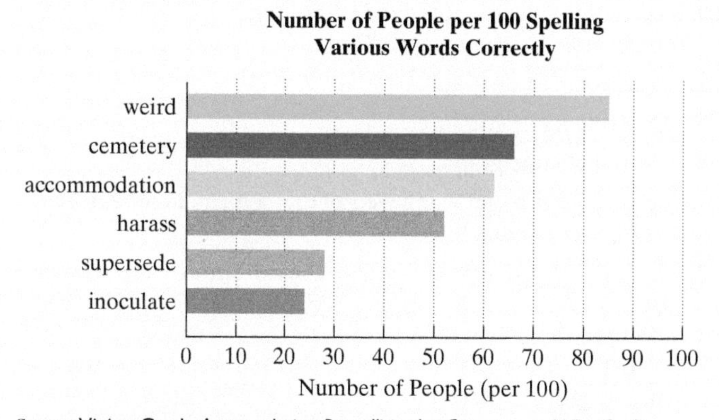

Source: Vivian Cook, *Accomodating Brocolli in the Cemetary or Why Can't Anybody Spell?*, Simon and Schuster, 2004

45. a. Estimate the number of people per 100 who spelled *weird* correctly.

b. In a group consisting of 8729 randomly selected people, estimate how many more people can correctly spell *weird* than *inoculate*.

46. a. Estimate the number of people per 100 who spelled *cemetery* correctly.

b. In a group consisting of 7219 randomly selected people, estimate how many more people can correctly spell *cemetery* than *supersede*.

The percentage of U.S. college freshmen claiming no religious affiliation has risen in recent decades. The bar graph shows the percentage of first-year college students claiming no religious affiliation for four selected years from 1980 through 2010. Use this information to solve Exercises 47–48.

Percentage of First-Year U.S. College Students Claiming No Religious Affiliation

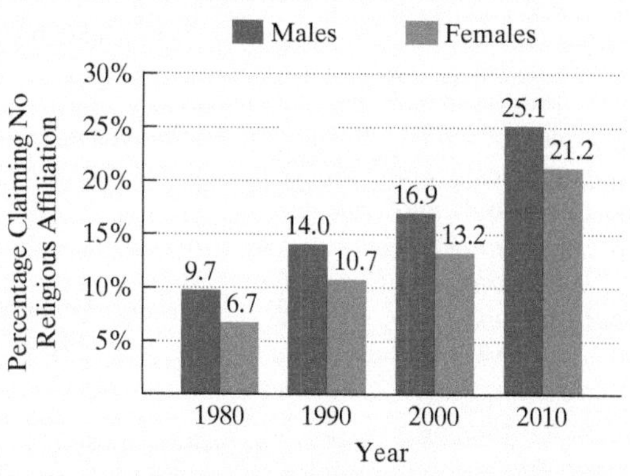

Source: John Macionis, *Sociology*, 14th Edition, Pearson, 2012.

47. a. Estimate the average yearly increase in the percentage of first-year college males claiming no religious affiliation. Round the percentage to the nearest tenth.

b. Estimate the percentage of first-year college males who will claim no religious affiliation in 2020.

48. a. Estimate the average yearly increase in the percentage of first-year college females claiming no religious affiliation. Round the percentage to the nearest tenth.

b. Estimate the percentage of first-year college females who will claim no religious affiliation in 2020.

According to a Gallup poll, in 2012 almost a third of Americans named Iran their country's greatest enemy. That number matched public sentiment in the United States toward Saddam Hussein's Iraq at the time of the 2003 invasion. The line graphs show the percentage of Americans who considered either Iraq or Iran their country's greatest enemy from 2001 through 2012. Use this information to solve Exercises 49–50.

Countries Americans Consider Their Greatest Enemy

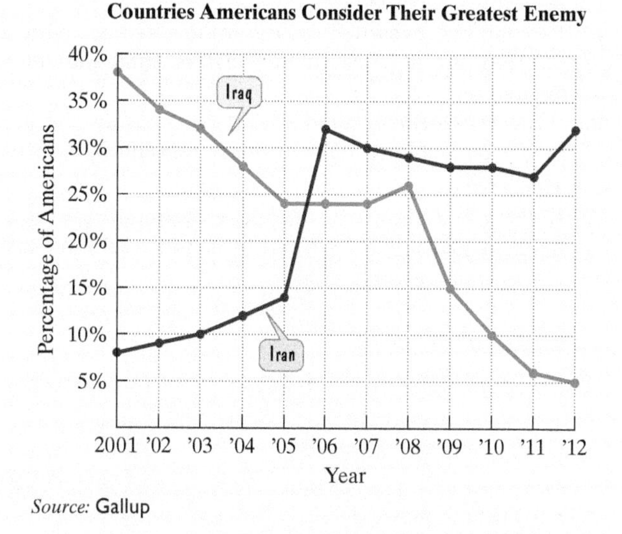

Source: Gallup

(In Exercises 49–50, refer to the graph at the bottom of the previous page.)

49. a. Find an estimate for the percentage of Americans who considered Iraq their country's greatest enemy in 2001.

b. Between which two years did the percentage of Americans who considered Iraq their country's greatest enemy decrease at the greatest rate?

c. In which year did 32% of Americans consider Iraq their country's greatest enemy?

50. a. Find an estimate for the percentage of Americans who considered Iran their country's greatest enemy in 2001.

b. Between which two years did the percentage of Americans who considered Iran their country's greatest enemy increase at the greatest rate?

c. In which year did 12% of Americans consider Iran their country's greatest enemy?

There is a strong scientific consensus that human activities are changing the Earth's climate. Scientists now believe that there is a striking correlation between atmospheric carbon dioxide concentration and global temperature. As both of these variables increase at significant rates, there are warnings of a planetary emergency that threatens to condemn coming generations to a catastrophically diminished future. The bar graphs give the average atmospheric concentration of carbon dioxide and the average global temperature for seven selected years. Use this information to solve Exercises 51–52.

Average Atmospheric Concentration of Carbon Dioxide

Year	Average Carbon Dioxide Concentration (parts per million)
1950	310
1960	317
1970	326
1980	339
1990	354
2000	369
2010	390

Average Global Temperature

Year	Average Global Temperature (degrees Fahrenheit)
1950	56.98
1960	57.04
1970	57.06
1980	57.35
1990	57.64
2000	57.67
2010	58.11

Source: National Oceanic and Atmospheric Administration

51. a. Estimate the yearly increase in the average atmospheric concentration of carbon dioxide. Express the answer in parts per million, rounded to the nearest hundredth.

b. Write a mathematical model that estimates the average atmospheric concentration of carbon dioxide, C, in parts per million, x years after 1950.

c. If the trend shown by the data continues, use your mathematical model from part (b) to project the average atmospheric concentration of carbon dioxide in 2050.

52. a. Estimate the yearly increase in the average global temperature, rounded to the nearest hundredth of a degree.

b. Write a mathematical model that estimates the average global temperature, T, in degrees Fahrenheit, x years after 1950.

c. If the trend shown by the data continues, use your mathematical model from part (b) to project the average global temperature in 2050.

Writing in Mathematics

53. What is estimation? When is it helpful to use estimation?

54. Explain how to round 218,543 to the nearest thousand and to the nearest hundred thousand.

55. Explain how to round 14.26841 to the nearest hundredth and to the nearest thousandth.

56. What does the $\approx$ symbol mean?

57. In this era of calculators and computers, why is there a need to develop estimation skills?

58. Describe a circle graph.

59. Describe a bar graph.

60. Describe a line graph.

61. What does it mean when we say that a formula models real-world phenomena?

62. In 1970, 5% of lawyers in the United States were women. By 2012, 32% of lawyers were women, indicating an increase of approximately 0.64% per year. (*Source*: Bureau of Labor Statistics) Describe how to use this information to write a mathematical model that estimates the percentage of women lawyers, W, x years after 1970.

63. Explain how to use the mathematical model from Exercise 62 to predict the percentage of U.S. lawyers who will be women in 2020.

64. Describe one way in which you use estimation in a nonacademic area of your life.

65. A forecaster at the National Hurricane Center needs to estimate the time until a hurricane with high probability of striking South Florida will hit Miami. Is it better to overestimate or underestimate? Explain your answer.

Critical Thinking Exercises

Make Sense? *In Exercises 66–69, determine whether each statement makes sense or does not make sense, and explain your reasoning.*

66. When buying several items at the market, I use estimation before going to the cashier to be sure I have enough money to pay for the purchase.

67. It's not necessary to use estimation skills when using my calculator.

68. Being able to compute an exact answer requires a different ability than estimating the reasonableness of the answer.

69. My mathematical model estimates the data for the past 10 years extremely well, so it will serve as an accurate prediction for what will occur in 2050.

70. Take a moment to read the verse preceding Exercises 3–8 that mentions the numbers π and e, whose decimal representations continue infinitely with no repeating patterns. The verse was written by the American mathematician (and accomplished amateur magician!) Martin Gardner (1914–2010), author of more than 60 books and best known for his "Mathematical Games" column, which ran in *Scientific American* for 25 years. Explain the humor in Gardner's question.

In Exercises 71–74, match the story with the correct graph. The graphs are labeled (a), (b), (c), and (d).

71. As the blizzard got worse, the snow fell harder and harder.

72. The snow fell more and more softly.

73. It snowed hard, but then it stopped. After a short time, the snow started falling softly.

74. It snowed softly, and then it stopped. After a short time, the snow started falling hard.

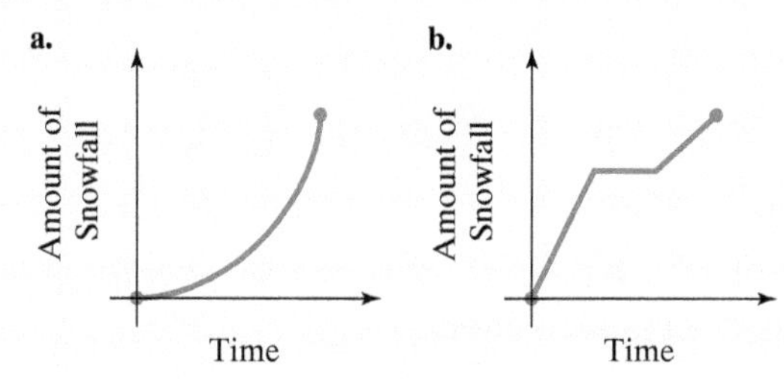

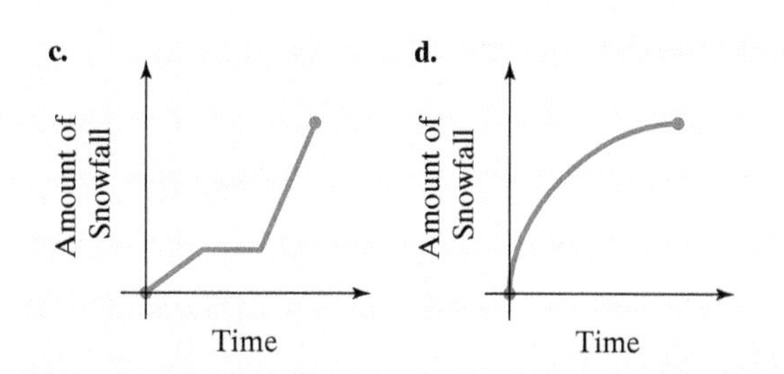

75. American children ages 2 to 17 spend 19 hours 40 minutes per week watching television. (*Source*: TV-Turnoff Network) From ages 2 through 17, inclusive, estimate the number of days an American child spends watching television. How many years, to the nearest tenth of a year, is that?

76. If you spend $1000 each day, estimate how long it will take to spend a billion dollars.

Group Exercises

77. Group members should devise an estimation process that can be used to answer each of the following questions. Use input from all group members to describe the best estimation process possible.

a. Is it possible to walk from San Francisco to New York in a year?

b. How much money is spent on ice cream in the United States each year?

78. Group members should begin by consulting an almanac, newspaper, magazine, or the Internet to find two graphs that show "intriguing" data changing from year to year. In one graph, the data values should be increasing relatively steadily. In the second graph, the data values should be decreasing relatively steadily. For each graph selected, write a mathematical model that estimates the changing variable x years after the graph's starting date. Then use each mathematical model to make predictions about what might occur in the future. Are there circumstances that might affect the accuracy of the prediction? List some of these circumstances.

1.3 Problem Solving

WHAT AM I SUPPOSED TO LEARN?

After you have read this section, you should be able to:

1 Solve problems using the organization of the four-step problem-solving process.

CRITICAL THINKING AND PROBLEM SOLVING are essential skills in both school and work. A model for problem solving was established by the charismatic teacher and mathematician George Polya (1887–1985) in *How to Solve It* (Princeton University Press, Princeton, NJ, 1957). This book, first published in 1945, has sold more than one million copies and is available in 17 languages. Using a four-step procedure for problem solving, Polya's book demonstrates how to think clearly in any field.

Solve problems using the organization of the four-step problem-solving process.

"If you don't know where you're going, you'll probably end up some place else."
—Yogi Berra

POLYA'S FOUR STEPS IN PROBLEM SOLVING

Step 1 **Understand the problem.** Read the problem several times. The first reading can serve as an overview. In the second reading, write down what information is given and determine exactly what it is that the problem requires you to find.

Step 2 **Devise a plan.** The plan for solving the problem might involve one or more of these suggested problem-solving strategies:

- Use inductive reasoning to look for a pattern.
- Make a systematic list or a table.
- Use estimation to make an educated guess at the solution. Check the guess against the problem's conditions and work backward to eventually determine the solution.
- Try expressing the problem more simply and solve a similar simpler problem.
- Use trial and error.
- List the given information in a chart or table.
- Try making a sketch or a diagram to illustrate the problem.
- Relate the problem to a similar problem that you have seen before. Try applying the procedures used to solve the similar problem to the new one.
- Look for a "catch" if the answer seems too obvious. Perhaps the problem involves some sort of trick question deliberately intended to lead the problem solver in the wrong direction.
- Use the given information to eliminate possibilities.
- Use common sense.

Step 3 **Carry out the plan and solve the problem.**

Step 4 **Look back and check the answer.** The answer should satisfy the conditions of the problem. The answer should make sense and be reasonable. If this is not the case, recheck the method and any calculations. Perhaps there is an alternate way to arrive at a correct solution.

GREAT QUESTION!

Should I memorize Polya's four steps in problem solving?

Not necessarily. Think of Polya's four steps as guidelines that will help you organize the process of problem solving, rather than a list of rigid rules that need to be memorized. You may be able to solve certain problems without thinking about or using every step in the four-step process.

The very first step in problem solving involves evaluating the given information in a deliberate manner. Is there enough given to solve the problem? Is the information relevant to the problem's solution, or are some facts not necessary to arrive at a solution?

EXAMPLE 1 *Finding What Is Missing*

Which necessary piece of information is missing and prevents you from solving the following problem?

A man purchased five shirts, each at the same discount price. How much did he pay for them?

SOLUTION

Step 1 **Understand the problem.** Here's what is given:

Number of shirts purchased: 5.

We must find how much the man paid for the five shirts.

Step 2 **Devise a plan.** The amount that the man paid for the five shirts is the number of shirts, 5, times the cost of each shirt. The discount price of each shirt is not given. This missing piece of information makes it impossible to solve the problem.

CHECK POINT 1 Which necessary piece of information is missing and prevents you from solving the following problem?

The bill for your meal totaled \$20.36, including the tax. How much change should you receive from the cashier?

EXAMPLE 2 *Finding What Is Unnecessary*

In the following problem, one more piece of information is given than is necessary for solving the problem. Identify this unnecessary piece of information. Then solve the problem.

A roll of E-Z Wipe paper towels contains 100 sheets and costs \$1.38. A comparable brand, Kwik-Clean, contains five dozen sheets per roll and costs \$1.23. If you need three rolls of paper towels, which brand is the better value?

SOLUTION

Step 1 **Understand the problem.** Here's what is given:

E-Z Wipe: 100 sheets per roll; \$1.38

Kwik-Clean: 5 dozen sheets per roll; \$1.23

Needed: 3 rolls.

We must determine which brand offers the better value.

Step 2 **Devise a plan.** The brand with the better value is the one that has the lower price per sheet. Thus, we can compare the two brands by finding the cost for one sheet of E-Z Wipe and one sheet of Kwik-Clean. The price per sheet, or the *unit price*, is the price of a roll divided by the number of sheets in the roll. The fact that three rolls are required is not relevant to the problem. This unnecessary piece of information is not needed to find which brand is the better value.

Step 3 **Carry out the plan and solve the problem.**

E-Z Wipe:

$$\text{price per sheet} = \frac{\text{price of a roll}}{\text{number of sheets per roll}} = \frac{\$1.38}{100 \text{ sheets}} = \$0.0138 \approx \$0.01$$

Kwik-Clean:

$$\text{price per sheet} = \frac{\text{price of a roll}}{\text{number of sheets per roll}} = \frac{\$1.23}{60 \text{ sheets}} = \$0.0205 \approx \$0.02$$

5 dozen = 5 × 12, or 60 sheets

By comparing unit prices, we see that E-Z Wipe, at approximately \$0.01 per sheet, is the better value.

Step 4 **Look back and check the answer.** We can double-check the arithmetic in each of our unit-price computations. We can also see if these unit prices satisfy the problem's conditions. The product of each brand's price per sheet and the number of sheets per roll should result in the given price for a roll.

E-Z Wipe: Check \$0.0138 — Kwik-Clean: Check \$0.0205

$\$0.0138 \times 100 = \$1.38$ — $\$0.0205 \times 60 = \$1.23$

These are the given prices for a roll of each respective brand.

The unit prices satisfy the problem's conditions.

Blitzer Bonus

Unit Prices and Sneaky Pricejacks

In *200% of Nothing* (John Wiley & Sons, 1993), author A. K. Dewdney writes, "It must be something of a corporate dream come true when a company charges more for a product and no one notices." He gives two examples of "sneaky pricejacks," both easily detected using unit prices. The manufacturers of Mennen Speed Stick deodorant increased the size of the package that held the stick, left the price the same, and reduced the amount of actual deodorant in the stick from 2.5 ounces to 2.25. Fabergé's Brut left the price and size of its cologne jar the same, but reduced its contents from 5 ounces to 4. Surprisingly, the new jar read, "Now, more Brut!" *Consumer Reports* contacted Fabergé to see how this could be possible. Their response: The new jar contained "more fragrance." *Consumer Reports* moaned, "Et tu Brut?"

A generalization of our work in Example 2 allows you to compare different brands and make a choice among various products of different sizes. When shopping at the supermarket, a useful number to keep in mind is a product's *unit price*. The **unit price** is the total price divided by the total units. Among comparable brands, the best value is the product with the lowest unit price, assuming that the units are kept uniform.

The word *per* is used to state unit prices. For example, if a 12-ounce box of cereal sells for \$3.00, its unit price is determined as follows:

$$\text{Unit price} = \frac{\text{total price}}{\text{total units}} = \frac{\$3.00}{12 \text{ ounces}} = \$0.25 \text{ per ounce.}$$

CHECK POINT 2 Solve the following problem. If the problem contains information that is not relevant to its solution, identify this unnecessary piece of information.

A manufacturer packages its apple juice in bottles and boxes. A 128-ounce bottle costs \$5.39, and a 9-pack of 6.75-ounce boxes costs \$3.15. Which packaging option is the better value?

EXAMPLE 3 *Applying the Four-Step Procedure*

By paying \$100 cash up front and the balance at \$20 a week, how long will it take to pay for a bicycle costing \$680?

SOLUTION

Step 1 **Understand the problem.** Here's what is given:

Cost of the bicycle: \$680

Amount paid in cash: \$100

Weekly payments: \$20.

If necessary, consult a dictionary to look up any unfamiliar words. The word *balance* means the amount still to be paid. We must find the balance to determine the number of weeks required to pay off the bicycle.

Step 2 **Devise a plan.** Subtract the amount paid in cash from the cost of the bicycle. This results in the amount still to be paid. Because weekly payments are \$20, divide the amount still to be paid by 20. This will give the number of weeks required to pay for the bicycle.

GREAT QUESTION!

Is there a strategy I can use to determine whether I understand a problem?

An effective way to see if you understand a problem is to restate the problem in your own words.

Step 3 **Carry out the plan and solve the problem.** Begin by finding the balance, the amount still to be paid for the bicycle.

$$\begin{array}{rl} \$680 & \text{cost of the bicycle} \\ -\$100 & \text{amount paid in cash} \\ \hline \$580 & \text{amount still to be paid} \end{array}$$

Now divide the \$580 balance by \$20, the payment per week. The result of the division is the number of weeks needed to pay off the bicycle.

$$\frac{\$580}{\frac{\$20}{\text{week}}} = \$580 \times \frac{\text{week}}{\$20} = \frac{580 \text{ weeks}}{20} = 29 \text{ weeks}$$

It will take 29 weeks to pay for the bicycle.

Step 4 **Look back and check the answer.** We can certainly double-check the arithmetic either by hand or with a calculator. We can also see if the answer, 29 weeks to pay for the bicycle, satisfies the condition that the bicycle costs \$680.

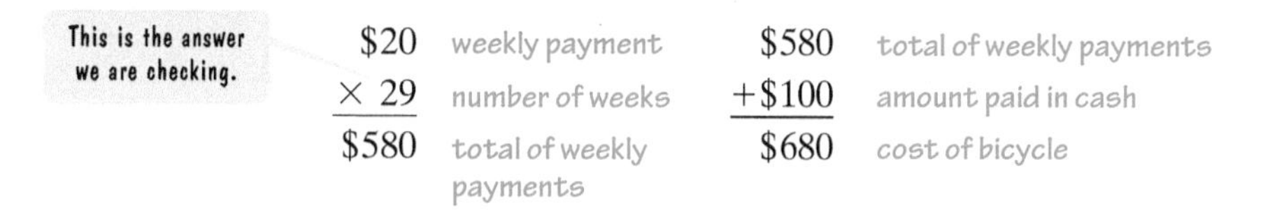

The answer of 29 weeks satisfies the condition that the cost of the bicycle is \$680.

CHECK POINT 3 By paying \$350 cash up front and the balance at \$45 per month, how long will it take to pay for a computer costing \$980?

Making lists is a useful strategy in problem solving.

EXAMPLE 4 *Solving a Problem by Making a List*

Suppose you are an engineer programming the automatic gate for a 50-cent toll. The gate should accept exact change only. It should not accept pennies. How many coin combinations must you program the gate to accept?

SOLUTION

Step 1 **Understand the problem.** The total change must always be 50 cents. One possible coin combination is two quarters. Another is five dimes. We need to count all such combinations.

Step 2 **Devise a plan.** Make a list of all possible coin combinations. Begin with the coins of larger value and work toward the coins of smaller value.

Step 3 **Carry out the plan and solve the problem.** First we must find all of the coins that are not pennies but can combine to form 50 cents. This includes half-dollars, quarters, dimes, and nickels. Now we can set up a table. We will use these coins as table headings.

Half-Dollars	Quarters	Dimes	Nickels

Blitzer Bonus

Trick Questions

Think about the following questions carefully before answering because each contains some sort of trick or catch.

Sample: Do they have a fourth of July in England?

Answer: Of course, they do. However, there is no national holiday on that date!

See if you can answer the questions that follow without developing mental whiplash. The answers appear in the answer section.

1. A farmer had 17 sheep. All but 12 died. How many sheep does the farmer have left?
2. Some months have 30 days. Some have 31. How many months have 28 days?
3. A doctor had a brother, but this brother had no brothers. What was the relationship between doctor and brother?
4. If you had only one match and entered a log cabin in which there was a candle, a fireplace, and a woodburning stove, which should you light first?

Half-Dollars	Quarters	Dimes	Nickels

Each row in the table (repeated above) will represent one possible combination for exact change. We start with the largest coin, the half-dollar. Only one half-dollar is needed to make exact change. No other coins are needed. Thus, we put a 1 in the half-dollars column and 0s in the other columns to represent the first possible combination.

Half-Dollars	Quarters	Dimes	Nickels
1	0	0	0

Likewise, two quarters are also exact change for 50 cents. We put a 0 in the half-dollars column, a 2 in the quarters column, and 0s in the columns for dimes and nickels.

Half-Dollars	Quarters	Dimes	Nickels
1	0	0	0
0	2	0	0

In this manner, we can find all possible combinations for exact change for the 50-cent toll. These combinations are shown in **Table 1.3**.

TABLE 1.3 Exact Change for 50 Cents: No Pennies

Half-Dollars	Quarters	Dimes	Nickels
1	0	0	0
0	2	0	0
0	1	2	1
0	1	1	3
0	1	0	5
0	0	5	0
0	0	4	2
0	0	3	4
0	0	2	6
0	0	1	8
0	0	0	10

Count the coin combinations shown in **Table 1.3**. How many coin combinations must the gate accept? You must program the gate to accept 11 coin combinations.

Step 4 **Look back and check the answer.** Double-check **Table 1.3** to make sure that no possible combinations have been omitted and that the total in each row is 50 cents. Double-check your count of the number of combinations.

CHECK POINT 4 Suppose you are an engineer programming the automatic gate for a 30-cent toll. The gate should accept exact change only. It should not accept pennies. How many coin combinations must you program the gate to accept?

Sketches and diagrams are sometimes useful in problem solving.

EXAMPLE 5 *Solving a Problem by Using a Diagram*

Four runners are in a one-mile race: Maria, Aretha, Thelma, and Debbie. Points are awarded only to the women finishing first or second. The first-place winner gets more points than the second-place winner. How many different arrangements of first- and second-place winners are possible?

SOLUTION

Step 1 **Understand the problem.** Three possibilities for first and second position are

Maria-Aretha
Maria-Thelma
Aretha-Maria.

Notice that Maria finishing first and Aretha finishing second is a different outcome than Aretha finishing first and Maria finishing second. Order makes a difference because the first-place winner gets more points than the second-place winner. We must count all possibilities for first and second position.

Step 2 **Devise a plan.** If Maria finishes first, then each of the other three runners could finish second:

First place	Second place	Possibilities for first and second place
Maria	Aretha	Maria-Aretha
	Thelma	Maria-Thelma
	Debbie	Maria-Debbie

Similarly, we can list each woman as the possible first-place runner. Then we will list the other three women as possible second-place runners. Next we will determine the possibilities for first and second place. This diagram will show how the runners can finish first or second.

Step 3 **Carry out the plan and solve the problem.** Now we complete the diagram started in step 2. The diagram is shown in **Figure 1.10**.

First place	Second place	Possibilities for first and second place
Maria	Aretha	Maria-Aretha
	Thelma	Maria-Thelma
	Debbie	Maria-Debbie
Aretha	Maria	Aretha-Maria
	Thelma	Aretha-Thelma
	Debbie	Aretha-Debbie
Thelma	Maria	Thelma-Maria
	Aretha	Thelma-Aretha
	Debbie	Thelma-Debbie
Debbie	Maria	Debbie-Maria
	Aretha	Debbie-Aretha
	Thelma	Debbie-Thelma

FIGURE 1.10 Possible ways for four runners to finish first and second

Because of the way **Figure 1.10** branches from first to second place, it is called a **tree diagram.** We will be using tree diagrams as a problem-solving tool in the study of uncertainty and probability.

Count the number of possibilities shown under the third column, "Possibilities for first and second place." Can you see that there are 12 possibilities? Therefore, 12 different arrangements of first- and second-place winners are possible.

Step 4 **Look back and check the answer.** Check the diagram in **Figure 1.10** to make sure that no possible first- and second-place outcomes have been left out. Double-check your count for the winning pairs of runners.

45. Jose, Bob, and Tony are college students living in adjacent dorm rooms. Bob lives in the middle dorm room. Their majors are business, psychology, and biology, although not necessarily in that order. The business major frequently uses the new computer in Bob's dorm room when Bob is in class. The psychology major and Jose both have 8 A.M. classes, and the psychology major knocks on Jose's wall to make sure he is awake. Determine Bob's major.

46. The figure represents a map of 13 countries. If countries that share a common border cannot be the same color, what is the minimum number of colors needed to color the map?

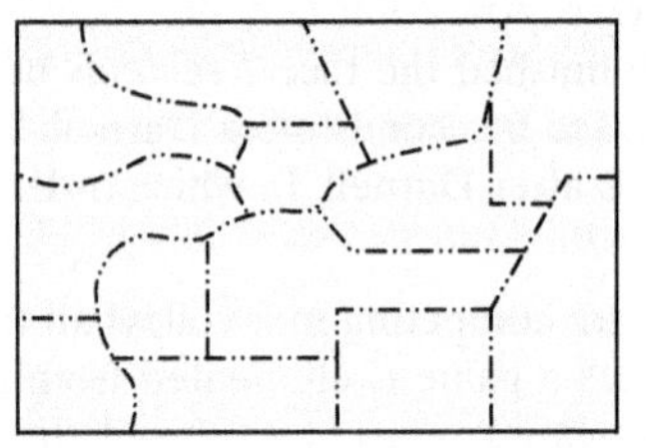

The sudoku (pronounced: sue-DOE-koo) craze, a number puzzle popular in Japan, hit the United States in 2005. A sudoku ("single number") puzzle consists of a 9-by-9 grid of 81 boxes subdivided into nine 3-by-3 squares. Some of the square boxes contain numbers. Here is an example:

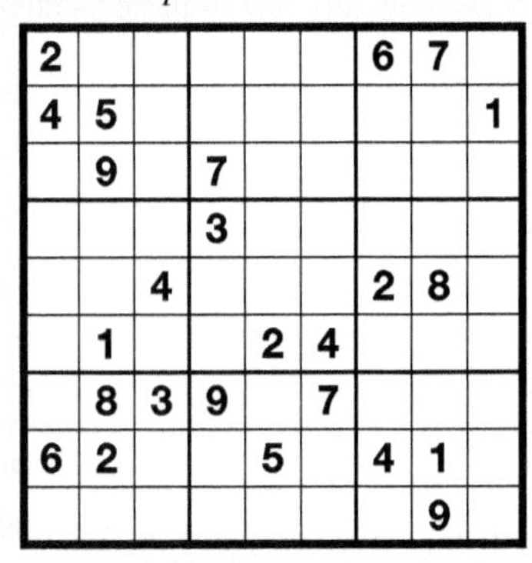

2						6	7	
4	5							1
	9		7					
			3					
		4				2	8	
	1			2	4			
	8	3	9		7			
6	2			5		4	1	
							9	

The objective is to fill in the remaining squares so that every row, every column, and every 3-by-3 square contains each of the digits from 1 through 9 exactly once. (You can work this puzzle in Exercise 66, perhaps consulting one of the dozens of sudoku books in which the numerals 1 through 9 have created a cottage industry for publishers. There's even a Sudoku for Dummies.*)*

Trying to slot numbers into small checkerboard grids is not unique to sudoku. In Exercises 47–50, we explore some of the intricate patterns in other arrays of numbers, including magic squares. A ***magic square*** *is a square array of numbers arranged so that the numbers in all rows, all columns, and the two diagonals have the same sum. Here is an example of a magic square in which the sum of the numbers in each row, each column, and each diagonal is 15:*

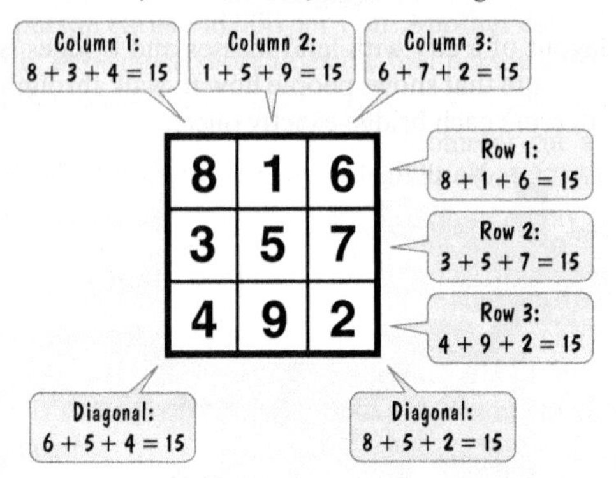

Exercises 47–48 are based on magic squares. (Be sure you have read the preceding discussion.)

47. a. Use the properties of a magic square to fill in the missing numbers.

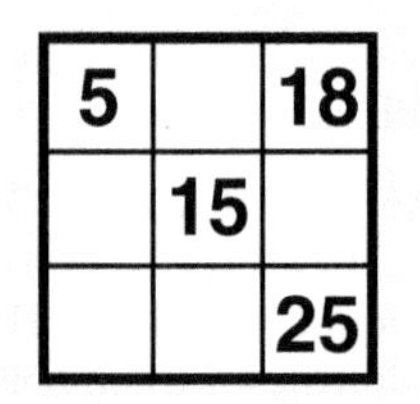

5		18
	15	
		25

b. Show that the number of letters in the word for each number in the square in part (a) generates another magic square.

48. a. Use the properties of a magic square to fill in the missing numbers.

96		37	45
	43		
		25	57
23		82	78

b. Show that if you reverse the digits for each number in the square in part (a), another magic square is generated. (*Source* for the *alphamagic square* in Exercise 47 and the *mirrormagic square* in Exercise 48: Clifford A. Pickover, *A Passion for Mathematics*, John Wiley & Sons, Inc., 2005)

49. As in sudoku, fill in the missing numbers in the 3-by-3 square so that it contains each of the digits from 1 through 9 exactly once. Furthermore, in this *antimagic square*, the rows, the columns, and the two diagonals must have *different sums*.

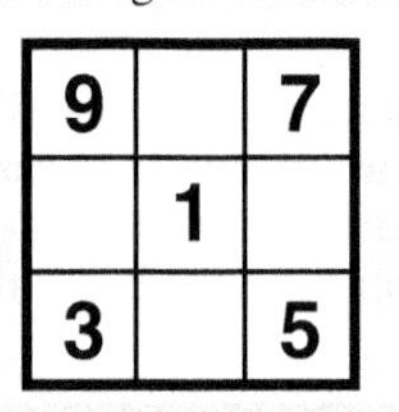

9		7
	1	
3		5

50. The missing numbers in the 4-by-4 array are one-digit numbers. The sums for each row, each column, and one diagonal are listed in the voice balloons outside the array. Find the missing numbers.

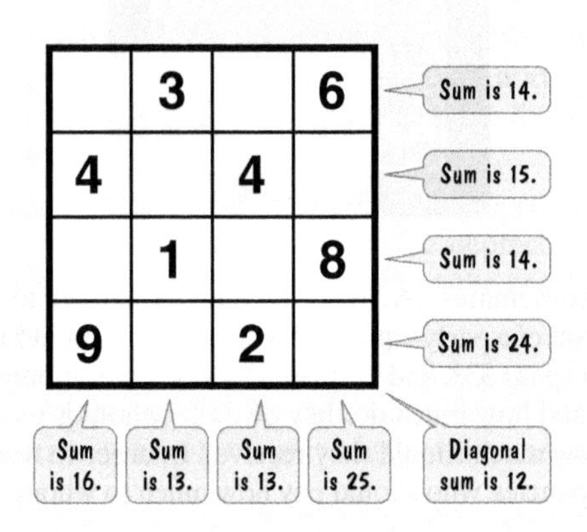

51. Some numbers in the printing of a division problem have become illegible. They are designated below by *. Fill in the blanks.

```
     1**
 **)4***
    28
    *56
    ***
     ***
     ***
       0
```

Writing in Mathematics

In Exercises 52–54, explain the plan needed to solve the problem.

52. If you know how much was paid for several pounds of steak, find the cost of one pound.

53. If you know a person's age, find the year in which that person was born.

54. If you know how much you earn each hour, find your yearly income.

55. Write your own problem that can be solved using the four-step procedure. Then use the four steps to solve the problem.

Critical Thinking Exercises

Make Sense? *In Exercises 56–59, determine whether each statement makes sense or does not make sense, and explain your reasoning.*

56. Polya's four steps in problem solving make it possible for me to solve any mathematical problem easily and quickly.

57. I used Polya's four steps in problem solving to deal with a personal problem in need of a creative solution.

58. I find it helpful to begin the problem-solving process by restating the problem in my own words.

59. When I get bogged down with a problem, there's no limit to the amount of time I should spend trying to solve it.

60. Gym lockers are to be numbered from 1 through 99 using metal numbers to be nailed onto each locker. How many 7s are needed?

61. You are on vacation in an isolated town. Everyone in the town was born there and has never left. You develop a toothache and check out the two dentists in town. One dentist has gorgeous teeth and one has teeth that show the effects of poor dental work. Which dentist should you choose and why?

62. India Jones is standing on a large rock in the middle of a square pool filled with hungry, man-eating piranhas. The edge of the pool is 20 feet away from the rock. India's mom wants to rescue her son, but she is standing on the edge of the pool with only two planks, each $19\frac{1}{2}$ feet long. How can India be rescued using the two planks?

63. One person tells the truth on Monday, Tuesday, Wednesday, and Thursday, but lies on all other days. A second person lies on Tuesday, Wednesday, and Thursday, but tells the truth on all other days. If both people state "I lied yesterday," then what day of the week is it today?

64. (This logic problem dates back to the eighth century.) A farmer needs to take his goat, wolf, and cabbage across a stream. His boat can hold him and one other passenger (the goat, wolf, or cabbage). If he takes the wolf with him, the goat will eat the cabbage. If he takes the cabbage, the wolf will eat the goat. Only when the farmer is present are the cabbage and goat safe from their respective predators. How does the farmer get everything across the stream?

65. As in sudoku, fill in the missing numbers along the sides of the triangle so that it contains each of the digits from 1 through 9 exactly once. Furthermore, each side of the triangle should contain four digits whose sum is 17.

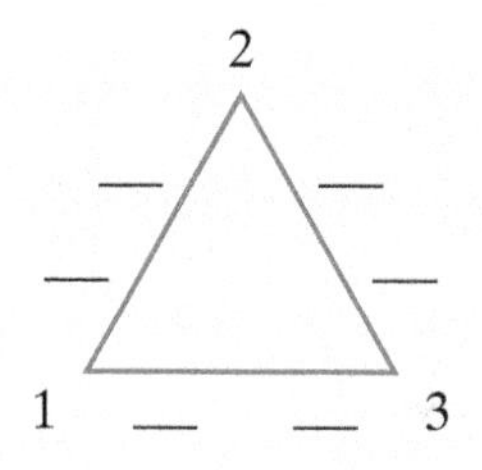

66. Solve the sudoku puzzle in the middle of the left column on page 40.

67. A version of this problem, called the *missing dollar problem*, first appeared in 1933. Three people eat at a restaurant and receive a total bill for $30. They divide the amount equally and pay $10 each. The waiter gives the bill and the $30 to the manager, who realizes there is an error: The correct charge should be only $25. The manager gives the waiter five $1 bills to return to the customers, with the restaurant's apologies. However, the waiter is dishonest, keeping $2 and giving back only $3 to the customers. In conclusion, each of the three customers has paid $9 and the waiter has stolen $2, giving a total of $29. However, the original bill was $30. Where has the missing dollar gone?

68. A firefighter spraying water on a fire stood on the middle rung of a ladder. When the smoke became less thick, the firefighter moved up 4 rungs. However it got too hot, so the firefighter backed down 6 rungs. Later, the firefighter went up 7 rungs and stayed until the fire was out. Then, the firefighter climbed the remaining 4 rungs and entered the building. How many rungs does the ladder have?

69. The Republic of Margaritaville is composed of four states: A, B, C, and D. According to the country's constitution, the congress will have 30 seats, divided among the four states according to their respective populations. The table shows each state's population.

POPULATION OF MARGARITAVILLE BY STATE

State	A	B	C	D	Total
Population (in thousands)	275	383	465	767	1890

Allocate the 30 congressional seats among the four states in a fair manner.

Group Exercises

Exercises 70–74 describe problems that have many plans for finding an answer. Group members should describe how the four steps in problem solving can be applied to find a solution. It is not necessary to actually solve each problem. Your professor will let the group know if the four steps should be described verbally by a group spokesperson or in essay form.

70. How much will it cost to install bicycle racks on campus to encourage students to use bikes, rather than cars, to get to campus?

71. How many new counselors are needed on campus to prevent students from waiting in long lines for academic advising?

72. By how much would taxes in your state have to be increased to cut tuition at community colleges and state universities in half?

73. Is your local electric company overcharging its customers?

74. Should solar heating be required for all new construction in your community?

75. Group members should describe a problem in need of a solution. Then, as in Exercises 70–74, describe how the four steps in problem solving can be applied to find a solution.

Chapter Summary, Review, and Test

SUMMARY – DEFINITIONS AND CONCEPTS	EXAMPLES
1.1 Inductive and Deductive Reasoning	
a. Inductive reasoning is the process of arriving at a general conclusion based on observations of specific examples. The conclusion is called a conjecture or a hypothesis. A case for which a conjecture is false is called a counterexample.	Ex. 1, p. 4; Ex. 2, p. 5; Ex. 3, p. 6; Ex. 4, p. 7
b. Deductive reasoning is the process of proving a specific conclusion from one or more general statements. The statement that is proved is called a theorem.	Ex. 5, p. 9
1.2 Estimation, Graphs, and Mathematical Models	
a. The procedure for rounding whole numbers is given in the box on page 15. The symbol $\approx$ means *is approximately equal to*.	Ex. 1, p. 15
b. Decimal parts of numbers are rounded in nearly the same way as whole numbers. However, digits to the right of the rounding place are dropped.	Ex. 2, p. 16
c. Estimation is the process of arriving at an approximate answer to a question. Computations can be estimated by using rounding that results in simplified arithmetic.	Ex. 3, p. 17; Ex. 4, p. 17
d. Estimation is useful when interpreting information given by circle, bar, or line graphs.	Ex. 5, p. 19; Ex. 6, p. 20; Ex. 7, p. 21
e. The process of finding formulas to describe real-world phenomena is called mathematical modeling. Such formulas, together with the meaning assigned to the variables, are called mathematical models.	Ex. 8, p. 23
1.3 Problem Solving	
Polya's Four Steps in Problem Solving **1.** Understand the problem. **2.** Devise a plan. **3.** Carry out the plan and solve the problem. **4.** Look back and check the answer.	Ex. 1, p. 30; Ex. 2, p. 31; Ex. 3, p. 32; Ex. 4, p. 33; Ex. 5, p. 35; Ex. 6, p. 36

Review Exercises

1.1

1. Which reasoning process is shown in the following example? Explain your answer.

All books by Stephen King have made the best-seller list. *Carrie* is a novel by Stephen King. Therefore, *Carrie* was on the best-seller list.

2. Which reasoning process is shown in the following example? Explain your answer.

All books by Stephen King have made the best-seller list. Therefore, it is highly probable that the novel King is currently working on will make the best-seller list.

In Exercises 3–10, identify a pattern in each list of numbers. Then use this pattern to find the next number.

3. 4, 9, 14, 19, ____

4. 7, 14, 28, 56, ____

5. 1, 3, 6, 10, 15, ____

6. $\frac{3}{4}, \frac{3}{5}, \frac{1}{2}, \frac{3}{7},$ ____

7. 40, −20, 10, −5, ____

8. 40, −20, −80, −140, ____

9. 2, 2, 4, 6, 10, 16, 26, ____

10. 2, 6, 12, 36, 72, 216, ____

11. Identify a pattern in the following sequence of figures. Then use the pattern to find the next figure in the sequence.

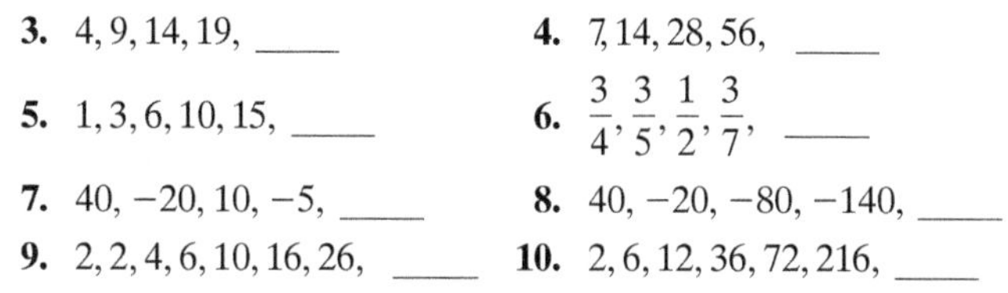

In Exercises 12–13, use inductive reasoning to predict the next line in each sequence of computations. Then perform the arithmetic to determine whether your conjecture is correct.

12.
$$2 = 4 - 2$$
$$2 + 4 = 8 - 2$$
$$2 + 4 + 8 = 16 - 2$$
$$2 + 4 + 8 + 16 = 32 - 2$$

13. $111 \div 3 = 37$

$222 \div 6 = 37$

$333 \div 9 = 37$

14. Consider the following procedure:

Select a number. Double the number. Add 4 to the product. Divide the sum by 2. Subtract 2 from the quotient.

a. Repeat the procedure for four numbers of your choice. Write a conjecture that relates the result of the process to the original number selected.

b. Represent the original number by the variable n and use deductive reasoning to prove the conjecture in part (a).

1.2

15. The number 923,187,456 is called a *pandigital square* because it uses all the digits from 1 to 9 once each and is the square of a number:

$$30{,}384^2 = 30{,}384 \times 30{,}384 = 923{,}187{,}456.$$

(*Source:* David Wells, *The Penguin Dictionary of Curious and Interesting Numbers*)

Round the pandigital square 923,187,456 to the nearest

a. hundred.

b. thousand.

c. hundred thousand.

d. million.

e. hundred million.

16. A magnified view of the boundary of this black "buglike" shape, called the Mandelbrot set, was illustrated in the Section 1.1 opener on page 2.

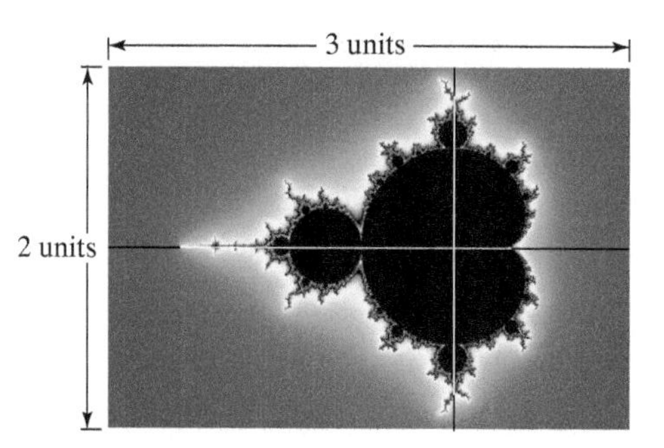

The area of the yellow rectangular region is the product of its length, 3 units, and its width, 2 units, or 6 square units. It is conjectured that the area of the black buglike region representing the Mandelbrot set is

$$\sqrt{6\pi - 1} - e \approx 1.5065916514855 \text{ square units.}$$

(*Source:* Robert P. Munafo, *Mandelbrot Set Glossary and Encyclopedia*)

Round the area of the Mandelbrot set to

a. the nearest tenth.

b. the nearest hundredth.

c. the nearest thousandth.

d. seven decimal places.

In Exercises 17–20, obtain an estimate for each computation by rounding the numbers so that the resulting arithmetic can easily be performed by hand or in your head. Then use a calculator to perform the computation. How reasonable is your estimate when compared to the actual answer?

17. $1.57 + 4.36 + 9.78$

18. 8.83×49

19. $19.894 \div 4.179$

20. 62.3% of 3847.6

In Exercises 21–24, determine each estimate without using a calculator. Then use a calculator to perform the computation necessary to obtain an exact answer. How reasonable is your estimate when compared to the actual answer?

21. Estimate the total cost of six grocery items if their prices are \$8.47, \$0.89, \$2.79, \$0.14, \$1.19, and \$4.76.

22. Estimate the salary of a worker who works for 78 hours at \$6.85 per hour.

23. At a yard sale, a person bought 21 books at \$0.85 each, two chairs for \$11.95 each, and a ceramic plate for \$14.65. Estimate the total amount spent.

24. The circle graph shows how the 17,487,475 students enrolled in U.S. colleges and universities in 2012 funded college costs. Estimate the number of students who covered these costs through grants and scholarships.

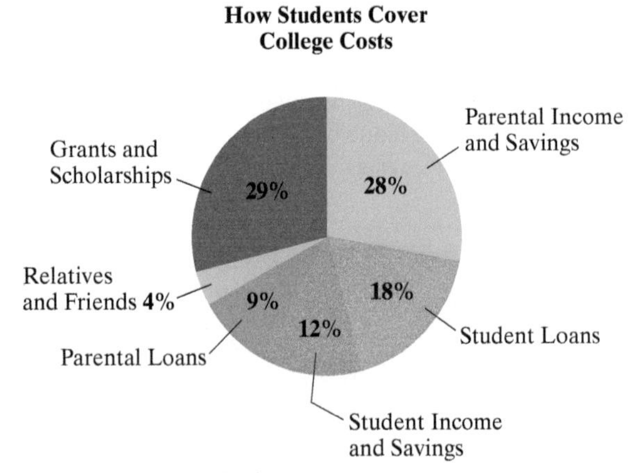

Source: Time, October 29, 2012

25. A small private school employs 10 teachers with salaries ranging from $817 to $992 per week. Which of the following is the best estimate of the monthly payroll for the teachers?

a. $30,000 **b.** $36,000

c. $42,000 **d.** $50,000

26. Select the best estimate for the number of seconds in a day.

a. 1500 **b.** 15,000

c. 86,000 **d.** 100,000

27. Imagine the entire global population as a village of precisely 200 people. The bar graph shows some numeric observations based on this scenario.

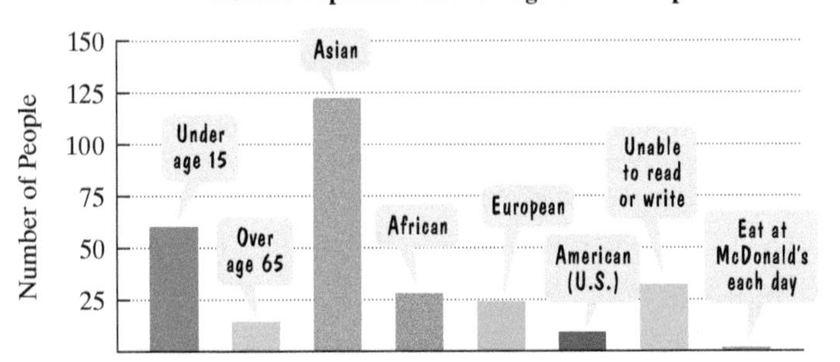

Source: Gary Rimmer, *Number Freaking*, The Disinformation Company Ltd.

a. Which group in the village has a population that exceeds 100? Estimate this group's population.

b. World population is approximately 33 million times the population of the village of 200 people. Use this observation to estimate the number of people in the world, in millions, unable to read or write.

28. The bar graph shows the percentage of people 25 years of age and older who were college graduates in the United States for seven selected years.

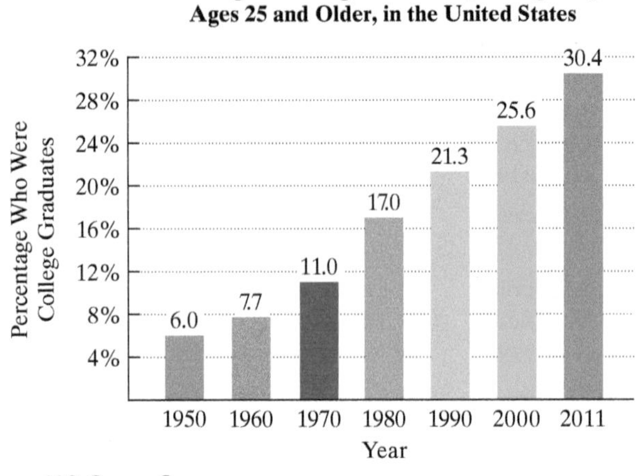

Source: U.S. Census Bureau

a. Estimate the average yearly increase in the percentage of college graduates.

b. If the trend shown by the graph continues, estimate the percentage of people 25 years of age and older who will be college graduates in 2020.

29. During a diagnostic evaluation, a 33-year-old woman experienced a panic attack a few minutes after she had been asked to relax her whole body. The graph shows the rapid increase in heart rate during the panic attack.

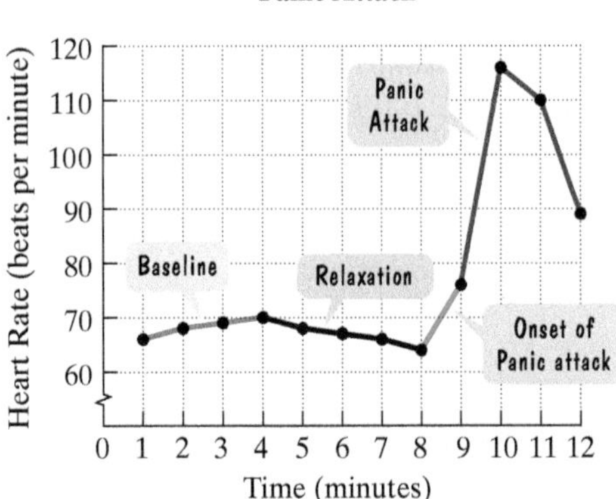

Source: Davis and Palladino, *Psychology*, Fifth Edition, Prentice Hall, 2007.

a. Use the graph to estimate the woman's maximum heart rate during the first 12 minutes of the diagnostic evaluation. After how many minutes did this occur?

b. Use the graph to estimate the woman's minimum heart rate during the first 12 minutes of the diagnostic evaluation. After how many minutes did this occur?

c. During which time period did the woman's heart rate increase at the greatest rate?

d. After how many minutes was the woman's heart rate approximately 75 beats per minute?

30. The bar graph shows the population of the United States, in millions, for five selected years.

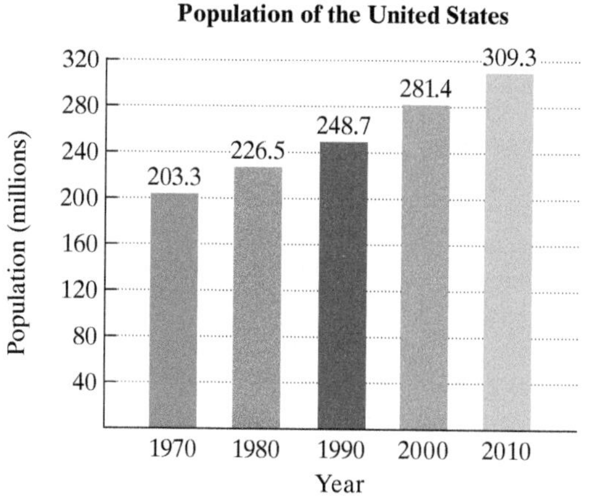

Source: U.S. Census Bureau

a. Estimate the yearly increase in the U.S. population. Express the answer in millions and do not round.

b. Write a mathematical model that estimates the U.S. population, p, in millions, x years after 1970.

c. Use the mathematical model from part (b) to project the U.S. population, in millions, in 2020.

1.3

31. What necessary piece of information is missing that prevents solving the following problem?

If 3 milligrams of a medicine is given for every 20 pounds of body weight, how many milligrams should be given to a 6-year-old child?

32. In the following problem, there is one more piece of information given than is necessary for solving the problem. Identify this unnecessary piece of information. Then solve the problem.

A taxicab charges \$3.00 for the first mile and \$0.50 for each additional half-mile. After a 6-mile trip, a customer handed the taxi driver a \$20 bill. Find the cost of the trip.

Use the four-step method in problem solving to solve Exercises 33–38.

33. If there are seven frankfurters in one pound, how many pounds would you buy for a picnic to supply 28 people with two frankfurters each?

34. A car rents for \$175 per week plus \$0.30 per mile. Find the rental cost for a three-week trip of 1200 miles.

35. You are choosing between two plans at a discount warehouse. Plan A offers an annual membership fee of \$100 and you pay 80% of the manufacturer's recommended list price. Plan B offers an annual membership fee of \$40 and you pay 90% of the manufacturer's recommended list price. If you anticipate purchasing \$1500 of merchandise in a year, which plan offers the better deal? By how much?

36. Miami is on Eastern Standard Time and San Francisco is on Pacific Standard Time, three hours earlier than Eastern Standard Time. A flight leaves Miami at 10 A.M. Eastern Standard Time, stops for 45 minutes in Houston, Texas, and arrives in San Francisco at 1:30 P.M. Pacific time. What is the actual flying time from Miami to San Francisco?

37. An automobile purchased for \$37,000 is worth \$2600 after eight years. Assuming that the value decreased steadily each year, what was the car worth at the end of the fifth year?

38. Suppose you are an engineer programming the automatic gate for a 35-cent toll. The gate is programmed for exact change only and will not accept pennies. How many coin combinations must you program the gate to accept?

Chapter 1 Test

1. Which reasoning process is shown in the following example?

The course policy states that if you turn in at least 80% of the homework, your lowest exam grade will be dropped. I turned in 90% of the homework, so my lowest grade will be dropped.

2. Which reasoning process is shown in the following example?

We examine the fingerprints of 1000 people. No two individuals in this group of people have identical fingerprints. We conclude that for all people, no two people have identical fingerprints.

In Exercises 3–6, find the next number, computation, or figure, as appropriate.

3. 0, 5, 10, 15, ____

4. $\frac{1}{6}, \frac{1}{12}, \frac{1}{24}, \frac{1}{48}$, ____

5. $3367 \times 3 = 10{,}101$

$3367 \times 6 = 20{,}202$

$3367 \times 9 = 30{,}303$

$3367 \times 12 = 40{,}404$ ____________

6. 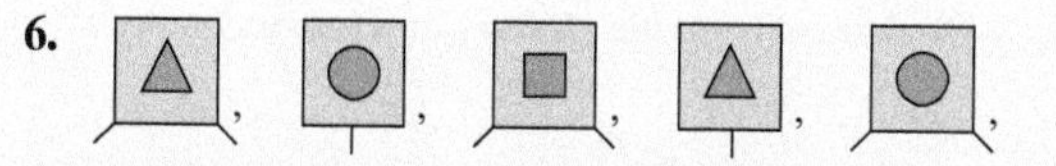 ______

7. Consider the following procedure:
Select a number. Multiply the number by 4. Add 8 to the product. Divide the sum by 2. Subtract 4 from the quotient.

a. Repeat this procedure for three numbers of your choice. Write a conjecture that relates the result of the process to the original number selected.

b. Represent the original number by the variable n and use deductive reasoning to prove the conjecture in part (a).

8. Round 3,279,425 to the nearest hundred thousand.

9. Round 706.3849 to the nearest hundredth.

In Exercises 10–13, determine each estimate without using a calculator. Different rounding results in different estimates, so there is not one single correct answer to each exercise. Use rounding to make the resulting calculations simple.

10. For a spring break vacation, a student needs to spend \$47.00 for gas, \$311.00 for food, and \$405.00 for a hotel room. If the student takes \$681.79 from savings, estimate how much more money is needed for the vacation.

11. The cost for opening a restaurant is \$485,000. If 19 people decide to share equally in the business, estimate the amount each must contribute.

12. Find an estimate of 0.48992×121.976.

13. The graph shows the composition of a typical American community's trash.

Types of Trash in an American Community by Percentage of Total Weight

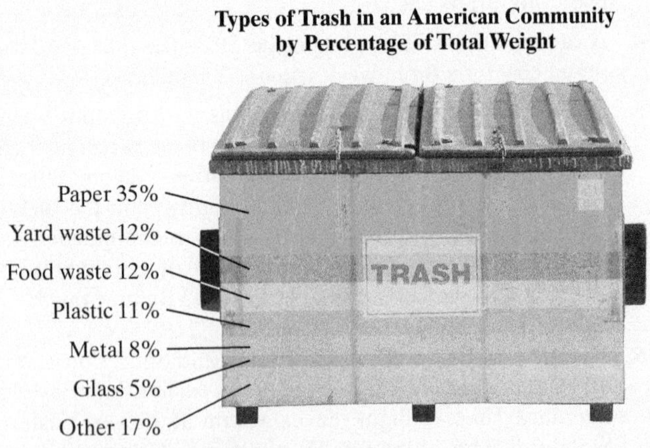

Source: U.S. Environmental Protection Agency

Across the United States, people generate approximately 512 billion pounds of trash per year. Estimate the number of pounds of trash in the form of plastic.

14. If the odometer of a car reads 71,911.5 miles and it averaged 28.9 miles per gallon, select the best estimate for the number of gallons of gasoline used.

a. 2400 **b.** 3200 **c.** 4000 **d.** 4800 **e.** 5600

15. The stated intent of the 1994 "don't ask, don't tell" policy was to reduce the number of discharges of gay men and lesbians from the military. Nearly 14,000 active-duty gay servicemembers were dismissed under the policy, which officially ended in 2011, after 18 years. The line graph shows the number of discharges under "don't ask, don't tell" from 1994 through 2010.

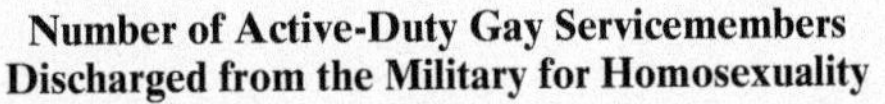

Number of Active-Duty Gay Servicemembers Discharged from the Military for Homosexuality

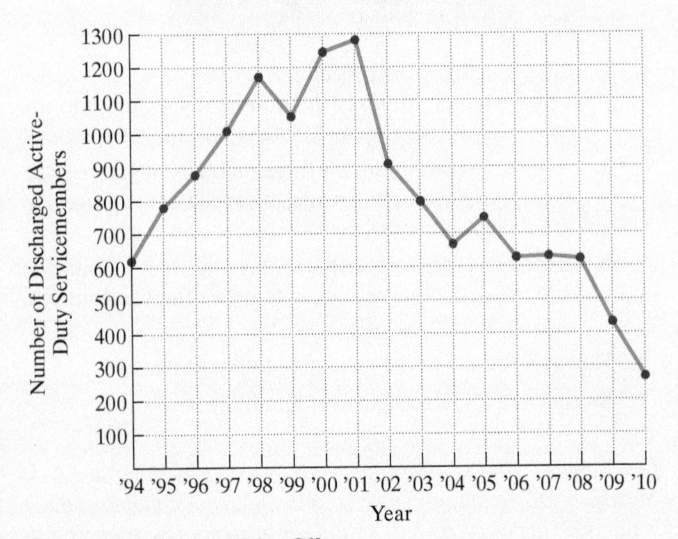

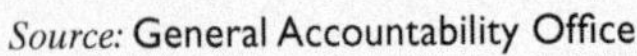

Source: General Accountability Office

a. For the period shown, in which year did the number of discharges reach a maximum? Find a reasonable estimate of the number of discharges for that year.

b. For the period shown, in which year did the number of discharges reach a minimum? Find a reasonable estimate of the number of discharges for that year.

c. In which one-year period did the number of discharges decrease at the greatest rate?

d. In which year were approximately 1000 gay servicemembers discharged under the "don't ask, don't tell" policy?

16. The bar graph shows a dramatic change in the high school grades of students who had just entered college between 1968 and 2010.

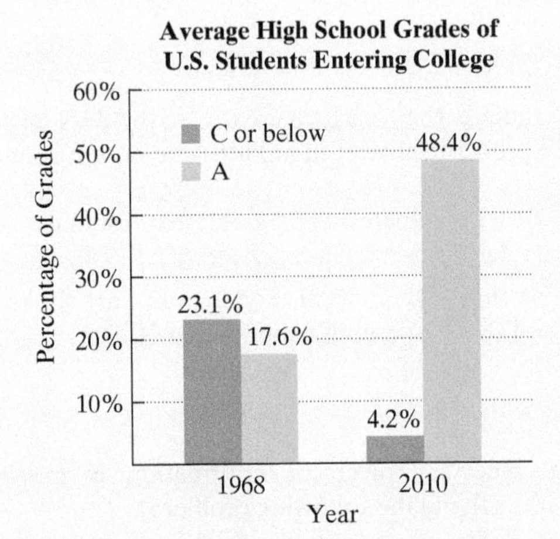

Source: John Macionis, *Sociology*, 14th Edition, Pearson, 2012.

a. Estimate the average yearly increase in the percentage of high school grades of A. Round to the nearest tenth of a percent.

b. Write a mathematical model that estimates the percentage of high school grades of A, p, x years after 1968.

c. If the trend shown by the graph continues, use your mathematical model from part (b) to project the percentage of high school grades of A in 2020.

17. The cost of renting a boat from Estes Rental is \$9 per 15 minutes. The cost from Ship and Shore Rental is \$20 per half-hour. If you plan to rent the boat for three hours, which business offers the better deal and by how much?

18. A bus operates between Miami International Airport and Miami Beach, 10 miles away. It makes 20 round trips per day carrying 32 passengers per trip. If the fare each way is \$11.00, how much money is taken in from one day's operation?

19. By paying \$50 cash up front and the balance at \$35 a week, how long will it take to pay for a computer costing \$960?

20. In 2000, the population of Greece was 10,600,000, with projections of a population decrease of 28,000 people per year. In the same year, the population of Belgium was 10,200,000, with projections of a population decrease of 12,000 people per year. (*Source:* United Nations)

According to these projections, which country will have the greater population in 2035 and by how many more people?

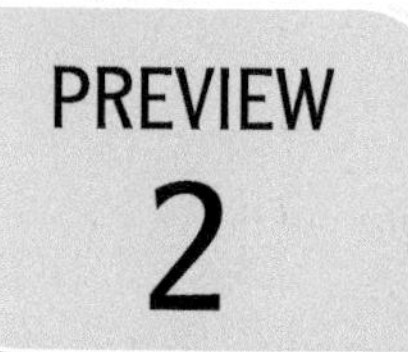

Ratio, Proportion, and Percent

Objective	Sample Problems		For help, go to page
When you finish this chapter you will be able to:			
1. Calculate ratios.	(a) Find the ratio of the pulley diameters. (4" and 10")	____________	50
	(b) Automotive Trades A small gasoline engine has a maximum cylinder volume of 520 cu cm and a compressed volume of 60 cu cm. Find the compression ratio.	____________	51
2. Solve proportions.	(a) Solve for x. $\frac{8}{x} = \frac{12}{15}$	____________	54
	(b) Solve for y. $\frac{4.4}{2.8} = \frac{y}{9.1}$	____________	
3. Solve problems involving proportions.	(a) Landscaping A mixture of plant food must be prepared by combining three parts of a concentrate with every 16 parts water. How much water should be added to 12 ounces of concentrate?	____________	57

Name ____________

Date ____________

Course/Section ____________

Objective	Sample Problems		For help, go to page
	(b) **Drafting** An architectural drawing of the living room of a house is $5\frac{1}{2}$ in. long and $4\frac{1}{2}$ in. wide. If the actual length of the living room is 22 ft, what is the actual width?	__________	64
	(c) **Manufacturing** A large production job is completed by four machines in 6 hours. The same size job must be finished in 2 hours the next time it is ordered. How many machines should be used to accomplish this task?	__________	69

(Answers to these preview problems are given in the Appendix. Also, worked solutions to many of these problems appear in the chapter Summary.)

If you are certain that you can work *all* these problems correctly, turn to page 79 for a set of practice problems. If you cannot work one or more of the preview problems, turn to the page indicated to the right of the problem. Those who wish to master this material with the greatest success should turn to Section 2-1 and begin work there.

Ratio, Proportion, and Percent

In this chapter, we cover three important and interrelated topics: ratio, proportion, and percent. Examples of ratios in the trades include the compression ratio of an automobile, the gear ratio of a machine, scale drawings, the pitch of a roof, the mechanical advantage of a pulley system, and the voltage ratio in a transformer. Two equal ratios form a proportion, and these special equations are used to solve a wide variety of problems in which three quantities are known and a fourth one is unknown. Percents are especially important in business and consumer applications, but they are also useful in trades and technical work. The following problem, is just one example of how percent is used by a **water treatment technician**:

To "shock" the water in a contaminated pipe properly, an operator needs to treat the water with 9.75 pounds of chlorine. The operator has available containers of liquid bleach that are 5% chlorine. If each gallon of the bleach weighs 8.34 pounds, how many gallons are needed to shock the water in the pipe?

2-1 Ratio and Proportion

Ratio A **ratio** is a comparison, using division, of two quantities of the same kind, both expressed in the same units. For example, the steepness of a hill can be written as the ratio of its height to its horizontal extent.

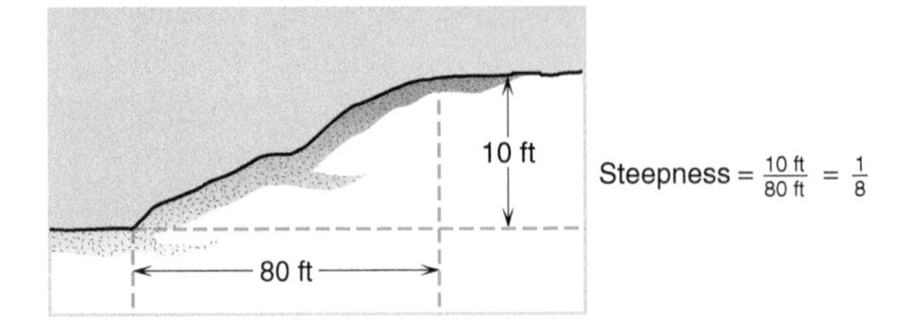

The ratio is usually written as a fraction in lowest terms, and you would read this ratio as either "one-eighth" or "one to eight."

The **gear ratio** of a gear system is defined as

$$\text{Gear ratio} = \frac{\text{number of teeth on the driven gear}}{\text{number of teeth on the driving gear}}$$

EXAMPLE 1 General Trades Find the gear ratio of the system shown if A is the driven gear and B is the driving gear, and where A has 64 teeth and B has 16 teeth.

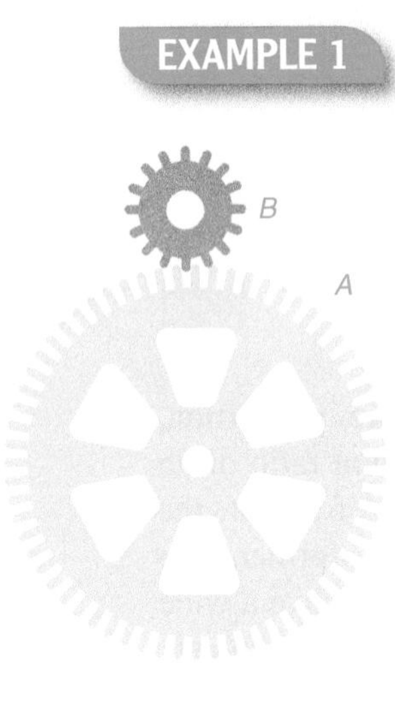

Gear ratio = ?

The ratio of the number of teeth on the driven gear to the number of teeth on the driving gear is

$$\text{Gear ratio} = \frac{64 \text{ teeth}}{16 \text{ teeth}} = \frac{4}{1}$$

Always write the fraction in lowest terms.

The gear ratio is 4 to 1. In technical work this is sometimes written as 4:1 and is read "four to one."

Typical gear ratios on a passenger car are

First gear:	3.54:1
Second gear:	1.90:1
Third gear:	1.31:1
Reverse:	3.25:1

A gear ratio of 3.54:1 means that the engine turns 3.54 revolutions for each revolution of the drive shaft. If the drive or rear-axle ratio is 3.72, the engine needs to make 3.54×3.72 or approximately 13.2 revolutions in first gear to turn the wheels one full turn.

Here are a few important examples of the use of ratios in practical work.

Pulley Ratios A pulley is a device that can be used to transfer power from one system to another. A pulley system can be used to lift heavy objects in a shop or to connect a power source to a piece of machinery. The ratio of the pulley diameters determines the relative pulley speeds.

EXAMPLE 2 **General Trades** Find the ratio of the diameter of pulley A to the diameter of pulley B in the following drawing.

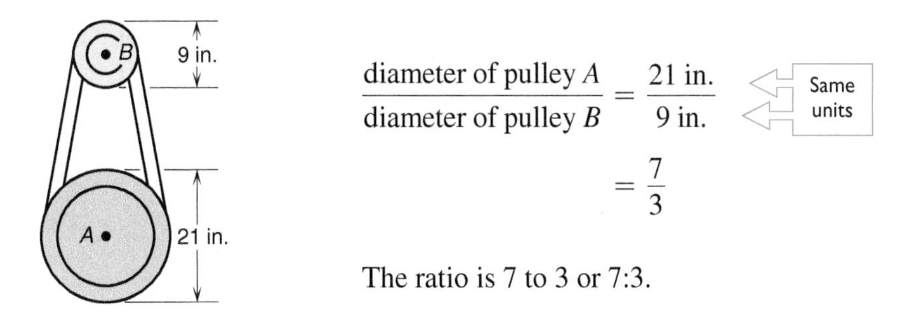

$$\frac{\text{diameter of pulley } A}{\text{diameter of pulley } B} = \frac{21 \text{ in.}}{9 \text{ in.}}$$

$$= \frac{7}{3}$$

The ratio is 7 to 3 or 7:3.

Notice that the units, inches, cancel from the ratio. A ratio is a fraction or decimal number, and it has no units. ●

Compression Ratio In an automobile engine there is a large difference between the volume of the cylinder space when a piston is at the bottom of its stroke and when it is at the top of its stroke. This difference in volumes is called the *engine displacement.* Automotive mechanics find it very useful to talk about the compression ratio of an automobile engine. The **compression ratio** of an engine compares the volume of the cylinder at maximum expansion to the volume of the cylinder at maximum compression.

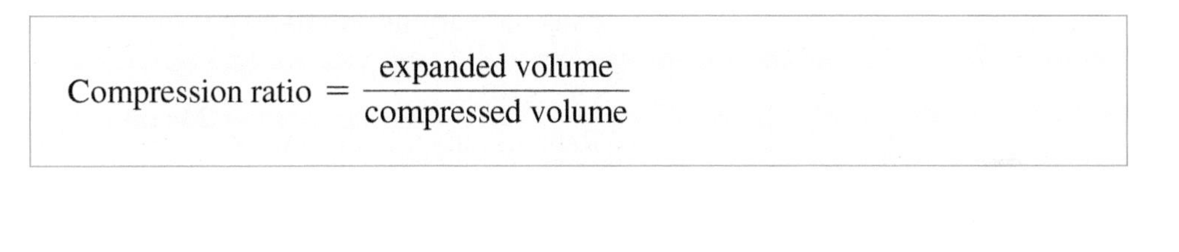

$$\text{Compression ratio} = \frac{\text{expanded volume}}{\text{compressed volume}}$$

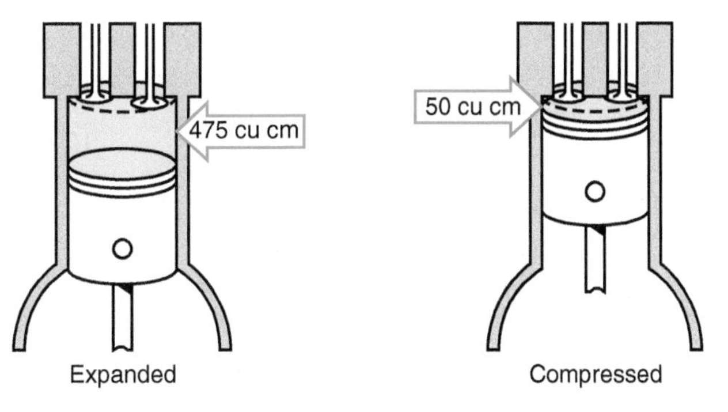

EXAMPLE 3 **Automotive Trades** Find the compression ratio of a gasoline engine if each cylinder has a maximum volume of 475 cu cm (cubic centimeters) and a minimum or compression volume of 50 cu cm.

$$\text{Compression ratio} = \frac{475 \text{ cu cm}}{50 \text{ cu cm}} = \frac{19}{2}$$

$$= 9.5$$

Compression ratios are always written so that the second number in the ratio is 1. This compression ratio would be written as $9\frac{1}{2}$ to 1. ●

Your Turn Now, for some practice in calculating ratios, work the following problems.

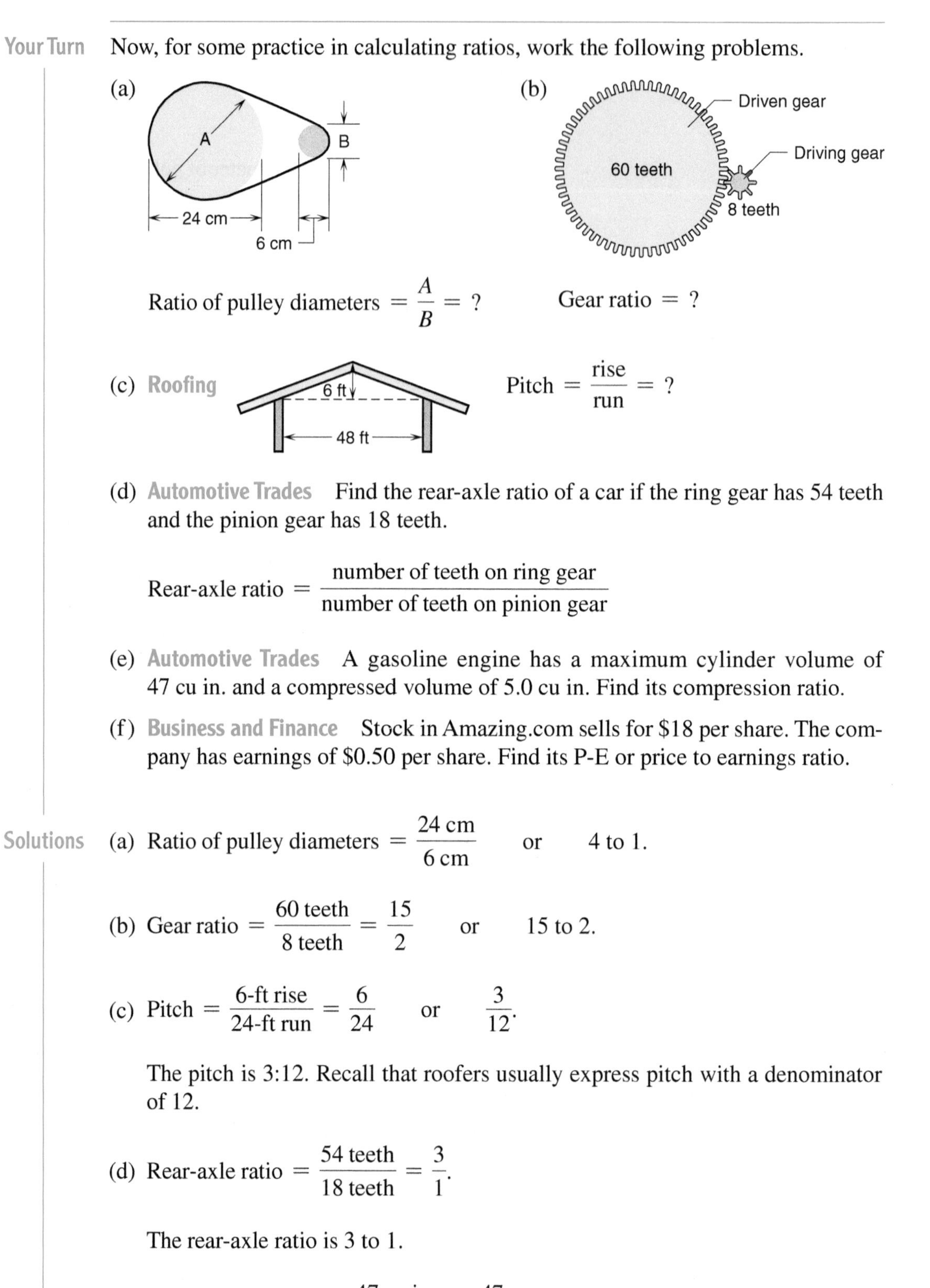

(a) Ratio of pulley diameters $= \frac{A}{B} = ?$

(b) Gear ratio $= ?$

(c) **Roofing** Pitch $= \frac{\text{rise}}{\text{run}} = ?$

(d) **Automotive Trades** Find the rear-axle ratio of a car if the ring gear has 54 teeth and the pinion gear has 18 teeth.

$$\text{Rear-axle ratio} = \frac{\text{number of teeth on ring gear}}{\text{number of teeth on pinion gear}}$$

(e) **Automotive Trades** A gasoline engine has a maximum cylinder volume of 47 cu in. and a compressed volume of 5.0 cu in. Find its compression ratio.

(f) **Business and Finance** Stock in Amazing.com sells for $18 per share. The company has earnings of $0.50 per share. Find its P-E or price to earnings ratio.

Solutions

(a) Ratio of pulley diameters $= \frac{24 \text{ cm}}{6 \text{ cm}}$ or 4 to 1.

(b) Gear ratio $= \frac{60 \text{ teeth}}{8 \text{ teeth}} = \frac{15}{2}$ or 15 to 2.

(c) Pitch $= \frac{6\text{-ft rise}}{24\text{-ft run}} = \frac{6}{24}$ or $\frac{3}{12}$.

The pitch is 3:12. Recall that roofers usually express pitch with a denominator of 12.

(d) Rear-axle ratio $= \frac{54 \text{ teeth}}{18 \text{ teeth}} = \frac{3}{1}$.

The rear-axle ratio is 3 to 1.

(e) Compression ratio $= \frac{47 \text{ cu in.}}{5.0 \text{ cu in.}} = \frac{47}{5.0}$ or 9.4 to 1.

(f) P-E $= \frac{\$18}{\$0.50} = \frac{\$18 \times 2}{\$0.50 \times 2} = \frac{\$36}{\$1}$ or 36 to 1.

Simple Equations To use ratios to solve a variety of problems, you must be able to solve a simple kind of algebraic equation. Consider this puzzle: "I'm thinking of a number. When

I multiply my number by 3, I get 15. What is my number?" Solve the puzzle and check your solution with ours.

If you answered "five," you're correct. Think about how you worked it out. Most people take the answer 15 and do the "reverse" of multiplying by 3. That is, they divide by 3. In symbols the problem would look like this:

If $3 \times \square = 15$

then $\square = 15 \div 3 = 5$

EXAMPLE 4 Let's try another one: A number multiplied by 40 gives 2200. Find the number.

Using symbols again,

$40 \times \square = 2200$

so $\square = 2200 \div 40 = \dfrac{2200}{40} = 55$

We have just solved a simple algebraic equation. But in algebra, instead of drawing boxes to represent unknown quantities, we use letters of the alphabet. For example, $40 \times \square$ could be written as $40 \times N$. Furthermore, we may signify multiplication in any one of these additional three ways:

- A raised dot — For example, $40 \cdot N$ or $8 \cdot 5$
- Writing a multiplier next to a letter. — For example, $40N$
- Enclosing in parentheses one or both of the numbers being multiplied. (This is especially useful when one or both of the numbers are fractions or decimals.) — For example, $8(5.6)$ or $\left(2\frac{1}{3}\right)\left(4\frac{5}{8}\right)$

EXAMPLE 5

$40 \times \square = 2200$

can be written $40 \cdot N = 2200$

or $40N = 2200$

To solve this type of equation, we divide 2200 by the multiplier of N, which is 40.

Your Turn For practice, solve these equations.

(a) $25n = 275$ (b) $6M = 96$

(c) $100x = 550$ (d) $12y = 99$

(e) $88 = 8P$ (f) $15 = 30a$

Solutions (a) $n = \dfrac{275}{25} = 11$ (b) $M = \dfrac{96}{6} = 16$

(c) $x = \dfrac{550}{100} = 5.5$ (d) $y = \dfrac{99}{12} = 8.25$

(e) Notice that P, the unknown quantity, is on the *right* side of the equation. You must divide the number by the multiplier of the unknown, so

$P = \dfrac{88}{8} = 11$

(f) Again, a, the unknown quantity, is on the right side, so

$$a = \frac{15}{30} = 0.5$$

Careful In problems like (f) some students mistakenly think that they must always divide the larger number by the smaller. That is not always correct. Remember, for an equation of this simple form, always divide by the number that multiplies the unknown. ●

Other types of equations will be solved, but only these simple equations are needed for our work with proportions and percent.

Proportions A **proportion** is an equation stating that two ratios are equal. For example,

$\frac{1}{3} = \frac{4}{12}$ is a proportion

Notice that the equation is true because the fraction $\frac{4}{12}$ expressed in lowest terms is equal to $\frac{1}{3}$.

Note When you are working with proportions, it is helpful to have a way of stating them in words. For example, the proportion

$\frac{2}{5} = \frac{6}{15}$ can be stated in words as

"Two is to five as six is to fifteen." ●

When one of the four numbers in a proportion is unknown, it is possible to find the value of that number. In the proportion

$$\frac{1}{3} = \frac{4}{12}$$

notice what happens when we multiply diagonally:

$\frac{1}{3} = \frac{4}{12} \rightarrow 1 \cdot 12 = 12$ $\qquad$ $\frac{1}{3} = \frac{4}{12} \rightarrow 3 \cdot 4 = 12$

These diagonal products are called the **cross-products** of the proportion. If the proportion is a true statement, the cross-products will always be equal. Here are more examples:

$\frac{5}{8} = \frac{10}{16} \rightarrow 5 \cdot 16 = 80$ and $8 \cdot 10 = 80$

$\frac{9}{12} = \frac{3}{4} \rightarrow 9 \cdot 4 = 36$ and $12 \cdot 3 = 36$

$\frac{10}{6} = \frac{5}{3} \rightarrow 10 \cdot 3 = 30$ and $6 \cdot 5 = 30$

This very important fact is called the cross-product rule.

The Cross-Product Rule

If $\frac{a}{b} = \frac{c}{d}$ then $a \cdot d = b \cdot c$.

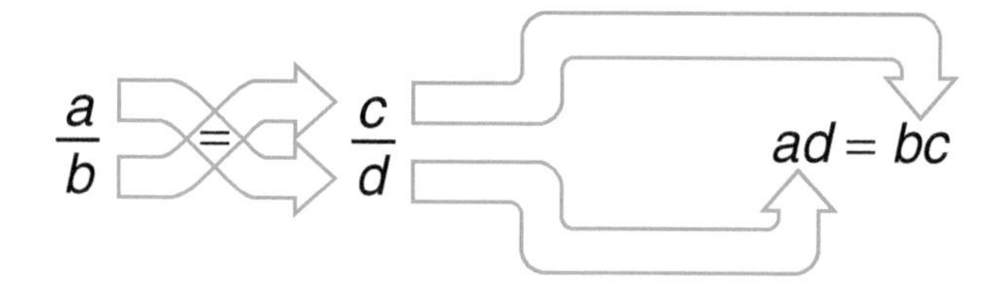

EXAMPLE 6 Find the cross-products for the proportion $\frac{3}{5} = \frac{12}{20}$.

The cross-products are $3 \cdot 20 = 60$ and $5 \cdot 12 = 60$.

The cross-product rule can be used to solve proportions, that is, to find the value of an unknown number in the proportion. For example, in the proportion

$$\frac{x}{4} = \frac{12}{16}$$

solving the proportion means finding the value of the unknown quantity x that makes the equation true. To do this:

First, use the cross-product rule.

If $\frac{x}{4} = \frac{12}{16}$ then $16 \cdot x = 4 \cdot 12$ or $16x = 48$

Then, solve this equation using the division technique.

$$x = \frac{48}{16} = 3$$

Finally, check your answer by replacing x with 3 in the original proportion equation.

$$\frac{3}{4} = \frac{12}{16}$$

Check 1: Find the cross-products.

$3 \cdot 16 = 48$ and $4 \cdot 12 = 48$ The answer is correct.

Check 2: Write $\frac{12}{16}$ in lowest terms.

$$\frac{12}{16} = \frac{4 \cdot 3}{4 \cdot 4} = \frac{3}{4}$$

Your Turn Now try this one:

$\frac{6}{N} = \frac{15}{10}$ Solve this proportion for N.

Solution **Step 1** Apply the cross-product rule.

If $\frac{6}{N} = \frac{15}{10}$ then $6 \cdot 10 = 15N$

or $15N = 60$

Step 2 Solve the equation.

$$N = \frac{60}{15} = 4$$

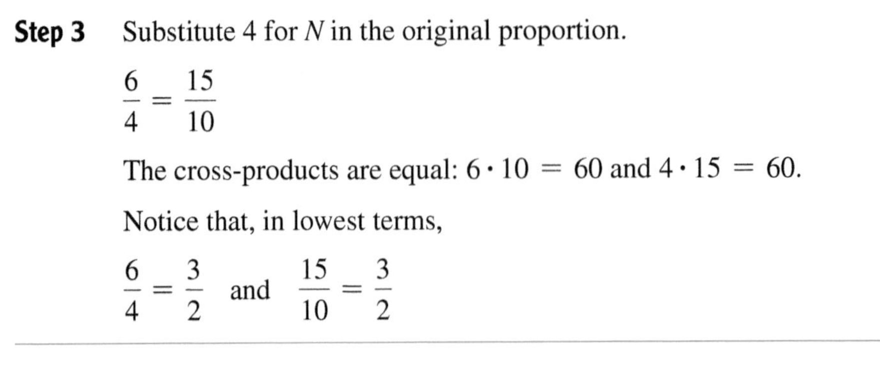

Step 3 Substitute 4 for N in the original proportion.

$$\frac{6}{4} = \frac{15}{10}$$

The cross-products are equal: $6 \cdot 10 = 60$ and $4 \cdot 15 = 60$.

Notice that, in lowest terms,

$$\frac{6}{4} = \frac{3}{2} \quad \text{and} \quad \frac{15}{10} = \frac{3}{2}$$

Note The unknown quantity can appear in any one of the four positions in a proportion. No matter where the unknown appears, solve the proportion the same way: write the cross-products and solve the resulting equation. ●

More Practice Here are more practice problems. Solve each proportion.

(a) $\frac{28}{40} = \frac{x}{100}$ (b) $\frac{12}{y} = \frac{8}{50}$ (c) $\frac{n}{6} = \frac{7}{21}$ (d) $\frac{12}{9} = \frac{32}{M}$

(e) $\frac{Y}{7} = \frac{3}{4}$ (f) $\frac{6}{5} = \frac{2}{T}$ (g) $\frac{2\frac{1}{2}}{3\frac{1}{2}} = \frac{w}{2}$ (h) $\frac{12}{E} = \frac{0.4}{1.5}$

Solutions

(a) $\frac{28}{40} = \frac{x}{100}$ $28 \cdot 100 = 40 \cdot x$ or $40x = 2800$

$x = 2800 \div 40$

$x = 70$

(b) $\frac{12}{y} = \frac{8}{50}$ $600 = 8y$ or $y = \frac{600}{8} = 75$

(c) $\frac{n}{6} = \frac{7}{21}$ $21n = 42$ $n = \frac{42}{21} = 2$

(d) $\frac{12}{9} = \frac{32}{M}$ $12M = 288$ $M = \frac{288}{12} = 24$

(e) $\frac{Y}{7} = \frac{3}{4}$ $4Y = 21$ $Y = \frac{21}{4} = 5\frac{1}{4}$ or 5.25

(f) $\frac{6}{5} = \frac{2}{T}$ $6T = 10$ $T = \frac{10}{6} = 1\frac{2}{3}$

(g) $\frac{2\frac{1}{2}}{3\frac{1}{2}} = \frac{w}{2}$ $3.5w = 5$ $w = \frac{5}{3.5} = 1\frac{3}{7}$

(h) $\frac{12}{E} = \frac{0.4}{1.5}$ $18 = 0.4E$ $E = \frac{18}{0.4} = 45$

A Closer Look You may have noticed that the two steps for solving a proportion can be simplified into one step. For example, in problem (a), to solve

$$\frac{28}{40} = \frac{x}{100}$$ we can write the answer directly as

$$x = \frac{28 \cdot 100}{40}$$

Always divide by the number that is diagonally opposite the unknown, and multiply the two remaining numbers that are diagonally opposite each other.

This shortcut comes in handy when using a calculator. For example, with a calculator, problem (h) becomes

12 [×] 1.5 [÷] .4 [=] → 45.

The numbers 12 and 1.5 are diagonally opposite each other in the proportion.

0.4 is diagonally opposite the unknown E. ●

Your Turn Practice this one-step process by solving the proportion

$$\frac{120}{25} = \frac{6}{Q}$$

Solution $Q = \dfrac{6 \cdot 25}{120} = 1.25$ Check it.

Practical Applications We can use proportions to solve a variety of problems involving ratios. If you are given the value of a ratio and one of its terms, it is possible to find the other term.

EXAMPLE 7

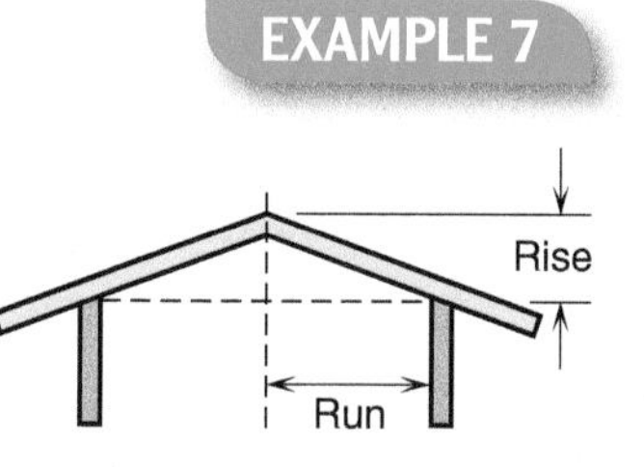

Roofing If the pitch of a roof is supposed to be 2:12, and the run is 20 ft, what must be the rise?

$$\text{Pitch} = \frac{\text{rise}}{\text{run}}$$

A ratio of 2:12 is equivalent to the fraction $\frac{2}{12}$; therefore, the equation becomes

$$\frac{2}{12} = \frac{\text{rise}}{20} \quad \text{or} \quad \frac{2}{12} = \frac{R}{20}$$

Find the cross-products. $12R = 40$

Then solve for R. $R = \dfrac{40}{12}$

The rise is 3 ft 4 inches. $\left(\dfrac{1}{3}\text{ ft} = 4\text{ in.}\right)$ $R = 3\dfrac{1}{3}\text{ ft}$ ●

The algebra you learned earlier in this chapter will enable you to solve any ratio problem of this kind. Here is another example.

EXAMPLE 8

Allied Health For medications provided in a liquid formulation, the amount of liquid given to a patient depends on the concentration of drug in the fluid. Medication Y is available only in a liquid formulation with a concentration of 100 mg/mL (milligrams per milliliter). Suppose a physician orders 225 mg of medication Y. To determine the amount of liquid required, first note that 100 mg/mL means that one milliliter of liquid contains 100 mg of the medication. Therefore, we can set up the following proportion:

$$\frac{1 \text{ mL}}{x \text{ mL}} = \frac{100 \text{ mg}}{225 \text{ mg}}$$

Solving for x, we have

$$100x = 225$$
$$x = 2.25 \text{ mL}$$

Therefore, the patient should take 2.25 mL of the liquid in order to receive 225 mg of medication Y.

Your Turn Try these problems.

(a) **Manufacturing** If the gear ratio on a mixing machine is 6:1 and the driving gear has 12 teeth, how many teeth are on the driven gear?

(b) **Manufacturing** The pulley system of an assembly belt has a pulley diameter ratio of 4. If the larger pulley has a diameter of 15 in., what is the diameter of the smaller pulley?

(c) **Automotive Trades** The compression ratio of a classic Datsun 280Z is 8.3 to 1. If the compressed volume of the cylinder is 36 cu cm, what is the expanded volume of the cylinder?

(d) **Construction** On a certain construction job, concrete is made using a volume ratio of 1 part cement to $2\frac{1}{2}$ parts sand and 4 parts gravel. How much sand should be mixed with 3 cu ft of cement?

(e) **Sports and Leisure** Manager Sparky Spittoon of the Huntville Hackers wants his ace pitcher Lefty Groove to improve his strikeouts-to-walks ratio to at least 5:2. If he has 65 strikeouts so far this season, what is the maximum number of walks he can give up and still keep Sparky happy?

(f) **Roofing** If the pitch of a roof must be 5:12, how much rise should there be over a run of 54 ft?

(g) **Allied Health** Medication TTQ is available only in a liquid formulation with a concentration of 125 mg/5 mL (milligrams per 5 milliliters). How much of this liquid formulation should be given to a patient if 500 mg of TTQ is ordered by the physician?

Solutions (a) Gear ratio $= \dfrac{\text{number of teeth on driven gear}}{\text{number of teeth on driving gear}}$

A ratio of 6:1 is equivalent to the fraction $\dfrac{6}{1}$.

Therefore,

$$\frac{6}{1} = \frac{x}{12}$$

or $72 = x$ The driven gear has 72 teeth.

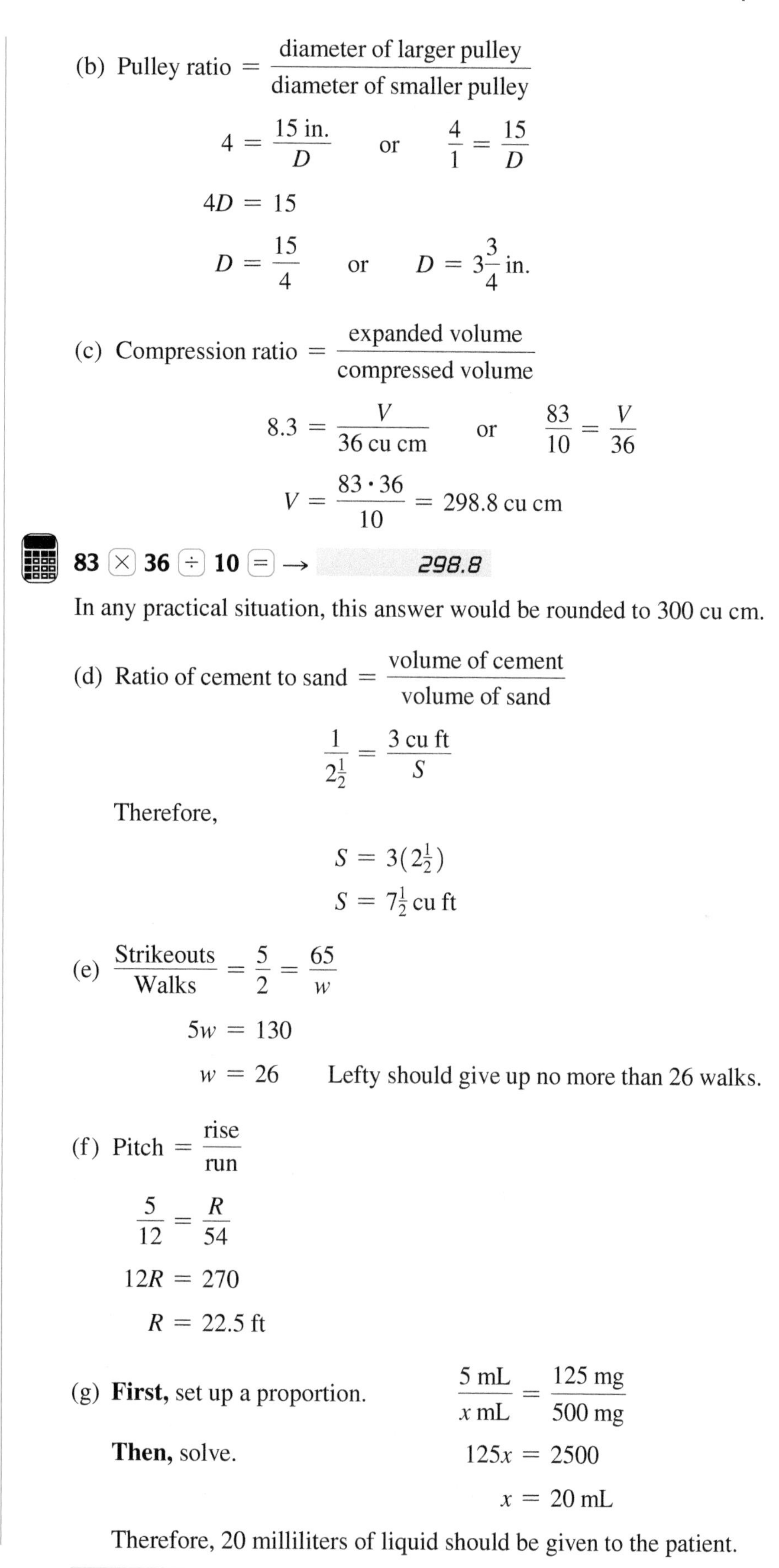

(b) $\text{Pulley ratio} = \dfrac{\text{diameter of larger pulley}}{\text{diameter of smaller pulley}}$

$$4 = \frac{15\text{ in.}}{D} \quad \text{or} \quad \frac{4}{1} = \frac{15}{D}$$

$$4D = 15$$

$$D = \frac{15}{4} \quad \text{or} \quad D = 3\frac{3}{4}\text{ in.}$$

(c) $\text{Compression ratio} = \dfrac{\text{expanded volume}}{\text{compressed volume}}$

$$8.3 = \frac{V}{36\text{ cu cm}} \quad \text{or} \quad \frac{83}{10} = \frac{V}{36}$$

$$V = \frac{83 \cdot 36}{10} = 298.8\text{ cu cm}$$

83 ⊠ 36 ⊟ 10 ⊜ → 298.8

(Calculator keystrokes: 83 [×] 36 [÷] 10 [=] → 298.8)

In any practical situation, this answer would be rounded to 300 cu cm.

(d) $\text{Ratio of cement to sand} = \dfrac{\text{volume of cement}}{\text{volume of sand}}$

$$\frac{1}{2\frac{1}{2}} = \frac{3\text{ cu ft}}{S}$$

Therefore,

$$S = 3(2\tfrac{1}{2})$$

$$S = 7\tfrac{1}{2}\text{ cu ft}$$

(e) $\dfrac{\text{Strikeouts}}{\text{Walks}} = \dfrac{5}{2} = \dfrac{65}{w}$

$$5w = 130$$

$w = 26$ Lefty should give up no more than 26 walks.

(f) $\text{Pitch} = \dfrac{\text{rise}}{\text{run}}$

$$\frac{5}{12} = \frac{R}{54}$$

$$12R = 270$$

$$R = 22.5\text{ ft}$$

(g) **First,** set up a proportion. $\dfrac{5\text{ mL}}{x\text{ mL}} = \dfrac{125\text{ mg}}{500\text{ mg}}$

Then, solve. $125x = 2500$

$$x = 20\text{ mL}$$

Therefore, 20 milliliters of liquid should be given to the patient.

Now turn to Exercises 2-1 for more practice on ratio and proportion.

Exercises 2-1 Ratio and Proportion

A. Complete the following tables.

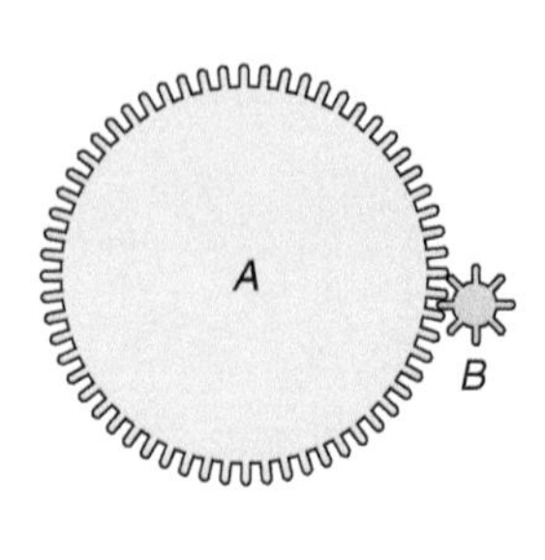

1.

	Teeth on Driven Gear *A*	Teeth on Driving Gear *B*	Gear Ratio, $\frac{A}{B}$
(a)	35	5	
(b)	12	7	
(c)		3	2 to 1
(d)	21		$3\frac{1}{2}$ to 1
(e)	15		1 to 3
(f)		18	1 to 2
(g)		24	2:3
(h)	30		3:5
(i)	27	18	
(j)	12	30	

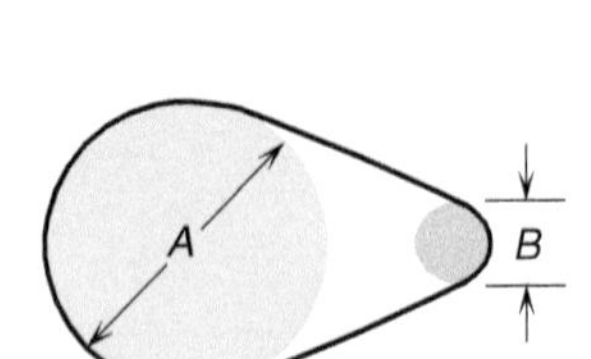

2.

	Diameter of Pulley *A*	Diameter of Pulley *B*	Pulley Ratio, $\frac{A}{B}$
(a)	16 in.	6 in.	
(b)	15 in.	12 in.	
(c)		8 in.	2 to 1
(d)	27 cm		4.5 to 1
(e)		10 cm	4 to 1
(f)	$8\frac{1}{8}$ in.	$3\frac{1}{4}$ in.	
(g)	8.46 cm	11.28 cm	
(h)	20.41 cm		3.14 to 1
(i)		12.15 cm	1 to 2.25
(j)	4.45 cm		0.25 to 1

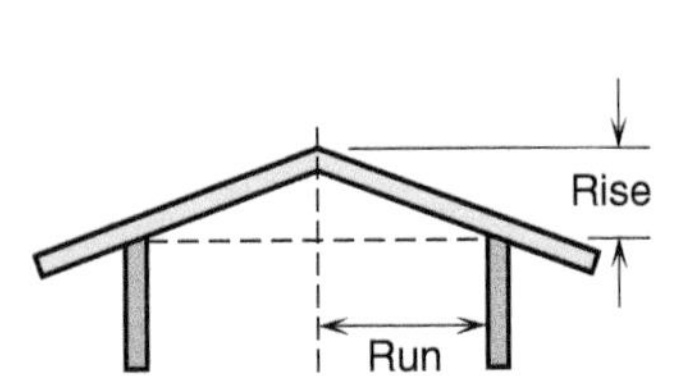

3.

	Rise	Run	Pitch
(a)	8 ft	6 ft	
(b)		24 ft	4:12
(c)	7 ft		3:12
(d)	14 ft 4 in.	25 ft	
(e)	9 ft	15 ft	
(f)		20 ft	2.4:12
(g)	3 ft		1.8:12
(h)		30 ft 6 in.	2:12

B. Solve these proportion equations.

1. $\frac{3}{2} = \frac{x}{8}$

2. $\frac{6}{R} = \frac{5}{72}$

3. $\frac{y}{60} = \frac{5}{3}$

4. $\frac{2}{15} = \frac{8}{H}$

5. $\frac{5}{P} = \frac{30}{7}$

6. $\frac{1}{6} = \frac{17}{x}$

7. $\frac{A}{2.5} = \frac{13}{10}$

8. $\frac{27}{M} = \frac{3}{0.8}$

9. $\frac{2}{5} = \frac{T}{4.5}$

10. $\frac{0.12}{N} = \frac{2}{7}$

11. $\frac{138}{23} = \frac{18}{x}$

12. $\frac{3.25}{1.5} = \frac{A}{0.6}$

13. $\frac{x}{34.86} = \frac{1.2}{8.3}$

14. $\frac{2\frac{1}{2}}{R} = \frac{1\frac{1}{4}}{3\frac{1}{4}}$

15. $\frac{2\text{ ft }6\text{ in.}}{4\text{ ft }3\text{ in.}} = \frac{L}{8\text{ ft }6\text{ in.}}$

16. $\frac{6.2\text{ cm}}{x} = \frac{1.2\text{ in.}}{11.4\text{ in.}}$

17. $\frac{3\text{ ft }4\text{ in.}}{4\text{ ft }2\text{ in.}} = \frac{3.2\text{ cm}}{x}$

18. $\frac{3\frac{1}{2}\text{ in.}}{W} = \frac{1.4}{0.05}$

C. Solve.

1. **Automotive Trades** The compression ratio in a certain engine is 9.6 to 1. If the expanded volume of a cylinder is 48 cu in., what is the compressed volume?

2. **Painting** If 1 gal of paint covers 360 sq ft, how many gallons will be needed to cover 2650 sq ft with two coats? (Assume that you cannot buy a fraction of a gallon.)

3. **Machine Trades** If 28 tapered pins can be machined from a steel rod 12 ft long, how many tapered pins can be made from a steel rod 9 ft long?

4. **Carpentry** If 6 lb of nails are needed for each thousand lath, how many pounds are required for 4250 lath?

5. **Masonry** For a certain kind of plaster work, 1.5 cu yd of sand are needed for every 100 sq yd of surface. How much sand will be needed for 350 sq yd of surface?

6. **Printing** The paper needed for a printing job weighs 12 lb per 500 sheets. How many pounds of paper are needed to run a job requiring 12,500 sheets?

7. **Machine Trades** A cylindrical oil tank 8 ft deep holds 420 gallons when filled to capacity. How many gallons remain in the tank when the depth of oil is $5\frac{1}{2}$ ft?

8. **Agriculture** A liquid fertilizer must be prepared by using one part of concentrate for every 32 parts of water. How much water should be added to 7 oz of concentrate?

9. **Welding** A 10-ft bar of I-beam weighs 208 lb. What is the weight of a 6-ft length?

10. **Photography** A photographer must mix a chemical in the ratio of 1 part chemical for every 7 parts of water. How many ounces of chemical should be used to make a 3-qt *total* mixture? (1 qt = 32 oz)

11. **General Trades** If you earn $684.80 for a 32-hour work week, how much would you earn for a 40-hour work week at the same hourly rate?

12. **Machine Trades** A machinist can produce 12 parts in 40 min. How many parts can the machinist produce in 4 hours?

13. **Automotive Trades** The headlights on a car are set so the light beam drops 2 in. for each 25 ft measured horizontally. If the headlights are mounted 30 in. above the ground, how far ahead of the car will they hit the ground?

14. **Machine Trades** A machinist creates $2\frac{3}{4}$ lb of steel chips in fabricating 16 rods. How many pounds of steel chips will be created in producing 120 rods?

15. **Agriculture** To prepare a pesticide spray, 3.5 lb of BIOsid is added to 30 gal of water. How much BIOsid should be added to a spray tank holding 325 gal? Round to the nearest 0.1 lb.

16. **Painting** A painter must thin some paint for use in a sprayer. If the recommended rate is $\frac{1}{2}$ pint of water per gallon of paint, how many pints of water should be added to $5\frac{1}{2}$ gallons of paint?

17. **Allied Health** The label on a concentrated drug solution indicates that it contains 85 mg of medication in 5 mL. If the patient is to receive 220 mg of solution, how much of the solution should be given? Round to the nearest tenth.

18. **Automotive Trades** In winter weather, fuel-line antifreeze must be added at a rate of one can per 8 gal of fuel. How many cans should be added for an 18-gal fuel tank?

19. **Culinary Arts** One small 0.5-kg package of Fromage de Cernex cheese contains 2000 calories. How many calories are contained in a large 10-kg package?

20. **Automotive Trades** The air-to-fuel ratio of an engine helps determine how efficiently the engine is running. In most cases, a ratio of 14.7:1 is ideal. A larger ratio indicates that the engine is running *lean,* while a smaller ratio indicates that it is running *rich.* Suppose a certain engine draws 160 lb of air in burning 12 lb of fuel. Find the air-to-fuel ratio, and state whether the engine is running lean or rich.

21. **Automotive Trades** In problem 20, it was stated that the ideal air-to-fuel ratio for an engine is 14.7:1. If a vehicle burns 9 lb of fuel, how many pounds of air should it draw to achieve the ideal ratio? Round to the nearest pound.

22. **Sports and Leisure** Power hitter Sammy Sockitome strikes out too much to suit manager Sparky Spittoon. Sammy is promised an incentive bonus of a million dollars if he can reduce his strikeout–to–home run ratio to 3:1. If Sammy hits 56 home runs, what is the maximum number of strikeouts he can have and still earn the bonus?

23. **Landscaping** A landscape architect is seeding a 6000-sq-ft lawn. If the seed manufacturer recommends using 6 lb of seed per 1500 sq ft, how many pounds of seed will be needed?

24. **Masonry** A mason needs to purchase mortar mix for a retaining wall consisting of 640 blocks. The guidelines for this mix suggest that 12 bags are required for every 100 blocks. Assuming that he cannot purchase part of a bag, how many bags will he need?

25. **Allied Health** Medication Q is available only in a liquid form with a concentration of 30 μg/mL (micrograms per milliliter). Determine how much

of the liquid should be given to a patient when the following amounts of Medication Q are ordered by the physician:

(a) 15 μg (b) 10 μg (c) 200 μg

(Round to two decimal digits if necessary.)

26. **Construction** Concrete requires cement, sand, and gravel in a ratio of 1 to 2 to 3 by volume for optimum strength. PTO Construction is pouring a small concrete foundation for which 38 bags of sand will be used. (a) How many bags of cement should be used? (b) How many bags of gravel should be used?

27. **Allied Health** Each tablet of medication Z contains 50 micrograms (μg) of drug. Determine how many tablets (or fractions of tablets) should be given when the following amounts of medication Z are ordered by the physician:

    (a) 100 μg (b) 75 μg (c) 230 μg

    (Round to the nearest half-tablet.)

28. **Construction** A building code requires one square foot (sq ft) of net-free vent area (NFVA) for every 300 sq ft of attic space. How many square feet of NFVA are required for a 1620-sq-ft attic?

29. **Agriculture** A 12-inch-wide conveyor unloads 5000 bushels of wheat per hour. At this speed, how many bushels per hour will an 18-inch-wide conveyor unload?

30. **Trades Management** A business owner is currently renting her shop space for $8460 per month. Her lease agreement states that her rent will be adjusted each July according to the CPI (Consumer Price Index). Specifically, the ratio of this June's CPI to the previous June's CPI will be multiplied by the current monthly rent to determine the new monthly rent. If this June's CPI is 226.765, and last June's CPI was 217.273, what will be her new monthly rent beginning in July? (Round your answer to the nearest cent.)

31. **Trades Management** A small welding shop employs four welders and one secretary. A workers' compensation insurance policy charges a premium of $10.59 per $100 of gross wages for the welders and $1.38 per $100 of gross wages for the secretary. If each welder earns $36,000 per year, and the secretary earns $28,000 per year, what is the total annual premium for this insurance?

32. **Construction** On a crisp fall day, a builder wants to drive from his house to a work site in the mountains to pour the concrete foundations for a cabin. The minimum temperature at which the concrete will set with adequate strength is 40°F. The temperature at his house is 60°F, and the cabin is at an altitude that is 5900 ft higher than the town where the builder lives. If temperature decreases by about 4°F for every 1000 ft of altitude increase, should the builder bother to drive to the work site?

33. **General Trades** A trades worker is considering a job offer in another city. Her current job pays $2950 per month and is in a city with a cost of living index of 98.3. The cost of living index in the new location is 128.5. If she were to maintain her present lifestyle, how much would she need to earn per month in the new job? (*Hint:* Cost of living must be directly proportional to salary).

34. **Automotive Trades** We calculated that the fuel cost of a certain gas-powered car is $12.92 more per 100 miles than the electrical cost

of a battery-powered car. If the cost of the battery-powered car was \$8000 more than the gas-powered car, how many miles of driving does it take to make up for this additional cost? (Round up to the next thousand.)

35. **Allied Health** The dosages of certain medications are based on a patient's body surface area (BSA) as measured in square meters. Suppose a physician prescribes a daily dosage of 250 mg/m^2 (milligrams per square meter) of medication D for a patient. If the patient has a BSA of 1.53 m^2, how many 60-mg capsules should the patient take per day? (Round down to the nearest whole number.)

Check your answers to the odd-numbered problems in the Appendix, then turn to Section 2-2.

Special Applications of Ratio and Proportion

In the previous section, we used the concepts of ratio and proportion to solve some simple applications. In this section we will learn about additional applications of ratio and proportion in the trades and technical areas.

Scale Drawings Proportion equations are found in a wide variety of practical situations. For example, when a drafter makes a drawing of a machine part, building layout, or other large structure, he or she must *scale it down.* The drawing must represent the object accurately, but it must be small enough to fit on the paper. The draftsperson reduces every dimension by some fixed ratio.

EXAMPLE 1 **Drafting** Drawings that are larger than life involve an expanded scale.

For the automobile shown, the ratio of the actual length to the scale-drawing length is equal to the ratio of the actual width to the scale-drawing width.

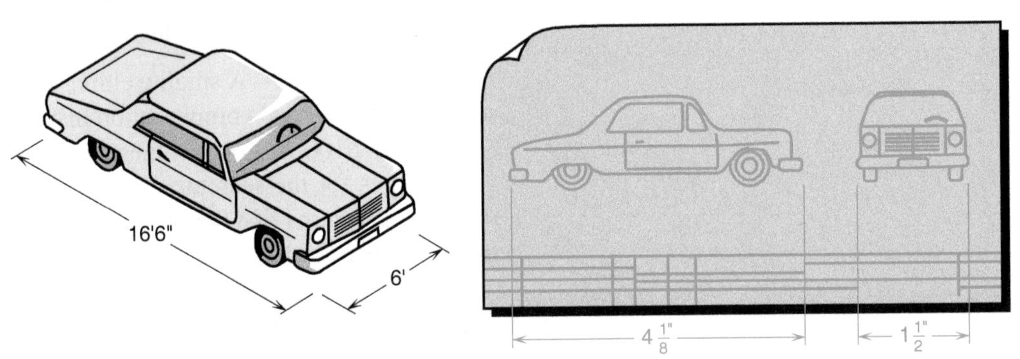

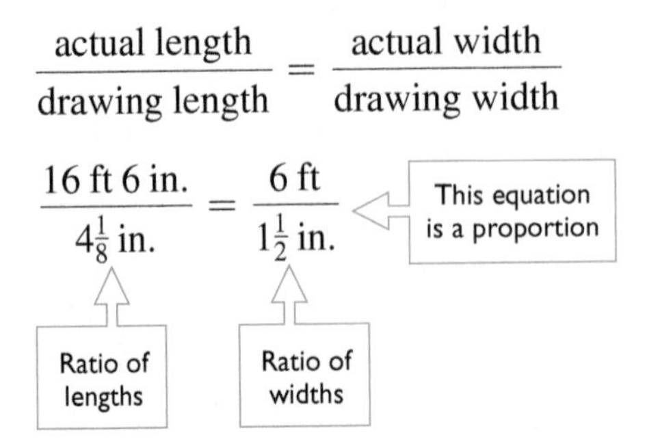

$$\frac{\text{actual length}}{\text{drawing length}} = \frac{\text{actual width}}{\text{drawing width}}$$

$$\frac{16\text{ ft }6\text{ in.}}{4\frac{1}{8}\text{ in.}} = \frac{6\text{ ft}}{1\frac{1}{2}\text{ in.}}$$

Rewrite all quantities in the same units (1 ft = 12 in.):

$$\frac{198\text{ in.}}{4\frac{1}{8}\text{ in.}} = \frac{72\text{ in.}}{1\frac{1}{2}\text{ in.}}$$

You should notice first of all that each side of this equation is a ratio. Each side is a ratio of *like* quantities: lengths on the left and widths on the right.

Second, notice that the ratio $\frac{198 \text{ in.}}{4\frac{1}{8} \text{ in.}}$ is equal to $\frac{48}{1}$.

Divide it out: $198 \div 4\frac{1}{8} = 198 \div \frac{33}{8}$

$$= \frac{198}{1} \times \frac{8}{33}$$

$$= 48$$

198 ⊠ **8** ⊞ **33** ⊟ → 48.

Notice also that the ratio $\frac{72 \text{ in.}}{1\frac{1}{2} \text{ in.}}$ is equal to $\frac{48}{1}$.

The common ratio $\frac{48}{1}$ is called the **scale factor** of the drawing.

EXAMPLE 2 **Architecture** In this problem, one of the dimensions is unknown.

Suppose that a rectangular room has a length of 18 ft and a width of 12 ft. An architectural scale drawing of this room is made so that, on the drawing, the length of the room is 4.5 in. What will be the width of the room on the drawing? What is the scale factor?

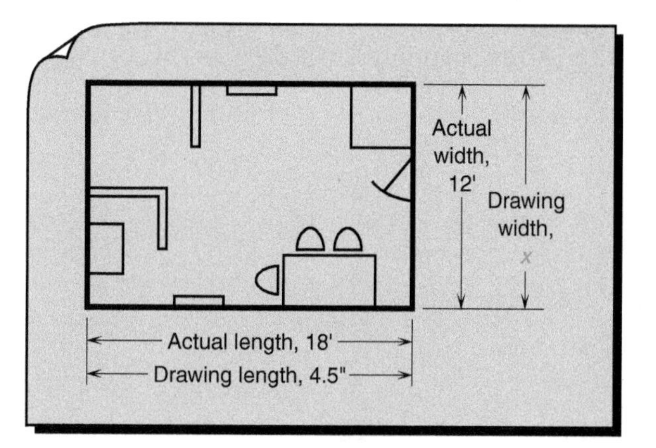

First, set up a ratio of lengths and a ratio of widths.

$$\text{Length ratio} = \frac{\text{actual length}}{\text{drawing length}}$$

$$= \frac{18 \text{ ft}}{4.5 \text{ in.}} = \frac{216 \text{ in.}}{4.5 \text{ in.}}$$ ← Convert 18 ft to inches so that the top and the bottom of the fraction have the same units.

$$\text{Width ratio} = \frac{\text{actual width}}{\text{drawing width}}$$

$$= \frac{12 \text{ ft}}{x \text{ in.}} = \frac{144 \text{ in.}}{x \text{ in.}}$$ ← Change 12 ft to 144 in. ← Let x = the drawing width

Second, write a proportion equation.

$$\frac{216}{4.5} = \frac{144}{x}$$

Third, solve this proportion. Cross-multiply to get

$216x = (4.5)144$

$216x = 648$

$x = 3$ in. The width of the room on the drawing is 3 in.

For the room drawing shown, the scale factor is

$$\text{Scale factor} = \frac{18\text{ ft}}{4.5\text{ in.}} = \frac{216\text{ in.}}{4.5\text{ in.}}$$

$$= 48 \quad \text{or} \quad 48 \text{ to } 1$$

One inch on the drawing corresponds to 48 in. or 4 ft on the actual object. We can express this as 1 in. = 4 ft. A draftsperson would divide by 4 and write it as $\frac{1}{4}$ in. = 1 ft.

Your Turn **Drafting** The drawing of the triangular plate shown has a height of 18 in. and a base length of 14 in.

(a) What will be the corresponding height in a reduced copy of this drawing if the base length in the copy is $2\frac{3}{16}$ in.?

(b) Find the scale factor of the reduction.

18"

14"

Solutions (a) $\dfrac{18\text{ in.}}{x} = \dfrac{14\text{ in.}}{2\frac{3}{16}\text{ in.}}$

Cross-multiply: $18(2\frac{3}{16}) = 14x$

$14x = 39\frac{3}{8}$

$x = 2\frac{13}{16}$ in.

2 (A b/c) **3** (A b/c) **16** (×) **18** (÷) **14** (=) → 2⌴13/16 (F↔D) (=) → 2.8125

(b) Scale factor $= \dfrac{18\text{ in.}}{2\frac{13}{16}\text{ in.}}$ or $\dfrac{14\text{ in.}}{2\frac{3}{16}\text{ in.}}$

$= 6\frac{2}{5}$ or 6.4 to 1

18 (÷) **2** (A b/c) **13** (A b/c) **16** (=) → 6⌴2/5 (F↔D) (=) → 6.4

Similar Figures In general, two geometric figures that have the same shape but are not the same size are said to be **similar figures**. The blueprint drawing and the actual object are a pair of similar figures. An enlarged photograph and the smaller original are similar.

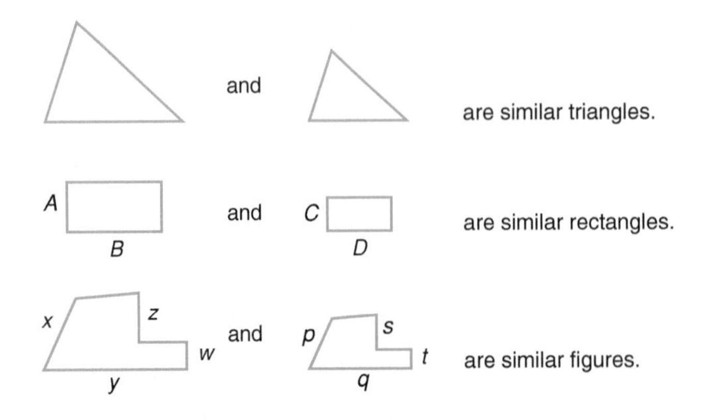

In any similar figures, all parts of corresponding dimensions have the same scale ratio. For example, in the preceding rectangles

$$\frac{A}{C} = \frac{B}{D}$$

In the irregular figures on the previous page,

$$\frac{x}{p} = \frac{y}{q} = \frac{z}{s} = \frac{w}{t} \text{ and so on}$$

The triangles shown here are *not* similar:

EXAMPLE 3

Landscaping A landscaper is designing a garden for a house that is not yet built. He needs to determine how long a shadow the house will cast into the garden area. To determine this, the landscaper, who is 6 ft tall, measures his shadow to be 8 ft long at a particular time on a summer afternoon.

If the roofline of the house will be 15 ft high where the landscaper was standing, how far from the edge of the house will its shadow extend at the same time of day?

To solve this problem we draw a sketch of the situation.

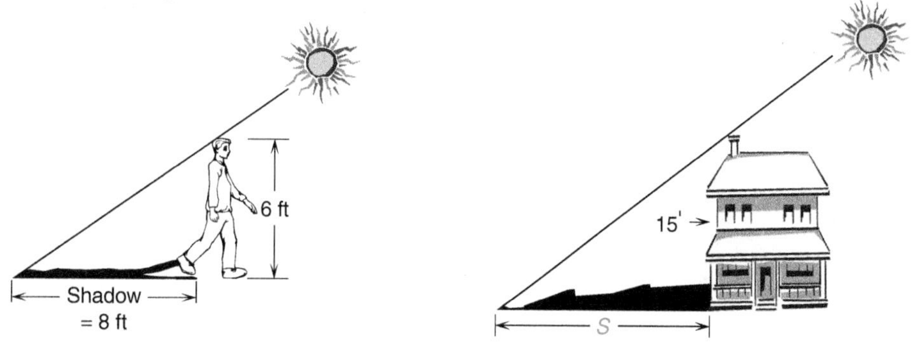

At the same time of day, the triangles formed by the objects, the sun's rays, and the shadows are similar. Therefore,

$$\frac{6 \text{ ft}}{15 \text{ ft}} = \frac{8 \text{ ft}}{S \text{ ft}}$$

$$S = \frac{15(8)}{6} = 20 \text{ ft}$$

The shadow cast by the house will extend 20 ft into the garden from the edge of the house.

Your Turn Find the missing dimension in each of the following pairs of similar figures.

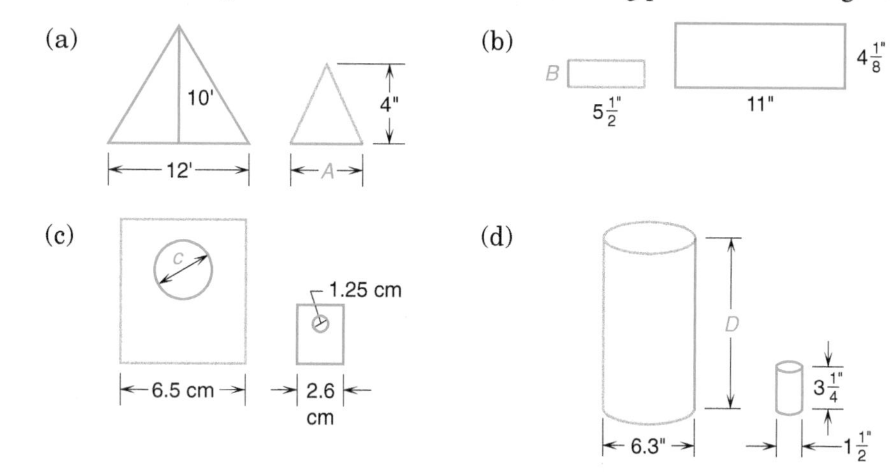

Solutions (a) $\frac{A}{144} = \frac{4}{120}$ Convert ft to in.

$A = \frac{4(144)}{120} = 4.8$ in.

(b) $\frac{B}{4\frac{1}{8}} = \frac{5\frac{1}{2}}{11}$

$B = \frac{(5\frac{1}{2})(4\frac{1}{8})}{11} = 2\frac{1}{16}$ in.

(c) $\frac{c}{1.25} = \frac{6.5}{2.6}$

$c = \frac{6.5(1.25)}{2.6} = 3.125$ cm

(d) $\frac{D}{3\frac{1}{4}} = \frac{6.3}{1\frac{1}{2}}$

$D = \frac{6.3(3\frac{1}{4})}{1\frac{1}{2}} = 13.65$ in.

Work problem (d) on a calculator this way:

3 [A b/c] **1** [A b/c] **4** [×] **6.3** [÷] **1.5** [=] → 13.65

Direct Proportion

Many trade problems can be solved by setting up a proportion involving four related quantities. But it is important that you recognize that there are *two* kinds of proportions—direct and inverse. Two quantities are said to be **directly proportional** if an increase in one quantity leads to a proportional increase in the other quantity, or if a decrease in one leads to a decrease in the other.

Direct proportion: increase → increase
or decrease → decrease

EXAMPLE 4

Electrical Trades The electrical resistance of a wire is directly proportional to its length—the longer the wire, the greater the resistance. If 1 ft of Nichrome heater element wire has a resistance of 1.65 ohms, what length of wire is needed to provide a resistance of 19.8 ohms?

Resistance = 1.65 ohms
1 ft
Resistance = 19.8 ohms
L

First, recognize that this problem involves a *direct* proportion. As the length of wire increases, the resistance increases proportionally.

As L increases . . . R increases

$$\frac{L}{1 \text{ ft}} = \frac{R}{1.65 \text{ ohms}}$$

Both ratios increase in size when L increases.

Second, set up a direct proportion and solve.

$$\frac{L}{1 \text{ ft}} = \frac{19.8 \text{ ohms}}{1.65 \text{ ohms}}$$

$$L = 12 \text{ ft}$$

Your Turn Solve each of the following problems by setting up a direct proportion.

(a) **Manufacturing** If a widget machine produces 88 widgets in 2 hours, how many will it produce in $3\frac{1}{2}$ hours?

(b) **Painting** If 1 gal of paint covers 825 sq ft, how much paint is needed to cover 2640 sq ft?

(c) **Automotive Trades** What is the cost of six air filters if eight filters cost $55.92?

(d) **Transportation** A diesel truck was driven 273 miles on 42 gal of fuel. How much fuel is needed for a trip of 600 miles? Round to the nearest gallon.

(e) **Industrial Technology** A cylindrical oil tank holds 450 gal when it is filled to its full height of 8 ft. When it contains oil to a height of 2 ft 4 in., how many gallons of oil are in the tank?

Solutions

(a) A direct proportion—the more time spent, the more widgets produced:

$$\frac{88}{x} = \frac{2 \text{ hours}}{3\frac{1}{2} \text{ hours}}$$

Cross-multiply:

$$2x = 308$$

$$x = 154 \text{ widgets}$$

88 ⊗ **3.5** ÷ **2** = → 154.

(b) A direct proportion—the more paint, the greater the area that can be covered:

$$\frac{1 \text{ gal}}{x \text{ gal}} = \frac{825 \text{ sq ft}}{2640 \text{ sq ft}}$$

$$x = 3.2 \text{ gal}$$

(c) A direct proportion—the less you get, the less you pay:

$$\frac{6 \text{ filters}}{8 \text{ filters}} = \frac{x}{\$55.92}$$

$$x = \$41.94$$

(d) A direct proportion—the more miles you drive, the more fuel it takes:

$$\frac{273 \text{ mi}}{600 \text{ mi}} = \frac{42 \text{ gal}}{x \text{ gal}}$$

$x \approx 92$ gallons (*Reminder:* ≈ means "approximately equal to")

(e) A direct proportion—the volume is directly proportional to the height:

$$\frac{450 \text{ gal}}{x \text{ gal}} = \frac{8 \text{ ft}}{2\frac{1}{3} \text{ ft}}$$

$2'\,4'' = 2\frac{4}{12}' = 2\frac{1}{3}'$

$$x = 131\frac{1}{4} \text{ gallons}$$

Inverse Proportion

Two quantities are said to be **inversely proportional** if an increase in one quantity leads to a proportional decrease in the other quantity, or if a decrease in one leads to an increase in the other.

> **Inverse Proportion:** increase → decrease
> or decrease → increase

For example, the time required for a trip of a certain length is *inversely* proportional to the speed of travel. The faster you go (*increase* in speed), the quicker you get there (*decrease* in time).

EXAMPLE 5 If a certain trip takes 2 hours at 50 mph, how long will it take at 60 mph?

The correct proportion equation is

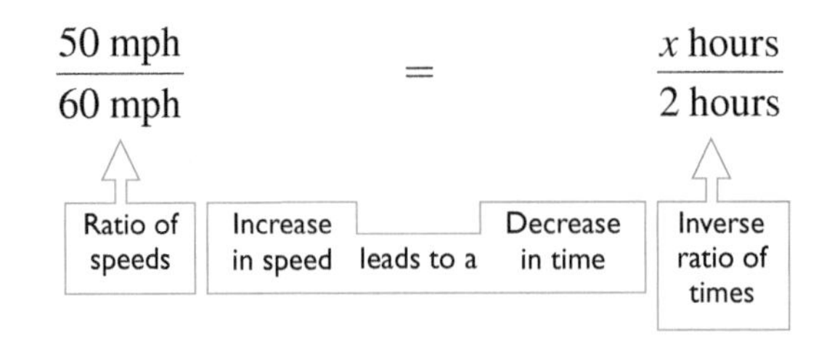

By inverting the time ratio, we have set it up so that both sides of the equation are in balance—both ratios decrease as speed increases.

Before attempting to solve the problem, make an estimate of the answer. We expect that the time to make the trip at 60 mph will be *less* than the time at 50 mph. The correct answer should be less than 2 hours.

Now solve it by cross-multiplying:

$$60x = 2 \cdot 50$$

$$x = 1\tfrac{2}{3} \text{ hours}$$

Learning Help Remember, in a *direct* proportion

$$\frac{A}{B} = \frac{C}{D}$$

These terms go together. If B and D are fixed, then an increase in A goes with an increase in C.

In an *inverse* proportion

$$\frac{X}{Y} = \frac{P}{Q}$$

These terms go together. If P and Y are fixed, then an increase in X goes with a decrease in Q.

Your Turn **Automotive Trades** In an automobile cylinder, the pressure is inversely proportional to the volume if the temperature does not change. If the volume of gas in the cylinder is 300 cu cm when the pressure is 20 psi, what is the volume when the pressure is increased to 80 psi?

Set this up as an inverse proportion and solve.

Solution Pressure is inversely proportional to volume. If the pressure increases, we expect the volume to decrease. The answer should be less than 300 cu cm.

Set up an inverse proportion. $$\frac{P_1}{P_2} = \frac{V_2}{V_1}$$

Substitute the given information. $$\frac{20 \text{ psi}}{80 \text{ psi}} = \frac{V}{300 \text{ cu cm}}$$

Cross-multiply. $$80V = 20 \cdot 300$$

$$V = 75 \text{ cu cm}$$

Gears and Pulleys A particularly useful kind of inverse proportion involves the relationship between the size of a gear or pulley and the speed with which it rotates.

In the figure in the margin, B is the driving gear.

Because gear A has twice as many teeth as gear B, when B makes two turns, A makes one turn. If gear B rotates at 20 turns per second, gear A will rotate at

10 turns per second. The speed of the gear is inversely proportional to the number of teeth.

$$\frac{\text{speed of gear } A}{\text{speed of gear } B} = \frac{\text{teeth in gear } B}{\text{teeth in gear } A}$$

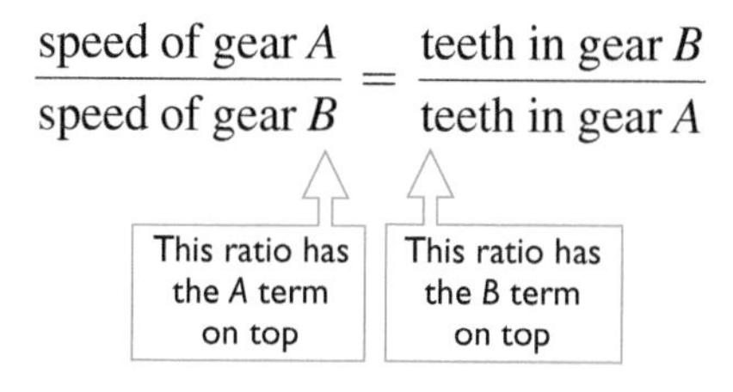

In this proportion, gear speed is measured in revolutions per minute, abbreviated rpm.

EXAMPLE 6 For the gear assembly shown on the previous page, if gear A turns at 40 rpm, what is the speed of gear B?

Because the relation is an inverse proportion, the smaller gear moves with the greater speed. We expect the speed of gear B to be faster than 40 rpm.

$$\frac{40 \text{ rpm}}{B} = \frac{8 \text{ teeth}}{16 \text{ teeth}}$$

$$8B = 640$$

$$B = 80 \text{ rpm}$$

On an automobile, the speed of the drive shaft is converted to rear axle motion by the ring and pinion gear system.

$$\frac{\text{drive shaft speed}}{\text{rear axle speed}} = \frac{\text{teeth in ring gear on axle}}{\text{teeth in pinion gear on drive shaft}}$$

This ratio has the drive shaft term on top | This ratio has the drive shaft term on the bottom

Again, gear speed is inversely proportional to the number of teeth on the gear.

Your Turn **Automotive Trades** If the pinion gear has 9 teeth and the ring gear has 40 teeth, what is the rear axle speed when the drive shaft turns at 1200 rpm?

Solution

$$\frac{1200 \text{ rpm}}{R} = \frac{40 \text{ teeth}}{9 \text{ teeth}}$$

Cross-multiply: $40R = 9 \cdot 1200$

$$R = 270 \text{ rpm}$$

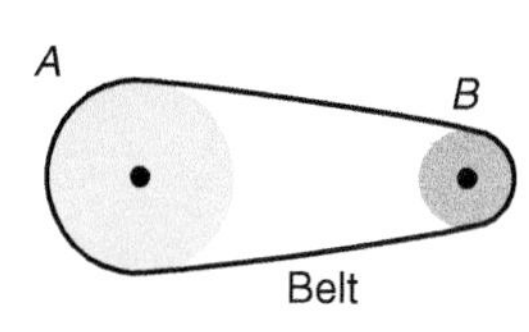

Pulleys transfer power in much the same way as gears. For the pulley system shown in the margin, the speed of a pulley is inversely proportional to its diameter.

Pulley A has a diameter twice that of pulley B. When pulley A makes one turn, pulley B will make two turns, assuming, of course, that there is no slippage of the belt.

$$\frac{\text{speed of pulley } A}{\text{speed of pulley } B} = \frac{\text{diameter of pulley } B}{\text{diameter of pulley } A}$$

This ratio has the A term on top | This ratio has the A term on the bottom

Your Turn If pulley B is 16 in. in diameter and is rotating at 240 rpm, what is the speed of pulley A if its diameter is 20 in.?

Solution

$$\frac{A}{240 \text{ rpm}} = \frac{16 \text{ in.}}{20 \text{ in.}}$$

Cross-multiply: $20A = 16 \cdot 240$

$$A = 192 \text{ rpm}$$

More Practice Solve each of the following problems by setting up an inverse proportion.

(a) **Machine Trades** A 9-in. pulley on a drill press rotates at 960 rpm. It is belted to a 5-in. pulley on an electric motor. Find the speed of the motor shaft.

(b) **Automotive Trades** A 12-tooth gear mounted on a motor shaft drives a larger gear. The motor shaft rotates at 1450 rpm. If the speed of the large gear is to be 425 rpm, how many teeth must be on the large gear?

(c) **Physics** For gases, pressure is inversely proportional to volume if the temperature does not change. If 30 cu ft of air at 15 psi is compressed to 6 cu ft, what is the new pressure?

(d) **Manufacturing** If five assembly machines can complete a given job in 3 hours, how many hours will it take for two assembly machines to do the same job?

(e) **Physics** The forces and lever arm distances for a lever obey an inverse proportion.

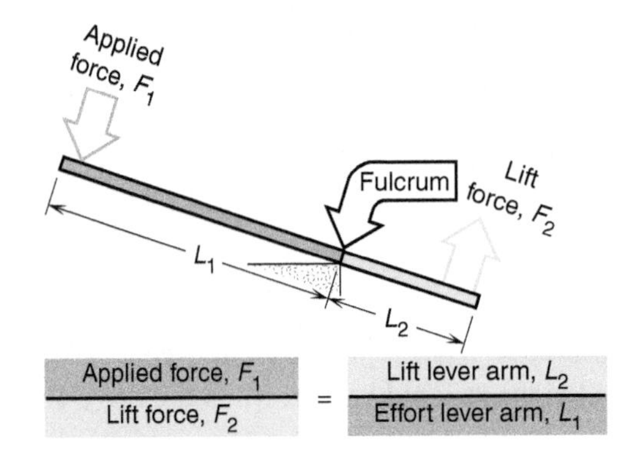

If a 100-lb force is applied to a 22-in. crowbar pivoted 2 in. from the end, what lift force is exerted?

Solutions

(a) $\frac{9 \text{ in.}}{5 \text{ in.}} = \frac{x}{960 \text{ rpm}}$ An inverse proportion: the larger pulley turns more slowly.

$$5x = 9 \cdot 960$$

$$x = 1728$$

(b) $\frac{12 \text{ teeth}}{x \text{ teeth}} = \frac{425 \text{ rpm}}{1450 \text{ rpm}}$ An inverse proportion: the larger gear turns more slowly.

$$425x = 12 \cdot 1450$$

$x = 40.941\ldots$ or 41 teeth, rounding to the nearest whole number. We can't have part of a gear tooth!

$$x \approx 41$$

(c) $\dfrac{30 \text{ cu ft}}{6 \text{ cu ft}} = \dfrac{P}{15 \text{ psi}}$ An inverse proportion: the higher the pressure, the smaller the volume.

$$6P = 30 \cdot 15$$
$$P = 75 \text{ psi}$$

(d) Careful on this one! An inverse proportion should be used. The *more* machines used, the *fewer* the hours needed to do the job.

$$\frac{5 \text{ machines}}{2 \text{ machines}} = \frac{x \text{ hours}}{3 \text{ hours}}$$
$$2x = 15$$
$$x = 7\tfrac{1}{2} \text{ hours}$$

Two machines will take much longer to do the job than will five machines.

(e) $\dfrac{100 \text{ lb}}{F} = \dfrac{2 \text{ in.}}{20 \text{ in.}}$ If the entire bar is 22 in. long, and $L_2 = 2$ in., then $L_1 = 20$ in.

$$2F = 20 \cdot 100$$
$$F = 1000 \text{ lb}$$

Now turn to Exercises 2-2 for a set of practice problems on these special applications of ratio and proportion.

Exercises 2-2 Special Applications of Ratio and Proportion

A. Complete the following tables.

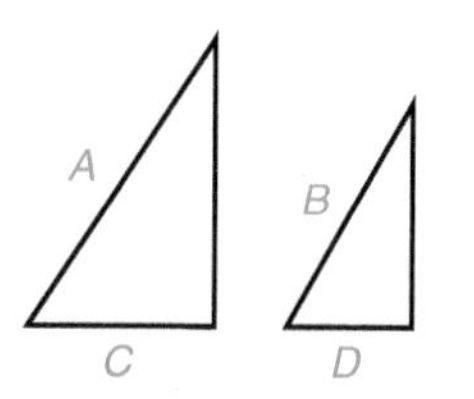

Similar triangles

1.

	A	B	C	D
(a)	$5\frac{1}{2}$ in.	$1\frac{1}{4}$ in.	$2\frac{3}{4}$ in.	
(b)		23.4 cm	20.8 cm	15.6 cm
(c)	12 ft		9 ft	6 ft
(d)	4.5 m	3.6 m		2.4 m

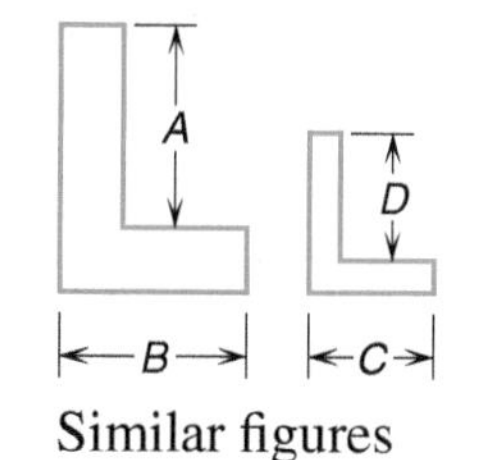

Similar figures

2.

	A	B	C	D
(a)	4 in.	5 in.	$3\frac{1}{2}$ in.	
(b)	5 ft		5 ft	2 ft
(c)	6.4 m	5.6 m		1.6 m
(d)		36 m	12 cm	14 cm

3.

	Number of Teeth on Gear 1	Number of Teeth on Gear 2	RPM of Gear 1	RPM of Gear 2
(a)	20	48	240	
(b)	25		150	420
(c)		40	160	100
(d)	32	40		1200

4.

	Diameter of Pulley 1	Diameter of Pulley 2	RPM of Pulley 1	RPM of Pulley 2
(a)	18 in.	24 in.	200	
(b)	12 in.		300	240
(c)		5 in.	400	640
(d)	14 in.	6 in.	300	

B. Practical Applications

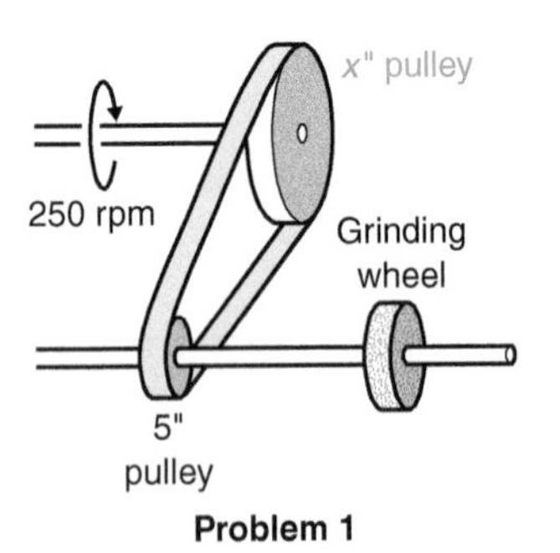

Problem 1

1. **Metalworking** A line shaft rotating at 250 rpm is connected to a grinding wheel by the pulley assembly shown. If the grinder shaft must turn at 1200 rpm, what size pulley should be attached to the line shaft?

2. **Architecture** The architectural drawing of an outside deck is $3\frac{1}{2}$ in. wide by $10\frac{7}{8}$ in. long. If the deck will actually be 14 ft wide, calculate the following:
   (a) The actual length of the deck
   (b) The scale factor

3. **Automotive Trades** Horsepower developed by an engine is directly proportional to its displacement. How many horsepower will be developed by an engine with a displacement of 240 cu in. if a 380-cu in. engine of the same kind develops 220 hp?

4. **Transportation** The distance necessary to stop a subway train at a given speed is inversely proportional to its deceleration. If a train traveling at 30 mph requires 180 ft to stop when decelerating at 0.18 g, what is the stopping distance at the same speed when it is decelerating at 0.15 g?

5. **Physics** A crowbar 28 in. long is pivoted 6 in. from the end. What force must be applied at the long end in order to lift a 400-lb object at the short end?

6. **Industrial Technology** If 60 gal of oil flow through a certain pipe in 16 minutes, how long will it take to fill a 450-gal tank using this pipe?

7. **Automotive Trades** If the alternator-to-engine drive ratio is 2.45 to 1, what rpm will the alternator have when the engine is idling at 400 rpm? (*Hint:* Use a direct proportion.)

8. **General Trades** The length of a wrench is inversely proportional to the amount of force needed to loosen a bolt. A wrench 6 in. long requires a force of 240 lb to loosen a rusty bolt. How much force would be required to loosen the same bolt using a 10-in. wrench?

9. **Construction** The Santa Barbara Planning Commission recently voted to restrict the size of home remodels by limiting the floor area to lot area ratio to a maximum of 0.45 to 1. Under these guidelines,
   (a) What would be the maximum allowable size of a remodel on an 11,800-sq-ft lot?
   (b) What size lot would be required in order to create a 3960-sq-ft remodel?

10. **Machine Trades** A pair of belted pulleys have diameters of 20 in. and 16 in., respectively. If the larger pulley turns at 2000 rpm, how fast will the smaller pulley turn?

11. **Manufacturing** A 15-tooth gear on a motor shaft drives a larger gear having 36 teeth. If the motor shaft rotates at 1200 rpm, what is the speed of the larger gear?

12. Electronics The power gain of an amplifier circuit is defined as

$$\text{Power gain} = \frac{\text{output power}}{\text{input power}}$$

If the audio power amplifier circuit has an input power of 0.72 watt and a power gain of 30, what output power will be available at the speaker?

13. Industrial Technology If 12 assemblers can complete a certain job in 4 hours, how long will the same job take if the number of assemblers is cut back to 8?

14. Electronics A 115-volt power transformer has 320 turns on the primary. If it delivers a secondary voltage of 12 volts, how many turns are on the secondary? (*Hint:* Use a direct proportion.)

15. Automotive Trades The headlights of a car are mounted at a height of 3.5 ft. If the light beam drops 1 in. per 35 ft, how far ahead in the road will the headlights illuminate?

16. Transportation A truck driver covers a certain stretch of the interstate in $4\frac{1}{2}$ hours traveling at the posted speed limit of 55 mph. If the speed limit is raised to 65 mph, how much time will the same trip require?

17. Machine Trades It is known that a cable with a cross-sectional area of 0.60 sq in. has a capacity to hold 2500 lb. If the capacity of the cable is proportional to its cross-sectional area, what size cable is needed to hold 4000 lb?

18. Masonry Cement, sand, and gravel are mixed to a proportion of 1:3:6 for a particular batch of concrete. How many cubic yards of each should be used to mix 125 cubic yards of concrete?

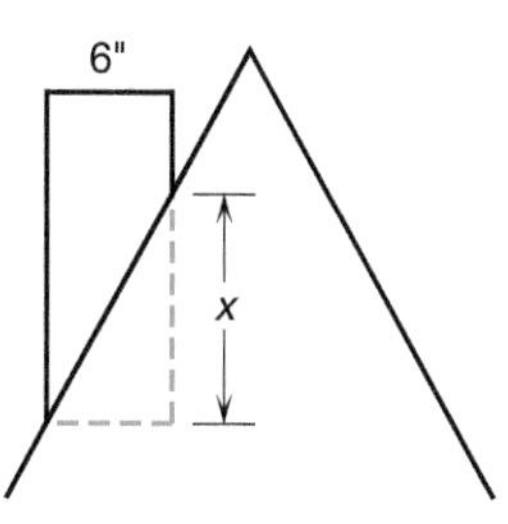

Problem 19

19. Roofing A cylindrical vent 6 in. in diameter must be cut at an angle to fit on a gable roof with a $\frac{2}{3}$ pitch. This means that for the vent itself the ratio of rise to run will be 2: 3. Find the height x of the cut that must be made on the cylinder to make it fit the slope of the roof. (See the figure.)

20. Architecture A wrought-iron gate for a new house will be 18 ft 9 in. long and 9 ft 6 in. high. An architect makes a drawing of the gate using a scale factor of $\frac{1}{4}$ in. = 1 ft. What will be the dimensions of the gate on the drawing?

21. Automotive Trades When a tire is inflated, the air pressure is inversely proportional to the volume of the air. If the pressure of a certain tire is 28 psi when the volume is 120 cu in., what is the pressure when the volume is 150 cu in.?

22. Electrical Trades The electrical resistance of a given length of wire is inversely proportional to the square of the diameter of the wire:

$$\frac{\text{resistance of wire } A}{\text{resistance of wire } B} = \frac{(\text{diameter of } B)^2}{(\text{diameter of } A)^2}$$

If a certain length of wire with a diameter of 34.852 mils has a resistance of 8.125 ohms, what is the resistance of the same length of the same composition wire with a diameter of 45.507 mils?

23. Life Skills If you are paid \$238.74 for $21\frac{1}{2}$ hours of work, what amount should you be paid for 34 hours of work at this same rate of pay?

24. **Sheet Metal Trades** If the triangular plate shown is cut into eight pieces along equally spaced dashed lines, find the height of each cut. Round to two decimal digits.

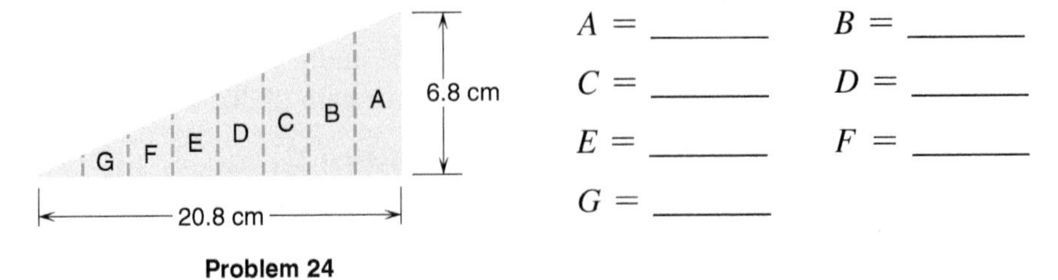

Problem 24

$A =$ ______ $B =$ ______

$C =$ ______ $D =$ ______

$E =$ ______ $F =$ ______

$G =$ ______

25. **Water/Wastewater Treatment** The time required for an outlet pipe to empty a tank is inversely proportional to the cross-sectional area of the pipe. A pipe with a cross-sectional area of 113.0 sq in. requires 6.4 hours to empty a certain tank. If the pipe was replaced with one with a cross-sectional area of 50.25 sq in., how long would it take this pipe to empty the same tank?

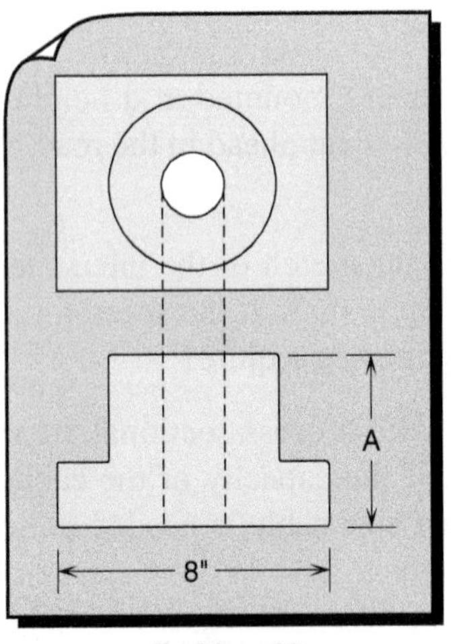

Problem 27

26. **Physics** A gas has a volume of 2480 cu cm at a pressure of 63.5 psi. What is the pressure when the gas is compressed to 1830 cu cm? (Round to the nearest tenth.)

27. **Machine Trades** The base of the flange shown in the drawing is actually 8 in. Its drawing width is 3 in. (a) What will be the actual dimension *A* if *A* is 2.25 in. on the drawing? (b) Find the scale factor of the drawing.

28. **Drafting** The drawing in the margin shows the actual length and width of a display panel. (a) What will be the corresponding drawing length of the panel if the drawing width is $2\frac{1}{4}$ in.? (b) Find the scale factor for this drawing.

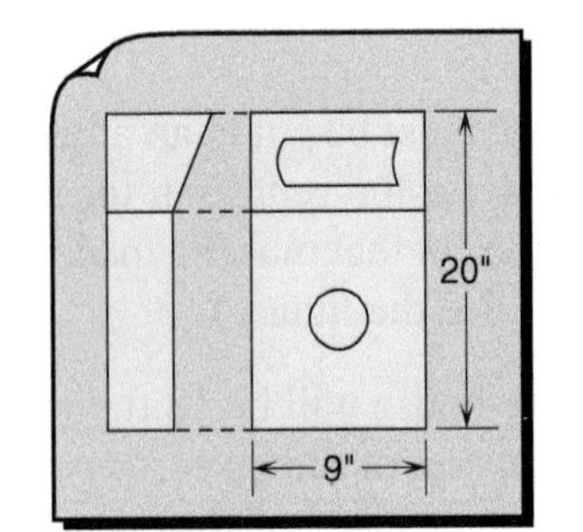

Problem 28

29. **Plumbing** If a 45-gal hot water tank holds 375 lb of water, what weight of water will a 55-gal tank hold? (Round to the nearest pound.)

30. **Automotive Trades** When different-size tires are put on a vehicle, the speedometer gear must be changed so that the mechanical speedometer will continue to give the correct reading. The number of teeth on the gear is inversely proportional to the size of the tires. Suppose that a driver decides to replace 24-in. tires with $26\frac{1}{2}$-in. ones. If the old speedometer gear had 18 teeth, how many teeth should the replacement gear have? (*Remember:* You cannot have a fraction of a tooth on a gear.)

31. **Manufacturing** A manufacturing company currently uses 24 workers to load and unload trucks. Each worker can move an average of 10 boxes per minute. A robotics firm has built a robot that can load and unload boxes at the rate of 15 boxes per minute. How many robots will it take to do the same job as the 24 humans?

When you have completed these exercises, check your answers to the odd-numbered problems in the Appendix, then turn to Section 2-3.

CHAPTER 2
SUMMARY

Ratio, Proportion, and Percent

Objective	Review
Calculate ratios. (p. 50)	A ratio is a comparison, using division, of two quantities of the same kind, both expressed in the same units. Final answers should be expressed either as a fraction in lowest terms or as a comparison to the number 1 using the word "to" or a colon (:). Example: Find the compression ratio C for an engine with maximum cylinder volume of 520 cu cm and minimum cylinder volume of 60 cu cm. $C = \frac{520 \text{ cu cm}}{60 \text{ cu cm}} = \frac{26}{3}$ or $8\frac{2}{3}$ to 1 or $8\frac{2}{3}:1$
Solve proportions. (p. 54)	A proportion is an equation stating that two ratios are equal: $\frac{a}{b} = \frac{c}{d}$ To solve a proportion, use the cross-product rule: $a \cdot d = b \cdot c$ Example: Solve: $\frac{8}{x} = \frac{12}{15}$ $12x = 120$ $x = 10$
Solve problems involving proportions. (pp. 57, 64)	Determine whether the problem involves a direct or an inverse proportion. Then set up the ratios accordingly and solve. Example: (a) An architectural drawing of a living room is $5\frac{1}{2}$ in. long and $4\frac{1}{2}$ in. wide. If the actual length of the room is 22 ft, find the actual width. Use a direct proportion. $\frac{5\frac{1}{2}''}{4\frac{1}{2}''} = \frac{22'}{x}$ $5\frac{1}{2} \cdot x = 99$ $x = 18'$ (b) A large production job is completed by four machines working for 6 hours. The same size job must be finished in 2 hours the next time it is ordered. How many machines should be used to accomplish this task? Use an inverse proportion. $\frac{4 \text{ machines}}{x \text{ machines}} = \frac{2 \text{ hr}}{6 \text{ hr}}$ $2x = 24$ $x = 12$ machines

PROBLEM SET 2 Ratio, Proportion, and Percent

Answers to odd-numbered problems are given in the Appendix.

A. Complete the following tables.

1.

	Diameter of Pulley *A*	Diameter of Pulley *B*	Pulley Ratio, $\frac{A}{B}$
(a)	12 in.		2 to 5
(b)	95 cm	38 cm	
(c)		15 in.	5 to 3

2.

	Teeth on Driven Gear *A*	Teeth on Driving Gear *B*	Gear Ratio, $\frac{A}{B}$
(a)	20	60	
(b)		10	6.5
(c)	56		4 to 3

B. Solve the following proportions.

1. $\frac{5}{6} = \frac{x}{42}$
2. $\frac{8}{15} = \frac{12}{x}$
3. $\frac{x}{12} = \frac{15}{9}$
4. $\frac{3\frac{1}{2}}{x} = \frac{5\frac{1}{4}}{18}$
5. $\frac{1.6}{5.2} = \frac{4.4}{x}$
6. $\frac{x}{12.4} = \frac{4 \text{ ft } 6 \text{ in.}}{6 \text{ ft } 3 \text{ in.}}$

C. Write each number as a percent.

1. 0.72
2. 0.06
3. 0.6
4. 0.358
5. 1.3
6. 3.03
7. 4
8. $\frac{7}{10}$
9. $\frac{1}{6}$
10. $2\frac{3}{5}$

D. Write each percent as a decimal number.

1. 4%
2. 37%
3. 11%
4. 94%
5. $1\frac{1}{4}$%
6. 0.09%
7. $\frac{1}{5}$%
8. 1.7%
9. $3\frac{7}{8}$%
10. 8.02%
11. 115%
12. 210%

E. Write each of the following percents as a fraction in lowest terms.

1. 28%
2. 375%
3. 81%
4. 4%
5. 0.5%
6. 70%
7. 14%
8. $41\frac{2}{3}$%

F. Solve.

1. 3 is _______ % of 5.
2. 5% of $120 is _______.
3. 25% of what number is 1.4?
4. 16 is what percent of 8?
5. 105% of 40 is _______.
6. 1.38 is _______ % of 1.15.
7. $7\frac{1}{4}$% of _______ is $2.10.
8. 250% of 50 is _______.
9. 0.05% of _______ is 4.
10. $8\frac{1}{4}$% of 1.2 is _______.

Name ____________________

Date ____________________

Course/Section ____________________

G. Solve.

1. **Metalworking** Extruded steel rods shrink 12% in cooling from furnace temperature to room temperature. If a standard tie rod is 34 in. exactly when it is formed, how long will it be after cooling?

2. **Metalworking** Cast iron contains up to 4.5% carbon, and wrought iron contains up to 0.08% carbon. How much carbon is in a 20-lb bar of each metal?

3. **Life Skills**
   (a) A real estate saleswoman sells a house for $664,500. Her company pays her 70% of the 1.5% commission on the sale. How much does she earn on the sale?
   (b) All salespeople in the Ace Department Store receive $360 per week plus a 6% commission. If you sold $3975 worth of goods in a week, what would be your income?
   (c) A salesman at the Wasteland TV Company sold five identical LED TV sets last week and earned $509.70 in commissions. If his commission rate is 6%, what does one of these models cost?

4. **Carpentry** What is the net price of a 10-in. band saw with a list price of $199.95 if it is on sale at a 35% discount?

5. **Life Skills** If the retail sales tax in your state is 6%, what would be the total cost of each of the following items?
   (a) An $18.99 pair of pliers.
   (b) A $17.49 adjustable wrench.
   (c) 69 cents worth of washers.
   (d) A $118.60 textbook.
   (e) A $139.99 five-drawer shop cabinet rollaway.

6. **Retail Merchandising** A computer printer sells for $376 after a 12% discount. What was its original or list price?

7. **Construction** How many running feet of matched 1-in. by 6-in. boards will be required to lay a subfloor in a room that is 28 ft by 26 ft? Add 20% to the area to allow for waste and matching.

8. **Sheet Metal Trades** In the Easy Does It Metal Shop, one sheet of metal is wasted for every 25 purchased. What percent of the sheets are wasted?

9. **Machine Trades** Complete the following table.

Measurement	Tolerance	Percent Tolerance
1.775 in.	±0.001 in.	(a)
1.775 in.	±0.05 in.	(b)
1.775 in.	(c)	±0.50%
310 mm	±0.1 mm	(d)
310 mm	(e)	±0.20%

10. **Masonry** A mason must purchase enough mortar mix to lay 1820 bricks. The guidelines for this mix suggest that about 15 bags are required for every 400 bricks.
    (a) Assuming that he cannot purchase a fraction of a bag, how many bags will he need?
    (b) At $6.40 per bag, what will be the total cost of the mix?

11. **Manufacturing** A production job is bid at \$6275, but cost overruns amount to 15%. What is the actual job cost?

12. **Metalworking** When heated, a metal rod expands 3.5%, to 15.23 cm. What is its cold length?

13. **Electrical Trades** An electrical resistor is rated at 4500 ohms ± 3%. Express this tolerance in ohms and state the actual range of resistance.

14. **Automotive Trades** A 140-hp automobile engine delivers only 126 hp to the driving wheels of the car. What is the efficiency of the transmission and drive mechanism?

15. **Metalworking** A steel casting has a hot length of 26.500 in. After cooling, the length is 26.255 in. What is the shrinkage expressed as a percent? Round to one decimal place.

16. **Automotive Trades** The parts manager for an automobile dealership can buy a part at a 25% discount off the retail price. If the retail price is \$46.75, how much does he pay?

17. **Manufacturing** An electric shop motor rated at 2.5 hp is found to deliver 1.8 hp to a vacuum pump when it is connected through a belt drive system. What is the efficiency of the drive system?

18. **Trades Management** To purchase a truck for his mobile welding service, Jerry arranges a 36-month loan of \$45,000 at 4.75% annual interest.
    (a) What total interest will he pay?
    (b) What monthly payment will he make? (Assume equal monthly payments on interest and principal.)

19. **HVAC** The motor to run a refrigeration system is rated at 12 hp, and the system has an efficiency of 76%. What is the effective cooling power output of the system?

20. **Interior Design** An interior designer is able to purchase a sofa from a design center for \$1922. His client would have paid \$2480 for the same sofa at a furniture store. What rate of discount was the designer receiving off the retail price?

21. **Life Skills** The commission rate paid to a manufacturer's rep varies according to the type of equipment sold. If his monthly statement showed \$124,600 in sales, and his total commission was \$4438, what was his average rate of commission to the nearest tenth of a percent?

22. **Masonry** Six square feet of a certain kind of brick wall contains 78 bricks. How many bricks are needed for 150 sq ft?

23. **Transportation** If 60 mph (miles per hour) is equivalent to 88 fps (feet per second), express
    (a) 45 mph in feet per second.
    (b) 22 fps in miles per hour.

24. **Automotive Trades** The headlights on a car are mounted at the height of 28 in. The light beam must illuminate the road for 400 ft. That is, the beam must hit the ground 400 ft ahead of the car.
    (a) What should be the drop ratio of the light beam in inches per foot?
    (b) What is this ratio in inches per 25 ft?

25. **Printing** A photograph measuring 8 in. wide by 12 in. long must be reduced to a width of $3\frac{1}{2}$ in. to fit on a printed page. What will be the corresponding length of the reduced photograph?

26. Machine Trades If 250 ft of wire weighs 22 lb, what will be the weight of 100 ft of the same wire?

27. Agriculture A sprayer discharges 600 cc of herbicide in 45 sec. For what period of time should the sprayer be discharged in order to apply 2000 cc of herbicide?

28. Trades Management An auto mechanic currently rents a 3460-sq-ft shop for $5363 per month. How much will his monthly rent be if he moves to a comparably priced 2740-sq-ft shop? Round to the nearest dollar.

29. Machine Trades Six steel parts weigh 1.8 lb. How many of these parts are in a box weighing 142 lb if the box itself weighs 7 lb?

30. Manufacturing Two belted pulleys have diameters of 24 in. and 10 in.
    (a) Find the pulley ratio.
    (b) If the larger pulley turns at 1500 rpm, how fast will the smaller pulley turn?

31. Printing If six printing presses can do a certain job in $2\frac{1}{2}$ hours, how long will it take four presses to do the same job? (*Hint:* Use an inverse proportion.)

32. Drafting Drafters usually use a scale of $\frac{1}{4}$ in. = 1 ft on their architectural drawings. Find the actual length of each of the following items if their blueprint length is given.
    (a) A printing press $2\frac{1}{4}$ in. long.
    (b) A building $7\frac{1}{2}$ in. long.
    (c) A rafter $\frac{11}{16}$ in. long.
    (d) A car $1\frac{7}{8}$ in. long.

33. Construction A certain concrete mix requires one sack of cement for every 650 lb of concrete. How many sacks of cement are needed for 3785 lb of concrete? (*Remember:* You cannot buy a fraction of a sack.)

34. Automotive Trades The rear axle of a car turns at 320 rpm when the drive shaft turns at 1600 rpm. If the pinion gear has 12 teeth, how many teeth are on the ring gear?

35. Physics If a 120-lb force is applied to a 36-in. crowbar pivoted 4 in. from the end, what lift force is exerted?

36. Machine Trades How many turns will a pinion gear having 16 teeth make if a ring gear having 48 teeth makes 120 turns?

37. Electrical Trades The current in a certain electrical circuit is inversely proportional to the line voltage. If a current of 0.40 A is delivered at 440 volts, what is the current of a similar system operating at 120 volts? Round to the nearest 0.01 A.

38. Printing A printer needs 12,000 good copies of a flyer for a particular job. Previous experience has shown that she can expect no more than a 5% spoilage rate on this type of job. How many should she print to ensure 12,000 clean copies?

39. General Trades If a mechanic's helper is paid $456.28 for $38\frac{1}{4}$ hours of work, how much should she receive for $56\frac{1}{2}$ hours at the same rate?

40. Manufacturing Two belted pulleys have diameters of $8\frac{3}{4}$ in. and $5\frac{5}{8}$ in. If the smaller pulley turns at 850 rpm, how fast will the larger one turn?

41. Trades Management Each production employee in a plant requires an average of 120 sq ft of work area. How many employees will be able to

work in an area that measures $8\frac{1}{16}$ in. by $32\frac{5}{8}$ in. on a blueprint if the scale of the drawing is $\frac{1}{4}$ in. $= 1$ ft?

42. **General Trades** Find the missing dimension in the following pair of similar figures.

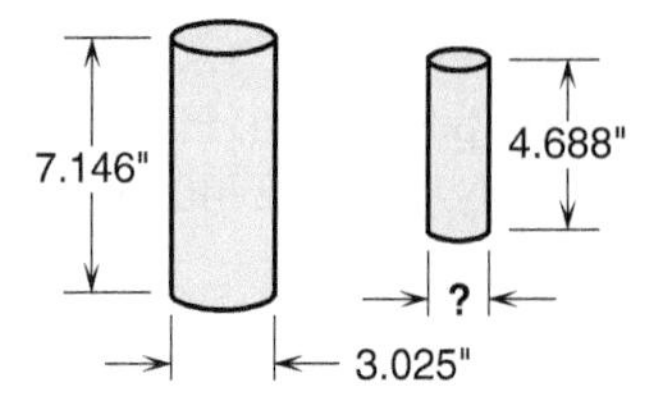

43. **Physics** In a closed container, the pressure is inversely proportional to the volume when the temperature is held constant. Find the pressure of a gas compressed to 0.386 cu ft if the pressure is 12.86 psi at 2.52 cu ft.

44. **Automotive Trades** The mechanical efficiency of a certain engine is specified to be 82.5%. This means that 82.5% of its indicated or theoretical horsepower becomes brake horsepower. If the indicated horsepower of the engine is 172, what is the brake horsepower? Round to the nearest whole number.

45. **Automotive Trades** An automobile engine loses approximately 3% of its power for every 1000 ft of elevation gain. A certain engine generates 180 horsepower (hp) at sea level. How much power will it generate at an elevation of 4000 ft? Round to the nearest whole number.

46. **Allied Health** Calculate the percent concentration of a solution created by adding 15 mL of a medication to 160 mL of water. Round your answer to the nearest tenth of a percent.

47. **Construction** The National Center for Real Estate Research released a study showing that houses advertised as "fixer-uppers" sell for an average of 24% less than comparable houses. How much would a fixer-upper sell for if a comparable house that was in good condition sold for $485,000?

48. **Automotive Trades** A headlight costs an auto service parts department $69.25. If the markup is 60%, what retail price will the customer be charged?

49. **Automotive Trades** During a compression check, the cylinder with the highest compression was measured at 156 psi (pounds per square inch), while the cylinder with the lowest compression was measured at 136 psi. If the maximum allowable reduction from the highest compression is 15%, does this engine fall within the allowable limit?

50. **Allied Health** A pre-op antiseptic solution is to be used to deliver 0.3 mg of atropine to the patient. There is, on hand, a solution of atropine containing 0.4 mg per 0.5 mL.
    (a) How much of the solution should be used to obtain the amount of atropine needed?
    (b) Suppose the only measuring device available is calibrated in minims (1 mL $=$ 16 minims). How much of the solution is needed in minims?

51. **Sports and Leisure** Use the following five steps to determine the NFL passing rating for quarterback Bubba Grassback.
    (a) Bubba completed 176 passes in 308 attempts. Calculate his pass completion rate as a percent. Subtract 30 from this number and multiply the result by 0.05.

(b) He has 11 touchdown passes in 308 attempts. Calculate the percent of his attempts that resulted in touchdowns. Multiply that number by 0.2.
(c) He has thrown 13 interceptions. Calculate the percent of his 308 attempts that have resulted in interceptions. Multiply this percent by 0.25, and then subtract the result from 2.375.
(d) Bubba passed for 2186 yards. Calculate the average number of yards gained per passing attempt. Subtract 3 from this number, and then multiply the result by 0.25.
(e) Add the four numbers obtained in parts (a), (b), (c), and (d).
(f) Divide the total in part (e) by 6 and then multiply by 100. This is Bubba's NFL quarterback passing rating.
(*Note:* Ratings for starting quarterbacks usually range from a low of about 50 to a high of about 110.)

52. **Allied Health** Medication Q is available only in tablets containing 30 mg of the drug. How many tablets (or fractions of tablets) should be administered if the physician orders 75 mg of medication Q?

53. **Allied Health** Medication TTQ is available only in a liquid formulation with a concentration of 25 μg/mL (micrograms per milliliter). How much of this liquid formulation should be administered if the following amounts are ordered by the physician?
(a) 300 μg (b) 150 μg (c) 20 μg

54. **Transportation** For every 1-mph reduction of average speed below 65 mph, a trucker will save 1.5% in fuel consumption. If a trucker reduces her average speed from 65 mph to 60 mph, how much will she save if she currently spends $4000 per week on fuel?

55. **Life Skills** A working person who needs an emergency loan, but who has no home or business to offer as security, may require the services of a company offering short-term paycheck advances. One such company offers a 14-day maximum advance of $255 for a fee of $45.
(a) What percent of the loan amount does the fee represent? (Round to the nearest hundredth of a percent.)
(b) Use a proportion to calculate the annual (365-day) percentage rate of this fee. (Round to the nearest percent.)

56. **Allied Health** Over the 20-year span from 1987 to 2007, the average life expectancy in the United States increased from 78.4 years to 80.8 years. By what percent did the life expectancy increase? (Round to the nearest tenth.)

57. **Meteorology** The cloudiest city in the United States—Astoria, Oregon—averages 240 cloudy days per year. What percent of the days of the year are sunny? (Use 1 year = 365 days and round to nearest percent.)

58. **Allied Health** In recent years, an increasing number of young people have been choosing to have weight-loss surgery. In 2010, approximately 5% of the statewide weight-loss surgeries in New York were performed on patients under the age of 25. If there were about 9400 total statewide weight-loss surgeries, how many of these were performed in 2010 on patients younger than 25 in New York?

59. **Construction** A contractor specializing in environmentally friendly (or green) construction proposes that he exceed the code requirements to install energy-saving upgrades in a new home. His computer software program estimates annual energy costs of $2140 without the upgrades and $960

with the upgrades. What percent of the $2140 will the residents save if they install the energy-saving upgrades? (Round to the nearest tenth.)

60. **Plumbing** A homeowner purchases a new hot-water system to use with her newly installed solar panels. The cost of the system is $8400, but tax credits and incentives bring the cost down to $4800. What percent of the original cost do the credits and incentives save her? (Round to the nearest tenth.)

61. **Retail Merchandising** The men's department reported the following sales totals, by size, for a particular shirt last year:

Small	$9400	Large	$19,200
Medium	$22,600	Extra Large	$12,800

If the store buyer has $40,000 to invest in the shirt this year, how much should she spend on each size if the amounts are in the same proportion as last year's sales?

62. **Water/Wastewater Treatment** To "shock" the water in a contaminated pipe, an operator needs to treat the water with 9.75 pounds of chlorine. The operator has available containers of liquid bleach that are 5% chlorine. If each gallon of the bleach solution weighs 8.34 pounds, how many gallons are needed to shock the water in the pipe? (Round to the nearest tenth.)

63. **Water/Wastewater Treatment** Water and wastewater formulas generally require concentrations to be expressed in parts per million (ppm). If a container of powdered pool chlorine contains 70% actual chlorine, how many parts per million is this equivalent to?

64. **Allied Health** A physician prescribes a daily dosage of 600 mg of medication G for a certain patient. Medication G is available only in an oral solution with a concentration of 100 mg/5 mL (milligrams per 5 milliliters). How many milliliters of the oral solution should the patient consume per day?

65. **Allied Health** Medication X comes in an oral solution with a concentration of 5 mg/mL (milligrams per milliliter). A doctor prescribes a daily dosage of 225 mg/m^2 (milligrams per square meter) for a particular patient. If the patient has a BSA of 1.42 m^2, how many milliliters of the solution should the patient consume per day? (See problem C-35 in Exercises 2-1. Round to the nearest milliliter.)

3

Measurement

YOU ARE FEELING CROWDED IN. PERHAPS IT WOULD BE A GOOD TIME TO MOVE TO A STATE WITH MORE ELBOW room. But which state? You can look up the population of each state, but that does not take into account the amount of land the population occupies. How is this land measured and how can you use this measure to select a place where wildlife outnumber humans?

In this chapter, we explore ways of measuring things in our English system, as well as in the metric system. Knowing how units of measure are used to describe your world can help you make decisions on issues ranging from where to live to alcohol consumption to determining proper dosages of medication.

Here's where you'll find these applications:

- Finding a state with lots of room to spread out is explored in Example 2 of Section 3.2.
- Measuring alcohol consumption is addressed in the Blitzer Bonus on page 110.
- Dosages of medication form the basis of Example 8 in Section 3.2 and Example 4 in Section 3.3.

Measuring Length; The Metric System

WHAT AM I SUPPOSED TO LEARN?

After you have read this section, you should be able to:

1. Use dimensional analysis to change units of measurement.
2. Understand and use metric prefixes.
3. Convert units within the metric system.
4. Use dimensional analysis to change to and from the metric system.

HAVE YOU SEEN EITHER OF THE *JURASSIC PARK* FILMS? The popularity of these movies reflects our fascination with dinosaurs and their incredible size. From end to end, the largest dinosaur from the Jurassic period, which lasted from 208 to 146 million years ago, was about 88 feet. To **measure** an object such as a dinosaur is to assign a number to its size. The number representing its measure from end to end is called its **length**. Measurements are used to describe properties of length, area, volume, weight, and temperature. Over the centuries, people have developed systems of measurement that are now accepted in most of the world.

Length

Every measurement consists of two parts: a number and a unit of measure. For example, if the length of a dinosaur is 88 feet, the number is 88 and the unit of measure is the foot. Many different units are commonly used in measuring length. The foot is from a system of measurement called the **English system**, which is generally used in the United States. In this system of measurement, length is expressed in such units as inches, feet, yards, and miles.

The result obtained from measuring length is called a **linear measurement** and is stated in **linear units**.

Linear units of measure were originally based on parts of the body. The Egyptians used the palm (equal to four fingers), the span (a handspan), and the cubit (length of forearm).

LINEAR UNITS OF MEASURE: THE ENGLISH SYSTEM

12 inches (in.) = 1 foot (ft)
3 feet = 1 yard (yd)
36 inches = 1 yard
5280 feet = 1 mile (mi)

Because many of us are familiar with the measures in the box, we find it simple to change from one measure to another, say from feet to inches. We know that there are 12 inches in a foot. To convert from 5 feet to a measure in inches, we multiply by 12. Thus, 5 feet = 5×12 inches = 60 inches.

1 Use dimensional analysis to change units of measurement.

Another procedure used to convert from one unit of measurement to another is called **dimensional analysis**. Dimensional analysis uses *unit fractions*. A **unit fraction** has two properties: The numerator and denominator contain different units and the value of the unit fraction is 1. Here are some examples of unit fractions:

$$\frac{12\text{ in.}}{1\text{ ft}};\quad \frac{1\text{ ft}}{12\text{ in.}};\quad \frac{3\text{ ft}}{1\text{ yd}};\quad \frac{1\text{ yd}}{3\text{ ft}};\quad \frac{5280\text{ ft}}{1\text{ mi}};\quad \frac{1\text{ mi}}{5280\text{ ft}}.$$

In each unit fraction, the numerator and denominator are equal measures, making the value of the fraction 1.

Let's see how to convert 5 feet to inches using dimensional analysis.

$$5\text{ ft} = ?\text{ in.}$$

We need to eliminate feet and introduce inches. The unit we need to introduce, inches, must appear in the numerator of the fraction. The unit we need to eliminate, feet, must appear in the denominator. Therefore, we choose the unit fraction with inches in the numerator and feet in the denominator. The units divide out as follows:

$$5 \text{ ft} = \frac{5 \cancel{\text{ft}}}{1} \cdot \frac{12 \text{ in.}}{1 \cancel{\text{ft}}} = 5 \cdot 12 \text{ in.} = 60 \text{ in.}$$

unit fraction

DIMENSIONAL ANALYSIS

To convert a measurement to a different unit, multiply by a unit fraction (or by unit fractions). The given unit of measurement should appear in the denominator of the unit fraction so that this unit cancels upon multiplication. The unit of measurement that needs to be introduced should appear in the numerator of the fraction so that this unit will be retained upon multiplication.

EXAMPLE 1 *Using Dimensional Analysis to Change Units of Measurement*

Convert:

a. 40 inches to feet **b.** 13,200 feet to miles **c.** 9 inches to yards.

SOLUTION

a. Because we want to convert 40 inches to feet, feet should appear in the numerator and inches in the denominator. We use the unit fraction

$$\frac{1 \text{ ft}}{12 \text{ in.}}$$

and proceed as follows:

This period ends the sentence and is not part of the abbreviated unit.

$$40 \text{ in.} = \frac{40 \cancel{\text{in.}}}{1} \cdot \frac{1 \text{ ft}}{12 \cancel{\text{in.}}} = \frac{40}{12} \text{ft} = 3\tfrac{1}{3} \text{ ft or } 3.\overline{3} \text{ ft.}$$

b. To convert 13,200 feet to miles, miles should appear in the numerator and feet in the denominator. We use the unit fraction

$$\frac{1 \text{ mi}}{5280 \text{ ft}}$$

and proceed as follows:

$$13{,}200 \text{ ft} = \frac{13{,}200 \cancel{\text{ft}}}{1} \cdot \frac{1 \text{ mi}}{5280 \cancel{\text{ft}}} = \frac{13{,}200}{5280} \text{mi} = 2\frac{1}{2} \text{ mi or } 2.5 \text{ mi.}$$

c. To convert 9 inches to yards, yards should appear in the numerator and inches in the denominator. We use the unit fraction

$$\frac{1 \text{ yd}}{36 \text{ in.}}$$

and proceed as follows:

$$9 \text{ in.} = \frac{9 \cancel{\text{in.}}}{1} \cdot \frac{1 \text{ yd}}{36 \cancel{\text{in.}}} = \frac{9}{36} \text{yd} = \frac{1}{4} \text{yd or } 0.25 \text{ yd.}$$

GREAT QUESTION!

When should I use a period for abbreviated units of measurement?

The abbreviations for units of measurement are written without a period, such as ft for feet, except for the abbreviation for inches (in.).

In each part of Example 1, we converted from a smaller unit to a larger unit. Did you notice that this results in a smaller number in the converted unit of measure? **Converting to a larger unit always produces a smaller number. Converting to a smaller unit always produces a larger number.**

CHECK POINT 1 Convert:

a. 78 inches to feet

b. 17,160 feet to miles

c. 3 inches to yards.

2 Understand and use metric prefixes.

Length and the Metric System

Although the English system of measurement is most commonly used in the United States, most industrialized countries use the metric system of measurement. One of the advantages of the metric system is that units are based on powers of ten, making it much easier than the English system to change from one unit of measure to another.

The basic unit for linear measure in the metric system is the meter (m). A meter is slightly longer than a yard, approximately 39 inches. Prefixes are used to denote a multiple or part of a meter. **Table 3.1** summarizes the more commonly used metric prefixes and their meanings.

kilodollar

hectodollar

dekadollar

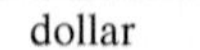

dollar

decidollar centidollar

Like our system of money, the metric system is based on powers of ten.

TABLE 3.1 Commonly Used Metric Prefixes

Prefix	Symbol	Meaning
kilo	k	$1000 \times$ base unit
hecto	h	$100 \times$ base unit
deka	da	$10 \times$ base unit
deci	d	$\frac{1}{10}$ of base unit
centi	c	$\frac{1}{100}$ of base unit
milli	m	$\frac{1}{1000}$ of base unit

GREAT QUESTION!

Does the "i" in the prefixes ending in "i" (deci, centi, milli) have any significance?

Prefixes ending in "i" are all fractional parts of one unit.

The prefixes kilo, centi, and milli are used more frequently than hecto, deka, and deci. **Table 3.2** applies all six prefixes to the meter. The first part of the symbol indicates the prefix and the second part (m) indicates meter.

TABLE 3.2 Commonly Used Units of Linear Measure in the Metric System

Symbol	Unit	Meaning
km	kilometer	1000 meters
hm	hectometer	100 meters
dam	dekameter	10 meters
m	meter	1 meter
dm	decimeter	0.1 meter
cm	centimeter	0.01 meter
mm	millimeter	0.001 meter

Kilometer is pronounced kil'-oh-met-er with the accent on the FIRST syllable. If pronounced correctly, kilometers should sound something like "kill all meters."

In the metric system, the kilometer is used to measure distances comparable to those measured in miles in the English system. One kilometer is approximately 0.6 mile, and one mile is approximately 1.6 kilometers.

Metric units of centimeters and millimeters are used to measure what the English system measures in inches. **Figure 3.1** on the next page shows that a centimeter is less than half an inch; there are 2.54 centimeters in an inch. The smaller markings on the bottom scale are millimeters. A millimeter is approximately the thickness of a dime. The length of a bee or a fly may be measured in millimeters.

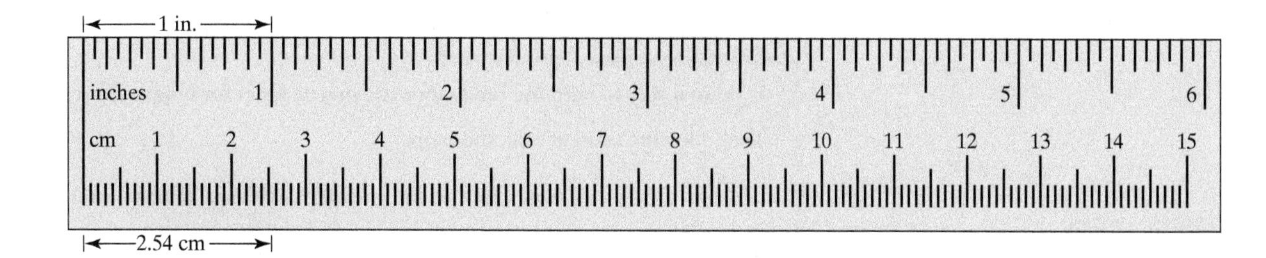

FIGURE 3.1

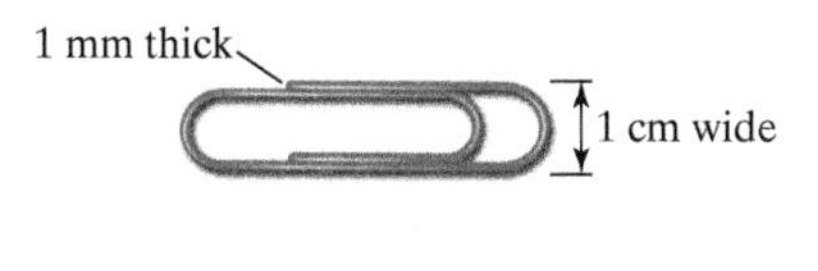

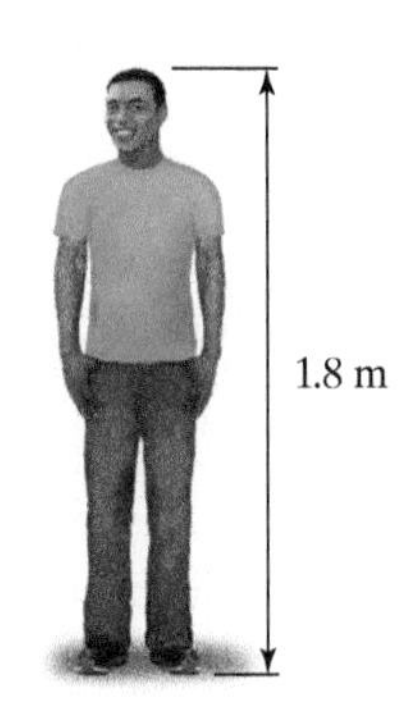

Those of us born in the United States have a good sense of what a length in the English system tells us about an object. An 88-foot dinosaur is huge, about 15 times the height of a 6-foot man. But what sense can we make of knowing that a whale is 25 meters long? The following lengths and the given approximations can help give you a feel for metric units of linear measure.

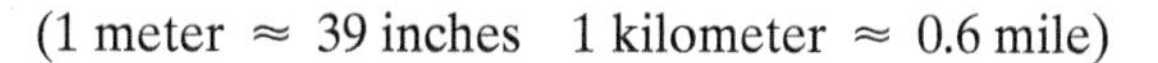

Item	Approximate Length
Width of lead in pencil	2 mm or 0.08 in.
Width of an adult's thumb	2 cm or 0.8 in.
Height of adult male	1.8 m or 6 ft
Typical room height	2.5 m or 8.3 ft
Length of medium-size car	5 m or 16.7 ft
Height of Empire State Building	381 m or 1270 ft
Average depth of ocean	4 km or 2.5 mi
Length of Manhattan Island	18 km or 11.25 mi
Distance from New York City to San Francisco	4800 km or 3000 mi
Radius of Earth	6378 km or 3986 mi
Distance from Earth to the moon	384,401 km or 240,251 mi

3 Convert units within the metric system.

Although dimensional analysis can be used to convert from one unit to another within the metric system, there is an easier, faster way to accomplish this conversion. The procedure is based on the observation that successively smaller units involve division by 10 and successively larger units involve multiplication by 10.

CHANGING UNITS WITHIN THE METRIC SYSTEM

Use the following chart to find equivalent measures of length:

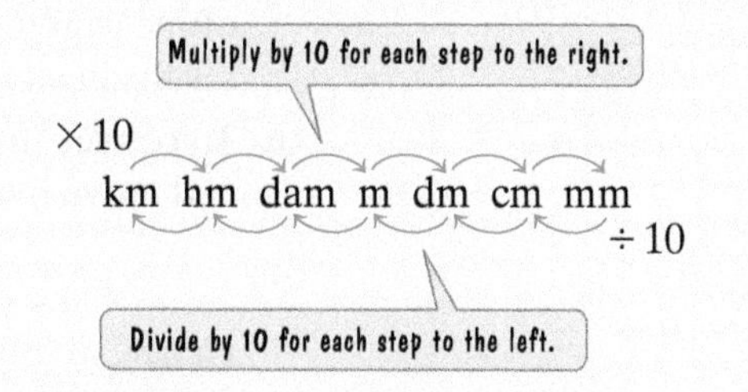

1. To change from a larger unit to a smaller unit (moving to the right in the diagram), multiply by 10 for each step to the right. Thus, move the decimal point in the given quantity one place to the right for each smaller unit until the desired unit is reached.
2. To change from a smaller unit to a larger unit (moving to the left in the diagram), divide by 10 for each step to the left. Thus, move the decimal point in the given quantity one place to the left for each larger unit until the desired unit is reached.

GREAT QUESTION!

Is there a way to help me remember the metric units for length from largest to smallest?

The following sentence should help:

King	Henry	died	Monday	drinking	chocolate	milk.
km	hm	dam	m	dm	cm	mm

Blitzer Bonus

The First Meter

The French first defined the meter in 1791, calculating its length as a romantic one ten-millionth of a line running from the Equator through Paris to the North Pole. Today's meter, officially accepted in 1983, is equal to the length of the path traveled by light in a vacuum during the time interval of 1/299,794,458 of a second.

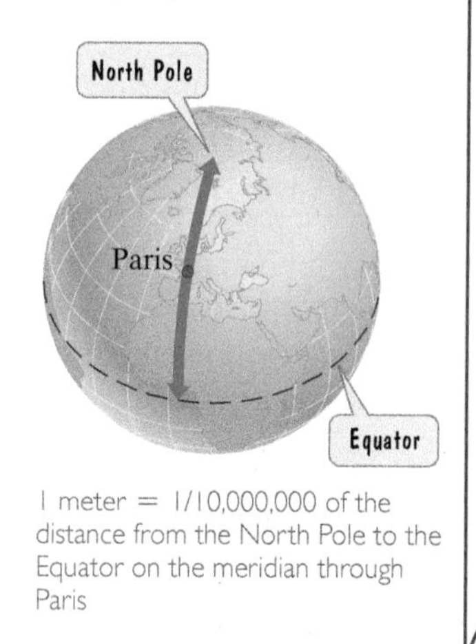

1 meter = 1/10,000,000 of the distance from the North Pole to the Equator on the meridian through Paris

EXAMPLE 2 *Changing Units within the Metric System*

a. Convert 504.7 meters to kilometers.

b. Convert 27 meters to centimeters.

c. Convert 704 mm to hm.

d. Convert 9.71 dam to dm.

SOLUTION

a. To convert from meters to kilometers, we start at meters and move three steps to the left to obtain kilometers:

km hm dam m dm cm mm.

Hence, we move the decimal point three places to the left:

504.7 m = 0.5047 km.

Thus, 504.7 meters converts to 0.5047 kilometer. Changing from a smaller unit of measurement (meter) to a larger unit of measurement (kilometer) results in an answer with a smaller number of units.

b. To convert from meters to centimeters, we start at meters and move two steps to the right to obtain centimeters:

km hm dam m dm cm mm.

Hence, we move the decimal point two places to the right:

27 m = 2700 cm.

Thus, 27 meters converts to 2700 centimeters. Changing from a larger unit of measurement (meter) to a smaller unit of measurement (centimeter) results in an answer with a larger number of units.

c. To convert from mm (millimeters) to hm (hectometers), we start at mm and move five steps to the left to obtain hm:

km hm dam m dm cm mm.

Hence, we move the decimal point five places to the left:

704 mm = 0.00704 hm.

d. To convert from dam (dekameters) to dm (decimeters), we start at dam and move two places to the right to obtain dm:

km hm dam m dm cm mm.

Hence, we move the decimal point two places to the right:

9.71 dam = 971 dm.

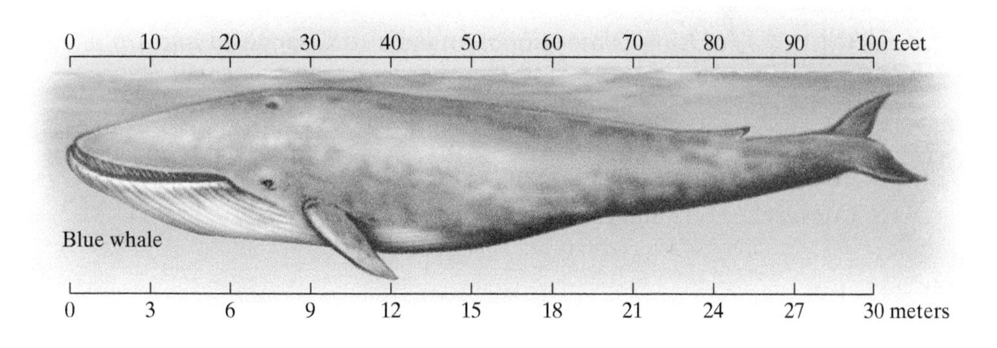

In Example 2(b), we showed that 27 meters converts to 2700 centimeters. This is the average length of the California blue whale, the longest of the great whales. Blue whales can have lengths that exceed 30 meters, making them over 100 feet long.

CHECK POINT 2

a. Convert 8000 meters to kilometers.

b. Convert 53 meters to millimeters.

c. Convert 604 cm to hm.

d. Convert 6.72 dam to cm.

Blitzer Bonus

Viruses and Metric Prefixes

Viruses are measured in attometers. An attometer is one quintillionth of a meter, or 10^{-18} meter, symbolized am. If a virus measures 1 am, you can place 10^{15} of them across a penciled 1 millimeter dot. If you were to enlarge each of these viruses to the size of the dot, they would stretch far into space, almost reaching Saturn.

Here is a list of all 20 metric prefixes. When applied to the meter, they range from the yottameter (10^{24} meters) to the yoctometer (10^{-24} meter).

LARGER THAN THE BASIC UNIT

Prefix	Symbol	Power of Ten	English Name
yotta-	Y	+24	septillion
zetta-	Z	+21	sextillion
exa-	E	+18	quintillion
peta-	P	+15	quadrillion
tera-	T	+12	trillion
giga-	G	+9	billion
mega-	M	+6	million
kilo-	k	+3	thousand
hecto-	h	+2	hundred
deca-	da	+1	ten

SMALLER THAN THE BASIC UNIT

Prefix	Symbol	Power of Ten	English Name
deci-	d	−1	tenth
centi-	c	−2	hundredth
milli-	m	−3	thousandth
micro-	μ	−6	millionth
nano-	n	−9	billionth
pico-	p	−12	trillionth
femto-	f	−15	quadrillionth
atto-	a	−18	quintillionth
zepto-	z	−21	sextillionth
yocto-	y	−24	septillionth

4 Use dimensional analysis to change to and from the metric system.

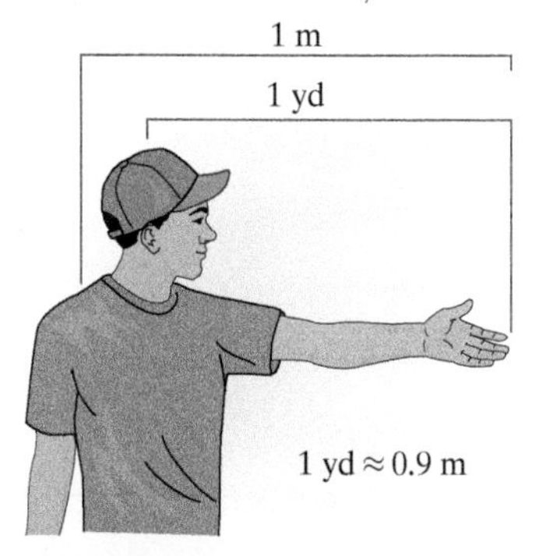

Although dimensional analysis is not necessary when changing units within the metric system, it is a useful tool when converting to and from the metric system. Some conversions are given in **Table 3.3**.

TABLE 3.3 English and Metric Equivalents

Equivalent	
1 inch (in.) = 2.54 centimeters (cm)	These conversions are exact.
1 foot (ft) = 30.48 centimeters (cm)	
1 yard (yd) ≈ 0.9 meter (m)	These conversions are approximate.
1 mile (mi) ≈ 1.6 kilometers (km)	

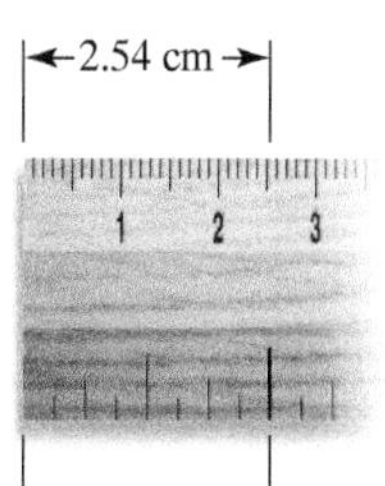

1 in. = 2.54 cm

TABLE 3.3 English and Metric Equivalents

1 inch (in.)	= 2.54 centimeters (cm)
1 foot (ft)	= 30.48 centimeters (cm)
1 yard (yd)	≈ 0.9 meter (m)
1 mile (mi)	≈ 1.6 kilometers (km)

1 mi ≈ 1.6 km

GREAT QUESTION!

Is the conversion in part (b) approximate or exact?

It's approximate. More accurately,

$$1 \text{ mi} \approx 1.61 \text{ km}.$$

Thus,

$$125 \text{ mi} \approx 125(1.61) \text{ km} \approx 201.25 \text{ km}.$$

EXAMPLE 3 *Using Dimensional Analysis to Change to and from the Metric System*

a. Convert 8 inches to centimeters.

b. Convert 125 miles to kilometers.

c. Convert 26,800 millimeters to inches.

SOLUTION

a. To convert 8 inches to centimeters, we use a unit fraction with centimeters in the numerator and inches in the denominator:

$$\frac{2.54 \text{ cm}}{1 \text{ in.}}. \quad \text{Table 3.3 shows that 1 in. = 2.54 cm.}$$

We proceed as follows.

$$8 \text{ in.} = \frac{8 \cancel{\text{in.}}}{1} \cdot \frac{2.54 \text{ cm}}{1 \cancel{\text{in.}}} = 8(2.54) \text{ cm} = 20.32 \text{ cm}$$

b. To convert 125 miles to kilometers, we use a unit fraction with kilometers in the numerator and miles in the denominator:

$$\frac{1.6 \text{ km}}{1 \text{ mi}}. \quad \text{Table 3.3 shows that 1 mi} \approx \text{1.6 km.}$$

Thus,

$$125 \text{ mi} \approx \frac{125 \cancel{\text{mi}}}{1} \cdot \frac{1.6 \text{ km}}{1 \cancel{\text{mi}}} = 125(1.6) \text{ km} = 200 \text{ km}.$$

c. To convert 26,800 millimeters to inches, we observe that **Table 3.3** has only a conversion factor between inches and centimeters. We begin by changing millimeters to centimeters:

$$26{,}800 \text{ mm} = 2680.0 \text{ cm}$$

Now we need to convert 2680 centimeters to inches. We use a unit fraction with inches in the numerator and centimeters in the denominator:

$$\frac{1 \text{ in.}}{2.54 \text{ cm}}.$$

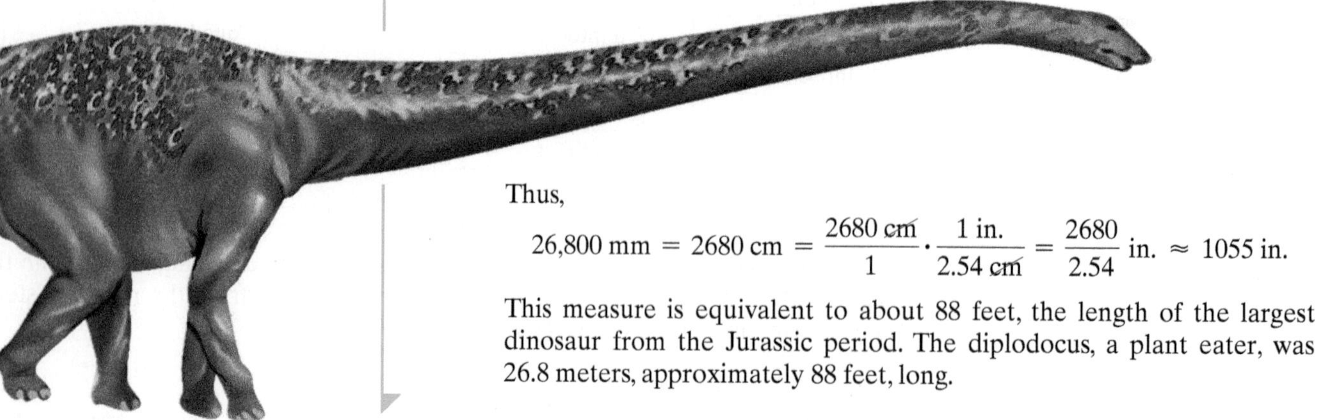

Thus,

$$26{,}800 \text{ mm} = 2680 \text{ cm} = \frac{2680 \cancel{\text{cm}}}{1} \cdot \frac{1 \text{ in.}}{2.54 \cancel{\text{cm}}} = \frac{2680}{2.54} \text{ in.} \approx 1055 \text{ in.}$$

This measure is equivalent to about 88 feet, the length of the largest dinosaur from the Jurassic period. The diplodocus, a plant eater, was 26.8 meters, approximately 88 feet, long.

CHECK POINT 3

a. Convert 8 feet to centimeters.

b. Convert 20 meters to yards.

c. Convert 30 meters to inches.

So far, we have used dimensional analysis to change units of length. Dimensional analysis may also be used to convert other kinds of measures, such as speed.

Blitzer Bonus

The Mars Climate Orbiter

If you think that using dimensional analysis to change to and from the metric system is no big deal, consider this: The Mars Climate Orbiter, launched on December 11, 1998, was lost when it crashed into Mars about a year later due to failure to properly convert English units into metric units. The price tag: $125 million!

EXAMPLE 4 *Using Dimensional Analysis*

a. The speed limit on many highways in the United States is 55 miles per hour (mi/hr). How many kilometers per hour (km/hr) is this?

b. If a high-speed train in Japan is capable of traveling at 200 kilometers per hour, how many miles per hour is this?

SOLUTION

a. To change miles per hour to kilometers per hour, we need to concentrate on changing miles to kilometers, so we need a unit fraction with kilometers in the numerator and miles in the denominator:

$$\frac{1.6\text{ km}}{1\text{ mi}}.$$ Table 3.3 shows that 1 mi ≈ 1.6 km.

Thus,

$$\frac{55\text{ mi}}{\text{hr}} \approx \frac{55\text{ mi}}{\text{hr}}\cdot\frac{1.6\text{ km}}{1\text{ mi}} = 55(1.6)\frac{\text{km}}{\text{hr}} = 88\text{ km/hr}.$$

This shows that 55 miles per hour is approximately 88 kilometers per hour.

b. To change 200 kilometers per hour to miles per hour, we must convert kilometers to miles. We need a unit fraction with miles in the numerator and kilometers in the denominator:

$$\frac{1\text{ mi}}{1.6\text{ km}}.$$ Table 3.3 shows that 1 mi ≈ 1.6 km.

Thus,

$$\frac{200\text{ km}}{\text{hr}} \approx \frac{200\text{ km}}{\text{hr}}\cdot\frac{1\text{ mi}}{1.6\text{ km}} = \frac{200}{1.6}\frac{\text{mi}}{\text{hr}} = 125\text{ mi/hr}.$$

A train capable of traveling at 200 kilometers per hour can therefore travel at about 125 miles per hour.

CHECK POINT 4 A road in Europe has a speed limit of 60 kilometers per hour. Approximately how many miles per hour is this?

Concept and Vocabulary Check

Fill in each blank so that the resulting statement is true.

1. The result obtained from measuring length is called a/an ________ measurement and is stated in ________ units.
2. In the English system, ________ in. = 1 ft, ________ ft = 1 yd, ________ in. = 1 yd, and ________ ft = 1 mi.
3. Fractions such as $\frac{12\text{ in.}}{1\text{ ft}}$ and $\frac{1\text{ yd}}{3\text{ ft}}$ are called ________ fractions. The value of such fractions is ________.
4. In the metric system, 1 km = ________ m, 1 hm = ________ m, 1 dam = ________ m, 1 dm = ________ m, 1 cm = ________ m, and 1 mm = ________ m.

In Exercises 5–8, determine whether each statement is true or false. If the statement is false, make the necessary change(s) to produce a true statement.

5. Dimensional analysis uses powers of 10 to convert from one unit of measurement to another. ______
6. One of the advantages of the English system is that units are based on powers of 10. ______
7. There are 2.54 inches in a centimeter. ______
8. The height of an adult male is approximately 6 meters. ______

Exercise Set 3.1

Practice Exercises

In Exercises 1–16, use dimensional analysis to convert the quantity to the indicated unit. If necessary, round the answer to two decimal places.

1. 30 in. to ft
2. 100 in. to ft
3. 30 ft to in.
4. 100 ft to in.
5. 6 in. to yd
6. 21 in. to yd
7. 6 yd to in.
8. 21 yd to in.
9. 6 yd to ft
10. 12 yd to ft
11. 6 ft to yd
12. 12 ft to yd
13. 23,760 ft to mi
14. 19,800 ft to mi
15. 0.75 mi to ft
16. 0.25 mi to ft

In Exercises 17–26, use the diagram in the box on page 89 to convert the given measurement to the unit indicated.

17. 5 m to cm
18. 8 dam to m
19. 16.3 hm to m
20. 0.37 hm to m
21. 317.8 cm to hm
22. 8.64 hm to cm
23. 0.023 mm to m
24. 0.00037 km to cm
25. 2196 mm to dm
26. 71 dm to km

In Exercises 27–44, use the following English and metric equivalents, along with dimensional analysis, to convert the given measurement to the unit indicated.

English and Metric Equivalents

1 in. = 2.54 cm
1 ft = 30.48 cm
1 yd ≈ 0.9 m
1 mi ≈ 1.6 km

27. 14 in. to cm
28. 26 in. to cm
29. 14 cm to in.
30. 26 cm to in.
31. 265 mi to km
32. 776 mi to km
33. 265 km to mi
34. 776 km to mi
35. 12 m to yd
36. 20 m to yd
37. 14 dm to in.
38. 1.2 dam to in.
39. 160 in. to dam
40. 180 in. to hm
41. 5 ft to m
42. 8 ft to m
43. 5 m to ft
44. 8 m to ft

Use 1 mi ≈ 1.6 km *to solve Exercises 45–48.*

45. Express 96 kilometers per hour in miles per hour.
46. Express 104 kilometers per hour in miles per hour.
47. Express 45 miles per hour in kilometers per hour.
48. Express 50 miles per hour in kilometers per hour.

Practice Plus

In Exercises 49–52, use the unit fractions

$$\frac{36 \text{ in.}}{1 \text{ yd}} \text{ and } \frac{2.54 \text{ cm}}{1 \text{ in.}}.$$

49. Convert 5 yd to cm.
50. Convert 8 yd to cm.
51. Convert 762 cm to yd.
52. Convert 1016 cm to yd.

In Exercises 53–54, use the unit fractions

$$\frac{5280 \text{ ft}}{1 \text{ mi}}, \frac{12 \text{ in.}}{1 \text{ ft}}, \text{ and } \frac{2.54 \text{ cm}}{1 \text{ in.}}.$$

53. Convert 30 mi to km.
54. Convert 50 mi to km.
55. Use unit fractions to express 120 miles per hour in feet per second.
56. Use unit fractions to express 100 miles per hour in feet per second.

Application Exercises

In Exercises 57–66, selecting from millimeter, meter, and kilometer, determine the best unit of measure to express the given length.

57. A person's height
58. The length of a football field
59. The length of a bee
60. The distance from New York City to Washington, D.C.
61. The distance around a one-acre lot
62. The length of a car
63. The width of a book
64. The altitude of an airplane
65. The diameter of a screw
66. The width of a human foot

In Exercises 67–74, select the best estimate for the measure of the given item.

67. The length of a pen
a. 30 cm **b.** 19 cm **c.** 19 mm

68. The length of this page
a. 2.5 mm **b.** 25 mm **c.** 250 mm

69. The height of a skyscraper
a. 325 m **b.** 32.5 km **c.** 325 km **d.** 3250 km

70. The length of a pair of pants
a. 700 cm **b.** 70 cm **c.** 7 cm

71. The height of a room
a. 4 mm **b.** 4 cm **c.** 4 m **d.** 4 dm

72. The length of a rowboat
a. 4 cm **b.** 4 dm **c.** 4 m **d.** 4 dam

73. The width of an electric cord

a. 4 mm **b.** 4 cm **c.** 4 dm **d.** 4 m

74. The dimensions of a piece of typing paper

a. 22 mm by 28 mm **b.** 22 cm by 28 cm

c. 22 dm by 28 dm **d.** 22 m by 28 m

75. A baseball diamond measures 27 meters along each side. If a batter scored two home runs in a game, how many kilometers did the batter run?

76. If you jog six times around a track that is 700 meters long, how many kilometers have you covered?

77. The distance from the Earth to the sun is about 93 million miles. What is this distance in kilometers?

78. The distance from New York City to Los Angeles is 4690 kilometers. What is the distance in miles?

Exercises 79–80 give the approximate length of some of the world's longest rivers. In each exercise, determine which is the longer river and by how many kilometers.

79. Nile: 4130 miles; Amazon: 6400 kilometers

80. Yangtze: 3940 miles; Mississippi: 6275 kilometers

Exercises 81–82 give the approximate height of some of the world's tallest mountains. In each exercise, determine which is the taller mountain and by how many meters. Round to the nearest meter.

81. K2: 8611 meters; Everest: 29,035 feet

82. Lhotse: 8516 meters; Kangchenjunga: 28,170 feet

Exercises 83–84 give the average rainfall of some of the world's wettest places. In each exercise, determine which location has the greater average rainfall and by how many inches. Round to the nearest inch.

83. Debundscha (Cameroon): 10,280 millimeters; Waialeale (Hawaii): 451 inches

84. Mawsynram (India): 11,870 millimeters; Cherrapunji (India): 498 inches

(Source for Exercises 79–84: Russell Ash, *The Top 10 of Everything 2009*)

Writing in Mathematics

85. Describe the two parts of a measurement.

86. Describe how to use dimensional analysis to convert 20 inches to feet.

87. Describe advantages of the metric system over the English system.

88. Explain how to change units within the metric system.

89. You jog 500 meters in a given period of time. The next day, you jog 500 yards over the same time period. On which day was your speed faster? Explain your answer.

90. What kind of difficulties might arise if the United States immediately eliminated all units of measure in the English system and replaced the system by the metric system?

91. The United States is the only Westernized country that does not use the metric system as its primary system of measurement. What reasons might be given for continuing to use the English system?

Critical Thinking Exercises

Make Sense? *In Exercises 92–95, determine whether each statement makes sense or does not make sense, and explain your reasoning.*

92. I can run 4000 meters in approximately one hour.

93. I ran 2000 meters and you ran 2000 yards in the same time, so I ran at a faster rate.

94. The most frequent use of dimensional analysis involves changing units within the metric system.

95. When multiplying by a unit fraction, I put the unit of measure that needs to be introduced in the denominator.

In Exercises 96–100, convert to an appropriate metric unit so that the numerical expression in the given measure does not contain any zeros.

96. 6000 cm

97. 900 m

98. 7000 dm

99. 11,000 mm

100. 0.0002 km

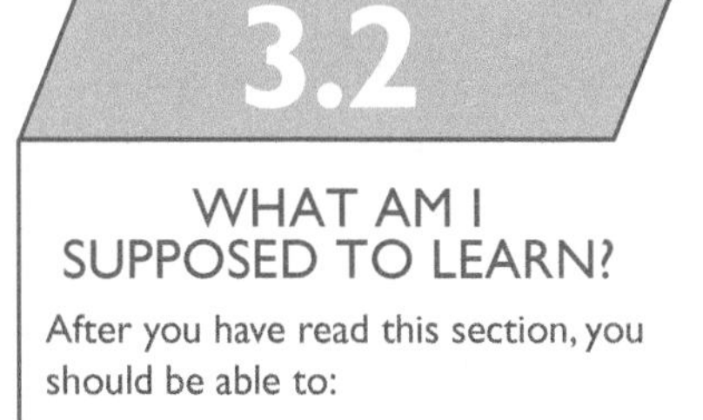

Measuring Area and Volume

WHAT AM I SUPPOSED TO LEARN?

After you have read this section, you should be able to:

1 Use square units to measure area.
2 Use dimensional analysis to change units for area.
3 Use cubic units to measure volume.
4 Use English and metric units to measure capacity.

ARE YOU FEELING A BIT CROWDED in? Although there are more people on the East Coast of the United States than there are bears, there are places in the Northwest where bears outnumber humans. The most densely populated state is New Jersey, averaging 1195.5 people per square mile. The least densely populated state is Alaska, averaging 1.2 persons per square mile. The U.S. average is 87.4 persons per square mile.

A square mile is one way of measuring the **area** of a state. A state's area is the region within its boundaries. Its **population density** is its population divided by its area. In this section, we discuss methods for measuring both area and volume.

Use square units to measure area.

Measuring Area

In order to measure a region that is enclosed by boundaries, we begin by selecting a *square unit.* A **square unit** is a square, each of whose sides is one unit in length, illustrated in **Figure 3.2**. The region in **Figure 3.2** is said to have an area of **one square unit**. The side of the square can be 1 inch, 1 centimeter, 1 meter, 1 foot, or one of any linear unit of measure. The corresponding units of area are the square inch (in.^{2}), the square centimeter (cm^2), the square meter (m^2), the square foot (ft^2), and so on. **Figure 3.3** illustrates 1 square inch and 1 square centimeter, drawn to actual size.

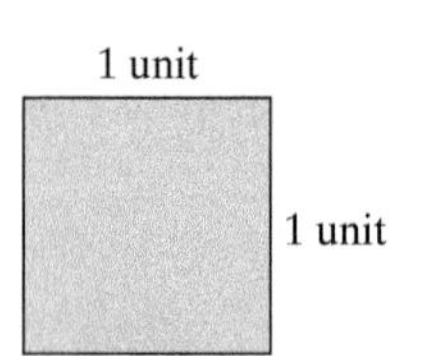

FIGURE 3.2 One square unit

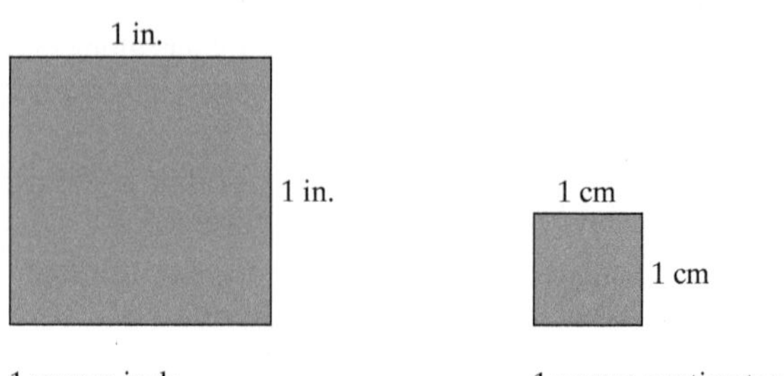

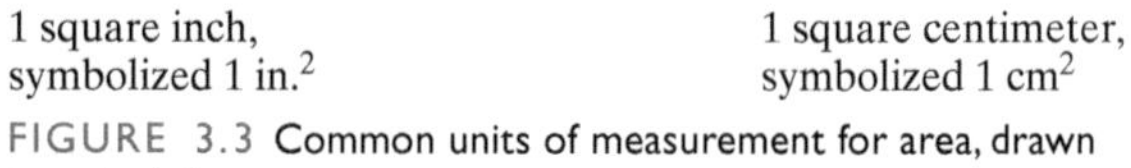

FIGURE 3.3 Common units of measurement for area, drawn to actual size

EXAMPLE 1 Measuring Area

What is the area of the region shown in **Figure 3.4**?

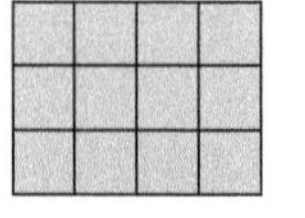

FIGURE 3.4

SOLUTION

We can determine the area of the region by counting the number of square units contained within the region. There are 12 such units. Therefore, the area of the region is 12 square units.

CHECK POINT 1 What is the area of the region represented by the first two rows in **Figure 3.4**?

Although there are 12 inches in one foot and 3 feet in one yard, these numerical relationships are not the same for square units.

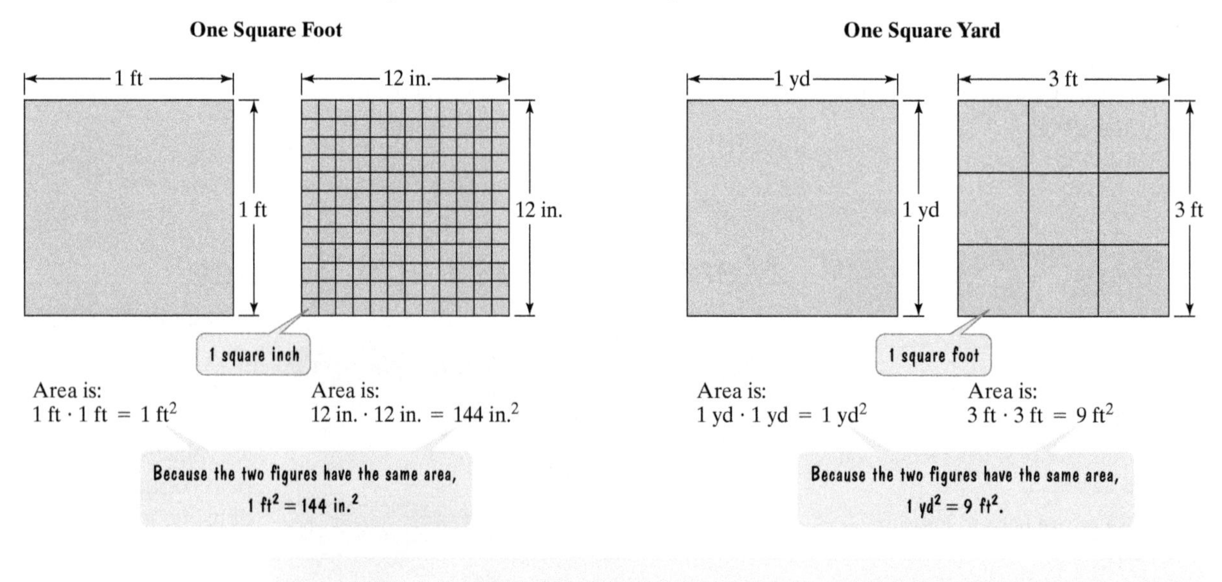

SQUARE UNITS OF MEASURE: THE ENGLISH SYSTEM

1 square foot (ft^2) = 144 square inches (in.^{2})
1 square yard (yd^2) = 9 square feet (ft^2)
1 acre (a) = 43,560 ft^2 or 4840 yd^2
1 square mile (mi^2) = 640 acres

GREAT QUESTION!

Which square units of measure are frequently used in everyday situations?

A small plot of land is usually measured in square feet, rather than a small fraction of an acre. Curiously, square yards are rarely used. However, square yards are commonly used for carpet and flooring measures.

EXAMPLE 2 *Using Square Units to Compute Population Density*

After Alaska, Wyoming is the least densely populated state. The population of Wyoming is 568,158 and its area is 97,814 square miles. What is Wyoming's population density?

SOLUTION

We compute the population density by dividing Wyoming's population by its area.

$$\text{population density} = \frac{\text{population}}{\text{area}} = \frac{568{,}158 \text{ people}}{97{,}814 \text{ square miles}}$$

Using a calculator and rounding to the nearest tenth, we obtain a population density of 5.8 people per square mile. This means that there is an average of only 5.8 people for each square mile of area.

CHECK POINT 2 The population of California is 37,691,912 and its area is 158,633 square miles. What is California's population density? Round to the nearest tenth.

2 Use dimensional analysis to change units for area.

EXAMPLE 3 *Using Dimensional Analysis on Units of Area*

Your author wrote *Thinking Mathematically* in Point Reyes National Seashore, 40 miles north of San Francisco. The national park consists of 75,000 acres with miles of pristine surf-washed beaches, forested ridges, and bays bordered by white cliffs. How large is the national park in square miles?

SOLUTION

We use the fact that 1 square mile = 640 acres to set up our unit fraction:

$$\frac{1 \text{ mi}^2}{640 \text{ acres}}.$$

Thus,

$$75{,}000 \text{ acres} = \frac{75{,}000 \not{\text{acres}}}{1} \cdot \frac{1 \text{ mi}^2}{640 \not{\text{acres}}} = \frac{75{,}000}{640} \text{ mi}^2 \approx 117 \text{ mi}^2.$$

The area of Point Reyes National Seashore is approximately 117 square miles.

CHECK POINT 3 The National Park Service administers approximately 84,000,000 acres of national parks. How large is this in square miles?

In Section 3.1, we saw that in most other countries, the system of measurement that is used is the metric system. In the metric system, the square centimeter is used instead of the square inch. The square meter replaces the square foot and the square yard.

The English system uses the acre and the square mile to measure large land areas, where one square mile = 640 acres. The metric system uses the hectare (symbolized ha and pronounced "hectair"). A hectare is about the area of two football fields placed side by side, approximately 2.5 acres. One square mile of land consists of approximately 260 hectares. Just as the hectare replaces the acre, the square kilometer is used instead of the square mile. One square kilometer is approximately 0.38 square mile.

Some basic approximate conversions for units of area are given in **Table 3.4**.

TABLE 3.4 English and Metric Equivalents for Area

1 square inch (in.^{2})	$\approx$ 6.5 square centimeters (cm^2)
1 square foot (ft^2)	$\approx$ 0.09 square meter (m^2)
1 square yard (yd^2)	$\approx$ 0.8 square meter (m^2)
1 square mile (mi^2)	$\approx$ 2.6 square kilometers (km^2)
1 acre	$\approx$ 0.4 hectare (ha)

EXAMPLE 4 *Using Dimensional Analysis on Units of Area*

A property in Italy is advertised at $545,000 for 6.8 hectares.

a. Find the area of the property in acres.

b. What is the price per acre?

SOLUTION

a. Using **Table 3.4**, we see that 1 acre $\approx$ 0.4 hectare. To convert 6.8 hectares to acres, we use a unit fraction with acres in the numerator and hectares in the denominator.

$$6.8 \text{ ha} \approx \frac{6.8 \text{ ha}}{1} \cdot \frac{1 \text{ acre}}{0.4 \text{ ha}} = \frac{6.8}{0.4} \text{ acres} = 17 \text{ acres}$$

The area of the property is approximately 17 acres.

b. The price per acre is the total price, $545,000, divided by the number of acres, 17.

$$\text{price per acre} = \frac{\$545{,}000}{17 \text{ acres}} \approx \$32{,}059/\text{acre}$$

The price is approximately $32,059 per acre.

CHECK POINT 4 A property in northern California is on the market at $415,000 for 1.8 acres.

a. Find the area of the property in hectares.

b. What is price per hectare?

3 Use cubic units to measure volume.

Measuring Volume

A shoe box and a basketball are examples of three-dimensional figures. **Volume** refers to the amount of space occupied by such figures. In order to measure this space, we begin by selecting a *cubic unit*. Two such cubic units are shown in **Figure 3.5**.

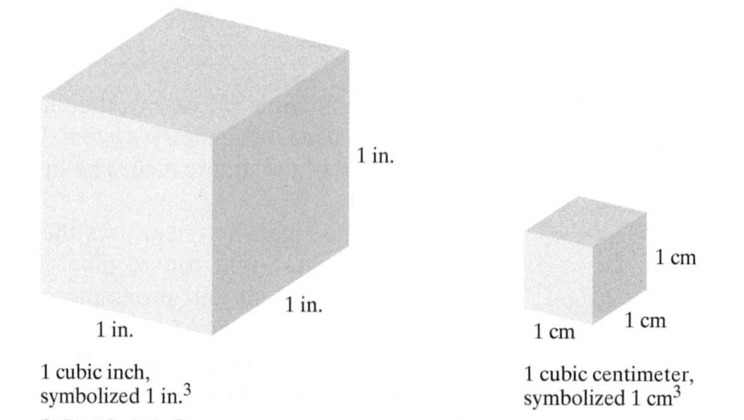

FIGURE 3.5 Common units of measurement for volume

The edges of a cube all have the same length. Other cubic units used to measure volume include 1 cubic foot (1 ft^3) and 1 cubic meter (1 m^3). One way to measure the volume of a solid is to calculate the number of cubic units contained in its interior.

EXAMPLE 5 *Measuring Volume*

What is the volume of the solid shown in **Figure 3.6**?

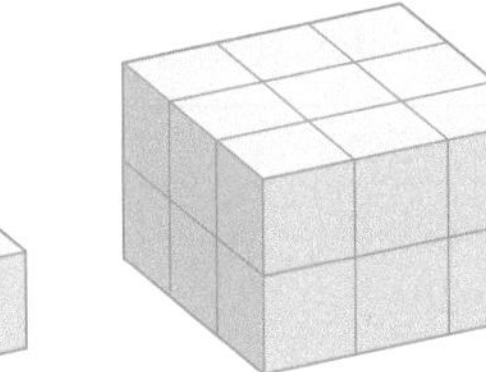

Cubic unit Volume = ?

FIGURE 3.6

SOLUTION

We can determine the volume of the solid by counting the number of cubic units contained within the region. Because we have drawn a solid three-dimensional figure on a flat two-dimensional page, some of the small cubic units in the back, right are hidden. The figures below show how the cubic units are used to fill the inside of the solid.

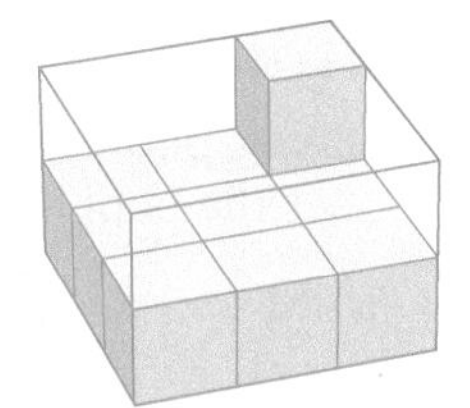

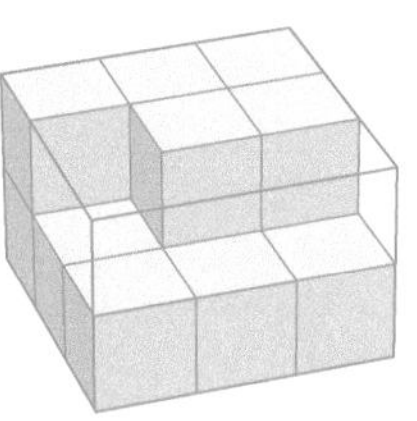

Do these figures help you to see that there are 18 cubic units inside the solid? The volume of the solid is 18 cubic units.

CHECK POINT 5 What is the volume of the region represented by the bottom row of blocks in **Figure 3.6**?

We have seen that there are 3 feet in a yard, but 9 square feet in a square yard. Neither of these relationships holds for cubic units. **Figure 3.7** illustrates that there are 27 cubic feet in a cubic yard. Furthermore, there are 1728 cubic inches in a cubic foot.

GREAT QUESTION!

I'm having difficulty seeing the detail in Figure 3.7. Can you help me out?

Cubing numbers is helpful:

$$3 \text{ ft} = 1 \text{ yd}$$
$$(3 \text{ ft})^3 = (1 \text{ yd})^3$$
$$3 \cdot 3 \cdot 3 \text{ ft}^3 = 1 \cdot 1 \cdot 1 \text{ yd}^3.$$

Conclusion: $27 \text{ ft}^3 = 1 \text{ yd}^3$

$$12 \text{ in.} = 1 \text{ ft}$$
$$(12 \text{ in.})^3 = (1 \text{ ft})^3$$
$$12 \cdot 12 \cdot 12 \text{ in.}^3 = 1 \cdot 1 \cdot 1 \text{ ft}^3$$

Conclusion: $1728 \text{ in.}^3 = 1 \text{ ft}^3$

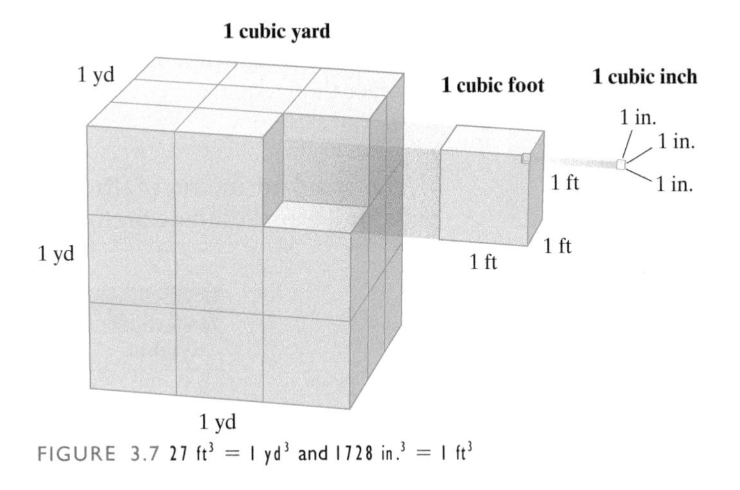

FIGURE 3.7 $27 \text{ ft}^3 = 1 \text{ yd}^3$ and $1728 \text{ in.}^3 = 1 \text{ ft}^3$

The measure of volume also includes the amount of fluid that a three-dimensional object can hold. This is often called the object's **capacity**. For example, we often refer to the capacity, in gallons, of a gas tank. A cubic yard has a capacity of about 200 gallons and a cubic foot has a capacity of about 7.48 gallons.

4 Use English and metric units to measure capacity.

Table 3.5 contains information about standard units of capacity in the English system.

TABLE 3.5 English Units for Capacity

2 pints (pt) = 1 quart (qt)	
4 quarts = 1 gallon (gal)	
1 gallon = 128 fluid ounces (fl oz)	
1 cup (c) = 8 fluid ounces	
Volume in Cubic Units	**Capacity**
1 cubic yard	about 200 gallons
1 cubic foot	about 7.48 gallons
231 cubic inches	about 1 gallon

EXAMPLE 6 *Volume and Capacity in the English System*

A swimming pool has a volume of 22,500 cubic feet. How many gallons of water does the pool hold?

SOLUTION

We use the fact that 1 cubic foot has a capacity of about 7.48 gallons to set up our unit fraction:

$$\frac{7.48 \text{ gal}}{1 \text{ ft}^3}.$$

We use this unit fraction to find the capacity of the 22,500 cubic feet.

$$22{,}500 \text{ ft}^3 \approx \frac{22{,}500 \text{ ft}^3}{1} \cdot \frac{7.48 \text{ gal}}{1 \text{ ft}^3} = 22{,}500(7.48) \text{ gal} = 168{,}300 \text{ gal}$$

The pool holds approximately 168,300 gallons of water.

CHECK POINT 6 A pool has a volume of 10,000 cubic feet. How many gallons of water does the pool hold?

1 liter

1 quart

As we have come to expect, things are simpler when the metric system is used to measure capacity. The basic unit is the **liter**, symbolized by L. A liter is slightly larger than a quart.

$$1 \text{ liter} \approx 1.0567 \text{ quarts}$$

The standard metric prefixes are used to denote a multiple or part of a liter. **Table 3.6** applies these prefixes to the liter.

TABLE 3.6 Units of Capacity in the Metric System

Symbol	Unit	Meaning
kL	kiloliter	1000 liters
hL	hectoliter	100 liters
daL	dekaliter	10 liters
L	liter	1 liter ≈ 1.06 quarts
dL	deciliter	0.1 liter
cL	centiliter	0.01 liter
mL	milliliter	0.001 liter

The following list should help give you a feel for capacity in the metric system.

Item	Capacity
Average cup of coffee	250 mL
12-ounce can of soda	355 mL
One quart of fruit juice	0.95 L
One gallon of milk	3.78 L
Average gas capacity of a car (about 18.5 gallons)	70 L

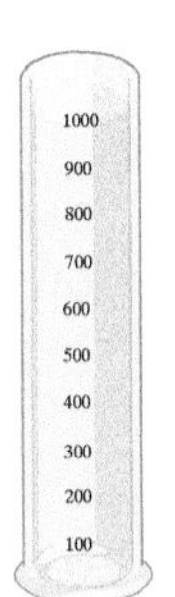

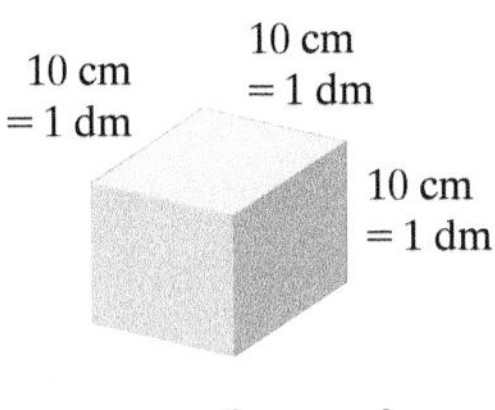

$1\text{ L} = 1000\text{ mL}$ $\quad 1000\text{ cm}^3 = 1\text{ dm}^3$

FIGURE 3.8

Figure 3.8 shows a 1-liter container filled with water. The water in the liter container will fit exactly into the cube shown to its right. The volume of this cube is 1000 cubic centimeters, or equivalently, 1 cubic decimeter. Thus,

$$1000\text{ cm}^3 = 1\text{ dm}^3 = 1\text{ L}.$$

Table 3.7 expands on this relationship between volume and capacity in the metric system.

TABLE 3.7 Volume and Capacity in the Metric System

Volume in Cubic Units		Capacity
1 cm^3	=	1 mL
$1\text{ dm}^3 = 1000\text{ cm}^3$	=	1 L
1 m^3	=	1 kL

A milliliter is the capacity of a cube measuring 1 centimeter on each side.

A liter is the capacity of a cube measuring 10 centimeters on each side.

EXAMPLE 7 *Volume and Capacity in the Metric System*

An aquarium has a volume of 36,000 cubic centimeters. How many liters of water does the aquarium hold?

SOLUTION

We use the fact that 1000 cubic centimeters corresponds to a capacity of 1 liter to set up our unit fraction:

$$\frac{1\text{ L}}{1000\text{ cm}^3}.$$

We use this unit fraction to find the capacity of the 36,000 cubic centimeters.

$$36{,}000\text{ cm}^3 = \frac{36{,}000\text{ cm}^3}{1} \cdot \frac{1\text{ L}}{1000\text{ cm}^3} = \frac{36{,}000}{1000}\text{ L} = 36\text{ L}$$

The aquarium holds 36 liters of water.

CHECK POINT 7 A fish pond has a volume of 220,000 cubic centimeters. How many liters of water does the pond hold?

Table 3.8 can be used to convert units of capacity to and from the metric system.

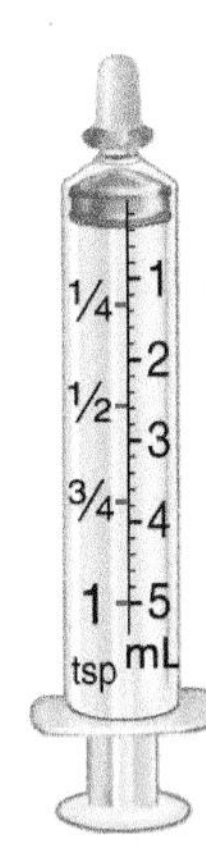

TABLE 3.8 English and Metric Equivalents for Capacity

1 teaspoon (tsp)	≈ 5 milliliters (mL)
1 tablespoon (tbsp)	≈ 15 milliliters (mL)
1 fluid ounce (fl oz)	≈ 30 milliliters (mL)
1 cup (c)	≈ 0.24 liter (L)
1 pint (pt)	≈ 0.47 liter (L)
1 quart (qt)	≈ 0.95 liter (L)
1 gallon (gal)	≈ 3.8 liters (L)

Our next example involves measuring dosages of medicine in liquid form. We have seen that

$$1 \text{ cm}^3 = 1 \text{ mL}.$$

Dosages of liquid medication are measured using cubic centimeters, or milliliters as they are also called. In the United States, cc, rather than cm^3, denotes cubic centimeters.

EXAMPLE 8 *Measuring Dosages of Medicine in Liquid Form*

A physician orders 10 cc of the drug Lexapro (used to treat depression and anxiety) to be administered to a patient in liquid form.

a. How many milliliters of the drug should be administered?

b. How many fluid ounces of the drug should be administered?

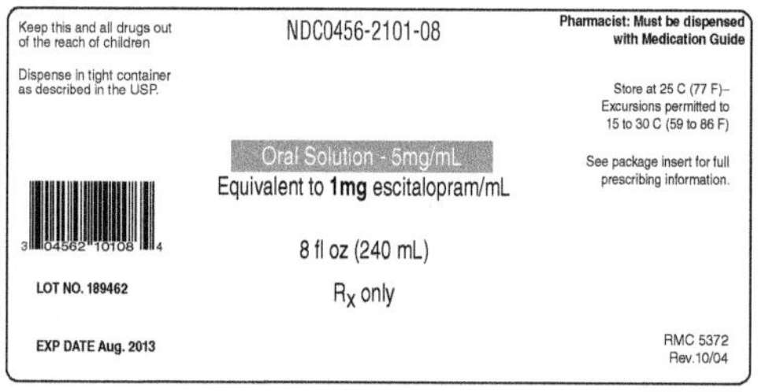

SOLUTION

a. We use a relationship between volume and capacity in the metric system: 1 cubic centimeter (cc) = 1 milliliter (mL). Because 10 cubic centimeters (cc) of the drug is to be administered, this is equivalent to 10 milliliters (mL) of Lexapro.

b. We now need to convert 10 milliliters to fluid ounces. **Table 3.8** on the previous page shows that 1 fluid ounce (fl oz) $\approx$ 30 milliliters (mL). We use

$$\frac{1 \text{ fl oz}}{30 \text{ mL}}$$

as our unit fraction.

$$10 \text{ mL} \approx \frac{10 \cancel{\text{mL}}}{1} \cdot \frac{1 \text{ fl oz}}{30 \cancel{\text{mL}}} = \frac{10}{30} \text{ fl oz} \approx 0.33 \text{ fl oz}$$

Approximately 0.33 fluid ounce (fl oz) of Lexapro should be administered.

CHECK POINT 8 A physician orders 20 cc of the antibiotic Omnicef to be administered every 12 hours.

a. How many milliliters of the drug should be administered?

b. How many fluid ounces of the drug should be administered? Round to two decimal places.

Concept and Vocabulary Check

Fill in each blank so that the resulting statement is true.

1. Area is measured in ________ units and volume is measured in ________ units.
2. In the English system, 1 ft^2 = ____________ $in.^2$ and 1 yd^2 = ____________ ft^2.
3. Because 1 mi^2 = 640 acres, the unit fraction needed to convert from acres to square miles is ________ and the unit fraction needed to convert from square miles to acres is ________.
4. In the English system, ____________ pt = 1 qt and ____________ qt = 1 gal.
5. The amount of fluid that a three-dimensional object can hold is called the object's ________, measured in the metric system using a basic unit called the ________.
6. A state's population density is its population divided by its ________.
7. 1 cm^3, or 1 cc, = ________ mL

In Exercises 8–10, determine whether each statement is true or false. If the statement is false, make the necessary change(s) to produce a true statement.

8. Because there are 3 feet in one yard, there are also 3 square feet in one square yard. ________
9. The English system uses $in.^2$ to measure large land areas. ________
10. One quart is approximately 1.06 liters. ________

Exercise Set 3.2

Practice Exercises

In Exercises 1–4, use the given figure to find its area in square units.

1. 2. 3. 4.

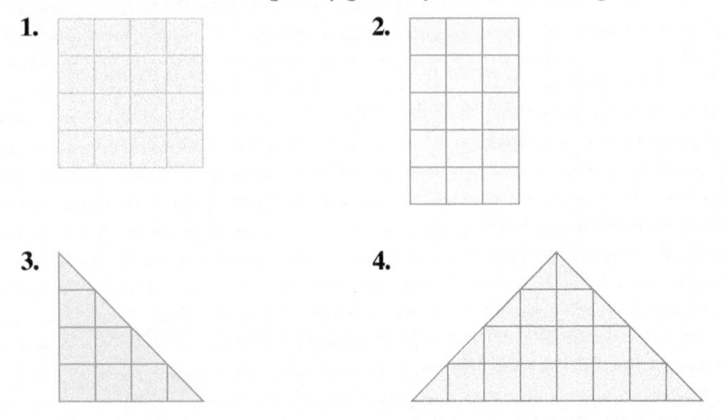

In Exercises 5–12, use ***Table 3.4*** *on page 98, along with dimensional analysis, to approximately convert the given square unit to the square unit indicated. Where necessary, round answers to two decimal places.*

5. 14 cm^2 to $in.^2$
6. 20 m^2 to ft^2
7. 30 m^2 to yd^2
8. 14 mi^2 to km^2
9. 10.2 ha to acres
10. 20.6 ha to acres
11. 14 $in.^2$ to cm^2
12. 20 $in.^2$ to cm^2

In Exercises 13–14, use the given figure to find its volume in cubic units.

13. 14.

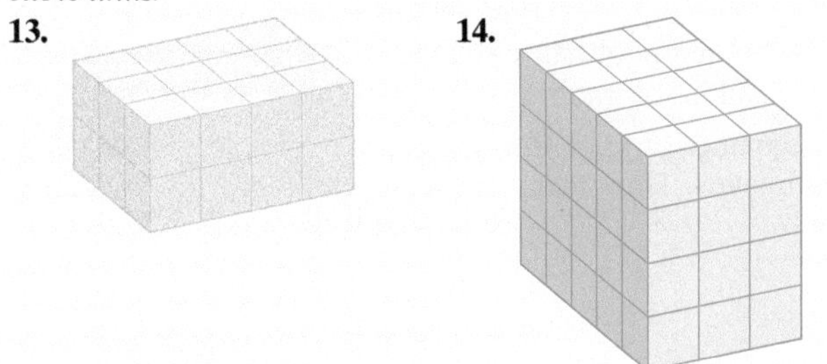

In Exercises 15–22, use ***Table 3.5*** *on page 100, along with dimensional analysis, to approximately convert the given unit to the unit indicated. Where necessary, round answers to two decimal places.*

15. 10,000 ft^3 to gal
16. 25,000 ft^3 to gal
17. 8 yd^3 to gal
18. 35 yd^3 to gal
19. 2079 $in.^3$ to gal
20. 6237 $in.^3$ to gal
21. 2700 gal to yd^3
22. 1496 gal to ft^3

In Exercises 23–32, use ***Table 3.7*** *on page 101, along with dimensional analysis, to convert the given unit to the unit indicated.*

23. 45,000 cm^3 to L
24. 75,000 cm^3 to L
25. 17 cm^3 to mL
26. 19 cm^3 to mL
27. 1.5 L to cm^3
28. 4.5 L to cm^3
29. 150 mL to cm^3
30. 250 mL to cm^3
31. 12 kL to dm^3
32. 16 kL to dm^3

In Exercises 33–48, use ***Table 3.8*** *on page 101, along with dimensional analysis, to convert the given unit to the unit indicated. Where necessary, round to two decimal places.*

33. 12 mL to tsp
34. 14 mL to tsp
35. 3 tbsp to mL

36. 4 tbsp to mL
37. 70 mL to fl oz
38. 80 mL to fl oz
39. 1.4 L to c
40. 2.6 L to c
41. 6 pt to L
42. 9 pt to L
43. 4 L to qt
44. 7 L to qt
45. 3 gal to L
46. 5 gal to L
47. 2000 mL to qt
48. 5000 mL to qt

Practice Plus

The bar graph shows the resident population and the land area of the United States for selected years from 1800 through 2010. Use the information shown by the graph to solve Exercises 49–52.

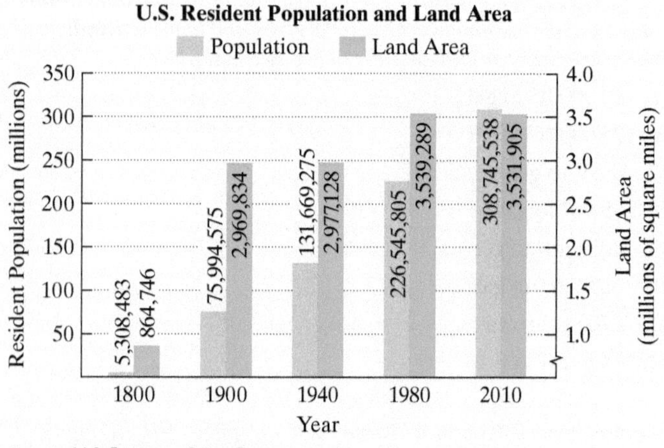

Source: U.S. Bureau of the Census

49. a. Find the population density of the United States, to the nearest tenth, in 1900 and in 2010.

b. Find the percent increase in population density, to the nearest tenth of a percent, from 1900 to 2010.

50. a. Find the population density of the United States, to the nearest tenth, in 1800 and in 2010.

b. Find the percent increase in population density, to the nearest tenth of a percent, from 1800 to 2010.

51. Find the population density of the United States, to the nearest tenth, expressed in people per square kilometer, in 1940.

52. Find the population density of the United States, to the nearest tenth, expressed in people per square kilometer, in 1980.

Application Exercises

In Exercises 53–54, find the population density, to the nearest tenth, for each state. Which state has the greater population density? How many more people per square mile inhabit the state with the greater density than inhabit the state with the lesser density?

53. Illinois population: 12,869,257 area: 57,914 mi^2
Ohio population: 11,544,951 area: 44,826 mi^2

54. New York population: 19,465,197 area: 54,555 mi^2
Rhode Island population: 1,051,302 area: 1545 mi^2

In Exercises 55–56, use the fact that 1 square mile = 640 acres to find the area of each national park to the nearest square mile.

55. Everglades National Park (Florida): 1,509,154 acres

56. Yosemite National Park (California): 761,268 acres

57. A property that measures 8 hectares is for sale.
a. How large is the property in acres?
b. If the property is selling for \$250,000, what is the price per acre?

58. A property that measures 100 hectares is for sale.
a. How large is the property in acres?
b. If the property is selling for \$350,000, what is the price per acre?

In Exercises 59–62, selecting from square centimeters, square meters, or square kilometers, determine the best unit of measure to express the area of the object described.

59. The top of a desk
60. A dollar bill
61. A national park
62. The wall of a room

In Exercises 63–66, select the best estimate for the measure of the area of the object described.

63. The area of the floor of a room
a. 25 cm^2 **b.** 25 m^2 **c.** 25 km^2

64. The area of a television screen
a. 2050 mm^2 **b.** 2050 cm^2 **c.** 2050 dm^2

65. The area of the face of a small coin
a. 6 mm^2 **b.** 6 cm^2 **c.** 6 dm^2

66. The area of a parcel of land in a large metropolitan area on which a house can be built
a. 900 cm^2 **b.** 900 m^2 **c.** 900 ha

67. A swimming pool has a volume of 45,000 cubic feet. How many gallons of water does the pool hold?

68. A swimming pool has a volume of 66,000 cubic feet. How many gallons of water does the pool hold?

69. A container of grapefruit juice has a volume of 4000 cubic centimeters. How many liters of juice does the container hold?

70. An aquarium has a volume of 17,500 cubic centimeters. How many liters of water does the aquarium hold?

Exercises 71–72 give the approximate area of some of the world's largest island countries. In each exercise, determine which country has the greater area and by how many square kilometers.

71. Philippines: 300,000 km^2; Japan: 145,900 mi^2

72. Iceland: 103,000 km^2; Cuba: 42,800 mi^2

Exercises 73–74 give the approximate area of some of the world's largest islands. In each exercise, determine which island has the greater area and by how many square miles. Round to the nearest square mile.

73. Baffin Island, Canada: 194,574 mi^2;
Sumatra, Indonesia: 443,070 km^2

74. Honshu, Japan: 87,805 mi^2;
Victoria Island, Canada: 217,300 km^2

(Source for Exercises 71–74: Russell Ash, *The Top 10 of Everything 2009*)

*Exercises 75–76 involve dosages of the anti-inflammatory drug indomethacin, administered in liquid form. Refer to the appropriate entries in **Table 3.8** on page 101 to convert given units to the unit indicated. Where necessary, round to two decimal places.*

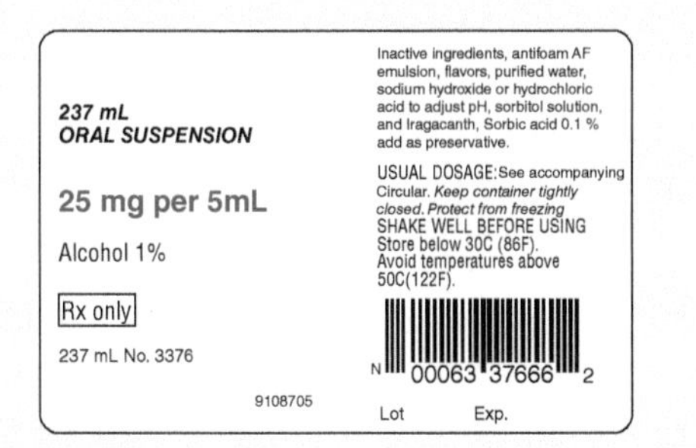

75. A physician orders 3 teaspoons daily of indomethacin in three equally divided doses.

a. How many milliliters of the drug should be administered daily?

b. How many cc of the drug should be administered daily?

c. How many fluid ounces of the drug should be administered daily?

d. How many fluid ounces of the drug should the patient receive in each divided dose?

76. A physician orders 4 teaspoons daily of indomethacin in four equally divided doses.

a. How many milliliters of the drug should be administered daily?

b. How many cc of the drug should be administered daily?

c. How many fluid ounces of the drug should be administered daily?

d. How many fluid ounces of the drug should the patient receive in each divided dose?

Writing in Mathematics

77. Describe how area is measured. Explain why linear units cannot be used.

78. New Mexico has a population density of 17 people per square mile. Describe what this means. Use an almanac or the Internet to compare this population density to that of the state in which you are now living.

79. Describe the difference between the following problems: How much fencing is needed to enclose a garden? How much fertilizer is needed for the garden?

80. Describe how volume is measured. Explain why linear or square units cannot be used.

81. For a swimming pool, what is the difference between the following units of measure: cubic feet and gallons? For each unit, write a sentence about the pool that makes the use of the unit appropriate.

82. If there are 10 decimeters in a meter, explain why there are not 10 cubic decimeters in a cubic meter.

Critical Thinking Exercises

Make Sense? *In Exercises 83–86, determine whether each statement makes sense or does not make sense, and explain your reasoning.*

83. The gas capacity of my car is approximately 40 meters.

84. The population density of Montana is approximately 6.5 people per mile.

85. Yesterday I drank 2000 cm^3 of water.

86. I read that one quart is approximately 0.94635295 liter.

87. Singapore has the highest population density of any country: 46,690 people per 1000 hectares. How many people are there per square mile?

88. Nebraska has a population density of 23.8 people per square mile and a population of 1,842,641. What is the area of Nebraska? Round to the nearest square mile.

89. A high population density is a condition common to extremely poor and extremely rich locales. Explain why this is so.

90. Although Alaska is the least densely populated state, over 90% of its land is protected federal property that is off-limits to settlement. A resident of Anchorage, Alaska, might feel hemmed in. In terms of "elbow room," what other important factor must be considered when calculating a state's population density?

91. Does an adult's body contain approximately 6.5 liters, kiloliters, or milliliters of blood? Explain your answer.

92. Is the volume of a coin approximately 1 cubic centimeter, 1 cubic millimeter, or 1 cubic decimeter? Explain your answer.

Group Exercise

93. If you could select any place in the world, where would you like to live? Look up the population and area of your ideal place, and compute its population density. Group members should share places to live and population densities. What trend, if any, does the group observe?

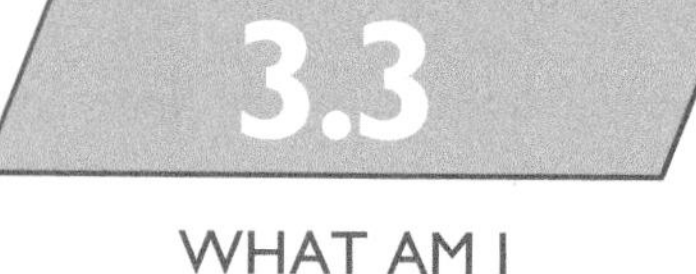

WHAT AM I SUPPOSED TO LEARN?

After you have read this section, you should be able to:

1. Apply metric prefixes to units of weight.
2. Convert units of weight within the metric system.
3. Use relationships between volume and weight within the metric system.
4. Use dimensional analysis to change units of weight to and from the metric system.
5. Understand temperature scales.

Measuring Weight and Temperature

YOU ARE WATCHING CNN INTERNATIONAL on cable television. The temperature in Honolulu, Hawaii, is reported as 30°C. Are Honolulu's tourists running around in winter jackets? In this section, we will make sense of Celsius temperature readings, as we discuss methods for measuring temperature and weight.

Measuring Weight

You step on the scale at the doctor's office to check your weight, discovering that you are 150 pounds. Compare this to your weight on the moon: 25 pounds. Why the difference? **Weight** is the measure of the gravitational pull on an object. The gravitational pull on the moon is only about one-sixth the gravitational pull on Earth. Although your weight varies depending on the force of gravity, your mass is exactly the same in all locations. **Mass** is a measure of the quantity of matter in an object, determined by its molecular structure. On Earth, as your weight increases, so does your mass. In this section, measurements are assumed to involve everyday situations on the surface of Earth. Thus, we will treat weight and mass as equivalent, and refer strictly to weight.

UNITS OF WEIGHT: THE ENGLISH SYSTEM

16 ounces (oz) = 1 pound (lb)

2000 pounds (lb) = 1 ton (T)

1 Apply metric prefixes to units of weight.

The basic metric unit of weight is the **gram** (g), used for very small objects such as a coin, a candy bar, or a teaspoon of salt. A nickel has a weight of about 5 grams.

As with meters, prefixes are used to denote a multiple or part of a gram. **Table 3.9** applies the common metric prefixes to the gram. The first part of the symbol indicates the prefix and the second part (g) indicates gram.

TABLE 3.9 Commonly Used Units of Weight in the Metric System

Symbol	Unit	Meaning
kg	kilogram	1000 grams
hg	hectogram	100 grams
dag	dekagram	10 grams
g	gram	1 gram
dg	decigram	0.1 gram
cg	centigram	0.01 gram
mg	milligram	0.001 gram

Weight of pineapple is 1kg, or 1000g.

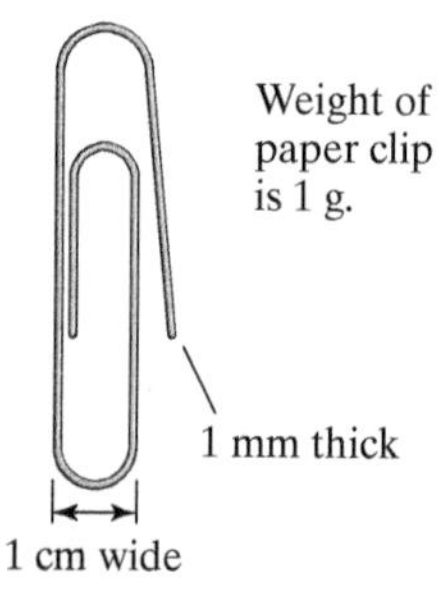

Weight of paper clip is 1 g.

In the metric system, the kilogram is the comparable unit to the pound in the English system. **A weight of 1 kilogram is approximately 2.2 pounds.** Thus, an average man has a weight of about 75 kilograms. Objects that we measure in pounds are measured in kilograms in most countries.

A milligram, equivalent to 0.001 gram, is an extremely small unit of weight and is used extensively in the pharmaceutical industry. If you look at the label on a bottle of tablets, you will see that the amounts of different substances in each tablet are expressed in milligrams.

The weight of a very heavy object is expressed in terms of the metric tonne (t), which is equivalent to 1000 kilograms, or about 2200 pounds. This is 10 percent more than the English ton (T) of 2000 pounds.

We change units of weight within the metric system exactly the same way that we changed units of length.

2 Convert units of weight within the metric system.

CHANGING UNITS OF WEIGHT WITHIN THE METRIC SYSTEM

Use the following diagram to find equivalent measures of weight:

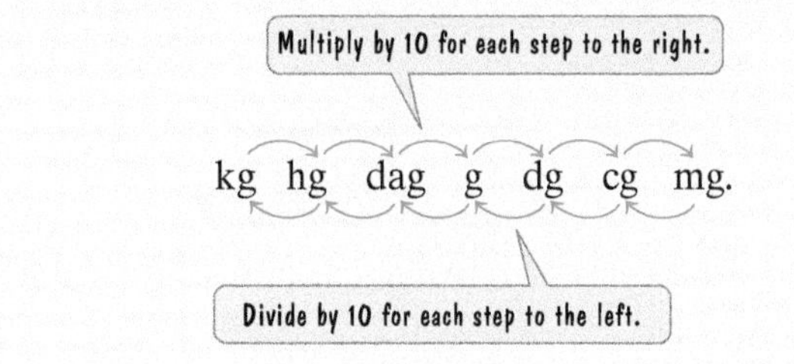

EXAMPLE 1 *Changing Units within the Metric System*

a. Convert 8.7 dg to mg.

b. Convert 950 mg to g.

SOLUTION

a. To convert from dg (decigrams) to mg (milligrams), we start at dg and move two steps to the right:

kg hg dag g dg cg mg.

Hence, we move the decimal point two places to the right:

$$8.7 \text{ dg} = 870 \text{ mg}.$$

b. To convert from mg (milligrams) to g (grams), we start at mg and move three steps to the left:

kg hg dag g dg cg mg.

Hence, we move the decimal point three places to the left:

$$950 \text{ mg} = 0.950 \text{ g}.$$

CHECK POINT 1

a. Convert 4.2 dg to mg.

b. Convert 620 cg to g.

---

3 Use relationships between volume and weight within the metric system.

We have seen a convenient relationship in the metric system between volume and capacity:

$$1000 \text{ cm}^3 = 1 \text{ dm}^3 = 1 \text{ L}.$$

This relationship can be extended to include weight based on the following:

One kilogram of water has a volume of 1 liter.

Thus,

$$1000 \text{ cm}^3 = 1 \text{ dm}^3 = 1 \text{ L} = 1 \text{ kg}.$$

Table 3.10 shows the relationships between volume and weight of water in the metric system.

TABLE 3.10 Volume and Weight of Water in the Metric System

Volume		Capacity		Weight
1 cm^3	=	1 mL	=	1 g
$1 \text{ dm}^3 = 1000 \text{ cm}^3$	=	1 L	=	1 kg
1 m^3	=	1 kL	=	1000 kg = 1 t

EXAMPLE 2 *Volume and Weight in the Metric System*

An aquarium holds 0.25 m^3 of water. How much does the water weigh?

SOLUTION

We use the fact that 1 m^3 of water = 1000 kg of water to set up our unit fraction:

$$\frac{1000 \text{ kg}}{1 \text{ m}^3}.$$

Thus,

$$0.25 \text{ m}^3 = \frac{0.25 \cancel{\text{m}^3}}{1} \cdot \frac{1000 \text{ kg}}{1 \cancel{\text{m}^3}} = 250 \text{ kg}.$$

The water weighs 250 kilograms.

CHECK POINT 2 An aquarium holds 0.145 m^3 of water. How much does the water weigh?

---

4 Use dimensional analysis to change units of weight to and from the metric system.

A problem like Example 2 involves more awkward computation in the English system. For example, if you know the aquarium's volume in cubic feet, you must also know that 1 cubic foot of water weighs about 62.5 pounds to determine the water's weight.

Dimensional analysis is a useful tool when converting units of weight between the English and metric systems. Some basic approximate conversions are given in **Table 3.11**.

1-ounce coin ≈ 28 grams

1-pound lobster ≈ 0.45 kilogram

TABLE 3.11 Weight: English and Metric Equivalents

English		Metric
1 ounce (oz)	≈	28 grams (g)
1 pound (lb)	≈	0.45 kilogram (kg)
1 ton (T)	≈	0.9 tonne (t)

1-ton bison ≈ 0.9 tonne

EXAMPLE 3 *Using Dimensional Analysis*

a. Convert 160 pounds to kilograms.

b. Convert 300 grams to ounces.

Blitzer Bonus

The SI System

The metric system is officially called the Système International d'Unités, abbreviated the SI system. Yemen, Brunei, and the United States are the only countries in the world not using the SI system.

In 1975, the United States prepared to adopt the SI system with the Metric Conversion Act. However, due to concerns in grassroots America, Congress made the conversion voluntary, effectively chasing it off. But it's not as bleak as you think; from metric tools to milligram measures of medication, we have been edging, inching, even centimetering toward the metric system.

SOLUTION

a. To convert 160 pounds to kilograms, we use a unit fraction with kilograms in the numerator and pounds in the denominator:

$$\frac{0.45 \text{ kg}}{1 \text{ lb}}.$$ Table 3.11 shows that 1 lb ≈ 0.45 kg.

Thus,

$$160 \text{ lb} \approx \frac{160 \text{ lb}}{1} \cdot \frac{0.45 \text{ kg}}{1 \text{ lb}} = 160(0.45) \text{ kg} = 72 \text{ kg}.$$

b. To convert 300 grams to ounces, we use a unit fraction with ounces in the numerator and grams in the denominator:

$$\frac{1 \text{ oz}}{28 \text{ g}}.$$ Table 3.11 shows that 1 oz ≈ 28 g.

Thus,

$$300 \text{ g} \approx \frac{300 \text{ g}}{1} \cdot \frac{1 \text{ oz}}{28 \text{ g}} = \frac{300}{28} \text{ oz} \approx 10.7 \text{ oz}.$$

CHECK POINT 3

a. Convert 120 pounds to kilograms.

b. Convert 500 grams to ounces.

EXAMPLE 4 *Dosages of Medication and Weight in the Metric System*

Drug dosage is frequently based on a patient's weight, measured in kilograms. For example, 20 milligrams of the drug Didronel (used to treat irregular bone formation) should be administered daily for each kilogram of a patient's weight. This can be expressed as 20 mg/kg. How many 400-milligram tablets should be given each day to a patient who weighs 180 pounds?

SOLUTION

- Convert 180 pounds to kilograms, using 1 lb ≈ 0.45 kg to set up the unit fraction.

$$180 \text{ lb} \approx \frac{180 \text{ lb}}{1} \cdot \frac{0.45 \text{ kg}}{1 \text{ lb}} = 180(0.45) \text{ kg} = 81 \text{ kg}$$

- Determine the dosage. We are given 20 mg/kg, meaning that 20 milligrams of the drug is to be given for each kilogram of a patient's weight. Multiply the patient's weight, 81 kilograms, by 20 to determine the dosage.

$$\text{Dosage} = \frac{81 \text{ kg}}{1} \cdot \frac{20 \text{ mg}}{1 \text{ kg}} = 81(20) \text{ mg} = 1620 \text{ mg}$$

- Determine the number of tablets that should be given each day. The patient should receive 1620 milligrams of Didronel daily. We are given that each tablet contains 400 milligrams.

$$\text{Number of tablets} = \frac{1620 \text{ mg}}{400 \text{ mg}} = 4.05$$

The patient should receive 4 tablets of Didronel daily.

CHECK POINT 4 The prescribed dosage of a drug is 6 mg/kg daily. How many 200-milligram tablets should be given each day to a patient who weighs 150 pounds?

Blitzer Bonus

Using the Metric System to Measure Blood-Alcohol Concentration

Blood-alcohol concentration (BAC) is measured in grams of alcohol per 100 milliliters of blood. To put this measurement into perspective, a 175-pound man has approximately 5 liters (5000 milliliters) of blood and a 12-ounce can of 6%-alcohol-by-volume beer contains about 15 grams of alcohol. Based on the time it takes for alcohol to be absorbed into the bloodstream, as well as its elimination at a rate of 10–15 grams per hour, **Figure 3.9** shows the effect on BAC of a number of drinks on individuals within weight classes. It is illegal to drive with a BAC at 0.08 g/100 mL, or 0.08 gram of alcohol per 100 milliliters of blood, or greater.

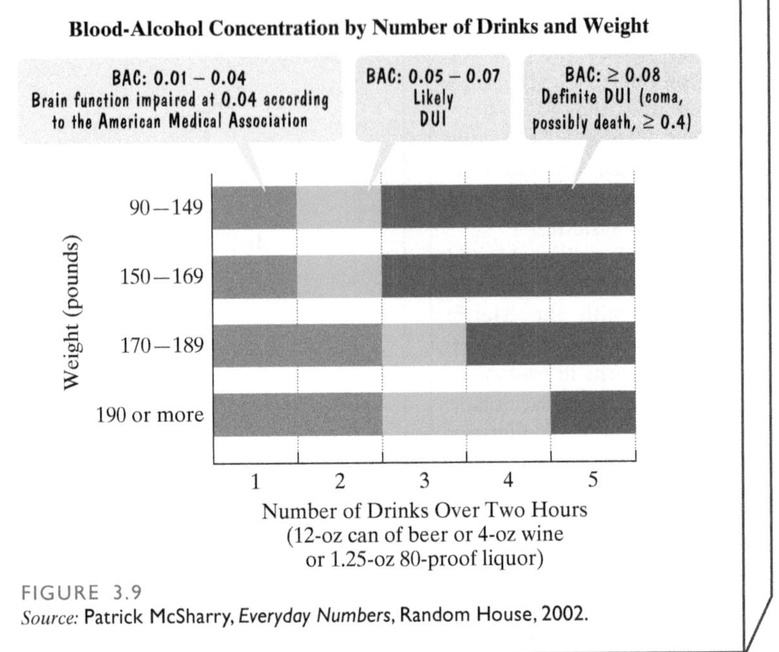

FIGURE 3.9
Source: Patrick McSharry, *Everyday Numbers*, Random House, 2002.

5 Understand temperature scales.

Measuring Temperature

You'll be leaving the cold of winter for a vacation to Hawaii. CNN International reports a temperature in Hawaii of 30°C. Should you pack a winter coat?

The idea of changing from Celsius readings—or is it Centigrade?—to familiar Fahrenheit readings can be disorienting. Reporting a temperature of 30°C doesn't have the same impact as the Fahrenheit equivalent of 86 degrees (don't pack the coat). Why these annoying temperature scales?

The **Fahrenheit temperature scale**, the one we are accustomed to, was established in 1714 by the German physicist Gabriel Daniel Fahrenheit. He took a mixture of salt and ice, then thought to be the coldest possible temperature, and called it 0 degrees. He called the temperature of the human body 96 degrees, dividing the space between 0 and 96 into 96 parts. Fahrenheit was wrong about body temperature. It was later found to be 98.6 degrees. On his scale, water froze (without salt) at 32 degrees and boiled at 212 degrees. The symbol ° was used to replace the word *degree*.

Twenty years later, the Swedish scientist Anders Celsius introduced another temperature scale. He set the freezing point of water at 0° and its boiling point at 100°, dividing the space into 100 parts. Degrees were called centigrade until 1948, when the name was officially changed to honor its inventor. However, *centigrade* is still commonly used in the United States.

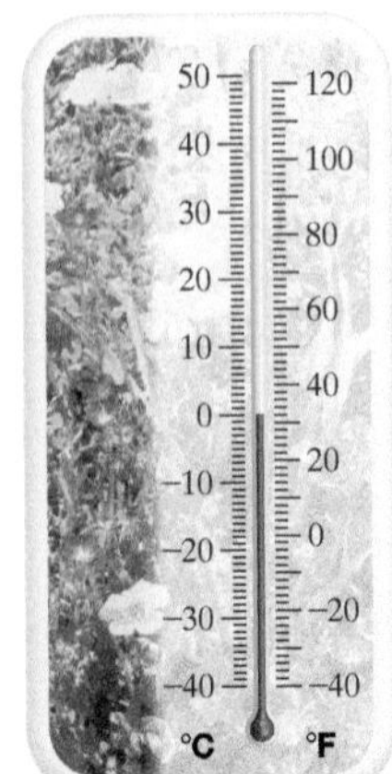

FIGURE 3.10 The Celsius scale is on the left and the Fahrenheit scale is on the right.

Figure 3.10 shows a thermometer that measures temperatures in both degrees Celsius (°C is the scale on the left) and degrees Fahrenheit (°F is the scale on the right). The thermometer should help orient you if you need to know what a temperature in °C means. For example, if it is 40°C, find the horizontal line representing this temperature on the left. Now read across to the °F scale on the right. The reading is above 100°, indicating heat wave conditions.

The following formulas can be used to convert from one temperature scale to the other:

FROM CELSIUS TO FAHRENHEIT

$$F = \frac{9}{5}C + 32$$

FROM FAHRENHEIT TO CELSIUS

$$C = \frac{5}{9}(F - 32)$$

GREAT QUESTION!

Because $\frac{9}{5} = 1.8$, can I use 1.8 instead of $\frac{9}{5}$ in the formula $F = \frac{9}{5}C + 32$?

Yes. The formula used to convert from Celsius to Fahrenheit can be expressed without the use of fractions:

$$F = 1.8C + 32.$$

Some students find this form of the formula easier to memorize.

EXAMPLE 5 *Converting from Celsius to Fahrenheit*

The bills from your European vacation have you feeling a bit feverish, so you decide to take your temperature. The thermometer reads 37°C. Should you panic?

SOLUTION

Use the formula

$$F = \frac{9}{5}C + 32$$

to convert 37°C from °C to °F. Substitute 37 for C in the formula and find the value of F.

$$F = \frac{9}{5}(37) + 32 = 66.6 + 32 = 98.6$$

No need to panic! Your temperature is 98.6°F, which is perfectly normal.

CHECK POINT 5 Convert 50°C from °C to °F.

EXAMPLE 6 *Converting from Fahrenheit to Celsius*

The temperature on a warm spring day is 77°F. Find the equivalent temperature on the Celsius scale.

SOLUTION

Use the formula

$$C = \frac{5}{9}(F - 32)$$

to convert 77°F from °F to °C. Substitute 77 for F in the formula and find the value of C.

$$C = \frac{5}{9}(77 - 32) = \frac{5}{9}(45) = 25$$

Thus, 77°F is equivalent to 25°C.

CHECK POINT 6 Convert 59°F from °F to °C.

Lake Baikal, Siberia, is one of the coldest places on Earth, reaching −76°F (−60°C) in winter. The lowest temperature possible is absolute zero. Scientists have cooled atoms to a few millionths of a degree above absolute zero.

Because temperature is a measure of heat, scientists do not find negative temperatures meaningful in their work. In 1948, the British physicist Lord Kelvin introduced a third temperature scale. He put 0 degrees at absolute zero, the coldest possible temperature, at which there is no heat and molecules stop moving. **Figure 3.11** on the next page illustrates the three temperature scales.

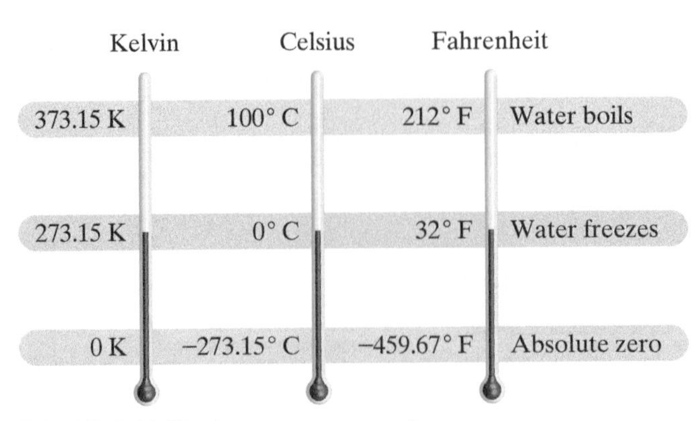

FIGURE 3.11 The three temperature scales

Figure 3.11 shows that water freezes at 273.15 K (read "K" or "Kelvins," not "degrees Kelvin") and boils at 373.15 K. The Kelvin scale is the same as the Celsius scale, except in its starting (zero) point. This makes it easy to go back and forth from Celsius to Kelvin.

FROM CELSIUS TO KELVIN

$$K = C + 273.15$$

FROM KELVIN TO CELSIUS

$$C = K - 273.15$$

Kelvin's scale was embraced by the scientific community. Today, it is the final authority, as scientists define Celsius and Fahrenheit in terms of Kelvins.

> **Blitzer Bonus**
>
> *Running a 5 K Race?*
>
> A 5 K race means a race at 5 Kelvins. This is a race so cold that no one would be able to move because all the participants would be frozen solid! The proper symbol for a race five kilometers long is a 5 km race.

Concept and Vocabulary Check

Fill in each blank so that the resulting statement is true.

1. In the English system, ________ oz = 1 lb and ________ lb = 1 T.
2. The basic metric unit of weight is the ________, used for very small objects such as a coin, a candy bar, or a teaspoon of salt.
3. A weight of 1 kilogram is approximately ________ pounds.
4. One kilogram of water has a volume of ________ liter(s).
5. On the Fahrenheit temperature scale, water freezes at ________ degrees and boils at ________ degrees.
6. On the Celsius temperature scale, water freezes at ________ degrees and boils at ________ degrees.

In Exercises 7–10, determine whether each statement is true or false. If the statement is false, make the necessary change(s) to produce a true statement.

7. 1 gram = 1000 kilograms ______
8. 1 gram ≈ 28 ounces ______
9. The formula $F = \frac{9}{5}C + 32$ is used to convert from Fahrenheit to Celsius. ______
10. The formula $C = \frac{1}{9}(F - 32)$ is used to convert from Fahrenheit to Celsius. ______

Exercise Set 3.3

Practice Exercises

In Exercises 1–10, convert the given unit of weight to the unit indicated.

1. 7.4 dg to mg
2. 6.9 dg to mg
3. 870 mg to g
4. 640 mg to g
5. 8 g to cg
6. 7 g to cg
7. 18.6 kg to g
8. 0.37 kg to g
9. 0.018 mg to g
10. 0.029 mg to g

In Exercises 11–18, use ***Table 3.10*** *on page 108 to convert the given measurement of water to the unit indicated.*

11. 0.05 m^3 to kg
12. 0.02 m^3 to kg
13. 4.2 kg to cm^3
14. 5.8 kg to cm^3

15. 1100 m^3 to t

16. 1500 t to m^3

17. 0.04 kL to g

18. 0.03 kL to g

In Exercises 19–30, use the following equivalents, along with dimensional analysis, to convert the given measurement to the unit indicated. When necessary, round answers to two decimal places.

$$16 \text{ oz} = 1 \text{ lb}$$
$$2000 \text{ lb} = 1 \text{ T}$$
$$1 \text{ oz} \approx 28 \text{ g}$$
$$1 \text{ lb} \approx 0.45 \text{ kg}$$
$$1 \text{ T} \approx 0.9 \text{ t}$$

19. 36 oz to lb

20. 26 oz to lb

21. 36 oz to g

22. 26 oz to g

23. 540 lb to kg

24. 220 lb to kg

25. 80 lb to g

26. 150 lb to g

27. 540 kg to lb

28. 220 kg to lb

29. 200 t to T

30. 100 t to T

In Exercises 31–38, convert the given Celsius temperature to its equivalent temperature on the Fahrenheit scale. Where appropriate, round to the nearest tenth of a degree.

31. 10°C

32. 20°C

33. 35°C

34. 45°C

35. 57°C

36. 98°C

37. −5°C

38. −10°C

In Exercises 39–50, convert the given Fahrenheit temperature to its equivalent temperature on the Celsius scale. Where appropriate, round to the nearest tenth of a degree.

39. 68°F

40. 86°F

41. 41°F

42. 50°F

43. 72°F

44. 90°F

45. 23°F

46. 14°F

47. 350°F

48. 475°F

49. −22°F

50. −31°F

Practice Plus

51. The nine points shown below represent Celsius temperatures and their equivalent Fahrenheit temperatures. Also shown is a line that passes through the points.

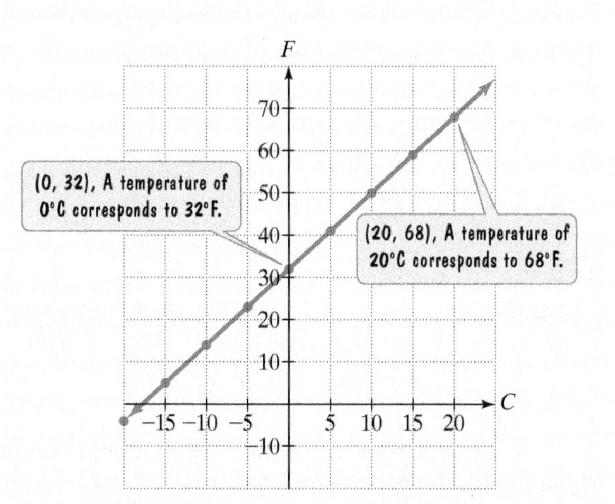

a. Use the coordinates of the two points identified by the voice balloons to compute the line's slope. Express the answer as a fraction reduced to lowest terms. What does this mean about the change in Fahrenheit temperature for each degree change in Celsius temperature?

b. Use the slope-intercept form of the equation of a line, $y = mx + b$, the slope from part (a), and the y-intercept shown by the graph to derive the formula used to convert from Celsius to Fahrenheit.

52. Solve the formula used to convert from Celsius to Fahrenheit for C and derive the other temperature conversion formula.

Application Exercises

In Exercises 53–59, selecting from milligram, gram, kilogram, and tonne, determine the best unit of measure to express the given item's weight.

53. A bee

54. This book

55. A tablespoon of salt

56. A Boeing 747

57. A stacked washer-dryer

58. A pen

59. An adult male

In Exercises 60–66, select the best estimate for the weight of the given item.

60. A newborn infant's weight

a. 3000 kg b. 300 kg
c. 30 kg d. 3 kg

61. The weight of a nickel

a. 5 kg b. 5 g c. 5 mg

62. A person's weight

a. 60 kg b. 60 g c. 60 dag

63. The weight of a box of cereal

a. 0.5 kg b. 0.5 g c. 0.5 t

64. The weight of a glass of water

a. 400 dg b. 400 g
c. 400 dag d. 400 hg

65. The weight of a regular-size car

a. 1500 dag b. 1500 hg c. 1500 kg d. 15,000 kg

66. The weight of a bicycle

a. 140 kg b. 140 hg c. 140 dag d. 140 g

67. Six items purchased at a grocery store weigh 14 kilograms. One of the items is detergent weighing 720 grams. What is the total weight, in kilograms, of the other five items?

68. If a nickel weighs 5 grams, how many nickels are there in 4 kilograms of nickels?

69. If the cost to mail a letter is 44 cents for mail weighing up to one ounce and 24 cents for each additional ounce or fraction of an ounce, find the cost of mailing a letter that weighs 85 grams.

70. Using the information given below the pictured finback whale, estimate the weight, in tons and kilograms, of the killer whale.

71. Which is more economical: purchasing the economy size of a detergent at 3 kilograms for \$3.15 or purchasing the regular size at 720 grams for 60¢?

Exercises 72–73 ask you to determine drug dosage by a patient's weight. Use the fact that 1 lb ≈ 0.45 kg.

72. The prescribed dosage of a drug is 10 mg/kg daily, meaning that 10 milligrams of the drug should be administered daily for each kilogram of a patient's weight. How many 400-milligram tablets should be given each day to a patient who weighs 175 pounds?

73. The prescribed dosage of a drug is 15 mg/kg daily, meaning that 15 milligrams of the drug should be administered daily for each kilogram of a patient's weight. How many 200-milligram tablets should be given each day to a patient who weighs 120 pounds?

The label on a bottle of Emetrol ("for food or drink indiscretions") reads

> *Each 5 mL teaspoonful contains glucose, 1.87 g; levulose, 1.87 g; and phosphoric acid, 21.5 mg.*

Use this information to solve Exercises 74–75.

74. a. Find the amount of glucose in the recommended dosage of two teaspoons.

b. If the bottle contains 4 ounces, find the quantity of glucose in the bottle. (1 oz ≈ 30 mL)

75. a. Find the amount of phosphoric acid in the recommended dosage of two teaspoons.

b. If the bottle contains 4 ounces, find the quantity of phosphoric acid in the bottle. (1 oz ≈ 30 mL)

In Exercises 76–79, select the best estimate of the Celsius temperature of

76. A very hot day.

a. 85°C **b.** 65°C **c.** 35°C **d.** 20°C

77. A warm winter day in Washington, D.C.

a. 10°C **b.** 30°C **c.** 50°C **d.** 70°C

78. A setting for a home thermostat.

a. 20°C **b.** 40°C **c.** 60°C **d.** 80°C

79. The oven temperature for cooking a roast.

a. 80°C **b.** 100°C **c.** 175°C **d.** 350°C

Exercises 80–81 give the average temperature of some of the world's hottest places. In each exercise, determine which location has the hotter average temperature and by how many degrees Fahrenheit. Round to the nearest tenth of a degree.

80. Assab, Eritrea: 86.8°F; Dalol, Ethiopia: 34.6°C

81. Berbera, Somalia: 86.2°F; Néma, Mauritania: 30.3°C

Exercises 82–83 give the average temperature of some of the world's coldest places. In each exercise, determine which location has the colder average temperature and by how many degrees Celsius. Round to the nearest tenth of a degree.

82. Plateau, Antarctica: −56.7°C;
Amundsen-Scott, Antarctica: −56.2°F

83. Eismitte, Greenland: −29.2°C;
Resolute, Canada: −11.6°F

(Source for Exercises 80–83: Russell Ash, *The Top 10 of Everything 2009*)

Writing in Mathematics

84. Describe the difference between weight and mass.

85. Explain how to use dimensional analysis to convert 200 pounds to kilograms.

86. Why do you think that countries using the metric system prefer the Celsius scale over the Fahrenheit scale?

87. Describe in words how to convert from Celsius to Fahrenheit.

88. Describe in words how to convert from Fahrenheit to Celsius.

89. If you decide to travel outside the United States, which one of the two temperature conversion formulas should you take? Explain your answer.

Critical Thinking Exercises

Make Sense? *In Exercises 90–93, determine whether each statement makes sense or does not make sense, and explain your reasoning.*

90. When I played high school basketball, I weighed 250 kilograms.

91. It's not realistic to convert 500 mg to g because measurements should not involve fractional units.

92. Both the English system and the metric system enable me to easily see relationships among volume, capacity, and weight.

93. A comfortable classroom temperature is 20°C.

In Exercises 94–101, determine whether each statement is true or false. If the statement is false, make the necessary change(s) to produce a true statement.

94. A 4-pound object weighs more than a 2000-gram object.

95. A 100-milligram object weighs more than a 2-ounce object.

96. A 50-gram object weighs more than a 2-ounce object.

97. A 10-pound object weighs more than a 4-kilogram object.

98. Flour selling at 3¢ per gram is a better buy than flour selling at 55¢ per pound.

99. The measures

32,600 g, 32.1 kg, 4 lb, 36 oz

are arranged in order, from greatest to least weight.

100. If you are taking aspirin to relieve cold symptoms, a reasonable dose is 2 kilograms four times a day.

101. A large dog weighs about 350 kilograms.

Group Exercise

102. Present a group report on the current status of the metric system in the United States. At present, does it appear that the United States will convert to the metric system? Who supports the conversion and who opposes it? Summarize each side's position. Give examples of how our current system of weights and measures is an economic liability. What are the current obstacles to metric conversion?

Chapter Summary, Review, and Test

SUMMARY – DEFINITIONS AND CONCEPTS	EXAMPLES
3.1 Measuring Length; The Metric System	
a. The result obtained from measuring length is called a linear measurement, stated in linear units.	
b. Linear Units: The English System 12 in. = 1 ft, 3 ft = 1 yd, 36 in. = 1 yd, 5280 ft = 1 mi	
c. Dimensional Analysis Multiply the given measurement by a unit fraction with the unit of measurement that needs to be introduced in the numerator and the unit of measurement that needs to be eliminated in the denominator.	Ex. 1, p. 87
d. Linear Units: The Metric System The basic unit is the meter (m), approximately 39 inches. 1 km = 1000 m, 1 hm = 100 m, 1 dam = 10 m, 1 dm = 0.1 m, 1 cm = 0.01 m, 1 mm = 0.001 m	
e. Changing Linear Units within the Metric System ×10 (left to right) km hm dam m dm cm mm ÷10 (right to left)	Ex. 2, p. 90
f. English and metric equivalents for length are given in **Table 3.3** on page 91.	Ex. 3, p. 92; Ex. 4, p. 93
3.2 Measuring Area and Volume	
a. The area measure of a plane region is the number of square units contained in the given region.	Ex. 1, p. 96
b. Square Units: The English System 1 ft^2 = 144 $in.^2$, 1 yd^2 = 9 ft^2, 1 a = 43,560 ft^2 = 4840 yd^2, 1 mi^2 = 640 a	Ex. 2, p. 97; Ex. 3, p. 97
c. English and metric equivalents for area are given in **Table 3.4** on page 98.	Ex. 4, p. 98
d. The volume measure of a three-dimensional figure is the number of cubic units contained in its interior.	Ex. 5, p. 99
e. Capacity refers to the amount of fluid that a three-dimensional object can hold. English units for capacity include pints, quarts, and gallons: 2 pt = 1 qt; 4 qt = 1 gal; one cubic yard has a capacity of about 200 gallons. See **Table 3.5** on page 100.	Ex. 6, p. 100

f. The basic unit for capacity in the metric system is the liter (L). One liter is about 1.06 quarts. Prefixes for the liter are the same as throughout the metric system.

g. **Table 3.7** on page 101 shows relationships between volume and capacity in the metric system. Ex. 7, p. 101

$$1 \text{ dm}^3 = 1000 \text{ cm}^3 = 1 \text{ L}$$

h. English and metric equivalents for capacity are given in **Table 3.8** on page 101. Ex. 8, p. 102

3.3 Measuring Weight and Temperature

a. Weight: The English System

$$16 \text{ oz} = 1 \text{ lb}, 2000 \text{ lb} = 1 \text{ T}$$

b. Units of Weight: The Metric System
The basic unit is the gram (g).

$$1000 \text{ grams } (1 \text{ kg}) \approx 2.2 \text{ lb},$$
$$1 \text{ kg} = 1000 \text{ g}, 1 \text{ hg} = 100 \text{ g}, 1 \text{ dag} = 10 \text{ g},$$
$$1 \text{ dg} = 0.1 \text{ g}, 1 \text{ cg} = 0.01 \text{ g}, 1 \text{ mg} = 0.001 \text{ g}$$

c. Changing Units of Weight within the Metric System Ex. 1, p. 107

× 10

kg hg dag g dg cg mg

÷ 10

d. One kilogram of water has a volume of 1 liter. **Table 3.10** on page 108 shows relationships between volume and weight of water in the metric system. Ex. 2, p. 108

e. English and metric equivalents for weight are given in **Table 3.11** on page 108. Ex. 3, p. 108; Ex. 4, p. 109

f. Temperature Scales: Celsius to Fahrenheit: $F = \frac{9}{5}C + 32$ Ex. 5, p. 111

g. Temperature Scales: Fahrenheit to Celsius: $C = \frac{5}{9}(F - 32)$ Ex. 6, p. 111

Review Exercises

3.1

In Exercises 1–4, use dimensional analysis to convert the quantity to the indicated unit.

1. 69 in. to ft
2. 9 in. to yd
3. 21 ft to yd
4. 13,200 ft to mi

In Exercises 5–10, convert the given linear measurement to the metric unit indicated.

5. 22.8 m to cm
6. 7 dam to m
7. 19.2 hm to m
8. 144 cm to hm
9. 0.5 mm to m
10. 18 cm to mm

In Exercises 11–16, use the given English and metric equivalents, along with dimensional analysis, to convert the given measurement to the unit indicated. Where necessary, round answers to two decimal places.

11. 23 in. to cm
12. 19 cm to in.
13. 330 mi to km
14. 600 km to mi
15. 14 m to yd
16. 12 m to ft

1 in. = 2.54 cm
1 ft = 30.48 cm
1 yd ≈ 0.9 m
1 mi ≈ 1.6 km

17. Express 45 kilometers per hour in miles per hour.

18. Express 60 miles per hour in kilometers per hour.

19. Arrange from smallest to largest: 0.024 km, 2400 m, 24,000 cm.

20. If you jog six times around a track that is 800 meters long, how many kilometers have you covered?

3.2

21. Use the given figure to find its area in square units.

22. Singapore, with an area of 268 square miles and a population of 4,425,700, is one of the world's most densely populated countries. Find Singapore's population density, to the nearest tenth. Describe what this means.

23. Acadia National Park on the coast of Maine consists of 47,453 acres. How large is the national park in square miles? Round to the nearest square mile. ($1 \text{ mi}^2 = 640$ a)

24. Given 1 acre ≈ 0.4 hectare, use dimensional analysis to find the size of a property in acres measured at 7.2 hectares.

25. Using 1 ft^2 ≈ 0.09 m^2, convert 30 m^2 to ft^2.

26. Using 1 mi^2 ≈ 2.6 km^2, convert 12 mi^2 to km^2.

27. Which one of the following is a reasonable measure for the area of a flower garden in a person's yard?
 a. 100 m^2 **b.** 0.4 ha **c.** 0.01 km^2

28. Use the given figure to find its volume in cubic units.

29. A swimming pool has a volume of 33,600 cubic feet. Given that 1 cubic foot has a capacity of about 7.48 gallons, how many gallons of water does the pool hold?

30. An aquarium has a volume of 76,000 cubic centimeters. How many liters of water does the aquarium hold?

In Exercises 31–35, use the given English and metric equivalents, along with dimensional analysis, to convert the given measurement to the unit indicated. Where necessary, round answers to two decimal places.

31. 22 mL to tsp

32. 5.4 L to c

33. 8 L to qt

34. 6 gal to L

1 tsp	≈ 5 mL
1 tbsp	≈ 15 mL
1 fl oz	≈ 30 mL
1 c	≈ 0.24 L
1 pt	≈ 0.47 L
1 qt	≈ 0.95 L
1 gal	≈ 3.8 L

35. A physician orders 15 cc of medication.
 a. How many milliliters of the drug should be administered?
 b. How many fluid ounces of the drug should be administered?

36. The capacity of a one-quart container of juice is approximately
 a. 0.1 kL **b.** 0.5 L **c.** 1 L **d.** 1 mL

37. There are 3 feet in a yard. Explain why there are not 3 square feet in a square yard. If helpful, illustrate your explanation with a diagram.

38. Explain why the area of Texas could not be measured in cubic miles.

3.3

In Exercises 39–42, convert the given unit of weight to the unit indicated.

39. 12.4 dg to mg

40. 12 g to cg

41. 0.012 mg to g

42. 450 mg to kg

In Exercises 43–44, use ***Table 3.10*** *on page 108 to convert the given measurement of water to the unit or units indicated.*

43. 50 kg to cm^3

44. 4 kL to dm^3 to g

45. Using 1 lb ≈ 0.45 kg, convert 210 pounds to kilograms.

46. Using 1 oz ≈ 28 g, convert 392 grams to ounces.

47. The prescribed dosage of a drug is 12 mg/kg daily. How many 400-milligram tablets should be given each day to a patient who weighs 220 pounds? (1 lb ≈ 0.45 kg)

48. If you are interested in your weight in the metric system, would it be best to report it in milligrams, grams, or kilograms? Explain why the unit you selected would be most appropriate. Explain why each of the other two units is not the best choice for reporting your weight.

49. Given 16 oz = 1 lb, use dimensional analysis to convert 36 ounces to pounds.

In Exercises 50–51, select the best estimate for the weight of the given item.

50. A dollar bill:
 a. 1 g **b.** 10 g **c.** 1 kg **d.** 4 kg

51. A hamburger:
 a. 3 kg **b.** 1 kg **c.** 200 g **d.** 5 g

In Exercises 52–56, convert the given Celsius temperature to its equivalent temperature on the Fahrenheit scale.

52. 15°C

53. 100°C

54. 5°C

55. 0°C

56. −25°C

In Exercises 57–62, convert the given Fahrenheit temperature to its equivalent temperature on the Celsius scale.

57. 59°F

58. 41°F

59. 212°F

60. 98.6°F

61. 0°F

62. 14°F

63. Is a decrease of 15° Celsius more or less than a decrease of 15° Fahrenheit? Explain your answer.

Chapter 3 Test

1. Change 807 mm to hm.

2. Given 1 inch = 2.54 centimeters, use dimensional analysis to change 635 centimeters to inches.

3. If you jog eight times around a track that is 600 meters long, how many kilometers have you covered?

In Exercises 4–6, write the most reasonable metric unit for length in each blank. Select from mm, cm, m, and km.

4. A human thumb is 20 ______ wide.

5. The height of the table is 45 ______.

6. The towns are 60 ______ apart.

7. If 1 mile ≈ 1.6 kilometers, express 80 miles per hour in kilometers per hour.

8. How many times greater is a square yard than a square foot?

9. Australia has a population of 20,090,400 and an area of 2,967,908 square miles. Find Australia's population density to the nearest tenth. Describe what this means.

10. Given 1 acre ≈ 0.4 hectare, use dimensional analysis to find the area of a property measured at 18 hectares.

11. The area of a dollar bill is approximately

a. 10 cm^2 **b.** 100 cm^2 **c.** 1000 cm^2 **d.** 1 m^2

12. There are 10 decimeters in a meter. Explain why there are not 10 cubic decimeters in a cubic meter. How many times greater is a cubic meter than a cubic decimeter?

13. The label on a bottle of Pepto Bismol indicates that the dosage should not exceed 16 tablespoons in 24 hours. How many fluid ounces is the maximum daily dose? (1 tbsp ≈ 15 mL; 1 fl oz ≈ 30 mL)

14. A swimming pool has a volume of 10,000 cubic feet. Given that 1 cubic foot has a capacity of about 7.48 gallons, how many gallons of water does the pool hold?

15. The capacity of a pail used to wash floors is approximately

a. 3 L **b.** 12 L **c.** 80 L **d.** 2 kL

16. Change 137 g to kg.

17. The prescribed dosage of a drug is 10 mg/kg daily. How many 200-milligram tablets should be given each day to a patient who weighs 130 pounds? (1 lb ≈ 0.45 kg)

In Exercises 18–19, write the most reasonable metric unit for weight in each blank. Select from mg, g, and kg.

18. My suitcase weighs 20 ______.

19. I took a 350 ______ aspirin.

20. Convert 30°C to Fahrenheit.

21. Convert 176°F to Celsius.

22. Comfortable room temperature is approximately

a. 70°C **b.** 50°C **c.** 30°C **d.** 20°C

4

Geometry

GEOMETRY IS THE STUDY OF THE SPACE YOU LIVE IN AND THE SHAPES THAT SURROUND YOU. YOU'RE EVEN MADE OF IT! THE HUMAN lung consists of nearly 300 spherical air sacs, geometrically designed to provide the greatest surface area within the limited volume of our bodies. Viewed in this way, geometry becomes an intimate experience.

For thousands of years, people have studied geometry in some form to obtain a better understanding of the world in which they live. A study of the shape of your world will provide you with many practical applications and perhaps help to increase your appreciation of its beauty.

Here's where you'll find these applications:

- A relationship between geometry and the visual arts is developed in Section 4.3 (Tessellations: pages 143–145).

4.1

WHAT AM I SUPPOSED TO LEARN?

After you have read this section, you should be able to:

1. Understand points, lines, and planes as the basis of geometry.
2. Solve problems involving angle measures.
3. Solve problems involving angles formed by parallel lines and transversals.

Points, Lines, Planes, and Angles

THE SAN FRANCISCO MUSEUM OF MODERN ART WAS constructed in 1995 to illustrate how art and architecture can enrich one another. The exterior involves geometric shapes, symmetry, and unusual facades. Although there are no windows, natural light streams in through a truncated cylindrical skylight that crowns the building. The architect worked with a scale model of the museum at the site and observed how light hit it during different times of the day. These observations were used to cut the cylindrical skylight at an angle that maximizes sunlight entering the interior.

Angles play a critical role in creating modern architecture. They are also fundamental in the study of geometry. The word "geometry" means "earth measure." Because it involves the mathematics of shapes, geometry connects mathematics to art and architecture. It also has many practical applications. You can use geometry at home when you buy carpet, build a fence, tile a floor, or determine whether a piece of furniture will fit through your doorway. In this chapter, we look at the shapes that surround us and their applications.

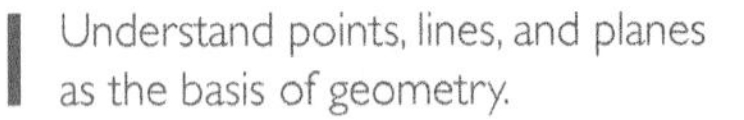

1 Understand points, lines, and planes as the basis of geometry.

Points, Lines, and Planes

Points, lines, and planes make up the basis of all geometry. Stars in the night sky look like points of light. Long stretches of overhead power lines that appear to extend endlessly look like lines. The top of a flat table resembles part of a plane. However, stars, power lines, and tabletops only approximate points, lines, and planes. Points, lines, and planes do not exist in the physical world. Representations of these forms are shown in **Figure 4.1**. A **point**, represented as a small dot, has no length, width, or thickness. No object in the real world has zero size. A **line**, connecting two points along the shortest possible path, has no thickness and extends infinitely in both directions. However, no familiar everyday object is infinite in length. A **plane** is a flat surface with no thickness and no boundaries. This page resembles a plane, although it does not extend indefinitely and it does have thickness.

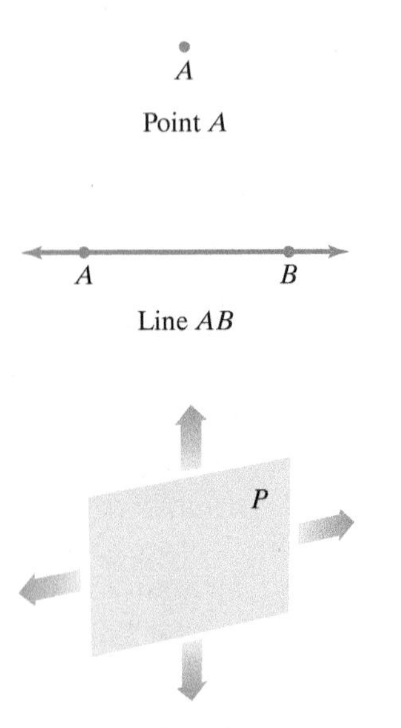

FIGURE 4.1 Representing a point, a line, and a plane

A line may be named using any two of its points. In **Figure 4.2(a)**, line AB can be symbolized $\overleftrightarrow{AB}$ or $\overleftrightarrow{BA}$. Any point on the line divides the line into three parts—the point and two **half-lines**. **Figure 4.2(b)** illustrates half-line AB, symbolized $\overset{\circ\!\!\longrightarrow}{AB}$. The open circle above the A in the symbol and in the diagram indicates that point A is not included in the half-line. A **ray** is a half-line with its endpoint included. **Figure 4.2(c)** illustrates ray AB, symbolized $\overrightarrow{AB}$. The closed dot above the A in the diagram shows that point A is included in the ray. A portion of a line joining two points and including the endpoints is called a **line segment**. **Figure 4.2(d)** illustrates line segment AB, symbolized $\overline{AB}$ or $\overline{BA}$.

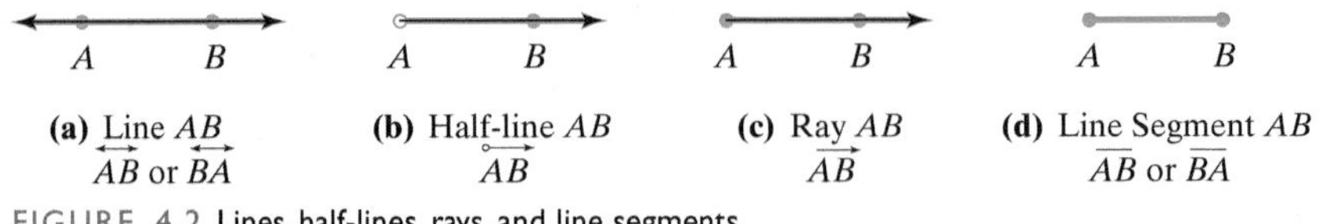

FIGURE 4.2 Lines, half-lines, rays, and line segments

Angles

An **angle**, symbolized $\measuredangle$, is formed by the union of two rays that have a common endpoint. One ray is called the **initial side** and the other the **terminal side**.

FIGURE 4.3 Clock with hands forming an angle

A rotating ray is often a useful way to think about angles. The ray in **Figure 4.3** rotates from 12 to 2. The ray pointing to 12 is the initial side and the ray pointing to 2 is the terminal side. The common endpoint of an angle's initial side and terminal side is the **vertex** of the angle.

Figure 4.4 shows an angle. The common endpoint of the two rays, B, is the vertex. The two rays that form the angle, $\overrightarrow{BA}$ and $\overrightarrow{BC}$, are the sides. The four ways of naming the angle are shown to the right of **Figure 4.4**.

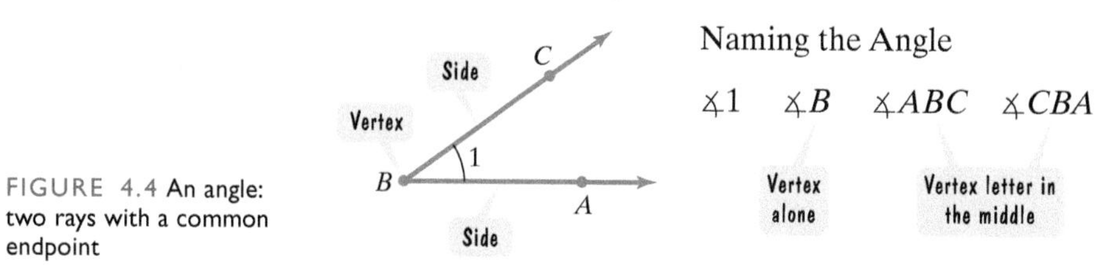

FIGURE 4.4 An angle: two rays with a common endpoint

2 Solve problems involving angle measures.

Measuring Angles Using Degrees

Angles are measured by determining the amount of rotation from the initial side to the terminal side. One way to measure angles is in **degrees**, symbolized by a small, raised circle °. Think of the hour hand of a clock. From 12 noon to 12 midnight, the hour hand moves around in a complete circle. By definition, the ray has rotated through 360 degrees, or 360°, shown in **Figure 4.5**. Using 360° as the amount of rotation of a ray back onto itself, **a degree, 1°, is $\frac{1}{360}$ of a complete rotation.**

FIGURE 4.5 A complete 360° rotation

EXAMPLE 1 Using Degree Measure

The hand of a clock moves from 12 to 2 o'clock, shown in **Figure 4.3**. Through how many degrees does it move?

SOLUTION

We know that one complete rotation is 360°. Moving from 12 to 2 o'clock is $\frac{2}{12}$, or $\frac{1}{6}$, of a complete revolution. Thus, the hour hand moves

$$\frac{1}{6} \times 360^\circ = \frac{360^\circ}{6} = 60^\circ$$

in going from 12 to 2 o'clock.

CHECK POINT 1 The hand of a clock moves from 12 to 1 o'clock. Through how many degrees does it move?

Figure 4.6 shows angles classified by their degree measurement. An **acute angle** measures less than 90° [see **Figure 4.6(a)**]. A **right angle**, one-quarter of a complete rotation, measures 90° [**Figure 4.6(b)**]. Examine the right angle—do you see a small square at the vertex? This symbol is used to indicate a right angle. An **obtuse angle** measures more than 90°, but less than 180° [**Figure 4.6(c)**]. Finally, a **straight angle**, one-half a complete rotation, measures 180° [**Figure 4.6(d)**]. The two rays in a straight angle form a straight line.

(a) Acute angle Less than 90°

(b) Right angle 90°

(c) Obtuse angle More than 90° but less than 180°

(d) Straight angle 180°

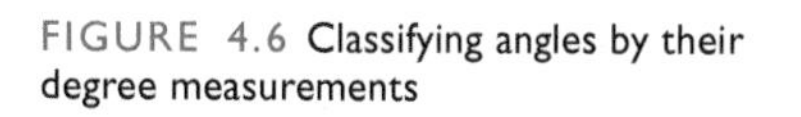

FIGURE 4.6 Classifying angles by their degree measurements

Figure 4.7 illustrates a **protractor**, used for finding the degree measure of an angle. As shown in the figure, we measure an angle by placing the center point of the protractor on the vertex of the angle and the straight side of the protractor along one side of the angle. The measure of $\measuredangle ABC$ is then read as 50°. Observe that the measure is not 130° because the angle is obviously less than 90°. We indicate the angle's measure by writing $m\measuredangle ABC = 50°$, read "the measure of angle ABC is 50°."

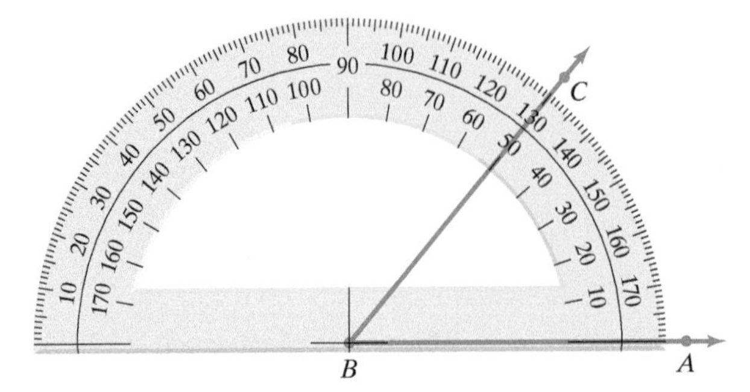

FIGURE 4.7 Using a protractor to measure an angle: $m\measuredangle ABC = 50°$

Two angles whose measures have a sum of 90° are called **complementary angles.** For example, angles measuring 70° and 20° are complementary angles because $70° + 20° = 90°$. For angles such as those measuring 70° and 20°, each angle is the **complement** of the other: The 70° angle is the complement of the 20° angle and the 20° angle is the complement of the 70° angle. **The measure of the complement can be found by subtracting the angle's measure from 90°.** For example, we can find the complement of a 25° angle by subtracting 25° from 90°: $90° - 25° = 65°$. Thus, an angle measuring 65° is the complement of one measuring 25°.

EXAMPLE 2 *Angle Measures and Complements*

Use **Figure 4.8** to find $m\measuredangle DBC$.

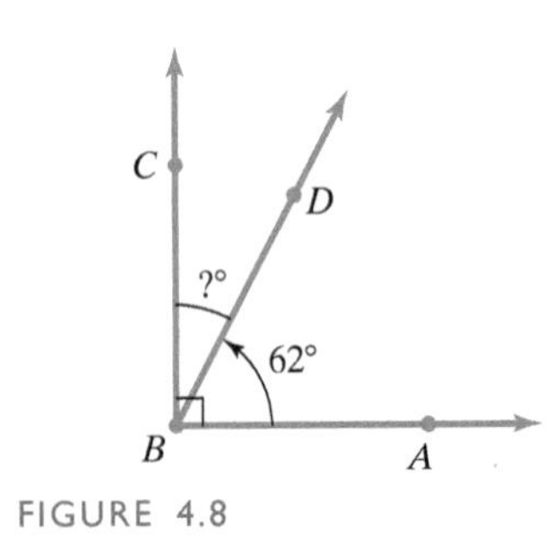

FIGURE 4.8

SOLUTION

The measure of $\measuredangle DBC$ is not yet known. It is shown as ?° in **Figure 4.8**. The acute angles $\measuredangle ABD$, which measures 62°, and $\measuredangle DBC$ form a right angle, indicated by the square at the vertex. This means that the measures of the acute angles add up to 90°. Thus, $\measuredangle DBC$ is the complement of the angle measuring 62°. The measure of $\measuredangle DBC$ is found by subtracting 62° from 90°:

$$m\measuredangle DBC = 90° - 62° = 28°.$$

The measure of $\measuredangle DBC$ can also be found using an algebraic approach.

$$m\measuredangle ABD + m\measuredangle DBC = 90°$$ The sum of the measures of complementary angles is 90°.

$$62° + m\measuredangle DBC = 90°$$ We are given $m\measuredangle ABD = 62°$.

$$m\measuredangle DBC = 90° - 62° = 28°$$ Subtract 62° from both sides of the equation.

CHECK POINT 2 In **Figure 4.8**, let $m\measuredangle DBC = 19°$. Find $m\measuredangle DBA$.

Two angles whose measures have a sum of 180° are called **supplementary angles.** For example, angles measuring 110° and 70° are supplementary angles because $110° + 70° = 180°$. For angles such as those measuring 110° and 70°, each angle is the **supplement** of the other: The 110° angle is the supplement of the 70° angle, and the 70° angle is the supplement of the 110° angle. **The measure of the supplement can be found by subtracting the angle's measure from 180°.** For example, we can find the supplement of a 25° angle by subtracting 25° from 180°: $180° - 25° = 155°$. Thus, an angle measuring 155° is the supplement of one measuring 25°.

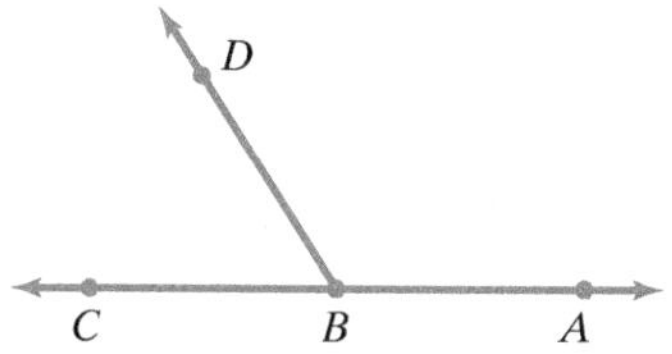

EXAMPLE 3 *Angle Measures and Supplements*

Figure 4.9 shows that $\measuredangle ABD$ and $\measuredangle DBC$ are supplementary angles. If $m\measuredangle ABD$ is 66° greater than $m\measuredangle DBC$, find the measure of each angle.

FIGURE 4.9

SOLUTION

Let $m\measuredangle DBC = x$. Because $m\measuredangle ABD$ is 66° greater than $m\measuredangle DBC$, then $m\measuredangle ABD = x + 66°$. We are given that these angles are supplementary.

$$m\measuredangle DBC + m\measuredangle ABD = 180°$$ The sum of the measures of supplementary angles is 180°.

$$x + (x + 66°) = 180°$$ Substitute the variable expressions for the measures.

$$2x + 66° = 180°$$ Combine like terms: $x + x = 2x$.

$$2x = 114°$$ Subtract 66° from both sides.

$$x = 57°$$ Divide both sides by 2.

Thus, $m\measuredangle DBC = 57°$ and $m\measuredangle ABD = 57° + 66° = 123°$.

CHECK POINT 3 In **Figure 4.9**, if $m\measuredangle ABD$ is 88° greater than $m\measuredangle DBC$, find the measure of each angle.

FIGURE 4.10

Figure 4.10 illustrates a highway sign that warns of a railroad crossing. When two lines intersect, the opposite angles formed are called **vertical angles**.

In **Figure 4.11**, there are two pairs of vertical angles. Angles 1 and 3 are vertical angles. Angles 2 and 4 are also vertical angles.

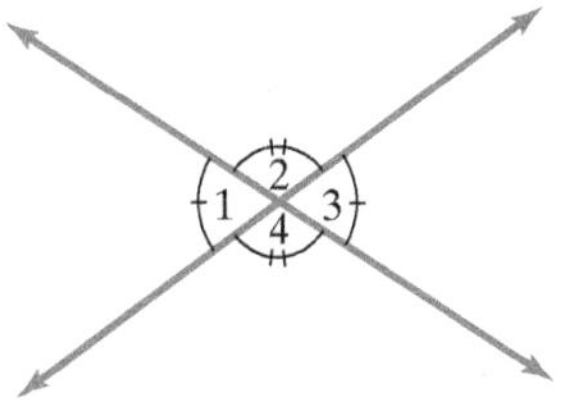

FIGURE 4.11

We can use **Figure 4.11** to show that vertical angles have the same measure. Let's concentrate on angles 1 and 3, each denoted by one tick mark. Can you see that each of these angles is supplementary to angle 2?

$$m\measuredangle 1 + m\measuredangle 2 = 180°$$ The sum of the measures of supplementary angles is 180°.

$$m\measuredangle 2 + m\measuredangle 3 = 180°$$

$$m\measuredangle 1 + m\measuredangle 2 = m\measuredangle 2 + m\measuredangle 3$$ Substitute $m\measuredangle 2 + m\measuredangle 3$ for 180° in the first equation.

$$m\measuredangle 1 = m\measuredangle 3$$ Subtract $m\measuredangle 2$ from both sides.

Using a similar approach, we can show that $m\measuredangle 2 = m\measuredangle 4$, each denoted by two tick marks in **Figure 4.11**.

Vertical angles have the same measure.

EXAMPLE 4 *Using Vertical Angles*

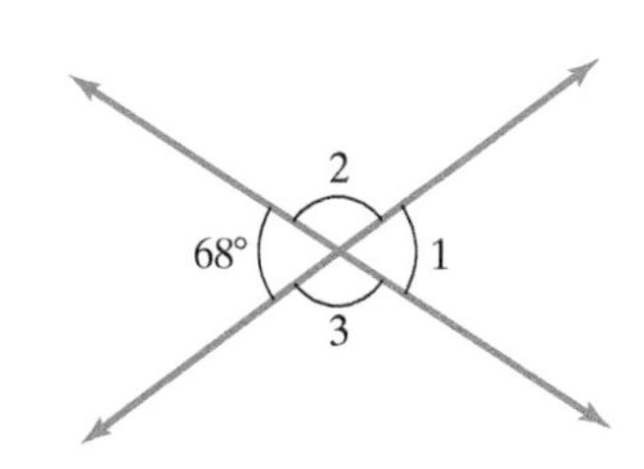

FIGURE 4.12

Figure 4.12 shows that the angle on the left measures 68°. Find the measures of the other three angles.

SOLUTION

Angle 1 and the angle measuring 68° are vertical angles. Because vertical angles have the same measure,

$$m\measuredangle 1 = 68°.$$

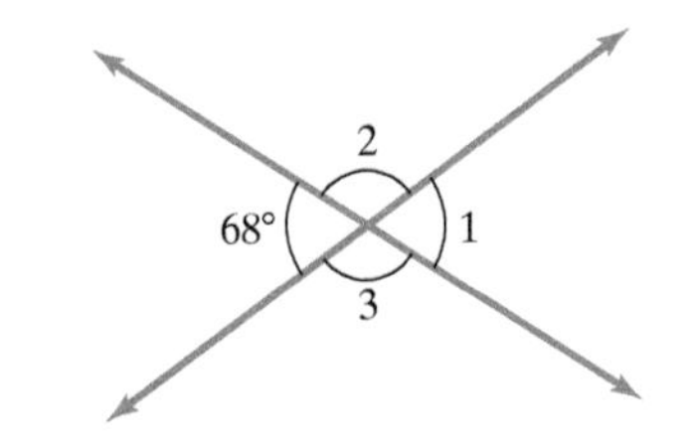

FIGURE 4.12 (repeated)

Angle 2 and the angle measuring 68° form a straight angle and are supplementary. Because their measures add up to 180°,

$$m\measuredangle 2 = 180° - 68° = 112°.$$

Angle 2 and angle 3 are also vertical angles, so they have the same measure. Because the measure of angle 2 is 112°,

$$m\measuredangle 3 = 112°.$$

CHECK POINT 4 In **Figure 4.12**, assume that the angle on the left measures 57°. Find the measures of the other three angles.

Parallel Lines

Parallel lines are lines that lie in the same plane and have no points in common. If two different lines in the same plane are not parallel, they have a single point in common and are called **intersecting lines**. If the lines intersect at an angle of 90°, they are called **perpendicular lines.**

If we intersect a pair of parallel lines with a third line, called a **transversal**, eight angles are formed, as shown in **Figure 4.13**. Certain pairs of these angles have special names, as well as special properties. These names and properties are summarized in **Table 4.1**.

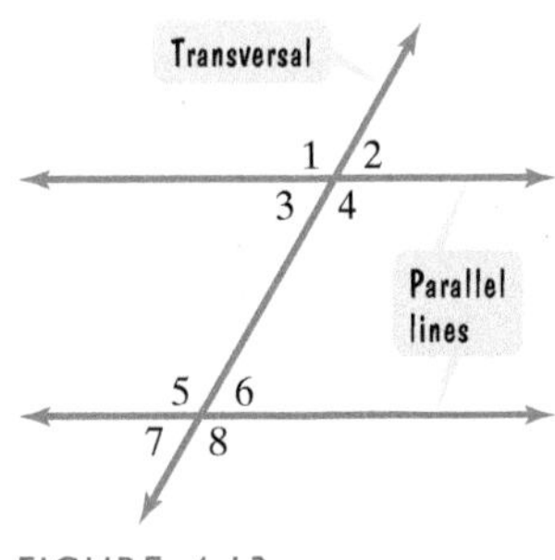

FIGURE 4.13

TABLE 4.1 Names of Angle Pairs Formed by a Transversal Intersecting Parallel Lines

Name	Description	Sketch	Angle Pairs Described	Property
Alternate interior angles	Interior angles that do not have a common vertex on alternate sides of the transversal		$\measuredangle 3$ and $\measuredangle 6$ $\measuredangle 4$ and $\measuredangle 5$	Alternate interior angles have the same measure. $m\measuredangle 3 = m\measuredangle 6$ $m\measuredangle 4 = m\measuredangle 5$
Alternate exterior angles	Exterior angles that do not have a common vertex on alternate sides of the transversal		$\measuredangle 1$ and $\measuredangle 8$ $\measuredangle 2$ and $\measuredangle 7$	Alternate exterior angles have the same measure. $m\measuredangle 1 = m\measuredangle 8$ $m\measuredangle 2 = m\measuredangle 7$
Corresponding angles	One interior and one exterior angle on the same side of the transversal		$\measuredangle 1$ and $\measuredangle 5$ $\measuredangle 2$ and $\measuredangle 6$ $\measuredangle 3$ and $\measuredangle 7$ $\measuredangle 4$ and $\measuredangle 8$	Corresponding angles have the same measure. $m\measuredangle 1 = m\measuredangle 5$ $m\measuredangle 2 = m\measuredangle 6$ $m\measuredangle 3 = m\measuredangle 7$ $m\measuredangle 4 = m\measuredangle 8$

3 Solve problems involving angles formed by parallel lines and transversals.

When two parallel lines are intersected by a transversal, the following relationships are true:

PARALLEL LINES AND ANGLE PAIRS

If parallel lines are intersected by a transversal,

- alternate interior angles have the same measure,
- alternate exterior angles have the same measure, and
- corresponding angles have the same measure.

Conversely, if two lines are intersected by a third line and a pair of alternate interior angles or a pair of alternate exterior angles or a pair of corresponding angles have the same measure, then the two lines are parallel.

EXAMPLE 5 *Finding Angle Measures When Parallel Lines Are Intersected by a Transversal*

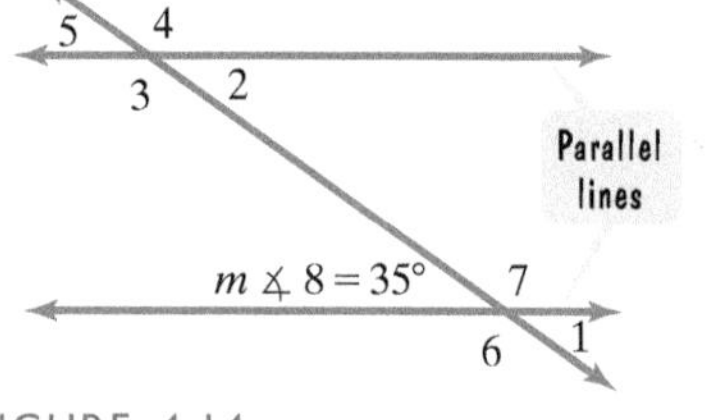

FIGURE 4.14

In **Figure 4.14**, two parallel lines are intersected by a transversal. One of the angles ($\measuredangle 8$) has a measure of 35°. Find the measure of each of the other seven angles.

SOLUTION

Look carefully at **Figure 4.14** and fill in the angle measures as you read each line in this solution.

$m\measuredangle 1 = 35°$ — $\measuredangle 8$ and $\measuredangle 1$ are vertical angles and vertical angles have the same measure.

$m\measuredangle 6 = 180° - 35° = 145°$ — $\measuredangle 8$ and $\measuredangle 6$ are supplementary.

$m\measuredangle 7 = 145°$ — $\measuredangle 6$ and $\measuredangle 7$ are vertical angles, so they have the same measure.

$m\measuredangle 2 = 35°$ — $\measuredangle 8$ and $\measuredangle 2$ are alternate interior angles, so they have the same measure.

$m\measuredangle 3 = 145°$ — $\measuredangle 7$ and $\measuredangle 3$ are alternate interior angles. Thus, they have the same measure.

$m\measuredangle 5 = 35°$ — $\measuredangle 8$ and $\measuredangle 5$ are corresponding angles. Thus, they have the same measure.

$m\measuredangle 4 = 180° - 35° = 145°$ — $\measuredangle 4$ and $\measuredangle 5$ are supplementary.

GREAT QUESTION!

Is there more than one way to solve Example 5?

Yes. For example, once you know that $m\measuredangle 2 = 35°$, $m\measuredangle 5$ is also 35° because $\measuredangle 2$ and $\measuredangle 5$ are vertical angles.

CHECK POINT 5 In **Figure 4.14**, assume that $m\measuredangle 8 = 29°$. Find the measure of each of the other seven angles.

Concept and Vocabulary Check

Fill in each blank so that the resulting statement is true.

1. $\overleftrightarrow{AB}$ symbolizes __________ AB, $\overset{\circ\!\!\rightarrow}{AB}$ symbolizes __________ AB, $\overrightarrow{AB}$ symbolizes __________ AB, and $\overline{AB}$ symbolizes __________ AB.

2. A/an __________ angle measures less than 90°, a/an __________ angle measures 90°, a/an __________ angle measures more than 90° and less than 180°, and a/an __________ angle measures 180°.

3. Two angles whose measures have a sum of 90° are called __________ angles. Two angles whose measures have a sum of 180° are called __________ angles.

4. When two lines intersect, the opposite angles are called __________ angles.

5. Lines that lie in the same plane and have no points in common are called __________ lines. If these lines are intersected by a third line, called a __________, eight angles are formed.

6. Lines that intersect at an angle of 90° are called __________ lines.

In Exercises 7–12, determine whether each statement is true or false. If the statement is false, make the necessary change(s) to produce a true statement.

7. A ray extends infinitely in both directions. ______
8. An angle is formed by the union of two lines that have a common endpoint. ______
9. A degree, 1°, is $\frac{1}{90}$ of a complete rotation. ______
10. A ruler is used for finding the degree measure of an angle. ______
11. The measure of an angle's complement is found by subtracting the angle's measure from 90°. ______
12. Vertical angles have the same measure. ______

Exercise Set 4.1

Practice Exercises

1. The hour hand of a clock moves from 12 to 5 o'clock. Through how many degrees does it move?
2. The hour hand of a clock moves from 12 to 4 o'clock. Through how many degrees does it move?
3. The hour hand of a clock moves from 1 to 4 o'clock. Through how many degrees does it move?
4. The hour hand of a clock moves from 1 to 7 o'clock. Through how many degrees does it move?

In Exercises 5–10, use the protractor to find the measure of each angle. Then classify the angle as acute, right, straight, or obtuse.

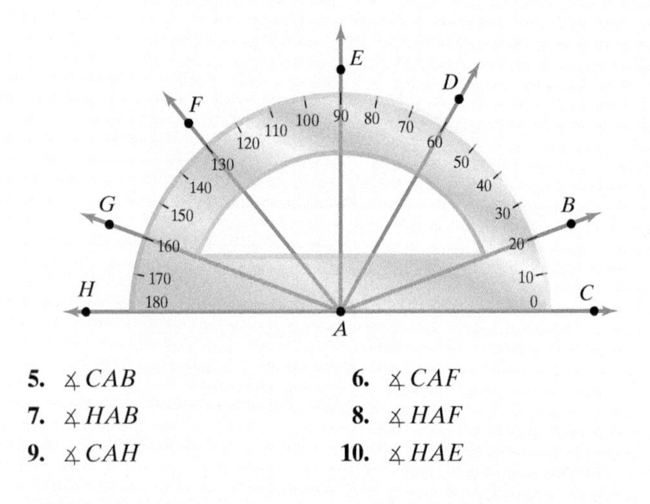

5. $\measuredangle CAB$
6. $\measuredangle CAF$
7. $\measuredangle HAB$
8. $\measuredangle HAF$
9. $\measuredangle CAH$
10. $\measuredangle HAE$

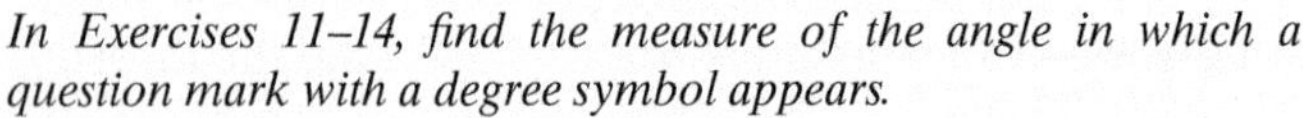

In Exercises 11–14, find the measure of the angle in which a question mark with a degree symbol appears.

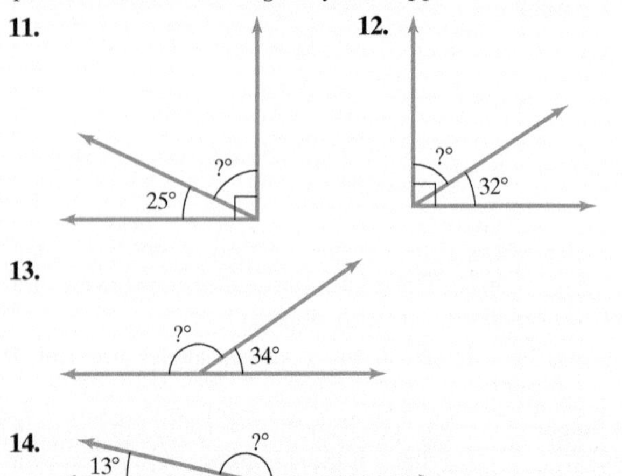

In Exercises 15–20, find the measure of the complement and the supplement of each angle.

15. 48°
16. 52°
17. 89°
18. 1°
19. 37.4°
20. $15\frac{1}{3}°$

In Exercises 21–24, use an algebraic equation to find the measures of the two angles described. Begin by letting x represent the degree measure of the angle's complement or its supplement.

21. The measure of the angle is 12° greater than its complement.
22. The measure of the angle is 56° greater than its complement.
23. The measure of the angle is three times greater than its supplement.
24. The measure of the angle is 81° more than twice that of its supplement.

In Exercises 25–28, find the measures of angles 1, 2, and 3.

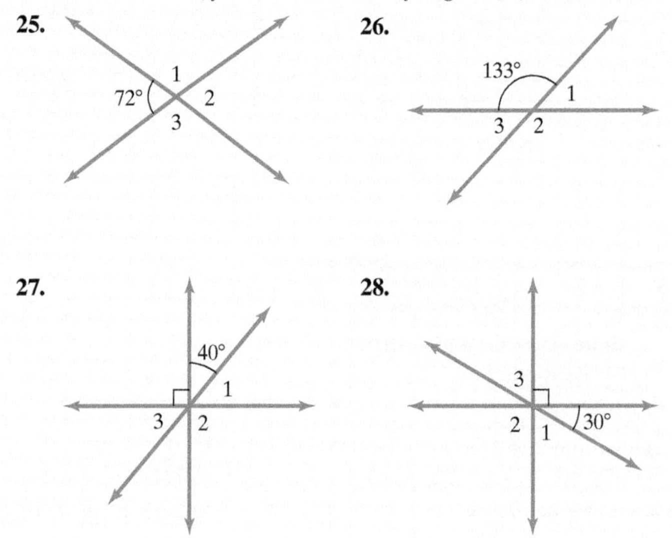

The figures for Exercises 29–30 show two parallel lines intersected by a transversal. One of the angle measures is given. Find the measure of each of the other seven angles.

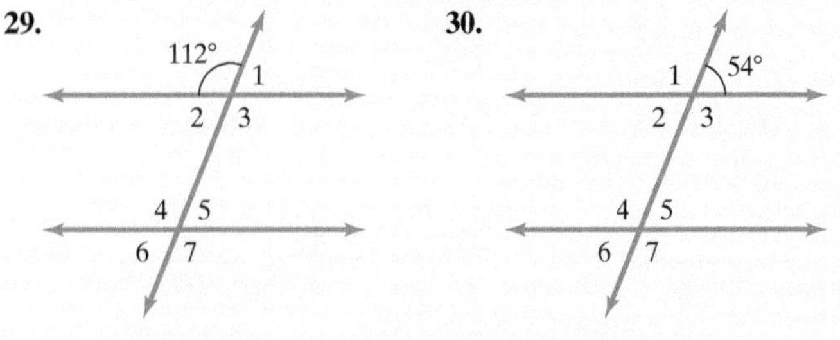

The figures for Exercises 31–34 show two parallel lines intersected by more than one transversal. Two of the angle measures are given. Find the measures of angles 1, 2, and 3.

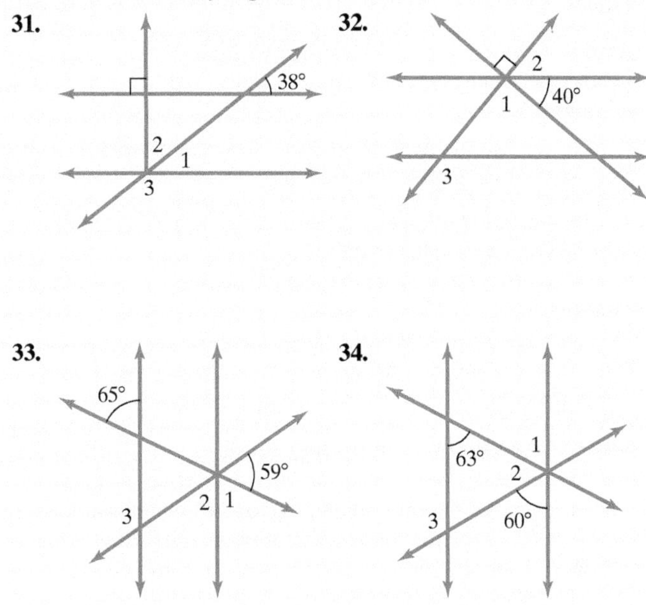

Use the following figure to determine whether each statement in Exercises 35–38 is true or false.

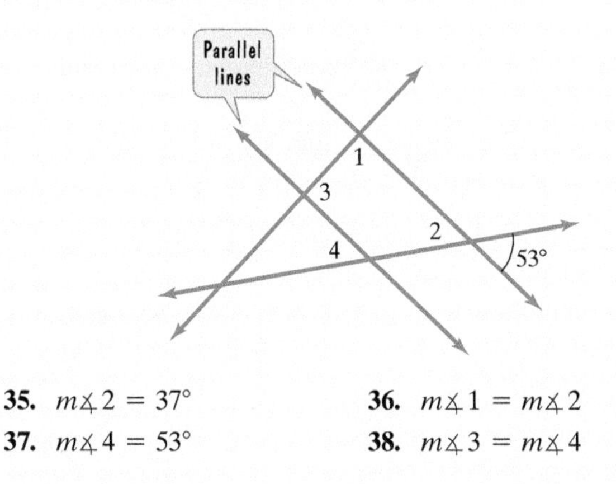

35. $m\measuredangle 2 = 37°$

36. $m\measuredangle 1 = m\measuredangle 2$

37. $m\measuredangle 4 = 53°$

38. $m\measuredangle 3 = m\measuredangle 4$

Use the following figure to determine whether each statement in Exercises 39–42 is true or false.

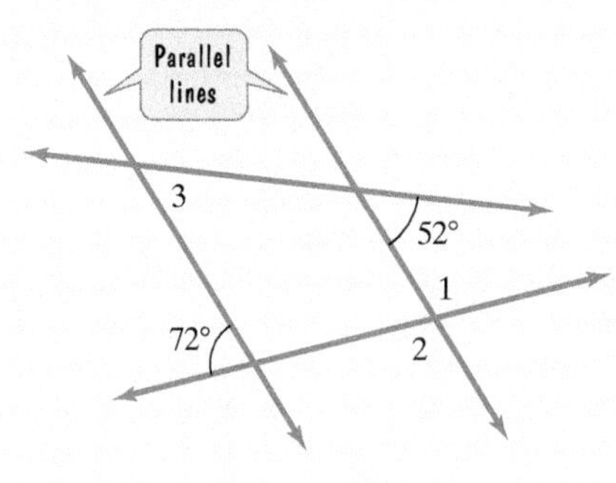

39. $m\measuredangle 1 = 38°$

40. $m\measuredangle 1 = 108°$

41. $m\measuredangle 2 = 52°$

42. $m\measuredangle 3 = 72°$

Practice Plus

In Exercises 43–46, use an algebraic equation to find the measure of each angle that is represented in terms of x.

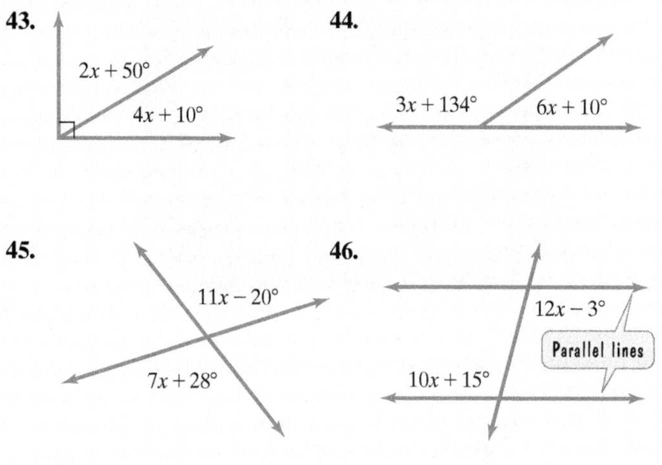

Because geometric figures consist of sets of points, we can apply set operations to obtain the union, ∪, or the intersection, ∩, of such figures. The union of two geometric figures is the set of points that belongs to either of the figures or to both figures. The intersection of two geometric figures is the set of points common to both figures. In Exercises 47–54, use the line shown to find each set of points.

A B C D

47. $\overline{AC} \cap \overline{BD}$

48. $\overline{AB} \cap \overline{BC}$

49. $\overline{AC} \cup \overline{BD}$

50. $\overline{AB} \cup \overline{BC}$

51. $\overrightarrow{BA} \cup \overrightarrow{BC}$

52. $\overrightarrow{CB} \cup \overrightarrow{CD}$

53. $\overrightarrow{AD} \cap \overrightarrow{DB}$

54. $\overline{AC} \cap \overrightarrow{CB}$

Application Exercises

55. The picture shows the top of an umbrella in which all the angles formed by the spokes have the same measure. Find the measure of each angle.

56. In the musical *Company*, composer Stephen Sondheim describes the marriage between two of the play's characters as "parallel lines who meet." What is the composer saying about this relationship?

57. The picture shows a window with parallel framing in which snow has collected in the corners. What property of parallel lines is illustrated by where the snow has collected?

In Exercises 58–59, consider the following uppercase letters from the English alphabet:

A E F H N T X Z.

58. Which letters contain parallel line segments?

59. Which letters contain perpendicular line segments?

Angles play an important role in custom bikes that are properly fitted to the biking needs of cyclists. One of the angles to help find the perfect fit is called the hip angle. The figure indicates that the hip angle is created when you're sitting on the bike, gripping the handlebars, and your leg is fully extended. Your hip is the vertex, with one ray extending to your shoulder and the other ray extending to the front-bottom of your foot.

The table indicates hip angles for various biking needs. Use this information to pedal through Exercises 60–63.

Hip Angle	Used For
$85° \leq$ hip angle $\leq 89°$	short-distance aggressive racing
$91° \leq$ hip angle $\leq 115°$	long-distance riding
$116° \leq$ hip angle $\leq 130°$	mountain biking

60. Which type or types of biking require an acute hip angle?

61. Which type or types of biking require an obtuse hip angle?

62. A racer who had an 89° hip angle decides to switch to long-distance riding. What is the maximum difference in hip angle for the two types of biking?

63. A racer who had an 89° hip angle decides to switch to mountain biking. What is the minimum difference in hip angle for the two types of biking?

(Source for Exercises 60–63: *Scholastic Math*, January 11, 2010)

Writing in Mathematics

64. Describe the differences among lines, half-lines, rays, and line segments.

65. What is an angle and what determines its size?

66. Describe each type of angle: acute, right, obtuse, and straight.

67. What are complementary angles? Describe how to find the measure of an angle's complement.

68. What are supplementary angles? Describe how to find the measure of an angle's supplement.

69. Describe the difference between perpendicular and parallel lines.

70. If two parallel lines are intersected by a transversal, describe the location of the alternate interior angles, the alternate exterior angles, and the corresponding angles.

71. Describe everyday objects that approximate points, lines, and planes.

72. If a transversal is perpendicular to one of two parallel lines, must it be perpendicular to the other parallel line as well? Explain your answer.

Critical Thinking Exercises

Make Sense? *In Exercises 73–76, determine whether each statement makes sense or does not make sense, and explain your reasoning.*

73. I drew two lines that are not parallel and that intersect twice.

74. I used the length of an angle's sides to determine that it was obtuse.

75. I'm working with two angles that are not complementary, so I can conclude that they are supplementary.

76. The rungs of a ladder are perpendicular to each side, so the rungs are parallel to each other.

77. Use the figure to select a pair of complementary angles.

a. $\measuredangle 1$ and $\measuredangle 4$

b. $\measuredangle 3$ and $\measuredangle 6$

c. $\measuredangle 2$ and $\measuredangle 5$

d. $\measuredangle 1$ and $\measuredangle 5$

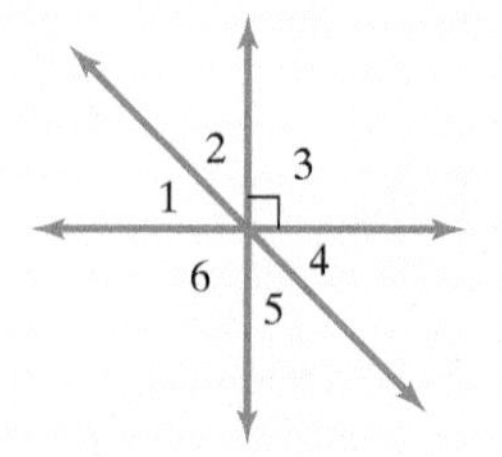

78. If $m\measuredangle AGB = m\measuredangle BGC$, and $m\measuredangle CGD = m\measuredangle DGE$, find $m\measuredangle BGD$.

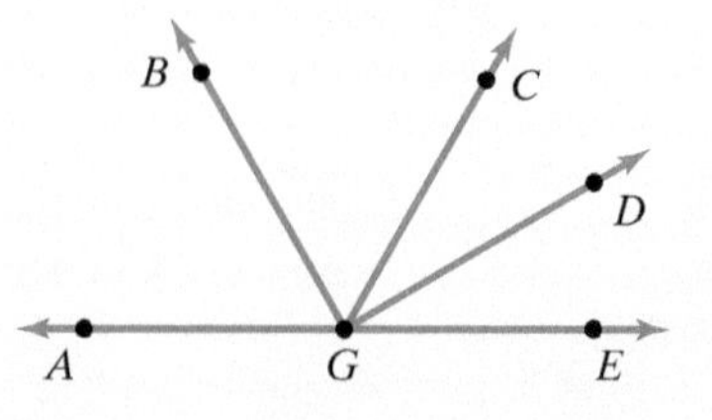

4.2

WHAT AM I SUPPOSED TO LEARN?

After you have read this section, you should be able to:

1. Solve problems involving angle relationships in triangles.
2. Solve problems involving similar triangles.
3. Solve problems using the Pythagorean Theorem.

Triangles

The Walter Pyramid, California State University, Long Beach

IN CHAPTER 1, WE DEFINED *deductive reasoning* as the process of proving a specific conclusion from one or more general statements. A conclusion that is proved to be true through deductive reasoning is called a **theorem**. The Greek mathematician Euclid, who lived more than 2000 years ago, used deductive reasoning. In his 13-volume book, *Elements,* Euclid proved over 465 theorems about geometric figures. Euclid's work established deductive reasoning as a fundamental tool of mathematics. Here's looking at Euclid!

A **triangle** is a geometric figure that has three sides, all of which lie on a flat surface or plane. If you start at any point along the triangle and trace along the entire figure exactly once, you will end at the same point at which you started. Because the beginning point and ending point are the same, the triangle is called a **closed** geometric figure. Euclid used parallel lines to prove one of the most important properties of triangles: The sum of the measures of the three angles of any triangle is 180°. Here is how he did it. He began with the following general statement:

EUCLID'S ASSUMPTION ABOUT PARALLEL LINES

Given a line and a point not on the line, one and only one line can be drawn through the given point parallel to the given line.

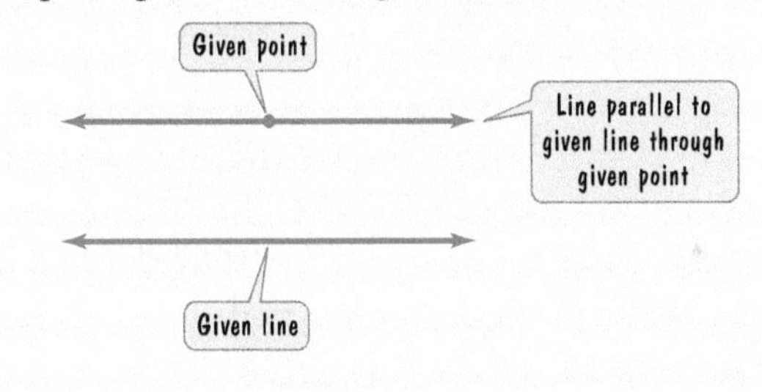

In **Figure 4.15**, triangle ABC represents any triangle. Using the general assumption given above, we draw a line through point B parallel to line AC.

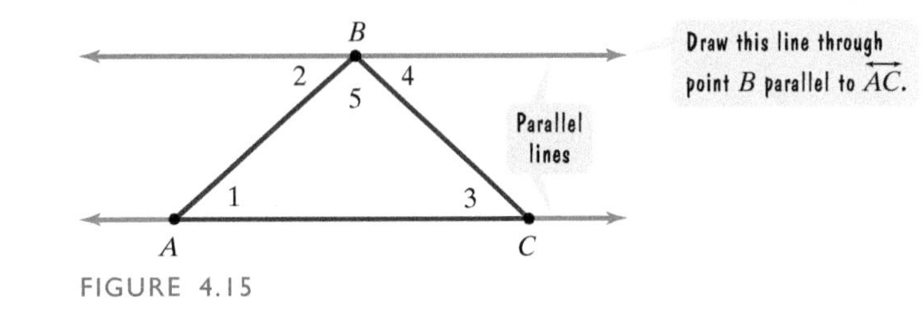

FIGURE 4.15

Because the lines are parallel, alternate interior angles have the same measure.

$$m\measuredangle 1 = m\measuredangle 2 \quad \text{and} \quad m\measuredangle 3 = m\measuredangle 4$$

Also observe that angles 2, 5, and 4 form a straight angle.

$$m\measuredangle 2 + m\measuredangle 5 + m\measuredangle 4 = 180°$$

Because $m\measuredangle 1 = m\measuredangle 2$, replace $m\measuredangle 2$ with $m\measuredangle 1$.

Because $m\measuredangle 3 = m\measuredangle 4$, replace $m\measuredangle 4$ with $m\measuredangle 3$.

$$m\measuredangle 1 + m\measuredangle 5 + m\measuredangle 3 = 180°$$

Because $\measuredangle 1$, $\measuredangle 5$, and $\measuredangle 3$ are the three angles of the triangle, this last equation shows that the measures of the triangle's three angles have a 180° sum.

THE ANGLES OF A TRIANGLE

The sum of the measures of the three angles of any triangle is 180°.

Solve problems involving angle relationships in triangles.

EXAMPLE 1 Using Angle Relationships in Triangles

Find the measure of angle A for triangle ABC in **Figure 4.16**.

FIGURE 4.16

SOLUTION

Because $m\measuredangle A + m\measuredangle B + m\measuredangle C = 180°$, we obtain

$m\measuredangle A + 120° + 17° = 180°$ The sum of the measures of a triangle's three angles is 180°.

$m\measuredangle A + 137° = 180°$ Simplify: $120° + 17° = 137°$.

$m\measuredangle A = 180° - 137°$ Find the measure of A by subtracting 137° from both sides of the equation.

$m\measuredangle A = 43°$ Simplify.

CHECK POINT 1 In **Figure 4.16**, suppose that $m\measuredangle B = 116°$ and $m\measuredangle C = 15°$. Find $m\measuredangle A$.

EXAMPLE 2 Using Angle Relationships in Triangles

Find the measures of angles 1 through 5 in **Figure 4.17**.

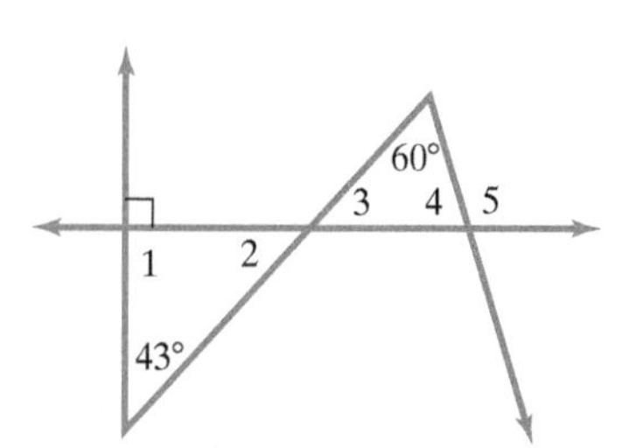

FIGURE 4.17

SOLUTION

Because $\measuredangle 1$ is supplementary to the right angle, $m\measuredangle 1 = 90°$.

$m\measuredangle 2$ can be found using the fact that the sum of the measures of the angles of a triangle is 180°.

$m\measuredangle 1 + m\measuredangle 2 + 43° = 180°$ The sum of the measures of a triangle's three angles is 180°.

$90° + m\measuredangle 2 + 43° = 180°$ We previously found that $m\measuredangle 1 = 90°$.

$m\measuredangle 2 + 133° = 180°$ Simplify: $90° + 43° = 133°$.

$m\measuredangle 2 = 180° - 133°$ Subtract 133° from both sides.

$m\measuredangle 2 = 47°$ Simplify.

$m\measuredangle 3$ can be found using the fact that vertical angles have equal measures: $m\measuredangle 3 = m\measuredangle 2$. Thus, $m\measuredangle 3 = 47°$.

$m\measuredangle 4$ can be found using the fact that the sum of the measures of the angles of a triangle is 180°. Refer to the triangle at the top of **Figure 4.17**.

$m\measuredangle 3 + m\measuredangle 4 + 60° = 180°$ The sum of the measures of a triangle's three angles is 180°.

$47° + m\measuredangle 4 + 60° = 180°$ We previously found that $m\measuredangle 3 = 47°$.

$m\measuredangle 4 + 107° = 180°$ Simplify: $47° + 60° = 107°$.

$m\measuredangle 4 = 180° - 107°$ Subtract 107° from both sides.

$m\measuredangle 4 = 73°$ Simplify.

Finally, we can find $m\angle 5$ by observing that angles 4 and 5 form a straight angle.

$$m\angle 4 + m\angle 5 = 180^\circ \quad \text{A straight angle measures } 180^\circ.$$
$$73^\circ + m\angle 5 = 180^\circ \quad \text{We previously found that } m\angle 4 = 73^\circ.$$
$$m\angle 5 = 180^\circ - 73^\circ \quad \text{Subtract } 73^\circ \text{ from both sides.}$$
$$m\angle 5 = 107^\circ \quad \text{Simplify.}$$

CHECK POINT 2 In **Figure 4.17**, suppose that the angle shown to measure 43° measures, instead, 36°. Further suppose that the angle shown to measure 60° measures, instead, 58°. Under these new conditions, find the measures of angles 1 through 5 in the figure.

GREAT QUESTION!

Does an isosceles triangle have exactly two equal sides or at least two equal sides?

We checked a variety of math textbooks and found two slightly different definitions for an isosceles triangle. One definition states that an isosceles triangle has *exactly* two sides of equal length. A second definition asserts that an isosceles triangle has *at least* two sides of equal length. (This makes an equilateral triangle, with three sides of the same length, an isosceles triangle.) In this book, we assume that an isosceles triangle has exactly two sides, but not three sides, of the same length.

Triangles can be described using characteristics of their angles or their sides.

TRIANGLES AND THEIR CHARACTERISTICS

Classification by Angles

Acute Triangle
All angles are acute.

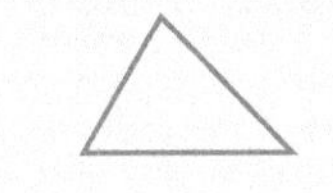

Right Triangle
One angle measures 90°.

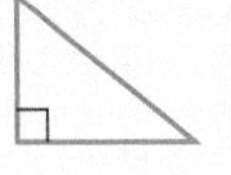

Obtuse Triangle
One angle is obtuse.

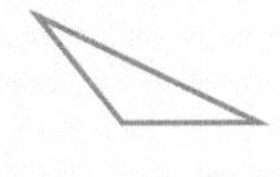

Classification by Sides

Isosceles Triangle
Two sides have equal length. (Angles opposite these sides have the same measure.)

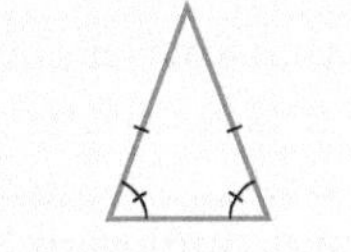

Equilateral Triangle
All sides have equal length. (Each angle measures 60°.)

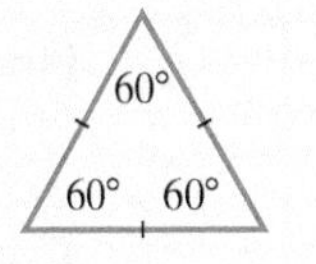

Scalene Triangle
No two sides are equal in length.

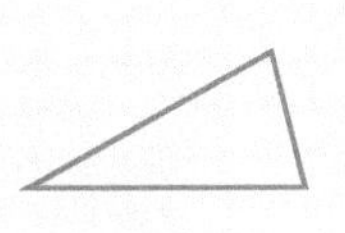

2 Solve problems involving similar triangles.

Pedestrian crossing

Similar Triangles

Shown in the margin is an international road sign. This sign is shaped just like the actual sign, although its size is smaller. Figures that have the same shape, but not the same size, are used in **scale drawings**. A scale drawing always pictures the exact shape of the object that the drawing represents. Architects, engineers, landscape gardeners, and interior decorators use scale drawings in planning their work.

Figures that have the same shape, but not necessarily the same size, are called **similar figures**. In **Figure 4.18**, triangles ABC and DEF are similar. Angles A and D measure the same number of degrees and are called **corresponding angles**. Angles C and F are corresponding angles, as are angles B and E. Angles with the same number of tick marks in **Figure 4.18** are the corresponding angles.

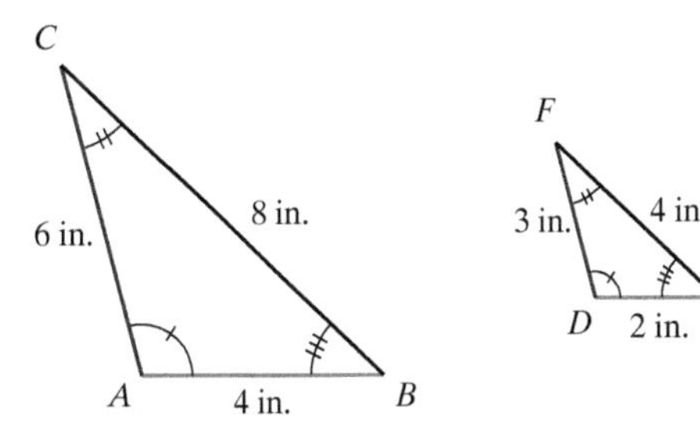

FIGURE 4.18

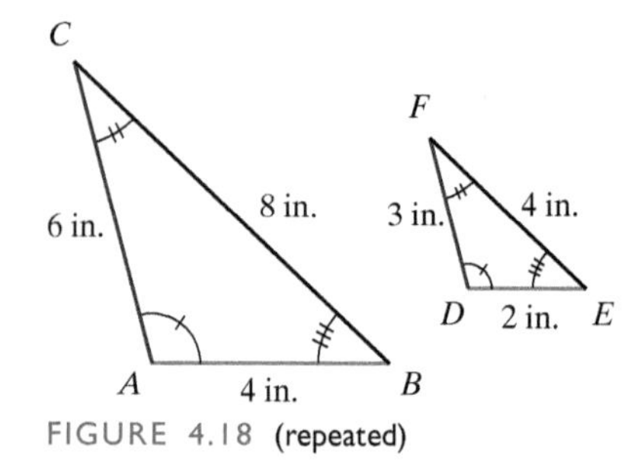

FIGURE 4.18 (repeated)

The sides opposite the corresponding angles are called **corresponding sides.** Thus, $\overline{CB}$ and $\overline{FE}$ are corresponding sides. $\overline{AB}$ and $\overline{DE}$ are also corresponding sides, as are $\overline{AC}$ and $\overline{DF}$. Corresponding angles measure the same number of degrees, but corresponding sides may or may not be the same length. For the triangles in **Figure 4.18**, each side in the smaller triangle is half the length of the corresponding side in the larger triangle.

The triangles in **Figure 4.18** illustrate what it means to be **similar triangles. Corresponding angles have the same measure and the ratios of the lengths of the corresponding sides are equal.**

$$\frac{\text{length of } \overline{AC}}{\text{length of } \overline{DF}} = \frac{6 \text{ in.}}{3 \text{ in.}} = \frac{2}{1}; \quad \frac{\text{length of } \overline{CB}}{\text{length of } \overline{FE}} = \frac{8 \text{ in.}}{4 \text{ in.}} = \frac{2}{1}; \quad \frac{\text{length of } \overline{AB}}{\text{length of } \overline{DE}} = \frac{4 \text{ in.}}{2 \text{ in.}} = \frac{2}{1}$$

In similar triangles, the lengths of the corresponding sides are proportional. Thus,

AC represents the length of $\overline{AC}$, DF the length of $\overline{DF}$, and so on.

$$\frac{AC}{DF} = \frac{CB}{FE} = \frac{AB}{DE}.$$

How can we quickly determine if two triangles are similar? **If the measures of two angles of one triangle are equal to those of two angles of a second triangle, then the two triangles are similar.** If the triangles are similar, then their corresponding sides are proportional.

EXAMPLE 3 *Using Similar Triangles*

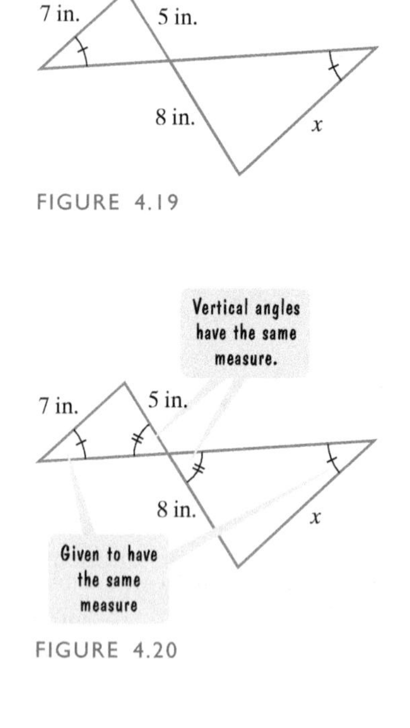

FIGURE 4.19

FIGURE 4.20

Explain why the triangles in **Figure 4.19** are similar. Then find the missing length, x.

SOLUTION

Figure 4.20 shows that two angles of the small triangle are equal in measure to two angles of the large triangle. One angle pair is given to have the same measure. Another angle pair consists of vertical angles with the same measure. Thus, the triangles are similar and their corresponding sides are proportional.

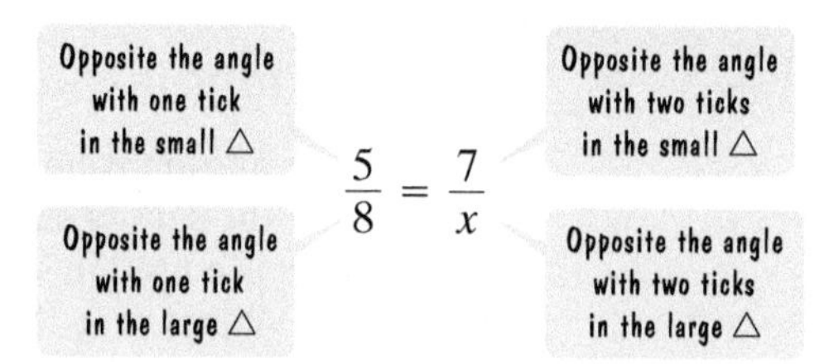

We solve $\frac{5}{8} = \frac{7}{x}$ for x by applying the cross-products principle for proportions that we discussed in Section 6.2: If $\frac{a}{b} = \frac{c}{d}$, then $ad = bc$.

$5x = 8 \cdot 7$	Apply the cross-products principle.
$5x = 56$	Multiply: $8 \cdot 7 = 56$.
$\frac{5x}{5} = \frac{56}{5}$	Divide both sides by 5.
$x = 11.2$	Simplify.

The missing length, x, is 11.2 inches.

CHECK POINT 3 Explain why the triangles in **Figure 4.21** are similar. Then find the missing length, x.

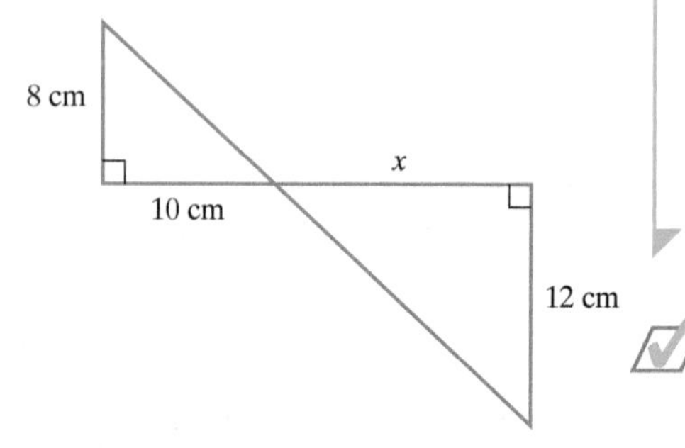

FIGURE 4.21

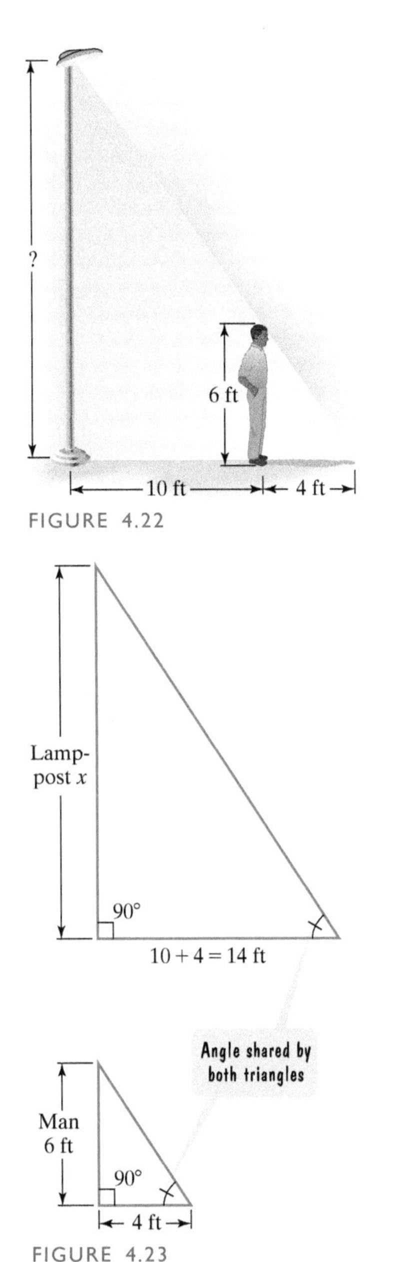

FIGURE 4.22

FIGURE 4.23

EXAMPLE 4 *Problem Solving Using Similar Triangles*

A man who is 6 feet tall is standing 10 feet from the base of a lamppost (see **Figure 4.22**). The man's shadow has a length of 4 feet. How tall is the lamppost?

SOLUTION

The drawing in **Figure 4.23** makes the similarity of the triangles easier to see. The large triangle with the lamppost on the left and the small triangle with the man on the left both contain 90° angles. They also share an angle. Thus, two angles of the large triangle are equal in measure to two angles of the small triangle. This means that the triangles are similar and their corresponding sides are proportional. We begin by letting x represent the height of the lamppost, in feet. Because corresponding sides of the two similar triangles are proportional,

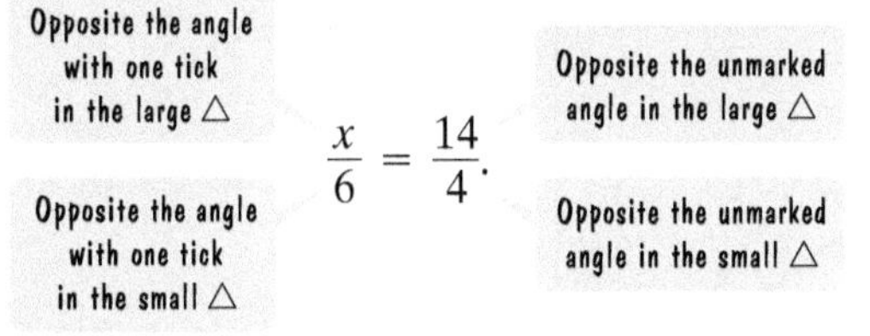

$$\frac{x}{6} = \frac{14}{4}.$$

We solve for x by applying the cross-products principle.

$$4x = 6 \cdot 14 \quad \text{Apply the cross-products principle.}$$
$$4x = 84 \quad \text{Multiply: } 6 \cdot 14 = 84.$$
$$\frac{4x}{4} = \frac{84}{4} \quad \text{Divide both sides by 4.}$$
$$x = 21 \quad \text{Simplify.}$$

The lamppost is 21 feet tall.

CHECK POINT 4 Find the height of the lookout tower shown in **Figure 4.24** using the figure that lines up the top of the tower with the top of a stick that is 2 yards long and 3.5 yards from the line to the top of the tower.

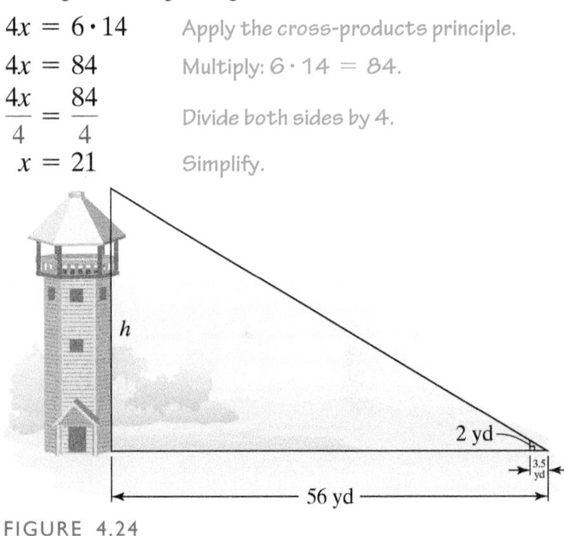

FIGURE 4.24

3 Solve problems using the Pythagorean Theorem.

The Pythagorean Theorem

The ancient Greek philosopher and mathematician Pythagoras (approximately 582–500 B.C.) founded a school whose motto was "All is number." Pythagoras is best remembered for his work with the **right triangle**, a triangle with one angle measuring 90°. The side opposite the 90° angle is called the **hypotenuse**. The other sides are called **legs**. Pythagoras found that if he constructed squares on each of the legs, as well as a larger square on the hypotenuse, the sum of the areas of the smaller squares is equal to the area of the larger square. This is illustrated in **Figure 4.25**.

This relationship is usually stated in terms of the lengths of the three sides of a right triangle and is called the **Pythagorean Theorem**.

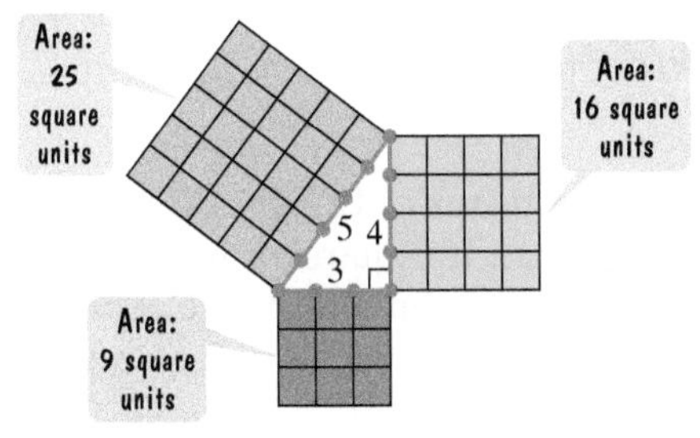

FIGURE 4.25 The area of the large square equals the sum of the areas of the smaller squares.

THE PYTHAGOREAN THEOREM

The sum of the squares of the lengths of the legs of a right triangle equals the square of the length of the hypotenuse.

If the legs have lengths a and b and the hypotenuse has length c, then

$$a^2 + b^2 = c^2.$$

B
c
a
Hypotenuse
Leg
A
b
C
Leg

Blitzer Bonus

The Universality of Mathematics

Is mathematics discovered or invented? The "Pythagorean" Theorem, credited to Pythagoras, was known in China, from land surveying, and in Egypt, from pyramid building, centuries before Pythagoras was born. The same mathematics is often discovered/invented by independent researchers separated by time, place, and culture.

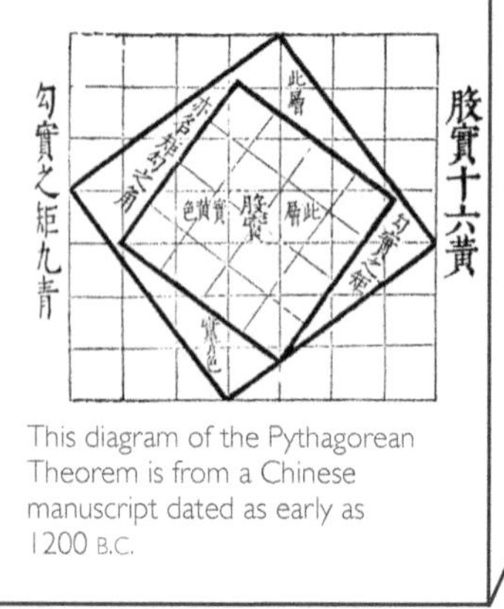

This diagram of the Pythagorean Theorem is from a Chinese manuscript dated as early as 1200 B.C.

EXAMPLE 5 *Using the Pythagorean Theorem*

Find the length of the hypotenuse c in the right triangle shown in **Figure 4.26**.

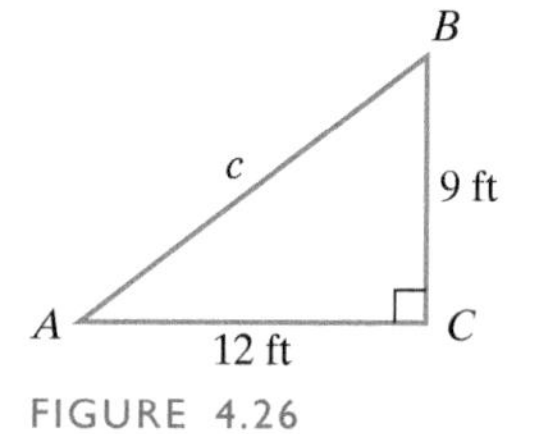

FIGURE 4.26

SOLUTION

Let $a = 9$ and $b = 12$. Substituting these values into $c^2 = a^2 + b^2$ enables us to solve for c.

$c^2 = a^2 + b^2$ Use the symbolic statement of the Pythagorean Theorem.

$c^2 = 9^2 + 12^2$ Let $a = 9$ and $b = 12$.

$c^2 = 81 + 144$ $9^2 = 9 \cdot 9 = 81$ and $12^2 = 12 \cdot 12 = 144$.

$c^2 = 225$ Add.

$c = \sqrt{225} = 15$ Solve for c by taking the positive square root of 225.

The length of the hypotenuse is 15 feet.

CHECK POINT 5 Find the length of the hypotenuse in a right triangle whose legs have lengths 7 feet and 24 feet.

EXAMPLE 6 *Using the Pythagorean Theorem*

a. A wheelchair ramp with a length of 122 inches has a horizontal distance of 120 inches. What is the ramp's vertical distance?

b. Construction laws are very specific when it comes to access ramps for the disabled. Every vertical rise of 1 inch requires a horizontal run of 12 inches. Does this ramp satisfy the requirement?

SOLUTION

a. The problem's conditions state that the wheelchair ramp has a length of 122 inches and a horizontal distance of 120 inches. **Figure 4.27** shows the right triangle that is formed by the ramp, the wall, and the ground. We can find x, the ramp's vertical distance, using the Pythagorean Theorem.

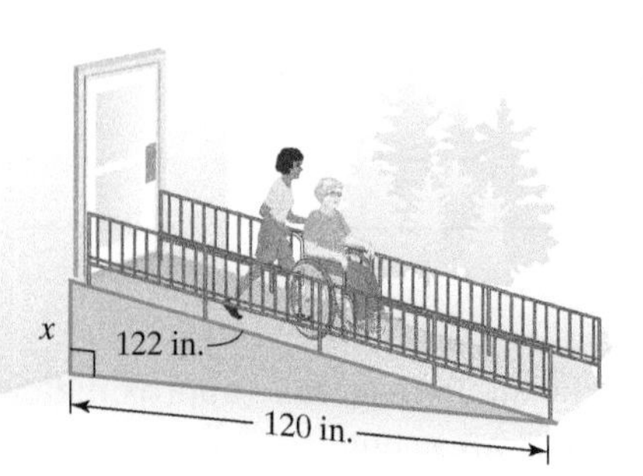

FIGURE 4.27

$$\underbrace{x^2}_{(\text{leg})^2} \quad \underbrace{+}_{\text{plus}} \quad \underbrace{120^2}_{(\text{leg})^2} \quad \underbrace{=}_{\text{equals}} \quad \underbrace{122^2}_{(\text{hypotenuse})^2}$$

$x^2 + 120^2 = 122^2$ This is the equation resulting from the Pythagorean Theorem.

$x^2 + 14{,}400 = 14{,}884$ Square 120 and 122.

$x^2 = 484$ Isolate x^2 by subtracting 14,400 from both sides.

$x = \sqrt{484} = 22$ Solve for x by taking the positive square root of 484.

The ramp's vertical distance is 22 inches.

b. Every vertical rise of 1 inch requires a horizontal run of 12 inches. Because the ramp has a vertical distance of 22 inches, it requires a horizontal distance of 22(12) inches, or 264 inches. The horizontal distance is only 120 inches, so this ramp does not satisfy construction laws for access ramps for the disabled.

CHECK POINT 6 A radio tower is supported by two wires that are each 130 yards long and attached to the ground 50 yards from the base of the tower. How far from the ground are the wires attached to the tower?

Blitzer Bonus

Curiosities Associated with the Pythagorean Theorem

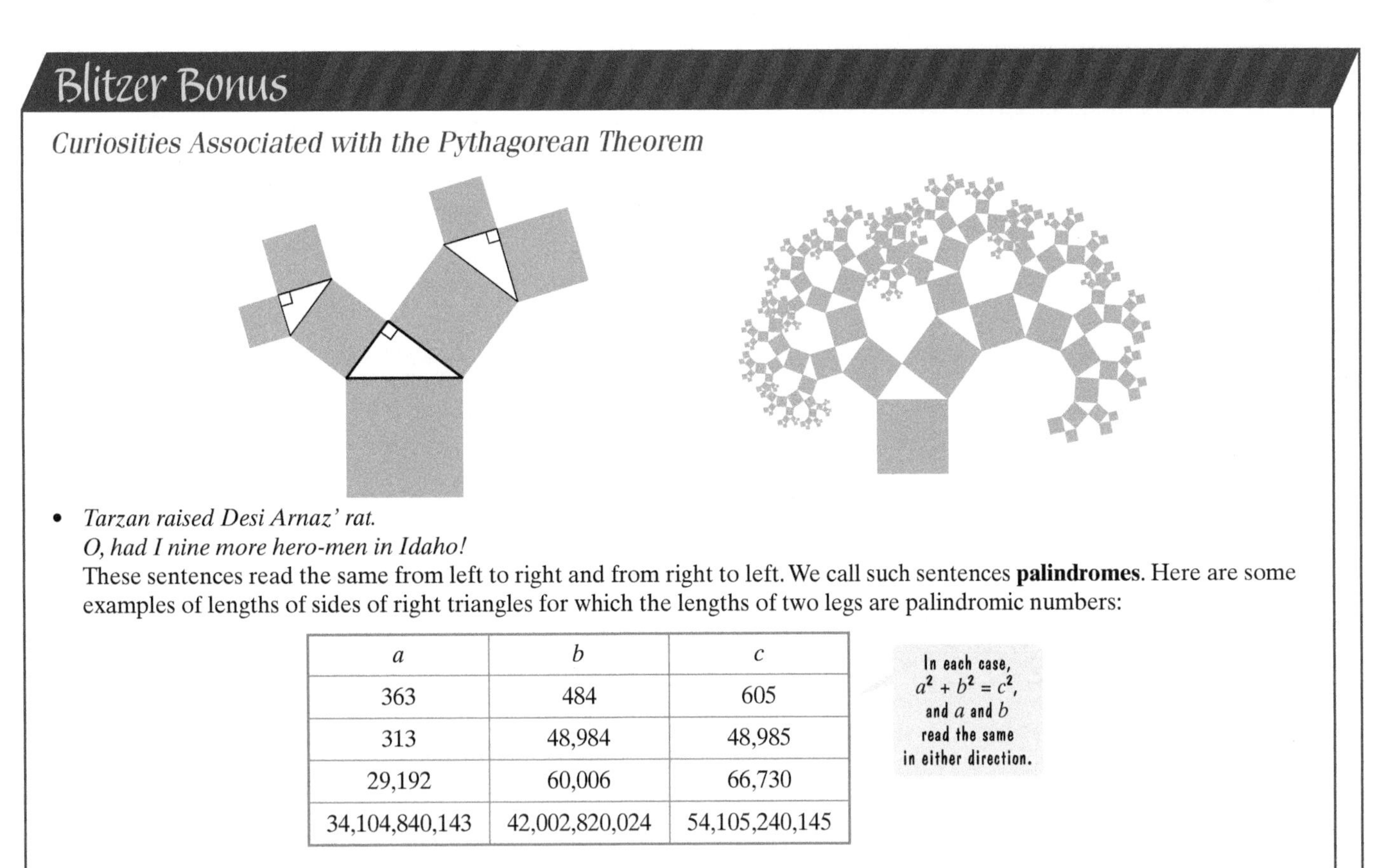

- *Tarzan raised Desi Arnaz' rat.*
  O, had I nine more hero-men in Idaho!
  These sentences read the same from left to right and from right to left. We call such sentences **palindromes**. Here are some examples of lengths of sides of right triangles for which the lengths of two legs are palindromic numbers:

a	b	c
363	484	605
313	48,984	48,985
29,192	60,006	66,730
34,104,840,143	42,002,820,024	54,105,240,145

In each case, $a^2 + b^2 = c^2$, and a and b read the same in either direction.

- The lengths of the sides of a right triangle can display unusual symmetric properties.

Palindromic number / Reverses of one another

a	b	c
33	56	65
3333	5656	6565

Reverses of one another

a	b	c
88,209	90,288	126,225

In each case, $a^2 + b^2 = c^2$.

- Some right triangles have unusual areas.

a	b	c	Area (square units)
443,531	6660	443,581	1,476,958,230 (Each of the ten digits, 0, 1, 2, 3, ..., 9 appears once.)
693	1924	2045	666,666 (See the Blitzer Bonus (Integers, Karma, Exponents).)

- There is a surprising relationship between the irrational number π and the Pythagorean Theorem.

$$\pi \approx 3.14159265$$

Let $a = 159$. Let $c = 265$.

Introducing the palindromic number $b = 212$, the resulting three numbers satisfy the Pythagorean Theorem.

a	b	c	$a^2 + b^2 = c^2$
159	212	265	$159^2 + 212^2 = 265^2$

Furthermore,

$$\frac{666}{212} \approx 3.1415 \approx \pi$$

See the Blitzer Bonus

This is the number we introduced above to form the sides of a right triangle.

Source: Alfred Posamentier, *The Pythagorean Theorem—The Story of Its Power and Beauty,* Prometheus Books, 2010.

Concept and Vocabulary Check

Fill in each blank so that the resulting statement is true.

1. The sum of the measures of the three angles of any triangle is __________.
2. A triangle in which each angle measures less than 90° is called a/an __________ triangle.
3. A triangle in which one angle measures more than 90° is called a/an __________ triangle.
4. A triangle with exactly two sides of the same length is called a/an __________ triangle.
5. A triangle whose sides are all the same length is called a/an __________ triangle.
6. A triangle that has no sides of the same length is called a/an __________ triangle.
7. Triangles that have the same shape, but not necessarily the same size, are called __________ triangles. For such triangles, corresponding angles have __________ and the lengths of the corresponding sides are __________.
8. The Pythagorean Theorem states that in any __________ triangle, the sum of the squares of the lengths of the __________ equals __________.

In Exercises 9–13, determine whether each statement is true or false. If the statement is false, make the necessary change(s) to produce a true statement.

9. Euclid's assumption about parallel lines states that given a line and a point not on the line, one and only one line can be drawn through the given point parallel to the given line. ______
10. A triangle cannot have both a right angle and an obtuse angle. ______
11. Each angle of an isosceles triangle measures 60°. ______
12. If the measures of two angles of one triangle are equal to those of two angles of a second triangle, then the two triangles have same size and shape. ______
13. In any triangle, the sum of the squares of the lengths of the two shorter sides equals the square of the length of the longest side. ______

Exercise Set 4.2

Practice Exercises

In Exercises 1–4, find the measure of angle A for the triangle shown.

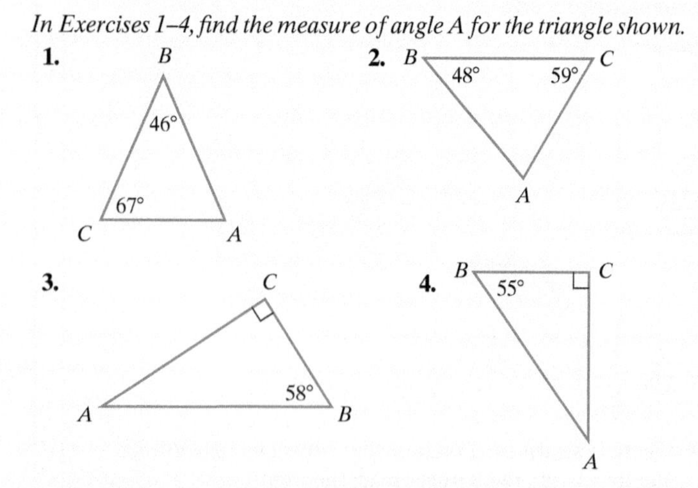

In Exercises 5–6, find the measures of angles 1 through 5 in the figure shown.

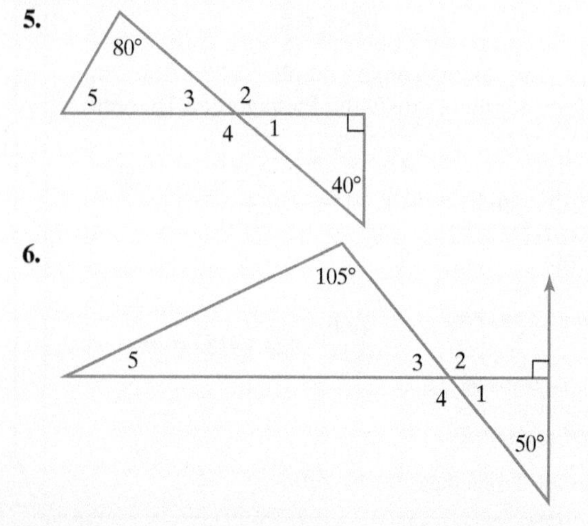

We have seen that isosceles triangles have two sides of equal length. The angles opposite these sides have the same measure. In Exercises 7–8, use this information to help find the measure of each numbered angle.

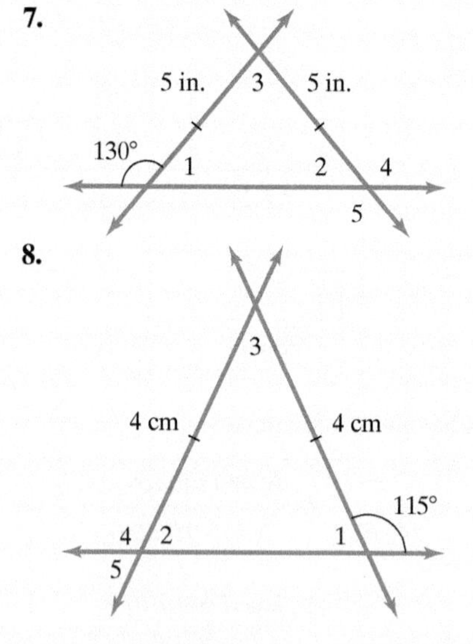

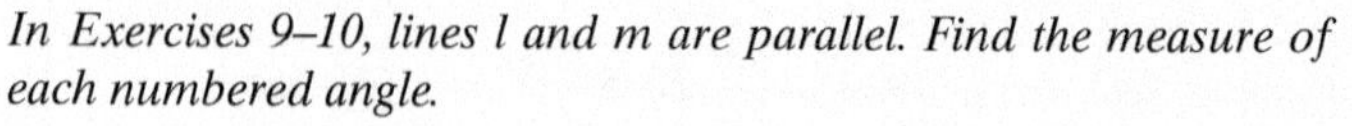
In Exercises 9–10, lines l and m are parallel. Find the measure of each numbered angle.

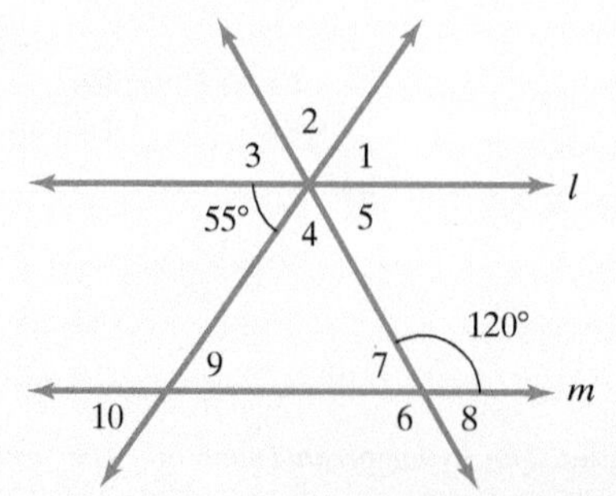

10.

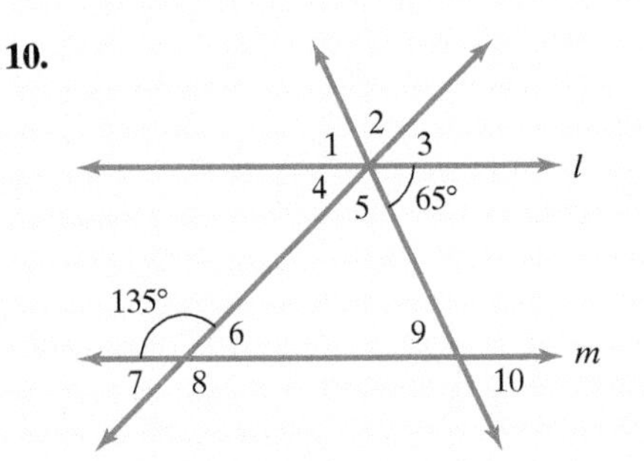

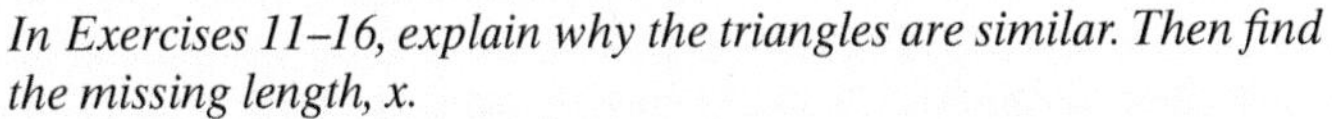

In Exercises 11–16, explain why the triangles are similar. Then find the missing length, x.

11. **12.** **13.** **14.** **15.** **16.**

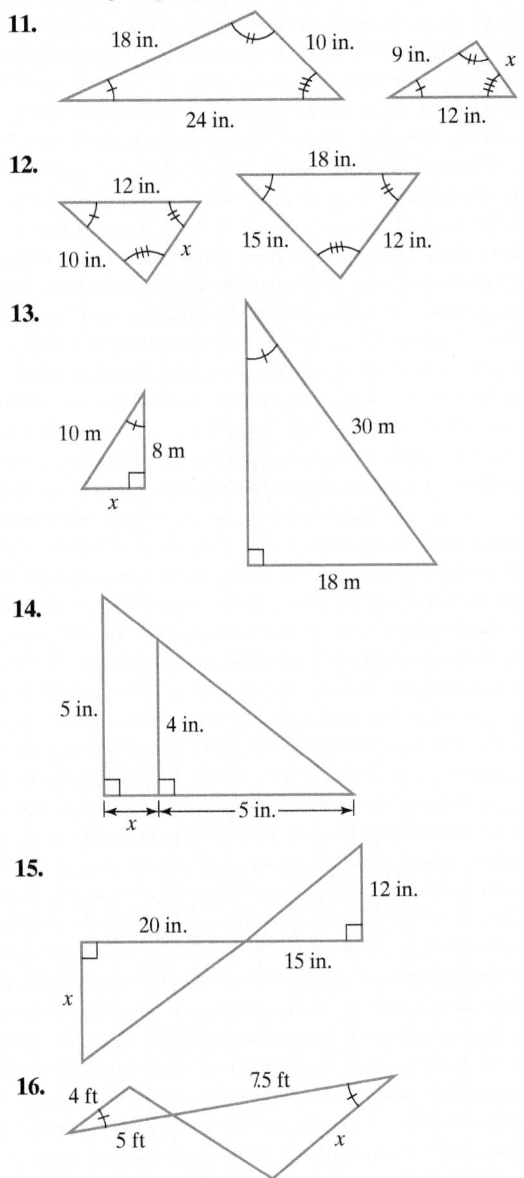

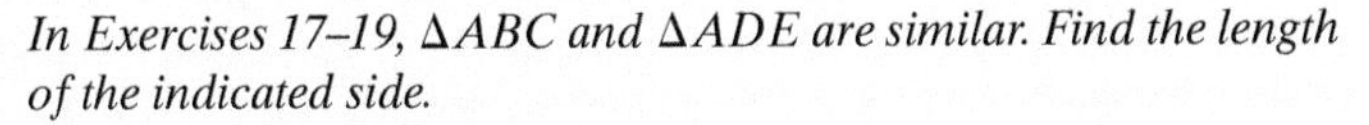

In Exercises 17–19, ΔABC and ΔADE are similar. Find the length of the indicated side.

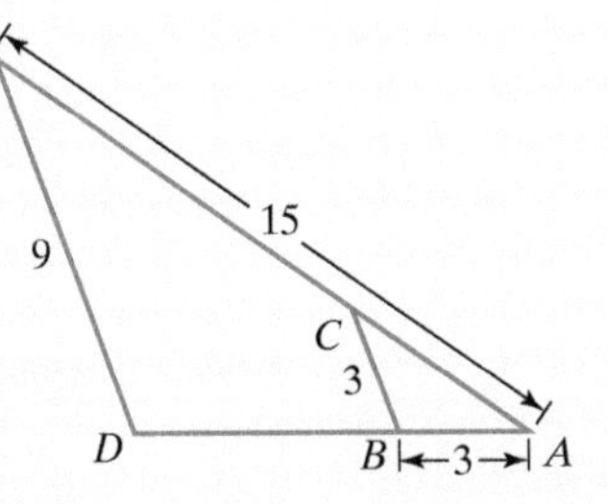

17. $\overline{CA}$ **18.** $\overline{DB}$ **19.** $\overline{DA}$

20. In the diagram for Exercises 17–19, suppose that you are not told that ΔABC and ΔADE are similar. Instead, you are given that $\overleftrightarrow{ED}$ and $\overleftrightarrow{CB}$ are parallel. Under these conditions, explain why the triangles must be similar.

In Exercises 21–26, use the Pythagorean Theorem to find the missing length in each right triangle. Use your calculator to find square roots, rounding, if necessary, to the nearest tenth.

21. **22.** **23.** **24.** **25.** **26.**

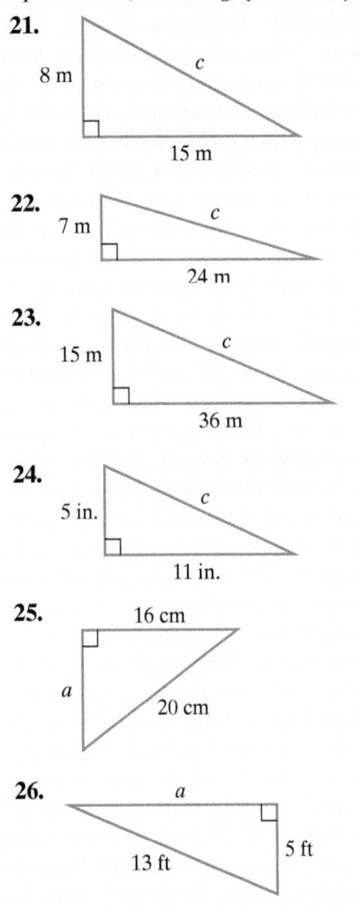

Practice Plus

Two triangles are ***congruent*** *if they have the same shape and the same size. In congruent triangles, the measures of corresponding angles are equal and the corresponding sides have the same length. The following triangles are congruent:*

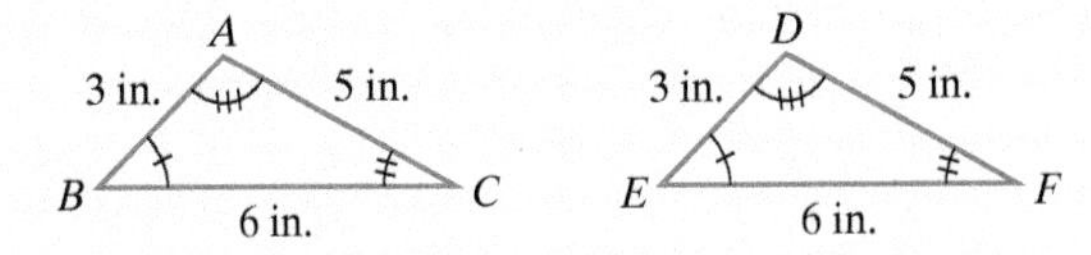

Any one of the following may be used to determine if two triangles are congruent.

Determining Congruent Triangles

1. Side-Side-Side (SSS)

If the lengths of three sides of one triangle equal the lengths of the corresponding sides of a second triangle, then the two triangles are congruent.

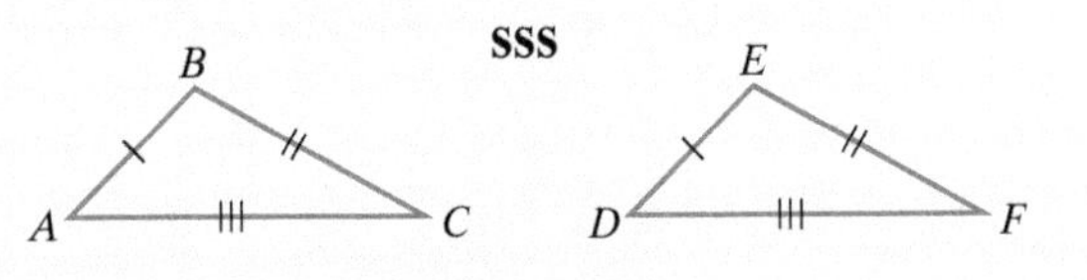

2. Side-Angle-Side (SAS)
If the lengths of two sides of one triangle equal the lengths of the corresponding sides of a second triangle and the measures of the angles between each pair of sides are equal, then the two triangles are congruent.

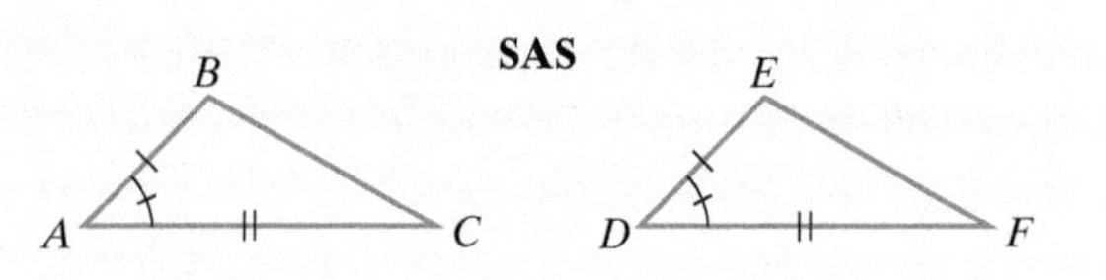

3. Angle-Side-Angle (ASA)
If the measures of two angles of one triangle equal the measures of two angles of a second triangle and the lengths of the sides between each pair of angles are equal, then the two triangles are congruent.

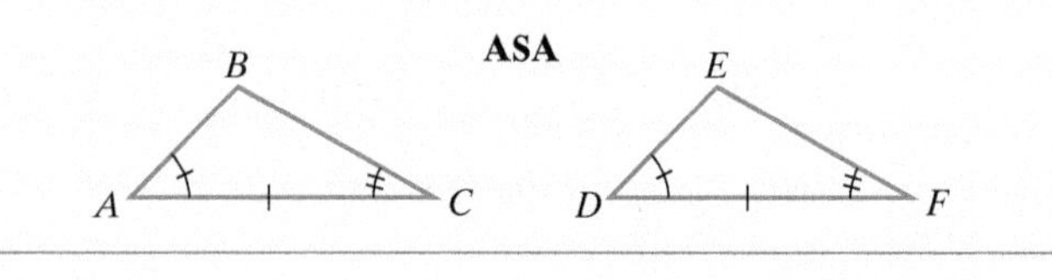

In Exercises 27–36, determine whether ΔI and ΔII are congruent. If the triangles are congruent, state the reason why, selecting from SSS, SAS, or ASA. (More than one reason may be possible.)

27.

28.

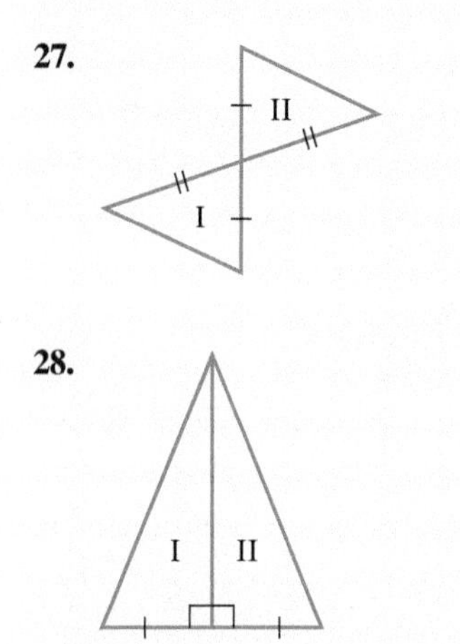

29.

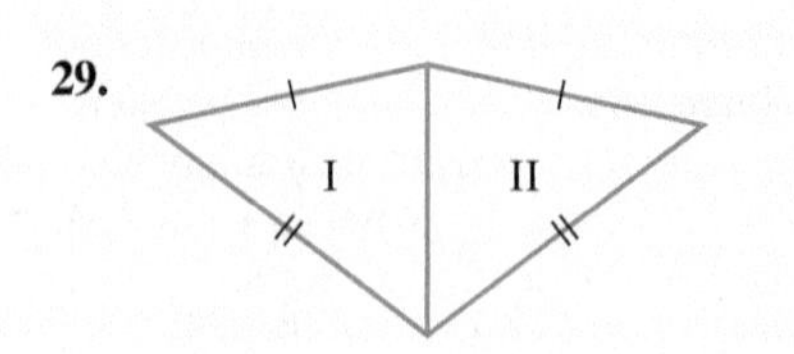

30.

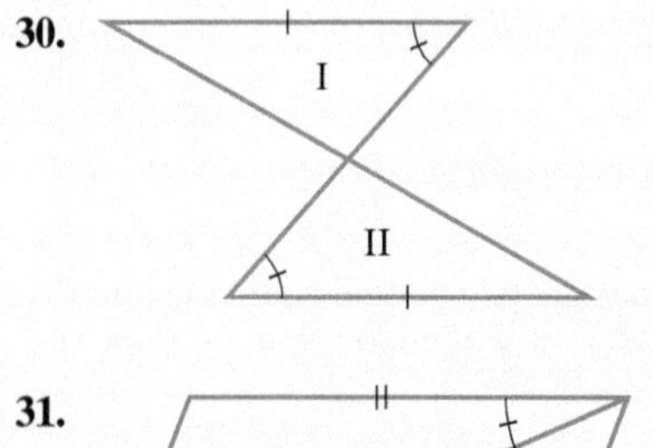

31.

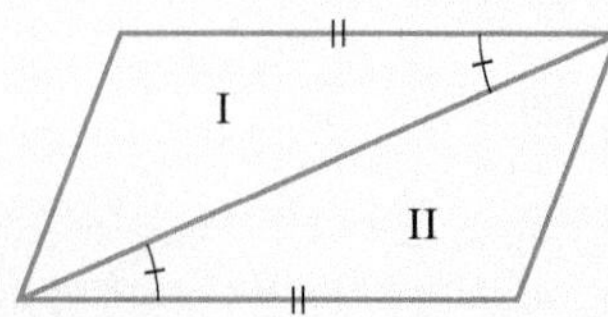

32.

33.

34.

35.

36.

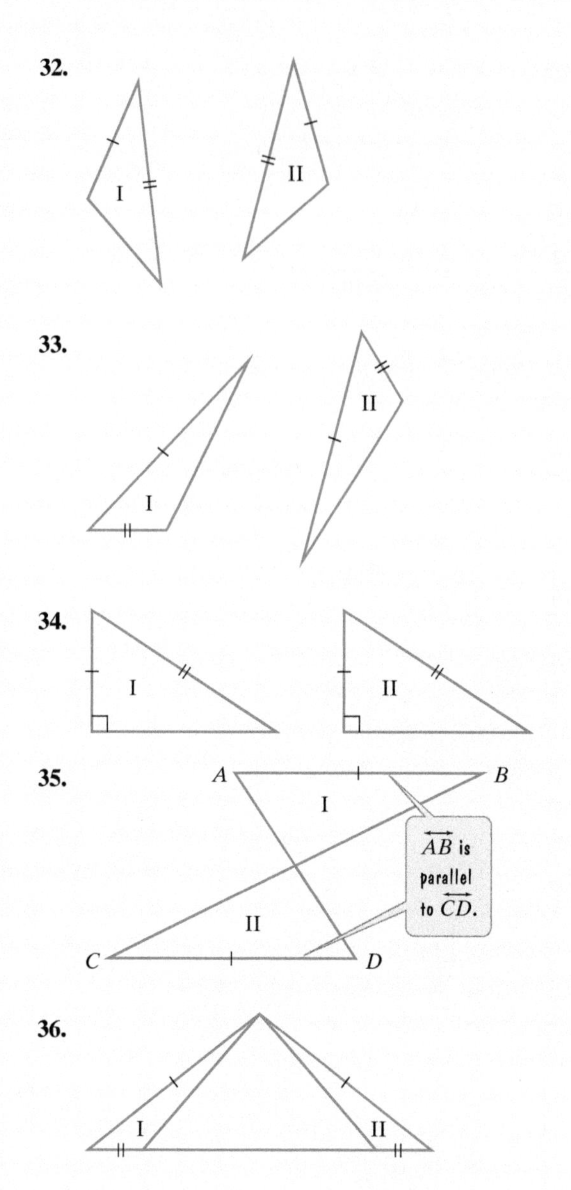

Application Exercises

Use similar triangles to solve Exercises 37–38.

37. A person who is 5 feet tall is standing 80 feet from the base of a tree and the tree casts an 86-foot shadow. The person's shadow is 6 feet in length. What is the tree's height?

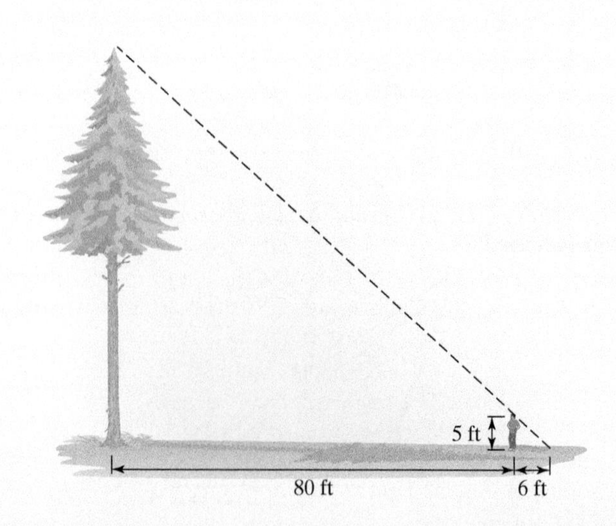

38. A tree casts a shadow 12 feet long. At the same time, a vertical rod 8 feet high casts a shadow that is 6 feet long. How tall is the tree?

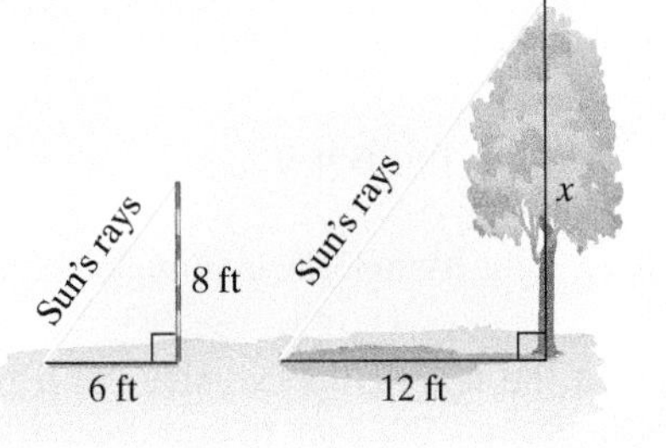

Use the Pythagorean Theorem to solve Exercises 39–46. Use your calculator to find square roots, rounding, if necessary, to the nearest tenth.

39. A baseball diamond is actually a square with 90-foot sides. What is the distance from home plate to second base?

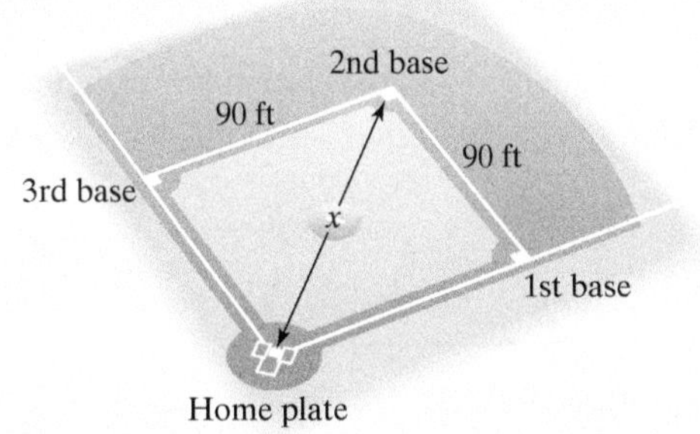

40. The base of a 20-foot ladder is 15 feet from the house. How far up the house does the ladder reach?

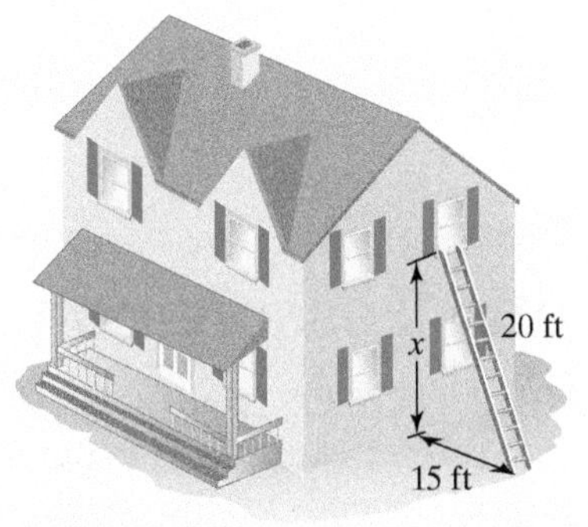

41. A flagpole has a height of 16 yards. It will be supported by three cables, each of which is attached to the flagpole at a point 4 yards below the top of the pole and attached to the ground at a point that is 9 yards from the base of the pole. Find the total number of yards of cable that will be required.

42. A flagpole has a height of 10 yards. It will be supported by three cables, each of which is attached to the flagpole at a point 4 yards below the top of the pole and attached to the ground at a point that is 8 yards from the base of the pole. Find the total number of yards of cable that will be required.

43. A rectangular garden bed measures 5 feet by 12 feet. A water faucet is located at one corner of the garden bed. A hose will be connected to the water faucet. The hose must be long enough to reach the opposite corner of the garden bed when stretched straight. Find the required length of hose.

44. A rocket ascends vertically after being launched from a location that is midway between two ground-based tracking stations. When the rocket reaches an altitude of 4 kilometers, it is 5 kilometers from each of the tracking stations. Assuming that this is a locale where the terrain is flat, how far apart are the two tracking stations?

45. If construction costs are $150,000 per *kilometer,* find the cost of building the new road in the figure shown.

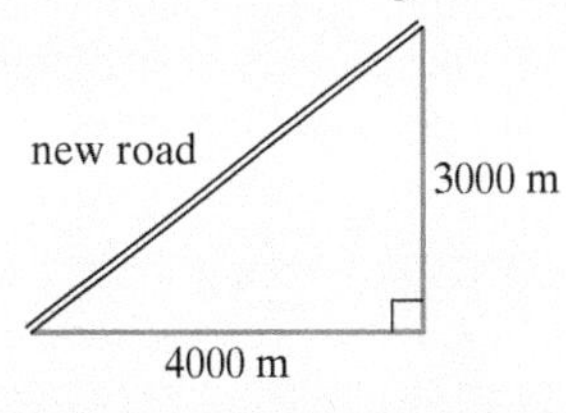

46. Picky, Picky, Picky This problem appeared on a high school exit exam:

Alex is building a ramp for a bike competition. He has two rectangular boards. One board is six meters and the other is five meters long. If the ramp has to form a right triangle, what should its height be?

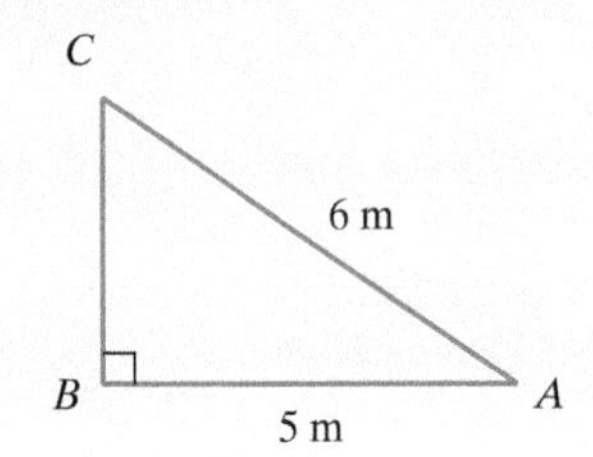

Students were asked to select the correct answer from the following options:

3 meters; 4 meters; 3.3 meters; 7.8 meters.

a. Among the available choices, which option best expresses the ramp's height? How many feet, to the nearest tenth of a foot, is this? Does a bike competition that requires riders to jump off these heights seem realistic? (ouch!)

b. Express the ramp's height to the nearest hundredth of a meter. By how many centimeters does this differ from the "correct" answer on the test? How many inches, to the nearest half inch, is this? Is it likely that a carpenter with a tape measure would make this error?

c. According to the problem, Alex has boards that measure 5 meters and 6 meters. A 6-meter board? How many feet, to the nearest tenth of a foot, is this? When was the last time you found a board of this length at Home Depot? (*Source: The New York Times,* April 24, 2005)

Writing in Mathematics

47. If the measures of two angles of a triangle are known, explain how to find the measure of the third angle.

48. Can a triangle contain two right angles? Explain your answer.

49. What general assumption did Euclid make about a point and a line in order to prove that the sum of the measures of the angles of a triangle is 180°?

50. What are similar triangles?

51. If the ratio of the corresponding sides of two similar triangles is 1 to $1\left(\frac{1}{1}\right)$, what must be true about the triangles?

52. What are corresponding angles in similar triangles?

53. Describe how to identify the corresponding sides in similar triangles.

54. In your own words, state the Pythagorean Theorem.

55. In the 1939 movie *The Wizard of Oz,* upon being presented with a Th.D. (Doctor of Thinkology), the Scarecrow proudly exclaims, "The sum of the square roots of any two sides of an isosceles triangle is equal to the square root of the remaining side." Did the Scarecrow get the Pythagorean Theorem right? In particular, describe four errors in the Scarecrow's statement.

Critical Thinking Exercises

Make Sense? *In Exercises 56–59, determine whether each statement makes sense or does not make sense, and explain your reasoning.*

56. I'm fencing off a triangular plot of land that has two right angles.

57. Triangle I is equilateral, as is triangle II, so the triangles are similar.

58. Triangle I is a right triangle, as is triangle II, so the triangles are similar.

59. If I am given the lengths of two sides of a triangle, I can use the Pythagorean Theorem to find the length of the third side.

60. Find the measure of angle R.

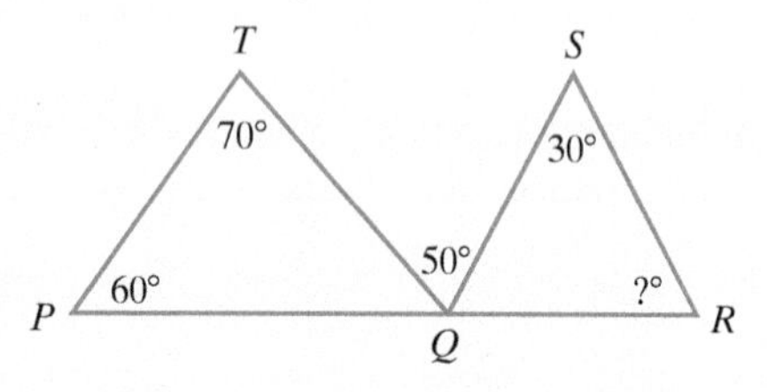

61. What is the length of $\overline{AB}$ in the accompanying figure?

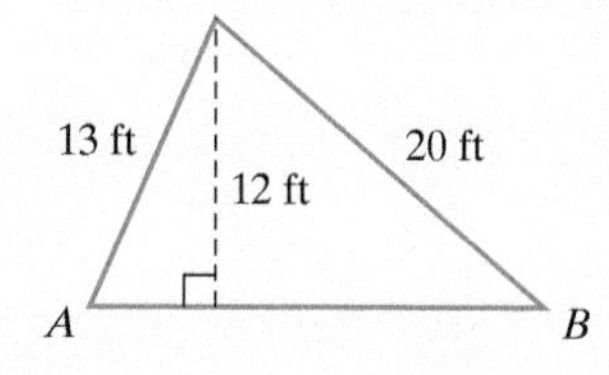

62. Use a quadratic equation to solve this problem. The width of a rectangular carpet is 7 meters shorter than the length, and the diagonal is 1 meter longer than the length. What are the carpet's dimensions?

WHAT AM I SUPPOSED TO LEARN?

After you have read this section, you should be able to:

1 Name certain polygons according to the number of sides.

2 Recognize the characteristics of certain quadrilaterals.

3 Solve problems involving a polygon's perimeter.

4 Find the sum of the measures of a polygon's angles.

5 Understand tessellations and their angle requirements.

Polygons, Perimeter, and Tessellations

YOU HAVE JUST PURCHASED A BEAUTIFUL PLOT OF LAND IN THE COUNTRY, shown in **Figure 4.28**. In order to have more privacy, you decide to put fencing along each of its four sides. The cost of this project depends on the distance around the four outside edges of the plot, called its **perimeter**, as well as the cost for each foot of fencing.

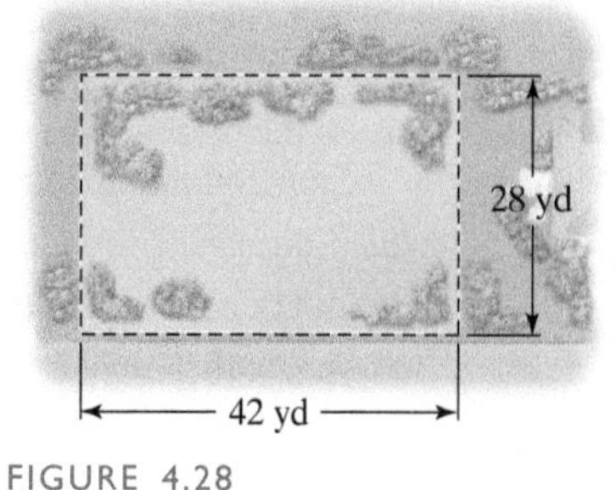

FIGURE 4.28

Your plot of land is a geometric figure: It has four straight sides that are line segments. The plot is on level ground, so that the four sides all lie on a flat surface, or plane. The plot is an example of a *polygon*. Any closed shape in the plane formed by three or more line segments that intersect only at their endpoints is a **polygon**.

1 Name certain polygons according to the number of sides.

A polygon is named according to the number of sides it has. We know that a three-sided polygon is called a **triangle**. A four-sided polygon is called a **quadrilateral**.

A polygon whose sides are all the same length and whose angles all have the same measure is called a **regular polygon**. **Table 4.2** provides the names of six polygons. Also shown are illustrations of regular polygons.

Table 4.2 Illustrations of Regular Polygons

Name	Picture	Name	Picture
Triangle 3 sides		Hexagon 6 sides	
Quadrilateral 4 sides		Heptagon 7 sides	
Pentagon 5 sides		Octagon 8 sides	

2 Recognize the characteristics of certain quadrilaterals.

Blitzer Bonus

Bees and Regular Hexagons

Bees use honeycombs to store honey and house larvae. They construct honey storage cells from wax. Each cell has the shape of a regular hexagon. The cells fit together perfectly, preventing dirt or predators from entering. Squares or equilateral triangles would fit equally well, but regular hexagons provide the largest storage space for the amount of wax used.

Quadrilaterals

The plot of land in **Figure 4.28** is a four-sided polygon, or a quadrilateral. However, when you first looked at the figure, perhaps you thought of the plot as a rectangular field. A **rectangle** is a special kind of quadrilateral in which both pairs of opposite sides are parallel, have the same measure, and whose angles are right angles. **Table 4.3** presents some special quadrilaterals and their characteristics.

TABLE 4.3 Types of Quadrilaterals

Name	Characteristics	Representation
Parallelogram	Quadrilateral in which both pairs of opposite sides are parallel and have the same measure. Opposite angles have the same measure.	
Rhombus	Parallelogram with all sides having equal length.	
Rectangle	Parallelogram with four right angles. Because a rectangle is a parallelogram, opposite sides are parallel and have the same measure.	
Square	A rectangle with all sides having equal length. Each angle measures 90°, and the square is a regular quadrilateral.	
Trapezoid	A quadrilateral with exactly one pair of parallel sides.	

3 Solve problems involving a polygon's perimeter.

Perimeter

The **perimeter**, P, of a polygon is the sum of the lengths of its sides. Perimeter is measured in linear units, such as inches, feet, yards, meters, or kilometers.

Example 1 involves the perimeter of a rectangle. Because perimeter is the sum of the lengths of the sides, the perimeter of the rectangle shown in **Figure 4.29** is $l + w + l + w$. This can be expressed as

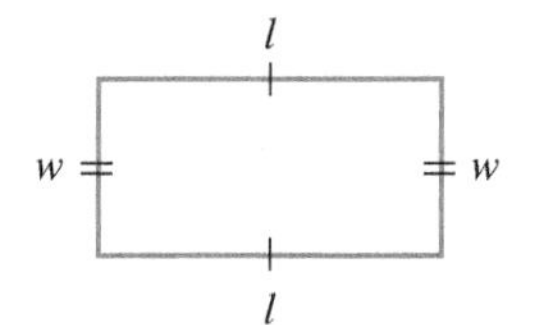

FIGURE 4.29
A rectangle with length l and width w

$$P = 2l + 2w.$$

EXAMPLE 1 *An Application of Perimeter*

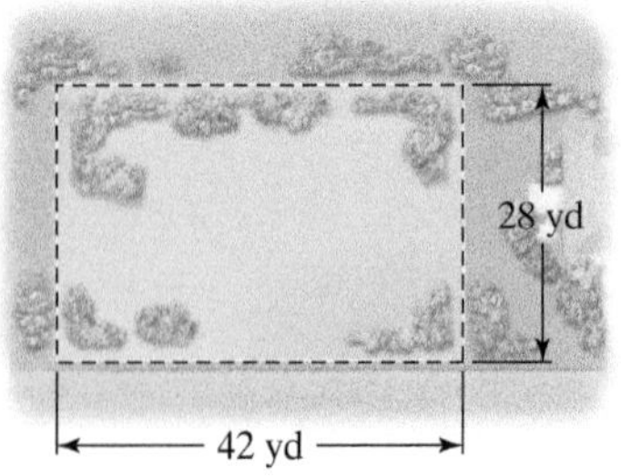

The rectangular field we discussed at the beginning of this section (see **Figure 4.28**) has a length of 42 yards and a width of 28 yards. If fencing costs \$5.25 per foot, find the cost to enclose the field with fencing.

FIGURE 4.28 **(repeated)**

SOLUTION

We begin by finding the perimeter of the rectangle in yards. Using 3 ft = 1 yd and dimensional analysis, we express the perimeter in feet. Finally, we multiply the perimeter, in feet, by \$5.25 because the fencing costs \$5.25 per foot.

The length, l, is 42 yards and the width, w, is 28 yards. The perimeter of the rectangle is determined using the formula $P = 2l + 2w$.

$$P = 2l + 2w = 2 \cdot 42 \text{ yd} + 2 \cdot 28 \text{ yd} = 84 \text{ yd} + 56 \text{ yd} = 140 \text{ yd}$$

Because 3 ft = 1 yd, we use the unit fraction $\frac{3 \text{ ft}}{1 \text{ yd}}$ to convert from yards to feet.

$$140 \text{ yd} = \frac{140 \cancel{\text{yd}}}{1} \cdot \frac{3 \text{ ft}}{1 \cancel{\text{yd}}} = 140 \cdot 3 \text{ ft} = 420 \text{ ft}$$

The perimeter of the rectangle is 420 feet. Now we are ready to find the cost of the fencing. We multiply 420 feet by \$5.25, the cost per foot.

$$\text{Cost} = \frac{420 \cancel{\text{feet}}}{1} \cdot \frac{\$5.25}{\cancel{\text{foot}}} = 420(\$5.25) = \$2205$$

The cost to enclose the field with fencing is \$2205.

CHECK POINT 1 A rectangular field has a length of 50 yards and a width of 30 yards. If fencing costs \$6.50 per foot, find the cost to enclose the field with fencing.

4 Find the sum of the measures of a polygon's angles.

The Sum of the Measures of a Polygon's Angles

We know that the sum of the measures of the three angles of any triangle is 180°. We can use inductive reasoning to find the sum of the measures of the angles of any polygon. Start by drawing line segments from a single point where two sides meet so that nonoverlapping triangles are formed. This is done in **Figure 4.30**.

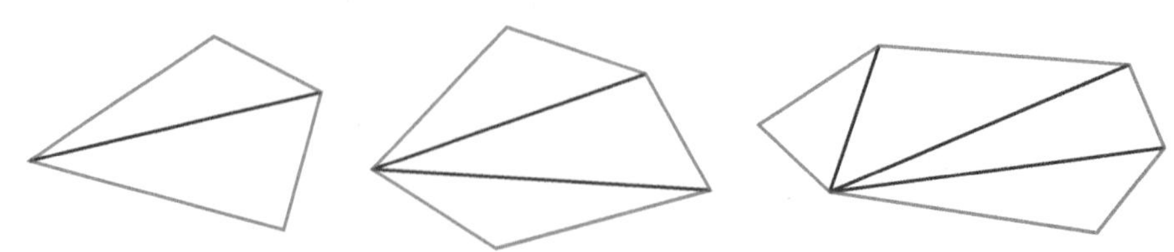

4 sides	5 sides	6 sides
2 triangles	3 triangles	4 triangles
Angle sum: 2(180°) = 360°	Angle sum: 3(180°) = 540°	Angle sum: 4(180°) = 720°

FIGURE 4.30

In each case, the number of triangles is two less than the number of sides of the polygon. Thus, for an n-sided polygon, there are $n - 2$ triangles. Because each triangle has an angle-measure sum of 180°, the sum of the measures for the angles in the $n - 2$ triangles is $(n - 2)180°$. Thus, the sum of the measures of the angles of an n-sided polygon is $(n - 2)180°$.

THE ANGLES OF A POLYGON

The sum of the measures of the angles of a polygon with n sides is

$$(n - 2)180°.$$

EXAMPLE 2 *Using the Formula for the Angles of a Polygon*

a. Find the sum of the measures of the angles of an octagon.

b. **Figure 4.31** shows a regular octagon. Find the measure of angle A.

c. Find the measure of exterior angle B.

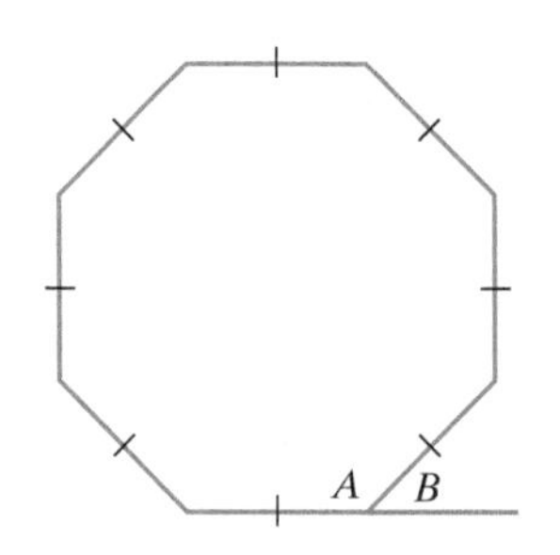

FIGURE 4.31 A regular octagon

SOLUTION

a. An octagon has eight sides. Using the formula $(n - 2)180°$ with $n = 8$, we can find the sum of the measures of its eight angles.
The sum of the measures of an octagon's angles is

$$\begin{aligned} &(n - 2)180° \\ &= (8 - 2)180° \\ &= 6 \cdot 180° \\ &= 1080°. \end{aligned}$$

b. Examine the regular octagon in **Figure 4.31**. Note that all eight sides have the same length. Likewise, all eight angles have the same degree measure. Angle A is one of these eight angles. We find its measure by taking the sum of the measures of all eight angles, 1080°, and dividing by 8.

$$m\measuredangle A = \frac{1080°}{8} = 135°$$

c. Because $\measuredangle B$ is the supplement of $\measuredangle A$,

$$m\measuredangle B = 180° - 135° = 45°.$$

CHECK POINT 2

a. Find the sum of the measures of the angles of a 12-sided polygon.

b. Find the measure of an angle of a regular 12-sided polygon.

5 Understand tessellations and their angle requirements.

Tessellations

A relationship between geometry and the visual arts is found in an art form called *tessellations*. A **tessellation**, or **tiling**, is a pattern consisting of the repeated use of the same geometric figures to completely cover a plane, leaving no gaps and no overlaps. **Figure 4.32** on the next page shows eight tessellations, each consisting of the repeated use of two or more regular polygons.

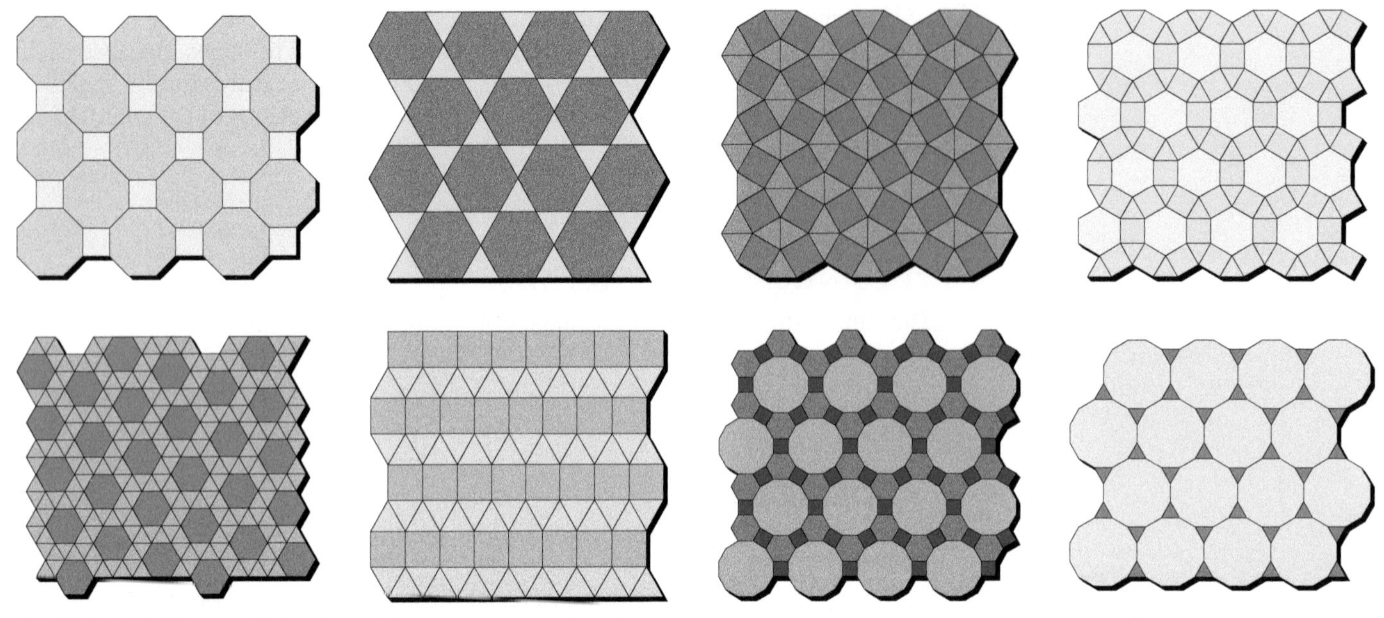

FIGURE 4.32 Eight tessellations formed by two or more regular polygons

In each tessellation in **Figure 4.32**, the same types of regular polygons surround every vertex (intersection point). Furthermore, **the sum of the measures of the angles that come together at each vertex is 360°, a requirement for the formation of a tessellation**. This is illustrated in the enlarged version of the tessellation in **Figure 4.33**. If you select any vertex and count the sides of the polygons that touch it, you'll see that vertices are surrounded by two regular octagons and a square. Can you see why the sum of the angle measures at every vertex is 360°?

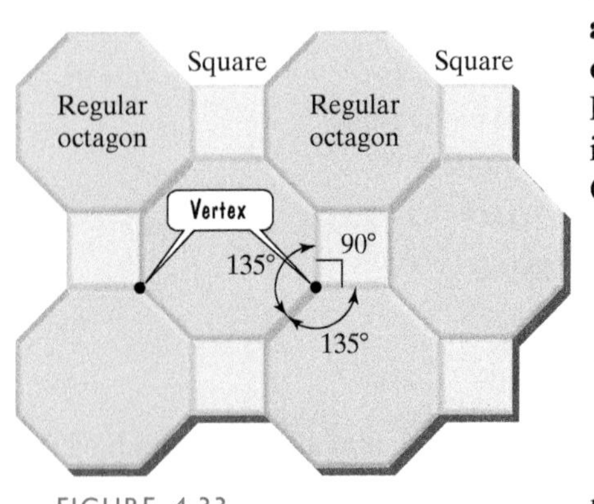

FIGURE 4.33

$$135° + 135° + 90° = 360°$$

In Example 2, we found that each angle of a regular octagon measures 135°.

Each angle of a square measures 90°.

The most restrictive condition in creating tessellations is that just *one type of regular polygon* may be used. With this restriction, there are only three possible tessellations, made from equilateral triangles or squares or regular hexagons, as shown in **Figure 4.34**.

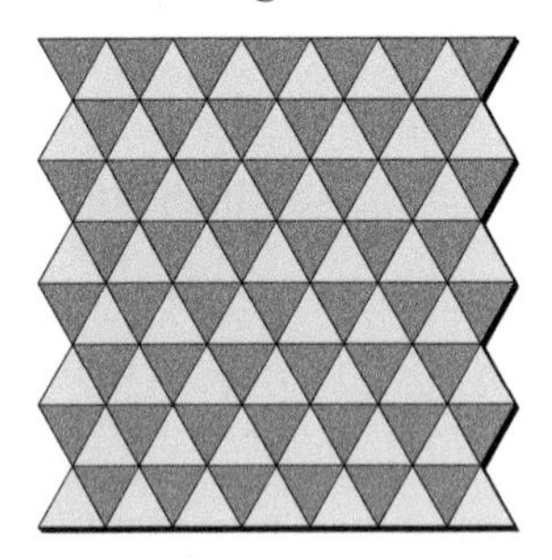

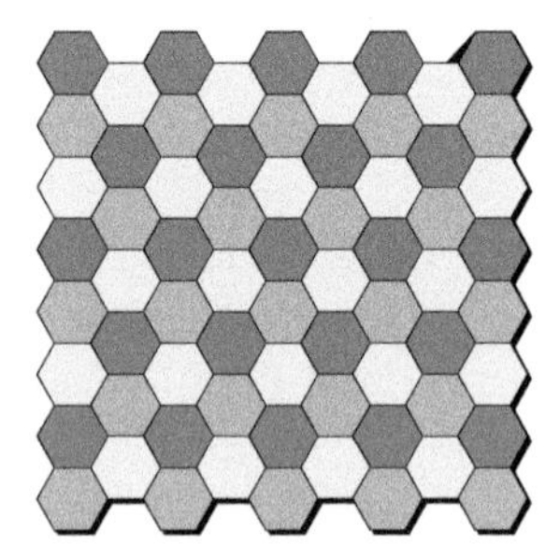

FIGURE 4.34 The three tessellations formed using one regular polygon

Each tessellation is possible because the angle sum at every vertex is 360°:

Six equilateral triangles at each vertex

$$60° + 60° + 60° + 60° + 60° + 60° = 360°$$

Four squares at each vertex

$$90° + 90° + 90° + 90° = 360°$$

Three regular hexagons at each vertex

$$120° + 120° + 120° = 360°.$$

Each angle measures $\frac{(n-2)180°}{n} = \frac{(6-2)180°}{6} = 120°$.

EXAMPLE 3 Angle Requirements of Tessellations

Explain why a tessellation cannot be created using only regular pentagons.

SOLUTION

Let's begin by applying $(n - 2)180°$ to find the measure of each angle of a regular pentagon. Each angle measures

$$\frac{(5-2)180°}{5} = \frac{3(180°)}{5} = 108°.$$

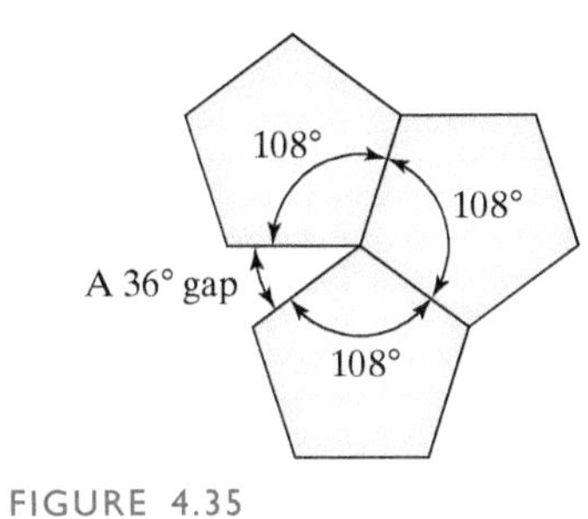

FIGURE 4.35

A requirement for the formation of a tessellation is that the measures of the angles that come together at each vertex is 360°. With each angle of a regular pentagon measuring 108°, **Figure 4.35** shows that three regular pentagons fill in $3 \cdot 108° = 324°$ and leave a $360° - 324°$, or a 36°, gap. Because the 360° angle requirement cannot be met, no tessellation by regular pentagons is possible.

"The regular division of the plane into congruent figures evoking an association in the observer with a familiar natural object is one of these hobbies or problems . . . I have embarked on this geometric problem again and again over the years, trying to throw light on different aspects each time. I cannot imagine what my life would be like if this problem had never occurred to me; one might say that I am head over heels in love with it, and I still don't know why."

—M. C. ESCHER

CHECK POINT 3 Explain why a tessellation cannot be created using only regular octagons.

Tessellations that are not restricted to the repeated use of regular polygons are endless in number. They are prominent in Islamic art, Italian mosaics, quilts, and ceramics. The Dutch artist M. C. Escher (1898–1972) created a dazzling array of prints, drawings, and paintings using tessellations composed of stylized interlocking animals. Escher's art reflects the mathematics that underlies all things, while creating surreal manipulations of space and perspective that make gentle fun of consensus reality.

Symmetry Drawing E85 (1952), M.C. Escher.

Concept and Vocabulary Check

Fill in each blank so that the resulting statement is true.

1. The distance around the sides of a polygon is called its ___________.
2. A four-sided polygon is a/an ___________, a five-sided polygon is a/an ___________, a six-sided polygon is a/an ___________, a seven-sided polygon is a/an ___________, and an eight-sided polygon is a/an ___________.
3. A polygon whose sides are all the same length and whose angles all have the same measure is called a/an ___________ polygon.
4. Opposite sides of a parallelogram are ___________ and ___________.
5. A parallelogram with all sides of equal length without any right angles is called a/an ___________.
6. A parallelogram with four right angles without all sides of equal length is called a/an ___________.
7. A parallelogram with four right angles and all sides of equal length is called a/an ___________.
8. A four-sided figure with exactly one pair of parallel sides is called a/an ___________.
9. The perimeter, P, of a rectangle with length l and width w is given by the formula ___________.
10. The sum of the measures of the angles of a polygon with n sides is ___________.
11. A pattern consisting of the repeated use of the same geometric figures to completely cover a plane, leaving no gaps and no overlaps, is called a/an ___________.

In Exercises 12–18, determine whether each statement is true or false. If the statement is false, make the necessary change(s) to produce a true statement.

12. Every parallelogram is a rhombus. ______
13. Every rhombus is a parallelogram. ______
14. All squares are rectangles. ______
15. Some rectangles are not squares. ______
16. No triangles are polygons. ______
17. Every rhombus is a regular polygon. ______
18. A requirement for the formation of a tessellation is that the sum of the measures of the angles that come together at each vertex is 360°. ______

Exercise Set 4.3

Practice Exercises

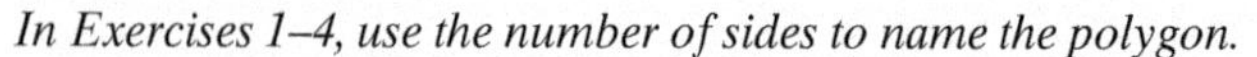

In Exercises 1–4, use the number of sides to name the polygon.

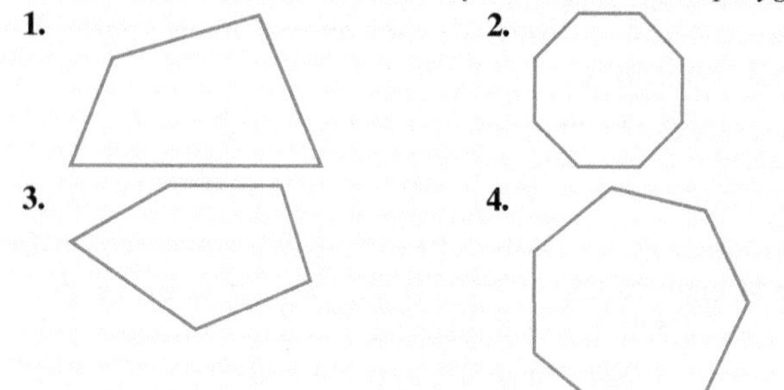

Use these quadrilaterals to solve Exercises 5–10.

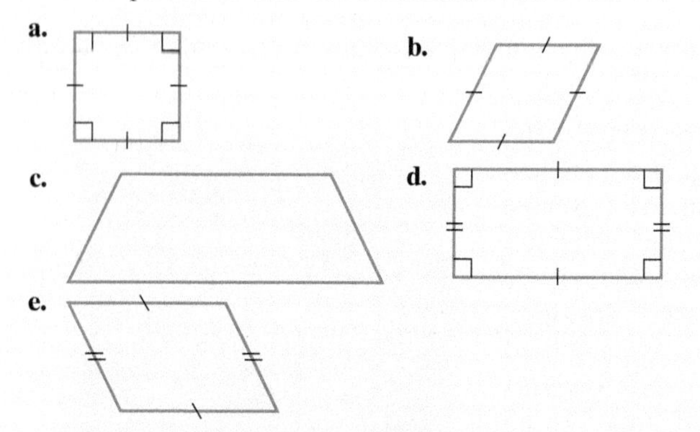

5. Which of these quadrilaterals have opposite sides that are parallel? Name these quadrilaterals.
6. Which of these quadrilaterals have sides of equal length that meet at a vertex? Name these quadrilaterals.
7. Which of these quadrilaterals have right angles? Name these quadrilaterals.
8. Which of these quadrilaterals do not have four sides of equal length? Name these quadrilaterals.
9. Which of these quadrilaterals is not a parallelogram? Name this quadrilateral.
10. Which of these quadrilaterals is/are a regular polygon? Name this/these quadrilateral(s).

In Exercises 11–20, find the perimeter of the figure named and shown. Express the perimeter using the same unit of measure that appears on the given side or sides.

11. Rectangle

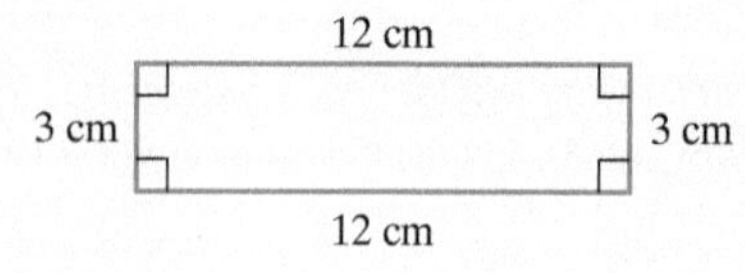

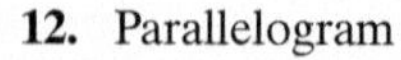

12. Parallelogram

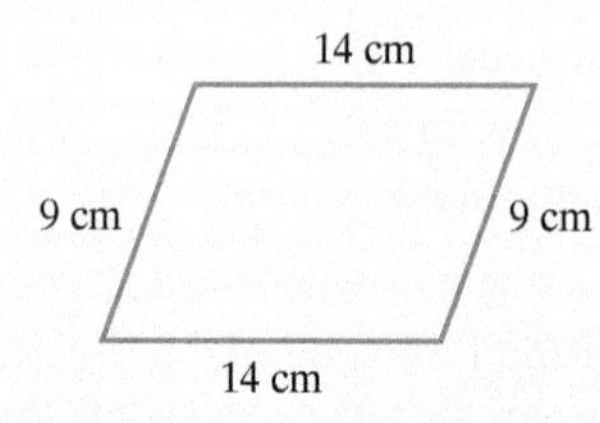

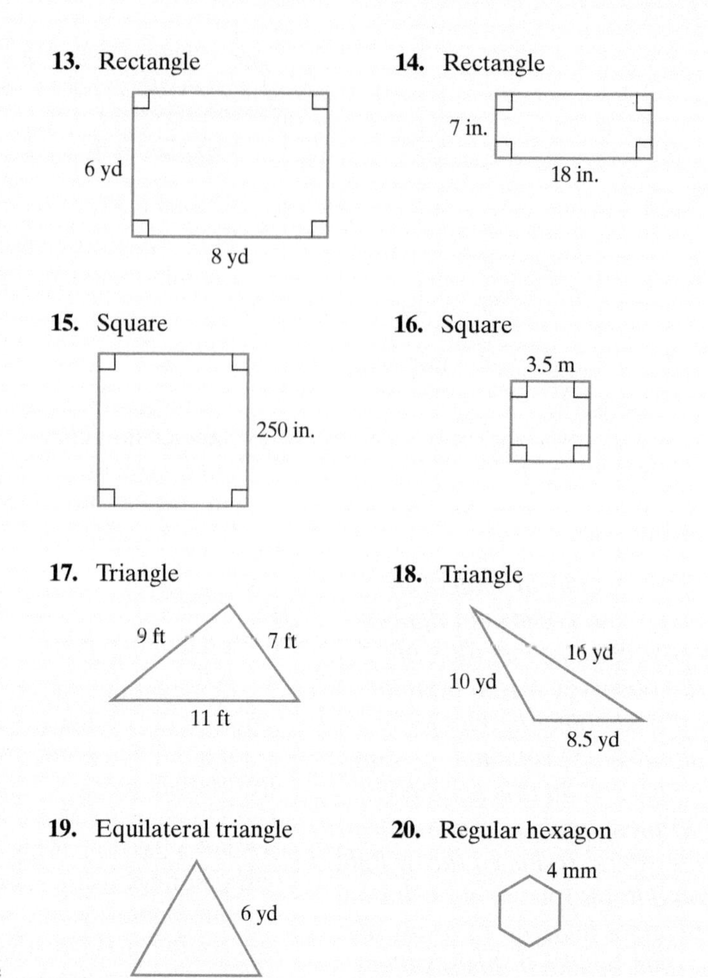

In Exercises 21–24, find the perimeter of the figure shown. Express the perimeter using the same unit of measure that appears on the given side or sides.

21.

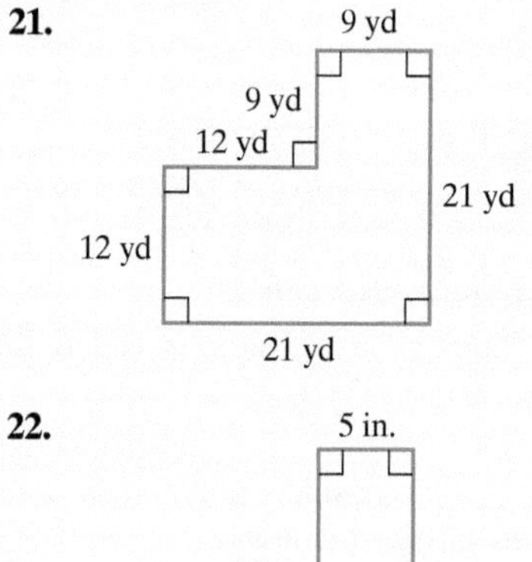

22.

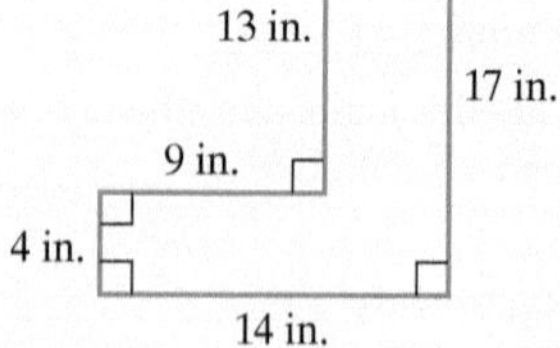

23.

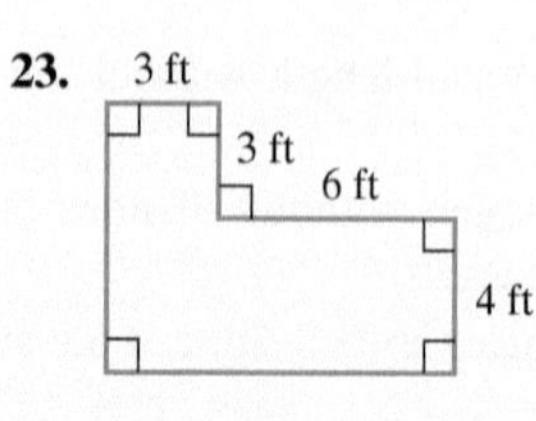

24.

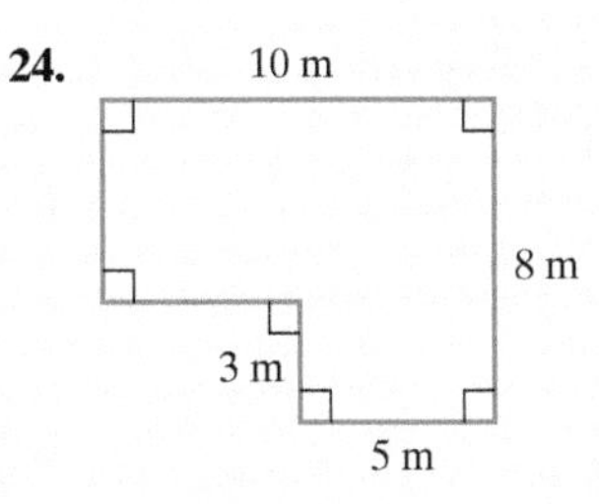

25. Find the sum of the measures of the angles of a five-sided polygon.

26. Find the sum of the measures of the angles of a six-sided polygon.

27. Find the sum of the measures of the angles of a quadrilateral.

28. Find the sum of the measures of the angles of a heptagon.

In Exercises 29–30, each figure shows a regular polygon. Find the measures of angle A and angle B.

29. 30.

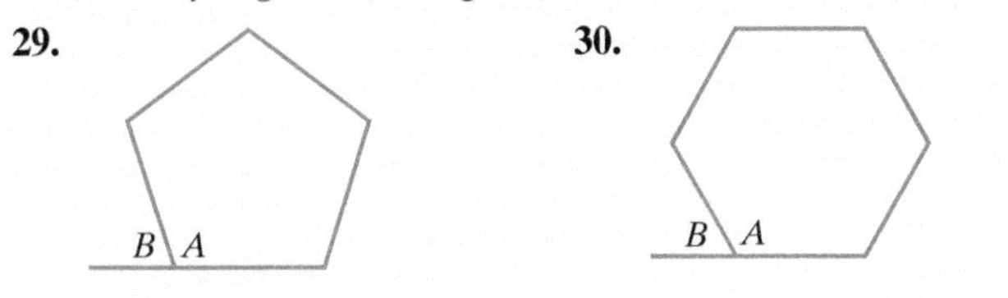

In Exercises 31–32, **a.** *Find the sum of the measures of the angles for the figure given;* **b.** *Find the measures of angle A and angle B.*

31. 32.

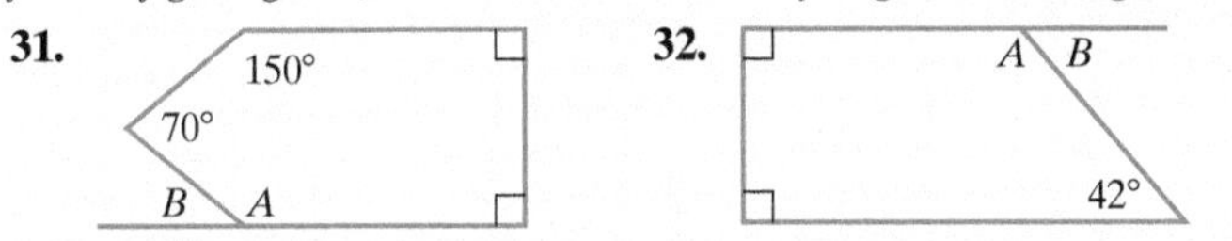

In Exercises 33–36, tessellations formed by two or more regular polygons are shown.

a. *Name the types of regular polygons that surround each vertex.*

b. *Determine the number of angles that come together at each vertex, as well as the measures of these angles.*

c. *Use the angle measures from part (b) to explain why the tessellation is possible.*

33.

34.

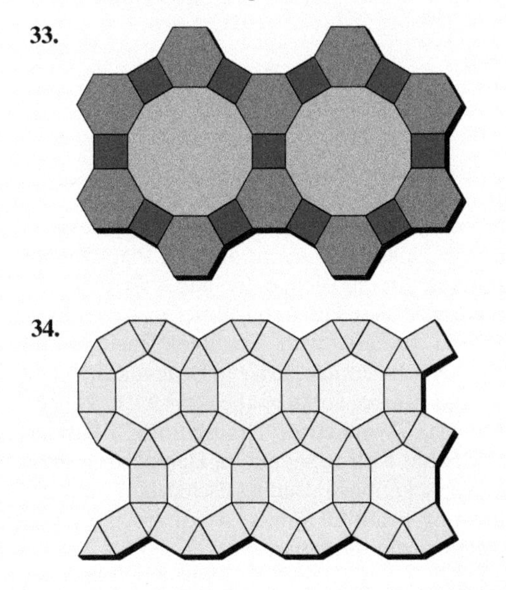

35.

36.

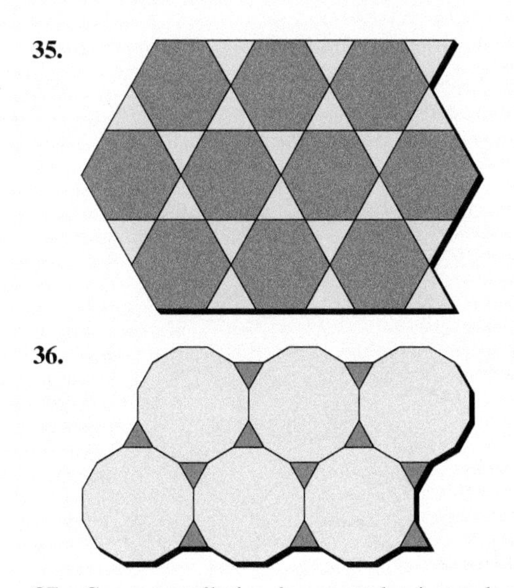

37. Can a tessellation be created using only regular nine-sided polygons? Explain your answer.

38. Can a tessellation be created using only regular ten-sided polygons? Explain your answer.

Practice Plus

In Exercises 39–42, use an algebraic equation to determine each rectangle's dimensions.

39. A rectangular field is four times as long as it is wide. If the perimeter of the field is 500 yards, what are the field's dimensions?

40. A rectangular field is five times as long as it is wide. If the perimeter of the field is 288 yards, what are the field's dimensions?

41. An American football field is a rectangle with a perimeter of 1040 feet. The length is 200 feet more than the width. Find the width and length of the rectangular field.

42. A basketball court is a rectangle with a perimeter of 86 meters. The length is 13 meters more than the width. Find the width and length of the basketball court.

In Exercises 43–44, use algebraic equations to find the measure of each angle that is represented in terms of x.

43.

44.

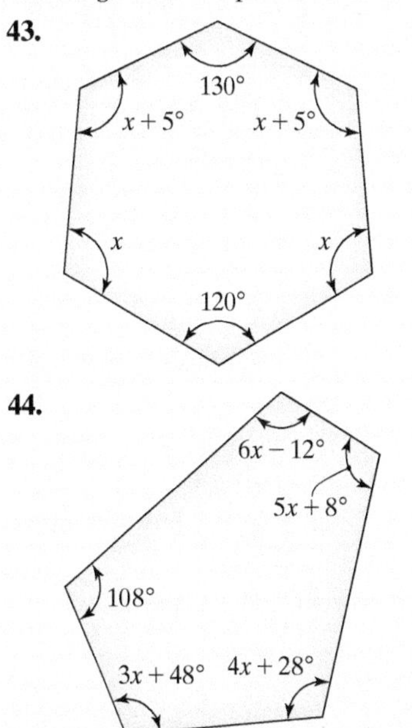

In the figure shown, the artist has cunningly distorted the "regular" polygons to create a fraudulent tessellation with discrepancies that are too subtle for the eye to notice. In Exercises 45–46, you will use mathematics, not your eyes, to observe the irregularities.

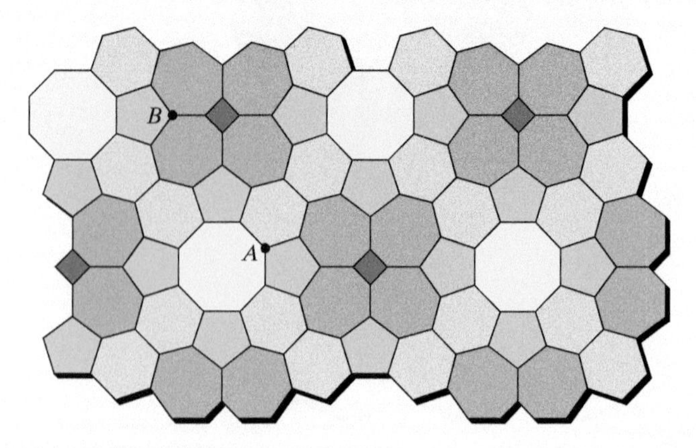

45. Find the sum of the angle measures at vertex A. Then explain why the tessellation is a fake.

46. Find the sum of the angle measures at vertex B. Then explain why the tessellation is a fake.

Application Exercises

47. A school playground is in the shape of a rectangle 400 feet long and 200 feet wide. If fencing costs \$14 per yard, what will it cost to place fencing around the playground?

48. A rectangular field is 70 feet long and 30 feet wide. If fencing costs \$8 per yard, how much will it cost to enclose the field?

49. One side of a square flower bed is 8 feet long. How many plants are needed if they are to be spaced 8 inches apart around the outside of the bed?

50. What will it cost to place baseboard around the region shown if the baseboard costs \$0.25 per foot? No baseboard is needed for the 2-foot doorway.

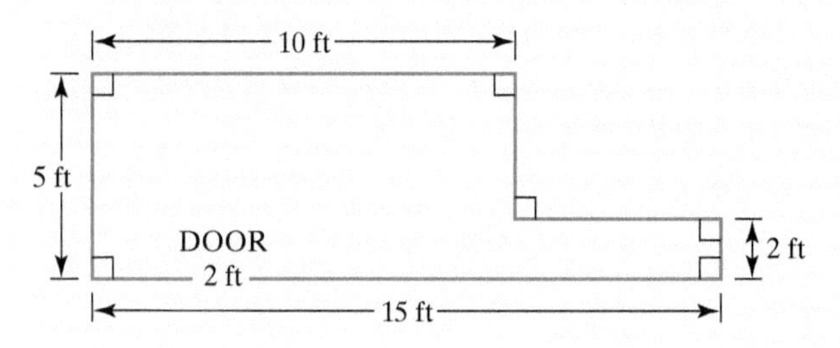

Writing in Mathematics

51. What is a polygon?

52. Explain why rectangles and rhombuses are also parallelograms.

53. Explain why every square is a rectangle, a rhombus, a parallelogram, a quadrilateral, and a polygon.

54. Explain why a square is a regular polygon, but a rhombus is not.

55. Using words only, describe how to find the perimeter of a rectangle.

56. Describe a practical situation in which you needed to apply the concept of a geometric figure's perimeter.

57. Describe how to find the measure of an angle of a regular pentagon.

Critical Thinking Exercises

Make Sense? *In Exercises 58–61, determine whether each statement makes sense or does not make sense, and explain your reasoning.*

58. I drew a polygon having two sides that intersect at their midpoints.

59. I find it helpful to think of a polygon's perimeter as the length of its boundary.

60. If a polygon is not regular, I can determine the sum of the measures of its angles, but not the measure of any one of its angles.

61. I used floor tiles in the shape of regular pentagons to completely cover my kitchen floor.

In Exercises 62–63, write an algebraic expression that represents the perimeter of the figure shown.

62.

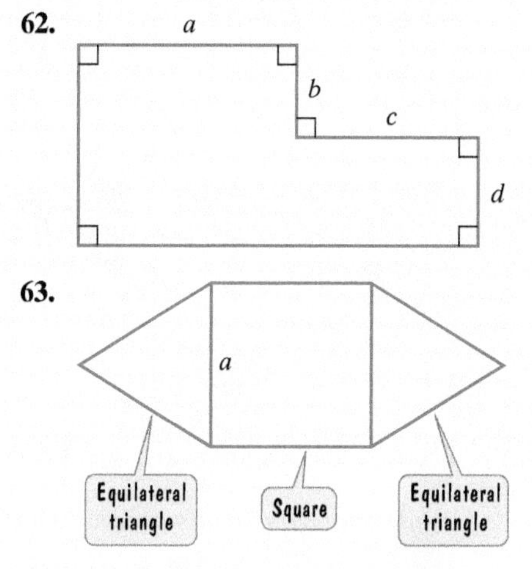

63.

64. Find $m\measuredangle 1$ in the figure shown.

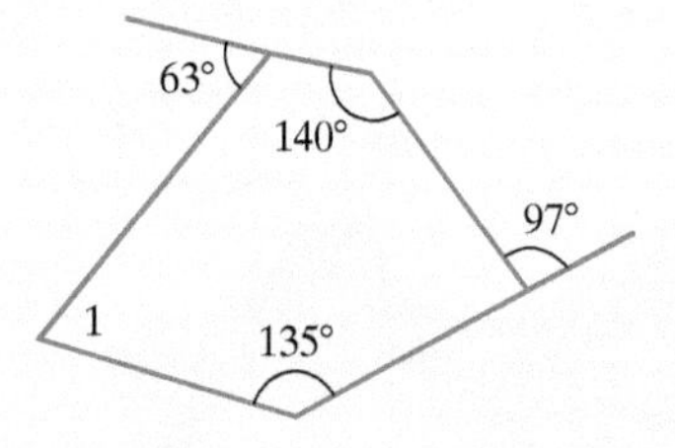

Group Exercise

65. Group members should consult sites on the Internet devoted to tessellations, or tilings, and present a report that expands upon the information in this section. Include a discussion of cultures that have used tessellations on fabrics, wall coverings, baskets, rugs, and pottery, with examples. Include the Alhambra, a fourteenth-century palace in Granada, Spain, in the presentation, as well as works by the artist M. C. Escher. Discuss the various symmetries (translations, rotations, reflections) associated with tessellations. Demonstrate how to create unique tessellations, including Escher-type patterns. Other than creating beautiful works of art, are there any practical applications of tessellations?

4.4

WHAT AM I SUPPOSED TO LEARN?

After you have read this section, you should be able to:

1. Use area formulas to compute the areas of plane regions and solve applied problems.
2. Use formulas for a circle's circumference and area.

Area and Circumference

The size of a house is described in square feet. But how do you know from the real estate ad whether the 1200-square-foot home with the backyard pool is large enough to warrant a visit? Faced with hundreds of ads, you need some way to sort out the best bets. What does 1200 square feet mean and how is this area determined? In this section, we discuss how to compute the areas of plane regions.

1 Use area formulas to compute the areas of plane regions and solve applied problems.

Formulas for Area

In Section 9.2, we saw that the area of a two-dimensional figure is the number of square units, such as square inches or square miles, it takes to fill the interior of the figure. For example, **Figure 4.36** shows that there are 12 square units contained within the rectangular region. The area of the region is 12 square units. Notice that the area can be determined in the following manner:

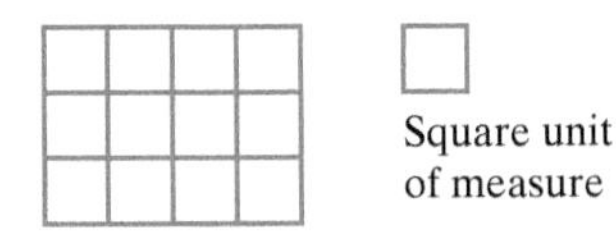

FIGURE 4.36 The area of the region on the left is 12 square units.

Distance across — Distance down

$$4 \text{ units} \times 3 \text{ units} = 4 \times 3 \times \text{units} \times \text{units}$$
$$= 12 \text{ square units.}$$

The area of a rectangular region, usually referred to as the area of a rectangle, is the product of the distance across (length) and the distance down (width).

AREA OF A RECTANGLE AND A SQUARE

The area, A, of a rectangle with length l and width w is given by the formula

$$A = lw.$$

The area, A, of a square with one side measuring s linear units is given by the formula

$$A = s^2.$$

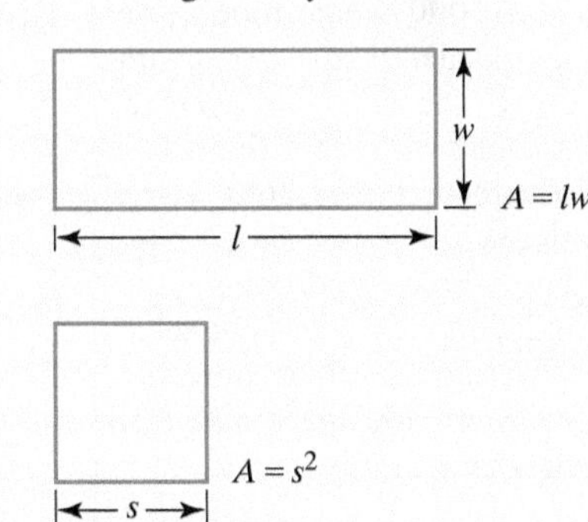

EXAMPLE 1 *Solving an Area Problem*

You decide to cover the path shown in **Figure 4.37** with bricks.

a. Find the area of the path.

b. If the path requires four bricks for every square foot, how many bricks are needed for the project?

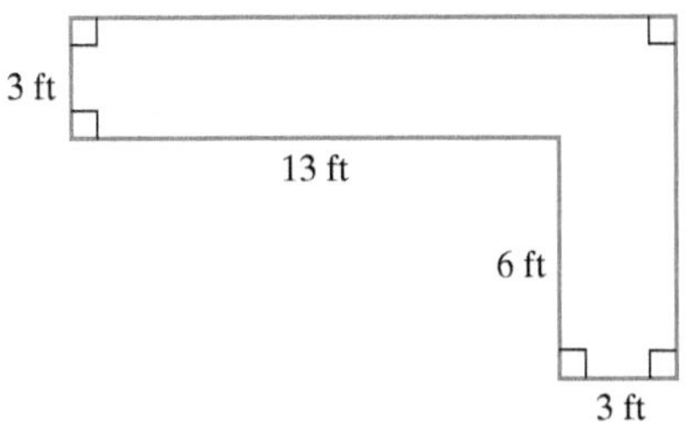

FIGURE 4.37

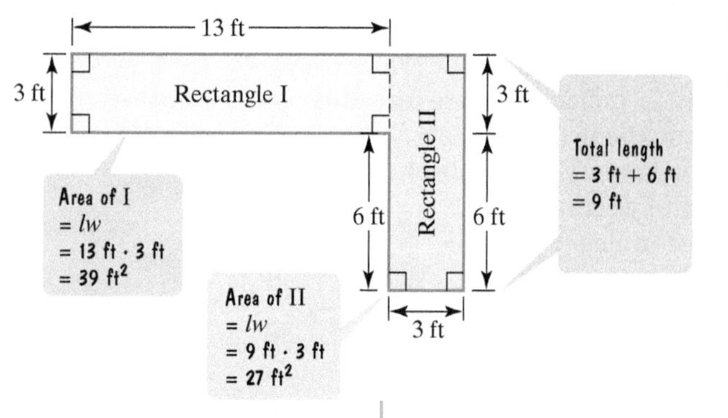

SOLUTION

a. Because we have a formula for the area of a rectangle, we begin by drawing a dashed line that divides the path into two rectangles. One way of doing this is shown at the left. We then use the length and width of each rectangle to find its area. The computations for area are shown in the green and blue voice balloons.

The area of the path is found by adding the areas of the two rectangles.

$$\text{Area of path} = 39 \text{ ft}^2 + 27 \text{ ft}^2 = 66 \text{ ft}^2$$

b. The path requires 4 bricks per square foot. The number of bricks needed for the project is the number of square feet in the path, its area, times 4.

$$\text{Number of bricks needed} = 66 \cancel{\text{ft}^2} \cdot \frac{4 \text{ bricks}}{\cancel{\text{ft}^2}} = 66 \cdot 4 \text{ bricks} = 264 \text{ bricks}$$

Thus, 264 bricks are needed for the project.

CHECK POINT 1 Find the area of the path described in Example 1, rendered on the right as a green region, by first measuring off a large rectangle as shown. The area of the path is the area of the large rectangle (the blue and green regions combined) minus the area of the blue rectangle. Do you get the same answer as we did in Example 1(a)?

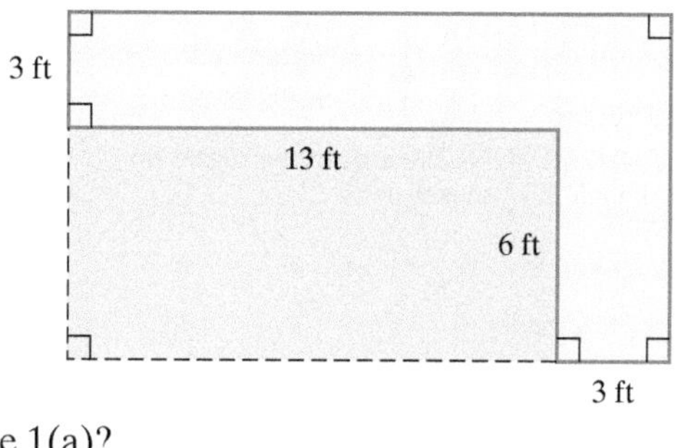

Blitzer Bonus

Appraising a House

A house is measured by an appraiser hired by a bank to help establish its value. The appraiser works from the outside, measuring off a rectangle. Then the appraiser adds the living spaces that lie outside the rectangle and subtracts the empty areas inside the rectangle. The final figure, in square feet, includes all the finished floor space in the house. Not included are the garage, outside porches, decks, or an unfinished basement.

A 1000-square-foot house is considered small, one with 2000 square feet average, and one with more than 2500 square feet pleasantly large. If a 1200–square-foot house has three bedrooms, the individual rooms might seem snug and cozy. With only one bedroom, the space may feel palatial!

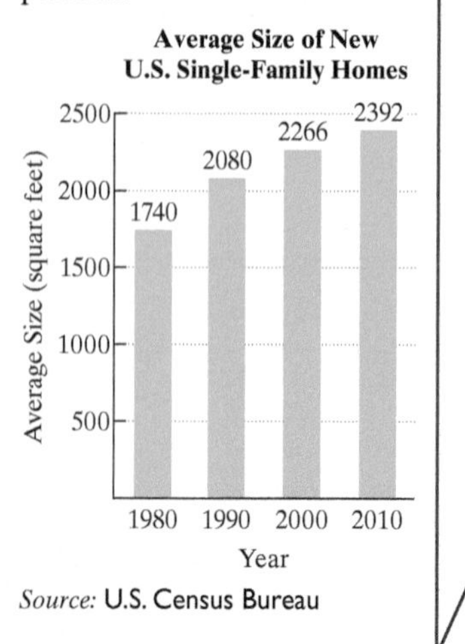

Source: U.S. Census Bureau

In Section 9.2, we saw that although there are 3 linear feet in a linear yard, there are 9 square feet in a square yard. If a problem requires measurement of area in square yards and the linear measures are given in feet, to avoid errors, first convert feet to yards. Then apply the area formula. This idea is illustrated in Example 2.

EXAMPLE 2 *Solving an Area Problem*

What will it cost to carpet a rectangular floor measuring 12 feet by 15 feet if the carpet costs $18.50 per square yard?

SOLUTION

We begin by converting the linear measures from feet to yards.

$$12 \text{ ft} = \frac{12 \cancel{\text{ft}}}{1} \cdot \frac{1 \text{ yd}}{3 \cancel{\text{ft}}} = \frac{12}{3} \text{ yd} = 4 \text{ yd}$$

$$15 \text{ ft} = \frac{15 \cancel{\text{ft}}}{1} \cdot \frac{1 \text{ yd}}{3 \cancel{\text{ft}}} = \frac{15}{3} \text{ yd} = 5 \text{ yd}$$

Next, we find the area of the rectangular floor in square yards.

$$A = lw = 5 \text{ yd} \cdot 4 \text{ yd} = 20 \text{ yd}^2$$

Finally, we find the cost of the carpet by multiplying the cost per square yard, \$18.50, by the number of square yards in the floor, 20.

$$\text{Cost of carpet} = \frac{\$18.50}{\cancel{yd^2}} \cdot \frac{20\ \cancel{yd^2}}{1} = \$18.50(20) = \$370$$

It will cost \$370 to carpet the floor.

CHECK POINT 2 What will it cost to carpet a rectangular floor measuring 18 feet by 21 feet if the carpet costs \$16 per square yard?

We can use the formula for the area of a rectangle to develop formulas for areas of other polygons. We begin with a parallelogram, a quadrilateral with opposite sides equal and parallel. The **height** of a parallelogram is the perpendicular distance between two of the parallel sides. Height is denoted by h in **Figure 4.38**. The **base**, denoted by b, is the length of either of these parallel sides.

FIGURE 4.38

FIGURE 4.39

In **Figure 4.39**, the orange triangular region has been cut off from the right of the parallelogram and attached to the left. The resulting figure is a rectangle with length b and width h. Because bh is the area of the rectangle, it also represents the area of the parallelogram.

AREA OF A PARALLELOGRAM

The area, A, of a parallelogram with height h and base b is given by the formula

$$A = bh.$$

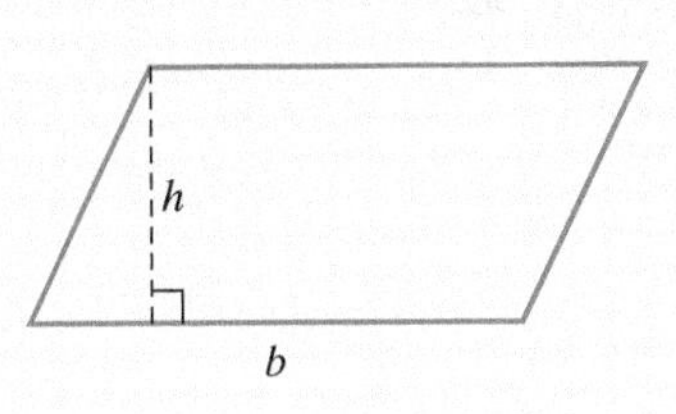

GREAT QUESTION!

Is the height of a parallelogram the length of one of its sides?

No. The height of a parallelogram is the perpendicular distance between two of the parallel sides. It is *not* the length of a side.

EXAMPLE 3 *Using the Formula for a Parallelogram's Area*

Find the area of the parallelogram in **Figure 4.40**.

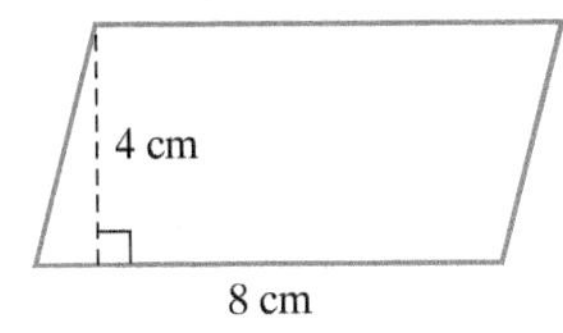

FIGURE 4.40

SOLUTION

As shown in the figure, the base is 8 centimeters and the height is 4 centimeters. Thus, $b = 8$ and $h = 4$.

$$A = bh$$

$$A = 8\text{ cm} \cdot 4\text{ cm} = 32\text{ cm}^2$$

The area is 32 square centimeters.

CHECK POINT 3 Find the area of a parallelogram with a base of 10 inches and a height of 6 inches.

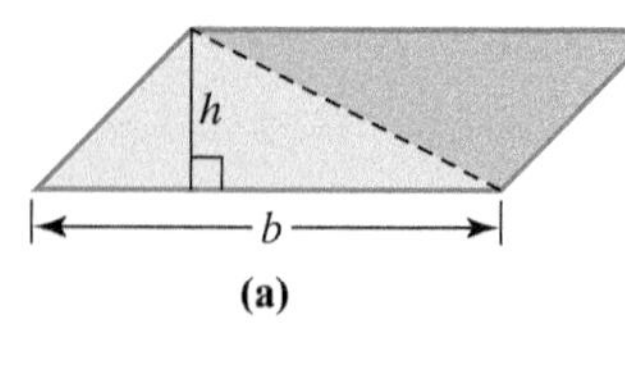

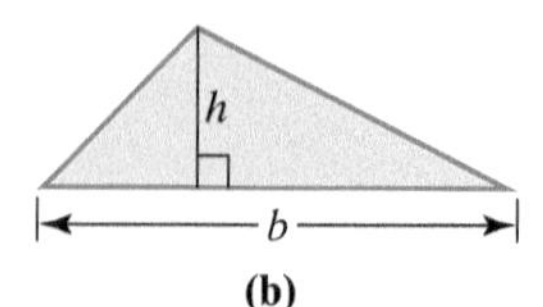

FIGURE 4.41

Figure 4.41 demonstrates how we can use the formula for the area of a parallelogram to obtain a formula for the area of a triangle. The area of the parallelogram in **Figure 4.41(a)** is given by $A = bh$. The diagonal shown in the parallelogram divides it into two triangles with the same size and shape. This means that the area of each triangle is one-half that of the parallelogram. Thus, the area of the triangle in **Figure 4.41(b)** is given by $A = \frac{1}{2}bh$.

AREA OF A TRIANGLE

The area, A, of a triangle with height h and base b is given by the formula

$$A = \frac{1}{2}bh.$$

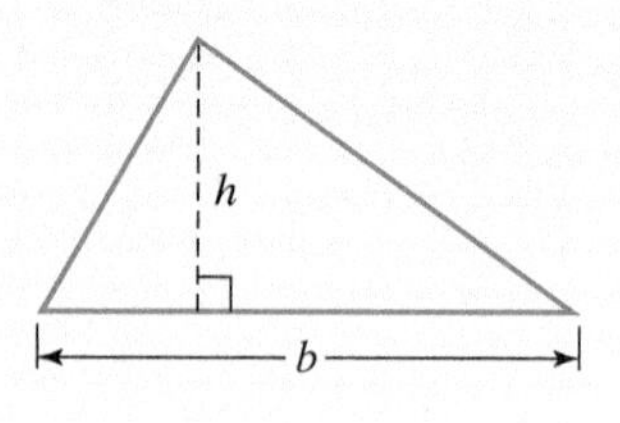

EXAMPLE 4 *Using the Formula for a Triangle's Area*

Find the area of each triangle in **Figure 4.42**.

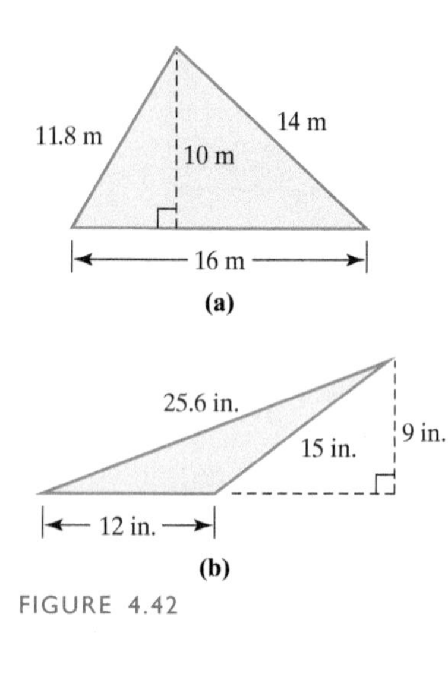

FIGURE 4.42

SOLUTION

a. In **Figure 4.42(a)**, the base is 16 meters and the height is 10 meters, so $b = 16$ and $h = 10$. We do not need the 11.8 meters or the 14 meters to find the area. The area of the triangle is

$$A = \frac{1}{2}bh = \frac{1}{2} \cdot 16 \text{ m} \cdot 10 \text{ m} = 80 \text{ m}^2.$$

The area is 80 square meters.

b. In **Figure 4.42(b)**, the base is 12 inches. The base line needs to be extended to draw the height. However, we still use 12 inches for b in the area formula. The height, h, is given to be 9 inches. The area of the triangle is

$$A = \frac{1}{2}bh = \frac{1}{2} \cdot 12 \text{ in.} \cdot 9 \text{ in.} = 54 \text{ in.}^2.$$

The area of the triangle is 54 square inches.

CHECK POINT 4 A sailboat has a triangular sail with a base of 12 feet and a height of 5 feet. Find the area of the sail.

The formula for the area of a triangle can be used to obtain a formula for the area of a trapezoid. Consider the trapezoid shown in **Figure 4.43**. The lengths of the two parallel sides, called the **bases**, are represented by a (the lower base) and b (the upper base). The trapezoid's height, denoted by h, is the perpendicular distance between the two parallel sides.

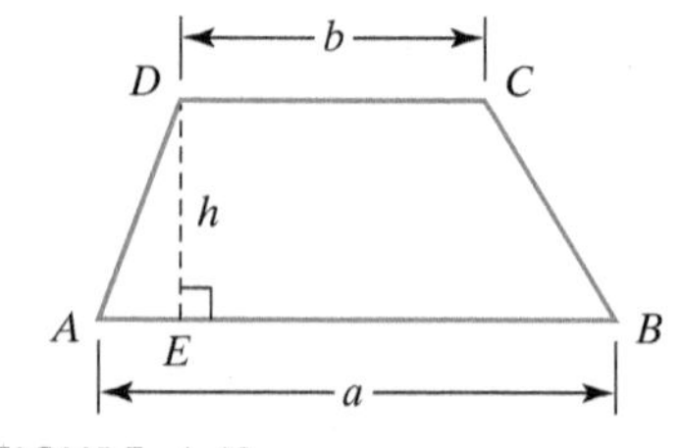

FIGURE 4.43

In **Figure 4.44**, we have drawn line segment BD, dividing the trapezoid into two triangles, shown in yellow and orange. The area of the trapezoid is the sum of the areas of these triangles.

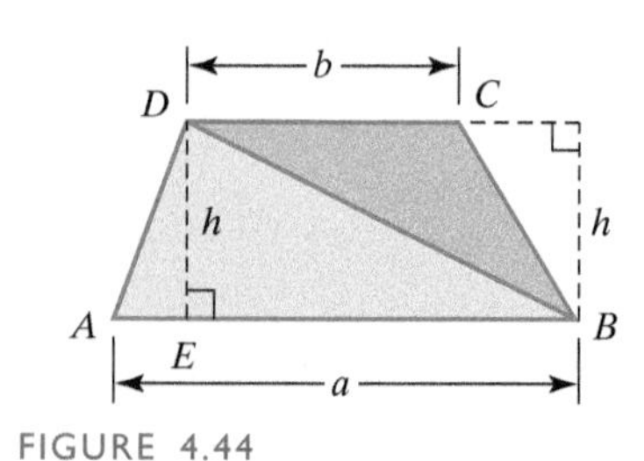

FIGURE 4.44

Area of trapezoid = Area of yellow Δ plus Area of orange Δ

$$A = \frac{1}{2}ah + \frac{1}{2}bh$$

$$= \frac{1}{2}h(a + b) \quad \text{Factor out } \frac{1}{2}h.$$

AREA OF A TRAPEZOID

The area, A, of a trapezoid with parallel bases a and b and height h is given by the formula

$$A = \frac{1}{2}h(a + b).$$

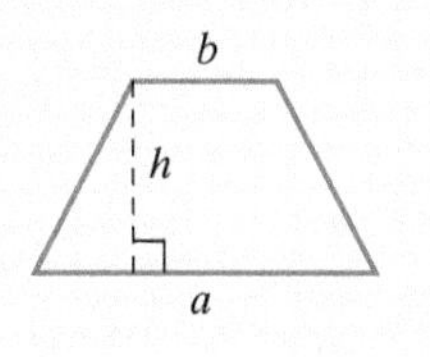

EXAMPLE 5 *Finding the Area of a Trapezoid*

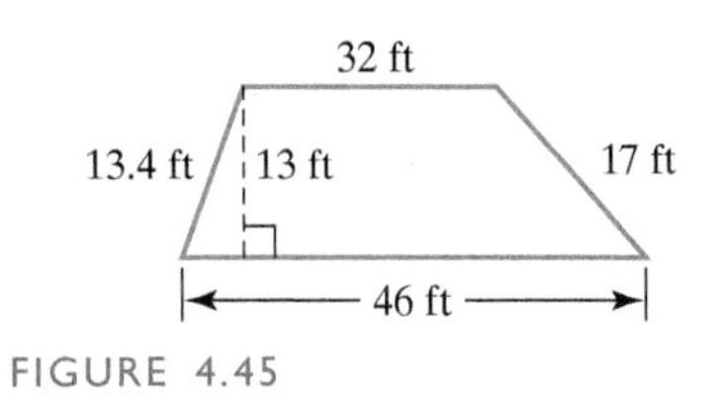

FIGURE 4.45

Find the area of the trapezoid in **Figure 4.45**.

SOLUTION

The height, h, is 13 feet. The lower base, a, is 46 feet, and the upper base, b, is 32 feet. We do not use the 17-foot and 13.4-foot sides in finding the trapezoid's area.

$$A = \frac{1}{2}h(a + b) = \frac{1}{2} \cdot 13 \text{ ft} \cdot (46 \text{ ft} + 32 \text{ ft})$$

$$= \frac{1}{2} \cdot 13 \text{ ft} \cdot 78 \text{ ft} = 507 \text{ ft}^2$$

The area of the trapezoid is 507 square feet.

CHECK POINT 5 Find the area of a trapezoid with bases of length 20 feet and 10 feet and height 7 feet.

2 Use formulas for a circle's circumference and area.

It's a good idea to know your way around a circle. Clocks, angles, maps, and compasses are based on circles. Circles occur everywhere in nature: in ripples on water, patterns on a butterfly's wings, and cross sections of trees. Some consider the circle to be the most pleasing of all shapes.

The point at which a pebble hits a flat surface of water becomes the center of a number of circular ripples.

A **circle** is a set of points in the plane equally distant from a given point, its **center**. **Figure 4.46** shows two circles. The **radius** (plural: radii), r, is a line segment from the center to any point on the circle. For a given circle, all radii have the same length. The **diameter**, d, is a line segment through the center whose endpoints both lie on the circle. For a given circle, all diameters have the same length. In any circle, the **length of the diameter is twice the length of the radius.**

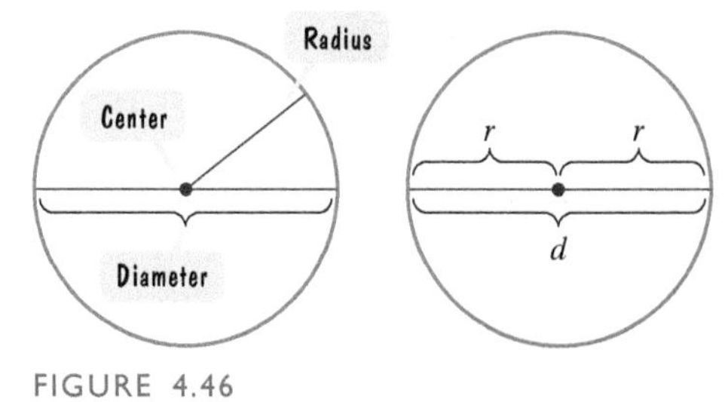

FIGURE 4.46

The words *radius* and *diameter* refer to both the line segments in **Figure 4.46** as well as to their linear measures. The distance around a circle (its perimeter) is called its **circumference**, C. For all circles, if you divide the circumference by the diameter, or by twice the radius, you will get the same number. This ratio is the irrational number π and is approximately equal to 3.14:

$$\frac{C}{d} = \pi \quad \text{or} \quad \frac{C}{2r} = \pi.$$

Thus,

$$C = \pi d \quad \text{or} \quad C = 2\pi r.$$

FINDING THE DISTANCE AROUND A CIRCLE

The circumference, C, of a circle with diameter d and radius r is

$$C = \pi d \quad \text{or} \quad C = 2\pi r.$$

When computing a circle's circumference by hand, round π to 3.14. When using a calculator, use the $\boxed{\pi}$ key, which gives the value of π rounded to approximately 11 decimal places. In either case, calculations involving π give approximate answers. These answers can vary slightly depending on how π is rounded. The symbol $\approx$ (is approximately equal to) will be written in these calculations.

EXAMPLE 6 *Finding a Circle's Circumference*

Find the circumference of the circle in **Figure 4.47**.

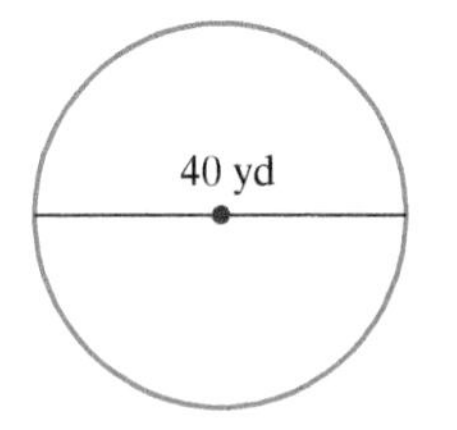

FIGURE 4.47

SOLUTION

The diameter is 40 yards, so we use the formula for circumference with d in it.

$$C = \pi d = \pi(40 \text{ yd}) = 40\pi \text{ yd} \approx 125.7 \text{ yd}$$

The distance around the circle is approximately 125.7 yards.

CHECK POINT 6 Find the circumference of a circle whose diameter measures 10 inches. Express the answer in terms of π and then round to the nearest tenth of an inch.

EXAMPLE 7 *Using the Circumference Formula*

How much trim, to the nearest tenth of a foot, is needed to go around the window shown in **Figure 4.48**?

FIGURE 4.48

SOLUTION

The trim covers the 6-foot bottom of the window, the two 8-foot sides, and the half-circle (called a semicircle) on top. The length needed is

$$6 \text{ ft} + 8 \text{ ft} + 8 \text{ ft} + \text{circumference of the semicircle.}$$

The circumference of the semicircle is half the circumference of a circle whose diameter is 6 feet.

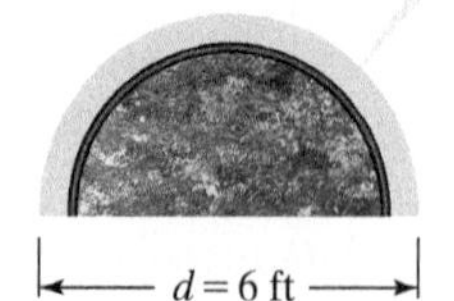

$$\text{Circumference of semicircle} = \frac{1}{2}\pi d$$
$$= \frac{1}{2}\pi(6 \text{ ft}) = 3\pi \text{ ft} \approx 9.4 \text{ ft}$$

Rounding the circumference to the nearest tenth (9.4 feet), the length of trim that is needed is approximately

$$6 \text{ ft} + 8 \text{ ft} + 8 \text{ ft} + 9.4 \text{ ft},$$

or 31.4 feet.

CHECK POINT 7 In **Figure 4.48**, suppose that the dimensions are 10 feet and 12 feet for the window's bottom and side, respectively. How much trim, to the nearest tenth of a foot, is needed to go around the window?

The irrational number π is also used to find the area of a circle in square units. This is because the ratio of a circle's area to the square of its radius is π:

$$\frac{A}{r^2} = \pi.$$

Multiplying both sides of this equation by r^2 gives a formula for determining a circle's area.

FINDING THE AREA OF A CIRCLE

The area, A, of a circle with radius r is

$$A = \pi r^2.$$

EXAMPLE 8 *Problem Solving Using the Formula for a Circle's Area*

Which one of the following is the better buy: a large pizza with a 16-inch diameter for \$15.00 or a medium pizza with an 8-inch diameter for \$7.50?

SOLUTION

The better buy is the pizza with the lower price per square inch. The radius of the large pizza is $\frac{1}{2} \cdot 16$ inches, or 8 inches, and the radius of the medium pizza is $\frac{1}{2} \cdot 8$ inches, or 4 inches. The area of the surface of each circular pizza is determined using the formula for the area of a circle.

$$\text{Large pizza: } A = \pi r^2 = \pi(8 \text{ in.})^2 = 64\pi \text{ in.}^2 \approx 201 \text{ in.}^2$$
$$\text{Medium pizza: } A = \pi r^2 = \pi(4 \text{ in.})^2 = 16\pi \text{ in.}^2 \approx 50 \text{ in.}^2$$

For each pizza, the price per square inch is found by dividing the price by the area:

$$\text{Price per square inch for large pizza} = \frac{\$15.00}{64\pi \text{ in.}^2} \approx \frac{\$15.00}{201 \text{ in.}^2} \approx \frac{\$0.07}{\text{in.}^2}$$

$$\text{Price per square inch for medium pizza} = \frac{\$7.50}{16\pi \text{ in.}^2} \approx \frac{\$7.50}{50 \text{ in.}^2} = \frac{\$0.15}{\text{in.}^2}$$

The large pizza costs approximately \$0.07 per square inch and the medium pizza costs approximately \$0.15 per square inch. Thus, the large pizza is the better buy.

TECHNOLOGY

You can use your calculator to obtain the price per square inch for each pizza in Example 8. The price per square inch for the large pizza, $\frac{15}{64\pi}$, is approximated by one of the following sequences of keystrokes:

Many Scientific Calculators

15 [÷] [(] 64 [×] [π] [)] [=]

Many Graphing Calculators

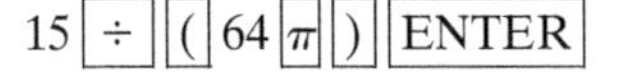

15 [÷] [(] 64 [π] [)] [ENTER]

In Example 8, did you at first think that the price per square inch would be the same for the large and the medium pizzas? After all, the radius of the large pizza is twice that of the medium pizza, and the cost of the large is twice that of the medium. However, the large pizza's area, 64π square inches, is *four times the area* of the medium pizza's, 16π square inches. Doubling the radius of a circle increases its area by a factor of 2^2, or 4. In general, if the radius of a circle is increased by k times its original linear measure, the area is multiplied by k^2. The same principle is true for any two-dimensional figure: If the shape of the figure is kept the same while linear dimensions are increased k times, the area of the larger, similar, figure is k^2 times greater than the area of the original figure.

CHECK POINT 8 Which one of the following is the better buy: a large pizza with an 18-inch diameter for \$20 or a medium pizza with a 14-inch diameter for \$14?

Concept and Vocabulary Check

Fill in each blank so that the resulting statement is true.

1. The area, A, of a rectangle with length l and width w is given by the formula ____________.
2. The area, A, of a square with one side measuring s linear units is given by the formula ____________.
3. The area, A, of a parallelogram with height h and base b is given by the formula ____________.
4. The area, A, of a triangle with height h and base b is given by the formula ____________.
5. The area, A, of a trapezoid with parallel bases a and b and height h is given by the formula ____________.
6. The circumference, C, of a circle with diameter d is given by the formula ____________.
7. The circumference, C, of a circle with radius r is given by the formula ____________.
8. The area, A, of a circle with radius r is given by the formula ____________.

In Exercises 9–13, determine whether each statement is true or false. If the statement is false, make the necessary change(s) to produce a true statement.

9. The area, A, of a rectangle with length l and width w is given by the formula $A = 2l + 2w$. ____________
10. The height of a parallelogram is the perpendicular distance between two of the parallel sides. ____________
11. The area of either triangle formed by drawing a diagonal in a parallelogram is one-half that of the parallelogram. ____________
12. In any circle, the length of the radius is twice the length of the diameter. ____________
13. The ratio of a circle's circumference to its diameter is the irrational number π. ____________

Exercise Set 4.4

Practice Exercises

In Exercises 1–14, use the formulas developed in this section to find the area of each figure.

1. 3 m; 6 m

2. 3 ft; 4 ft

3. 4 in.; 4 in.

4. 3 cm; 3 cm

5. 50 cm; 44 cm; 42 cm; 44 cm; 50 cm

6. 58 ft; 46 ft; 43 ft; 46 ft; 58 ft

7. 8 in.; 14 in.

8. 33 m; 30 m

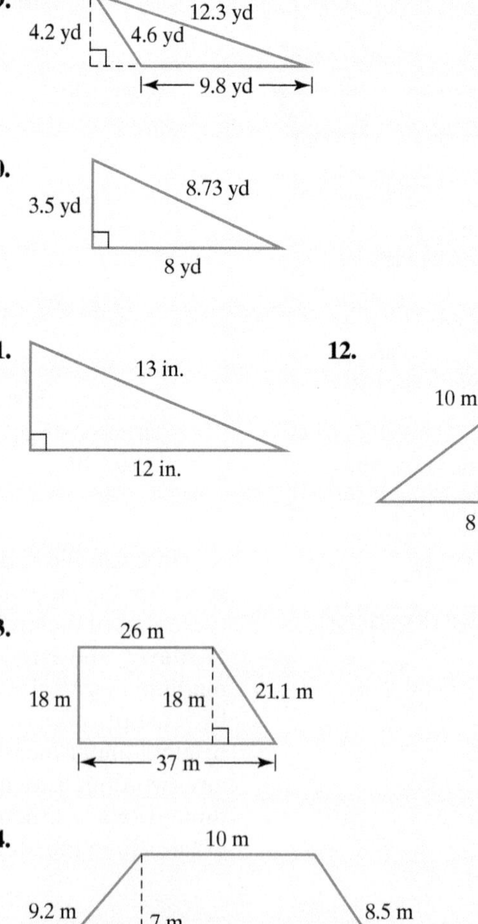

In Exercises 15–18, find the circumference and area of each circle. Express answers in terms of π and then round to the nearest tenth.

15. **16.** **17.** **18.**

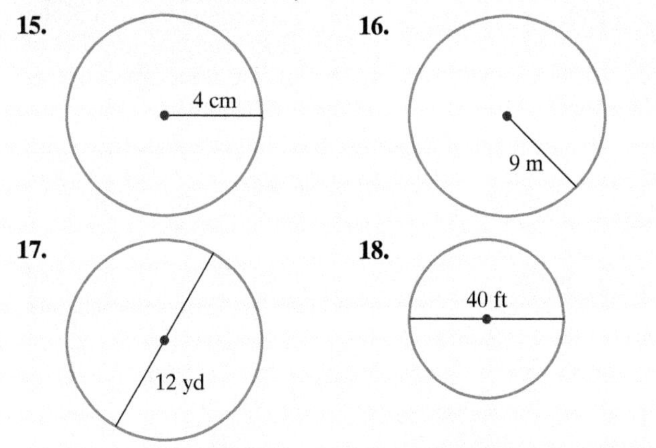

Find the area of each figure in Exercises 19–24. Where necessary, express answers in terms of π and then round to the nearest tenth.

19. **20.** **21.** **22.**

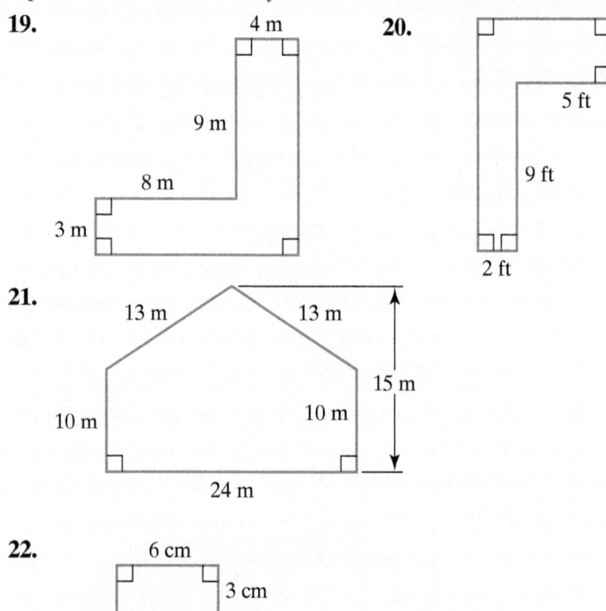

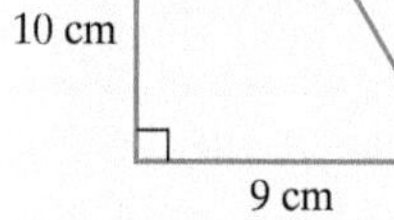

23.

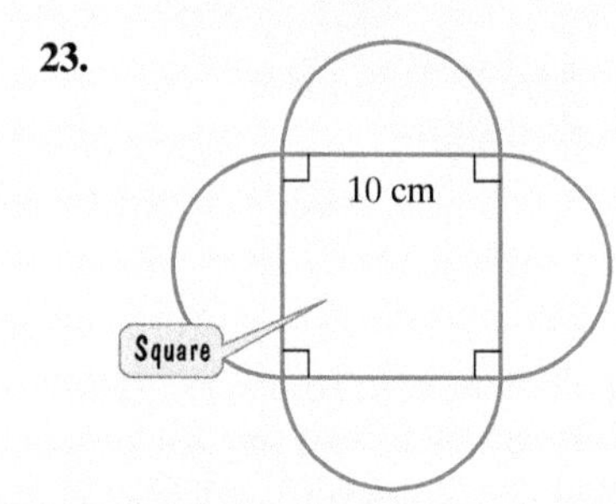

24.

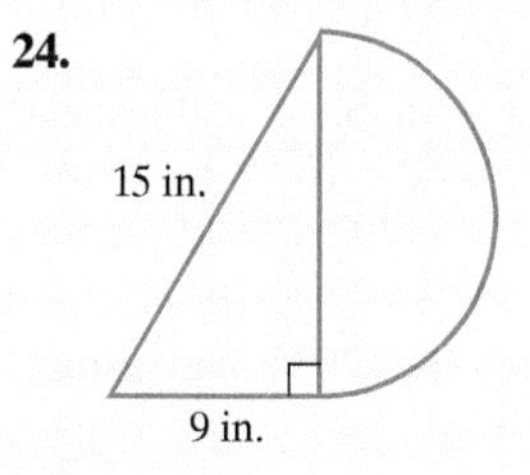

In Exercises 25–28, find a formula for the total area, A, of each figure in terms of the variable(s) shown. Where necessary, use π in the formula.

25.

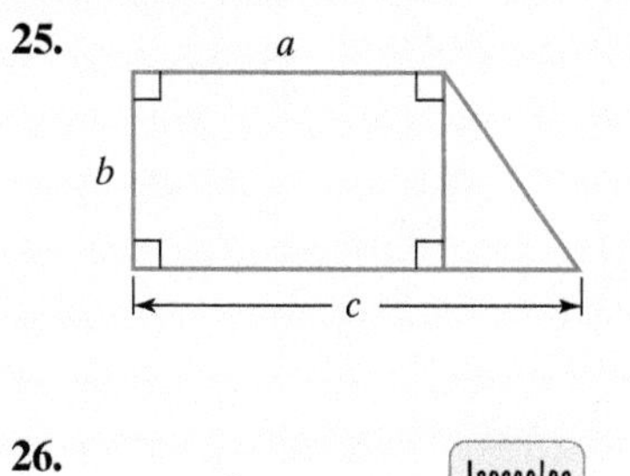

26.

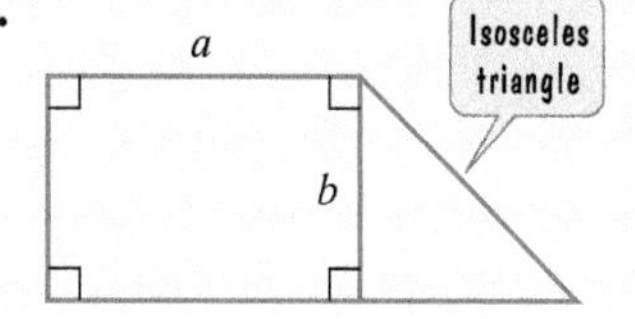

27.

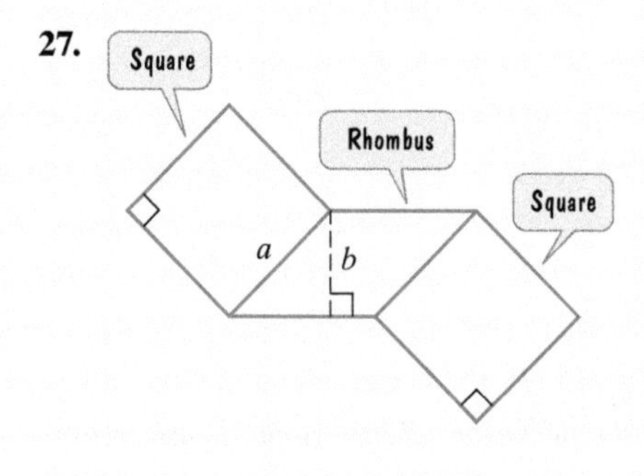

28.

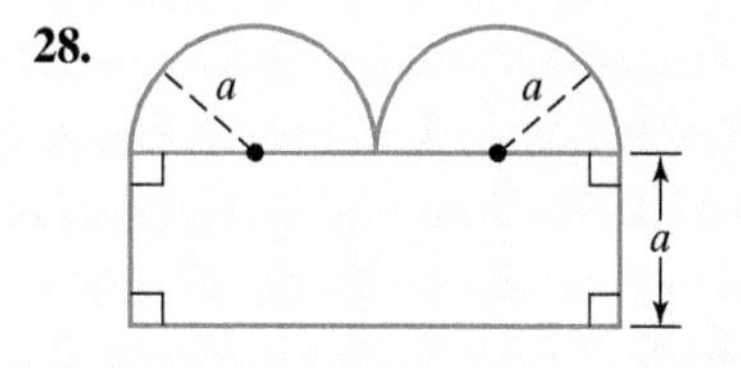

Practice Plus

In Exercises 29–30, find the area of each shaded region.

29.

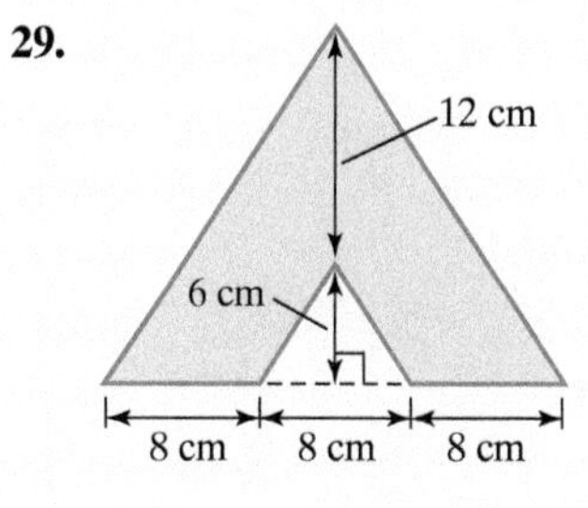

30.

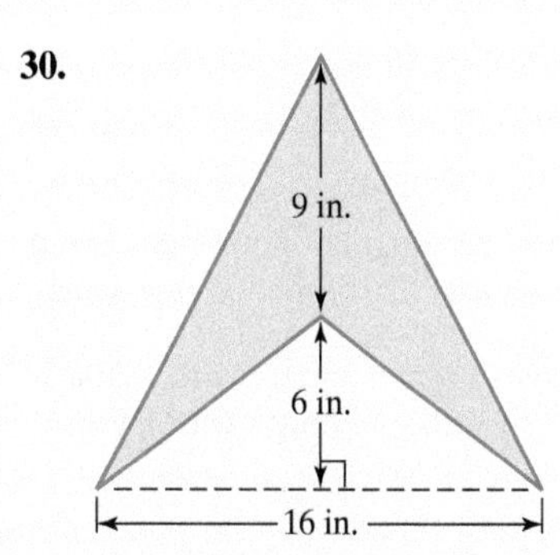

In Exercises 31–34, find the area of each shaded region in terms of π.

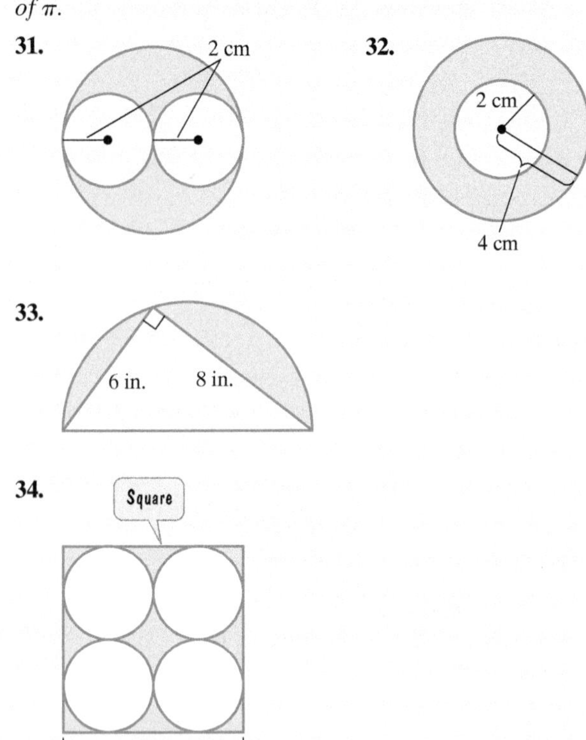

In Exercises 35–36, find the perimeter and the area of each figure. Where necessary, express answers in terms of π and round to the nearest tenth.

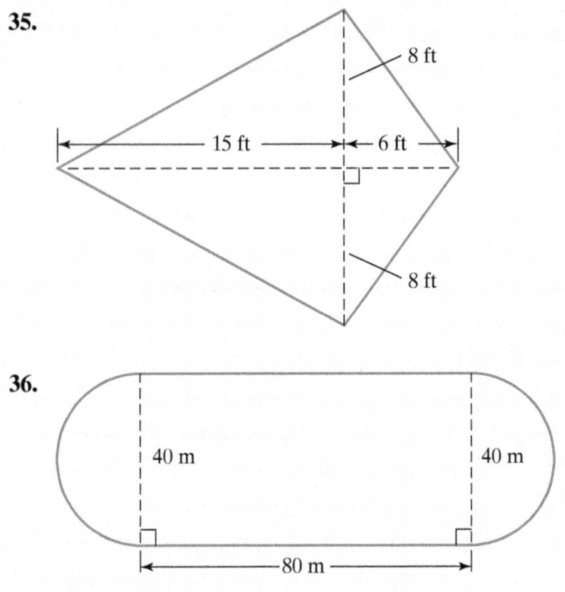

Application Exercises

37. What will it cost to carpet a rectangular floor measuring 9 feet by 21 feet if the carpet costs $26.50 per square yard?

38. A plastering contractor charges $18 per square yard. What is the cost of plastering 60 feet of wall in a house with a 9-foot ceiling?

39. A rectangular kitchen floor measures 12 feet by 15 feet. A stove on the floor has a rectangular base measuring 3 feet by 4 feet, and a refrigerator covers a rectangular area of the floor measuring 4 feet by 5 feet. How many square feet of tile will be needed to cover the kitchen floor not counting the area used by the stove and the refrigerator?

40. A rectangular room measures 12 feet by 15 feet. The entire room is to be covered with rectangular tiles that measure 3 inches by 2 inches. If the tiles are sold at ten for $1.20, what will it cost to tile the room?

41. The lot in the figure shown, except for the house, shed, and driveway, is lawn. One bag of lawn fertilizer costs $25 and covers 4000 square feet.

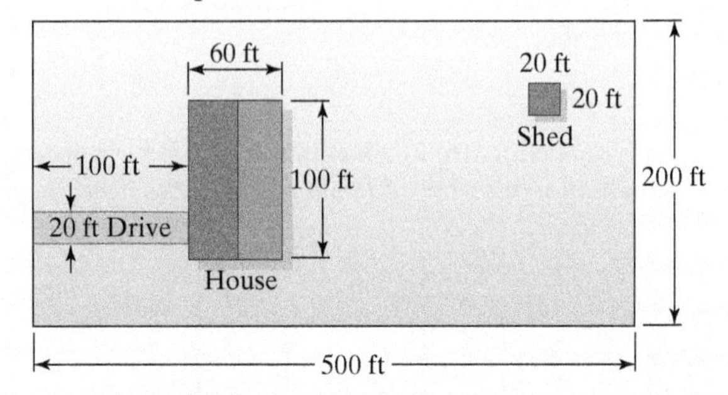

a. Determine the minimum number of bags of fertilizer needed for the lawn.

b. Find the total cost of the fertilizer.

42. Taxpayers with an office in their home may deduct a percentage of their home-related expenses. This percentage is based on the ratio of the office's area to the area of the home. A taxpayer with an office in a 2200-square-foot home maintains a 20 foot by 16 foot office. If the yearly utility bills for the home come to $4800, how much of this is deductible?

43. You are planning to paint the house whose dimensions are shown in the figure.

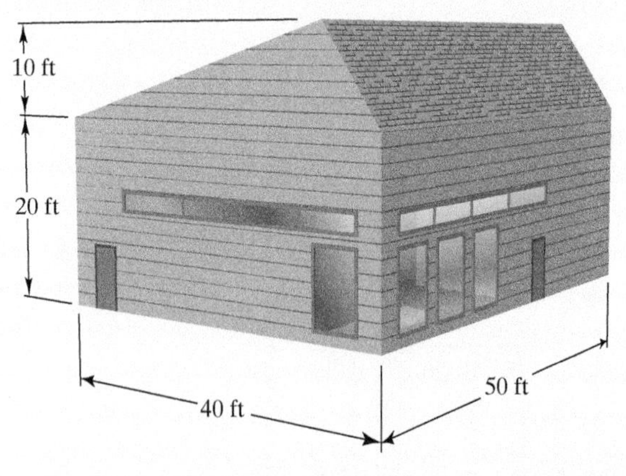

a. How many square feet will you need to paint? (There are four windows, each 8 feet by 5 feet; two windows, each 30 feet by 2 feet; and two doors, each 80 inches by 36 inches, that do not require paint.)

b. The paint that you have chosen is available in gallon cans only. Each can covers 500 square feet. If you want to use two coats of paint, how many cans will you need for the project?

c. If the paint you have chosen sells for $26.95 per gallon, what will it cost to paint the house?

The diagram shows the floor plan for a one-story home. Use the given measurements to solve Exercises 44–46. (A calculator will be helpful in performing the necessary computations.)

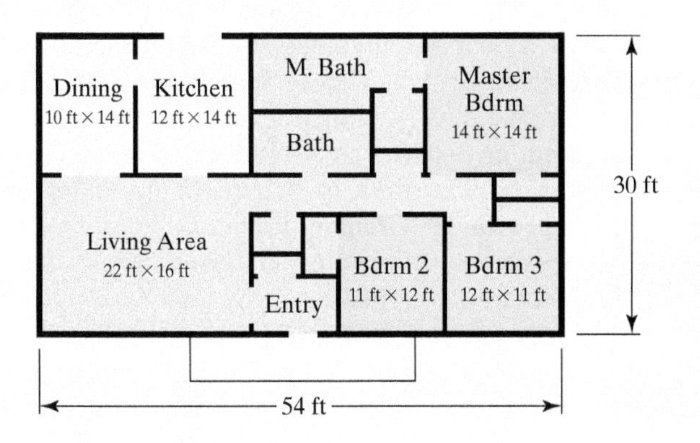

44. If construction costs \$95 per square foot, find the cost of building the home.

45. If carpet costs \$17.95 per square yard and is available in whole square yards only, find the cost of carpeting the three bedroom floors.

46. If ceramic tile costs \$26.95 per square yard and is available in whole square yards only, find the cost of installing ceramic tile on the kitchen and dining room floors.

In Exercises 47–48, express the required calculation in terms of π and then round to the nearest tenth.

47. How much fencing is required to enclose a circular garden whose radius is 20 meters?

48. A circular rug is 6 feet in diameter. How many feet of fringe is required to edge this rug?

49. How many plants spaced every 6 inches are needed to surround a circular garden with a 30-foot radius?

50. A stained glass window is to be placed in a house. The window consists of a rectangle, 6 feet high by 3 feet wide, with a semicircle at the top. Approximately how many feet of stripping, to the nearest tenth of a foot, will be needed to frame the window?

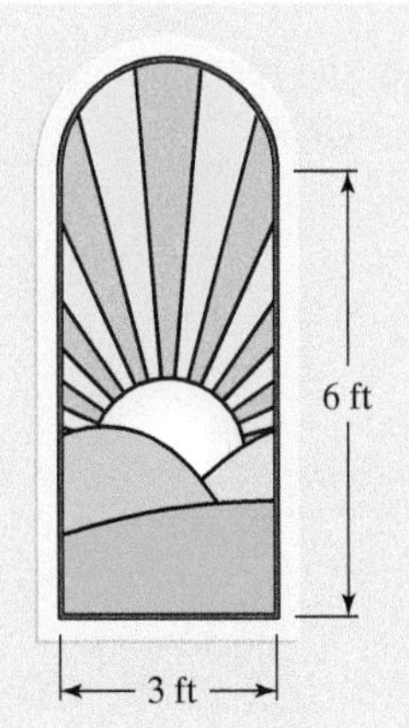

51. Which one of the following is a better buy: a large pizza with a 14-inch diameter for \$12 or a medium pizza with a 7-inch diameter for \$5?

52. Which one of the following is a better buy: a large pizza with a 16-inch diameter for \$12 or two small pizzas, each with a 10-inch diameter, for \$12?

Writing in Mathematics

53. Using the formula for the area of a rectangle, explain how the formula for the area of a parallelogram ($A = bh$) is obtained.

54. Using the formula for the area of a parallelogram ($A = bh$), explain how the formula for the area of a triangle $\left(A = \frac{1}{2}bh\right)$ is obtained.

55. Using the formula for the area of a triangle, explain how the formula for the area of a trapezoid is obtained.

56. Explain why a circle is not a polygon.

57. Describe the difference between the following problems: How much fencing is needed to enclose a circular garden? How much fertilizer is needed for a circular garden?

Critical Thinking Exercises

Make Sense? *In Exercises 58–61, determine whether each statement makes sense or does not make sense, and explain your reasoning.*

58. The house is a 1500-square-foot mansion with six bedrooms.

59. Because a parallelogram can be divided into two triangles with the same size and shape, the area of a triangle is one-half that of a parallelogram.

60. I used $A = \pi r^2$ to determine the amount of fencing needed to enclose my circular garden.

61. I paid \$10 for a pizza, so I would expect to pay approximately \$20 for the same kind of pizza with twice the radius.

62. You need to enclose a rectangular region with 200 feet of fencing. Experiment with different lengths and widths to determine the maximum area you can enclose. Which quadrilateral encloses the most area?

63. Suppose you know the cost for building a rectangular deck measuring 8 feet by 10 feet. If you decide to increase the dimensions to 12 feet by 15 feet, by how much will the cost increase?

64. A rectangular swimming pool measures 14 feet by 30 feet. The pool is surrounded on all four sides by a path that is 3 feet wide. If the cost to resurface the path is \$2 per square foot, what is the total cost of resurfacing the path?

65. A proposed oil pipeline will cross 16.8 miles of national forest. The width of the land needed for the pipeline is 200 feet. If the U.S. Forest Service charges the oil company \$32 per acre, calculate the total cost. (1 mile = 5280 feet and 1 acre = 43,560 square feet.)

Volume and Surface Area

WHAT AM I SUPPOSED TO LEARN?

After you have read this section, you should be able to:

1. Use volume formulas to compute the volumes of three-dimensional figures and solve applied problems.
2. Compute the surface area of a three-dimensional figure.

YOU ARE CONSIDERING GOING TO JUDGE JUDY'S WEB site and filling out a case submission form to appear on her TV show. The case involves your contractor, who promised to install a water tank that holds 500 gallons of water. Upon delivery, you noticed that capacity was not printed anywhere, so you decided to do some measuring. The tank is shaped like a giant tuna can, with a circular top and bottom. You measured the radius of each circle to be 3 feet and you measured the tank's height to be 2 feet 4 inches. You know that 500 gallons is the capacity of a solid figure with a volume of about 67 cubic feet. Now you need some sort of method to compute the volume of the water tank. In this section, we discuss how to compute the volumes of various solid, three-dimensional figures. Using a formula you will learn in the section, you can determine whether the evidence indicates you can win a case against the contractor if you appear on *Judge Judy*. Or do you risk joining a cast of bozos who entertain television viewers by being loudly castigated by the judge? (Before a possible ear-piercing "Baloney, sir, you're a geometric idiot!", we suggest working Exercise 45 in Exercise Set 4.5.)

1 Use volume formulas to compute the volumes of three-dimensional figures and solve applied problems.

Formulas for Volume

We saw that **volume** refers to the amount of space occupied by a solid object, determined by the number of cubic units it takes to fill the interior of that object. For example, **Figure 4.49** shows that there are 18 cubic units contained within the box. The volume of the box, called a **rectangular solid**, is 18 cubic units. The box has a length of 3 units, a width of 3 units, and a height of 2 units. The volume, 18 cubic units, may be determined by finding the product of the length, the width, and the height:

$$\text{Volume} = 3 \text{ units} \cdot 3 \text{ units} \cdot 2 \text{ units} = 18 \text{ units}^3.$$

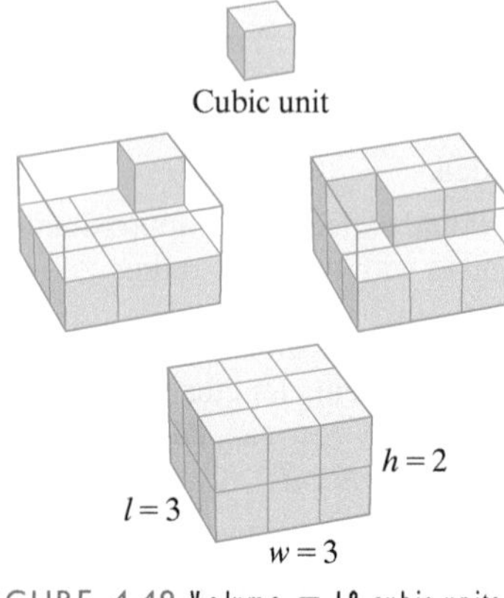

FIGURE 4.49 Volume = 18 cubic units

In general, the volume, V, of a rectangular solid is the product of its length, l, its width, w, and its height, h:

$$V = lwh.$$

If the length, width, and height are the same, the rectangular solid is called a **cube**. Formulas for these boxlike shapes are given below.

VOLUMES OF BOXLIKE SHAPES

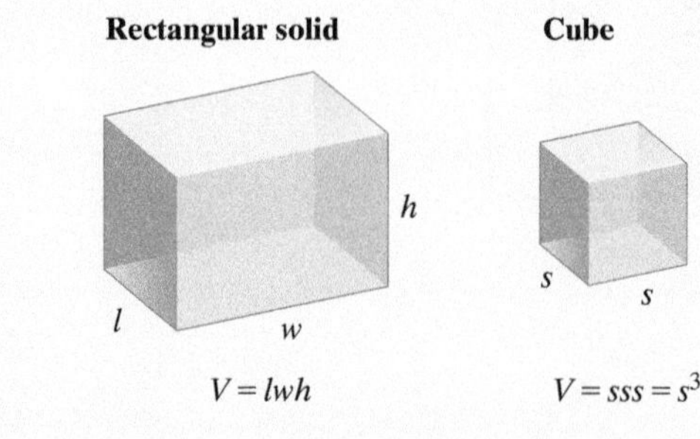

EXAMPLE 1 Finding the Volume of a Rectangular Solid

Find the volume of the rectangular solid in **Figure 4.50**.

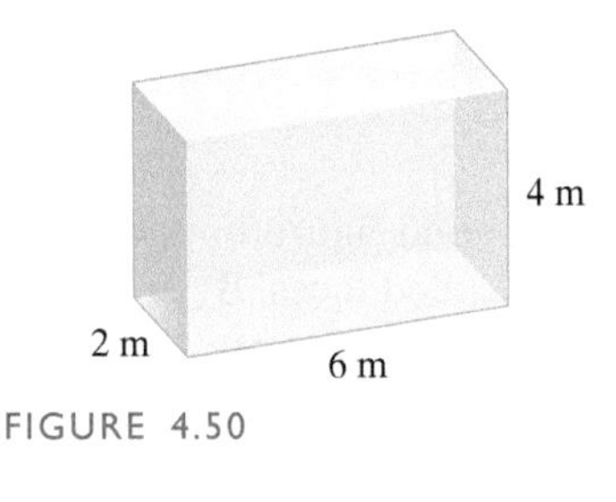

FIGURE 4.50

SOLUTION

As shown in the figure, the length is 6 meters, the width is 2 meters, and the height is 4 meters. Thus, $l = 6$, $w = 2$, and $h = 4$.

$$V = lwh = 6\text{ m} \cdot 2\text{ m} \cdot 4\text{ m} = 48\text{ m}^3$$

The volume of the rectangular solid is 48 cubic meters.

CHECK POINT 1 Find the volume of a rectangular solid with length 5 feet, width 3 feet, and height 7 feet.

We saw that although there are 3 feet in a yard, there are 27 cubic feet in a cubic yard. If a problem requires measurement of volume in cubic yards and the linear measures are given in feet, to avoid errors, first convert feet to yards. Then apply the volume formula. This idea is illustrated in Example 2.

EXAMPLE 2 Solving a Volume Problem

You are about to begin work on a swimming pool in your yard. The first step is to have a hole dug that is 90 feet long, 60 feet wide, and 6 feet deep. You will use a truck that can carry 10 cubic yards of dirt and charges $35 per load. How much will it cost you to have all the dirt hauled away?

SOLUTION

We begin by converting feet to yards:

$$90\text{ ft} = \frac{90\text{ ft}}{1} \cdot \frac{1\text{ yd}}{3\text{ ft}} = \frac{90}{3}\text{ yd} = 30\text{ yd}.$$

Similarly, 60 ft = 20 yd and 6 ft = 2 yd. Next, we find the volume of dirt that needs to be dug out and hauled off.

$$V = lwh = 30\text{ yd} \cdot 20\text{ yd} \cdot 2\text{ yd} = 1200\text{ yd}^3$$

Now, we find the number of loads that the truck needs to haul off all the dirt. Because the truck carries 10 cubic yards, divide the number of cubic yards of dirt by 10.

$$\text{Number of truckloads} = \frac{1200\text{ yd}^3}{\frac{10\text{ yd}^3}{\text{trip}}} = \frac{1200\text{ yd}^3}{1} \cdot \frac{\text{trip}}{10\text{ yd}^3} = \frac{1200}{10}\text{ trips} = 120\text{ trips}$$

Because the truck charges $35 per trip, the cost to have all the dirt hauled away is the number of trips, 120, times the cost per trip, $35.

$$\text{Cost to haul all dirt away} = \frac{120\text{ trips}}{1} \cdot \frac{\$35}{\text{trip}} = 120(\$35) = \$4200$$

The dirt-hauling phase of the pool project will cost you $4200.

CHECK POINT 2 Find the volume, in cubic yards, of a cube whose edges each measure 6 feet.

A rectangular solid is an example of a **polyhedron**, a solid figure bounded by polygons. A rectangular solid is bounded by six rectangles, called faces. By contrast, a **pyramid** is a polyhedron whose base is a polygon and whose sides are triangles. **Figure 4.51** shows a pyramid with a rectangular base drawn inside a rectangular solid. The contents of three pyramids with rectangular bases exactly fill a rectangular solid of the same base and height. Thus, the formula for the volume of the pyramid is $\frac{1}{3}$ that of the rectangular solid.

FIGURE 4.51 The volume of a pyramid is $\frac{1}{3}$ the volume of a rectangular solid having the same base and the same height.

VOLUME OF A PYRAMID

The volume, V, of a pyramid is given by the formula

$$V = \frac{1}{3}Bh,$$

where B is the area of the base and h is the height (the perpendicular distance from the top to the base).

EXAMPLE 3 *Using the Formula for a Pyramid's Volume*

Capped with a pointed spire on top of its 48 stories, the Transamerica Tower in San Francisco is a pyramid with a square base. The pyramid is 256 meters (853 feet) tall. Each side of the square base has a length of 52 meters. Although San Franciscans disliked it when it opened in 1972, they have since accepted it as part of the skyline. Find the volume of the building.

The Transamerica Tower's 3678 windows take cleaners one month to wash. Its foundation is sunk 15.5 m (52 ft) into the ground and is designed to move with earth tremors.

SOLUTION

First find the area of the square base, represented as B in the volume formula. Because each side of the square base is 52 meters, the area of the square base is

$$B = 52 \text{ m} \cdot 52 \text{ m} = 2704 \text{ m}^2.$$

The area of the square base is 2704 square meters. Because the pyramid is 256 meters tall, its height, h, is 256 meters. Now we apply the formula for the volume of a pyramid:

$$V = \frac{1}{3}Bh = \frac{1}{3} \cdot \frac{2704 \text{ m}^2}{1} \cdot \frac{256 \text{ m}}{1} = \frac{2704 \cdot 256}{3} \text{ m}^3 \approx 230{,}741 \text{ m}^3.$$

The volume of the building is approximately 230,741 cubic meters.

The San Francisco pyramid is relatively small compared to the Great Pyramid outside Cairo, Egypt. Built in about 2550 B.C. by a labor force of 100,000, the Great Pyramid is approximately 11 times the volume of San Francisco's pyramid.

CHECK POINT 3 A pyramid is 4 feet tall. Each side of the square base has a length of 6 feet. Find the pyramid's volume.

Radius

Height

FIGURE 4.52

Not every three-dimensional figure is a polyhedron. Take, for example, the right circular cylinder shown in **Figure 4.52**. Its shape should remind you of a soup can or a stack of coins. The right circular cylinder is so named because the top and bottom are circles, and the side forms a right angle with the top and bottom. The formula for the volume of a right circular cylinder is given as follows:

VOLUME OF A RIGHT CIRCULAR CYLINDER

The volume, V, of a right circular cylinder is given by the formula

$$V = \pi r^2 h,$$

where r is the radius of the circle at either end and h is the height.

Right circular cylinder

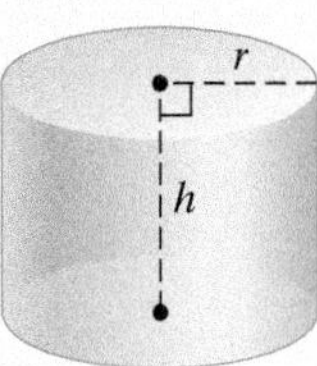

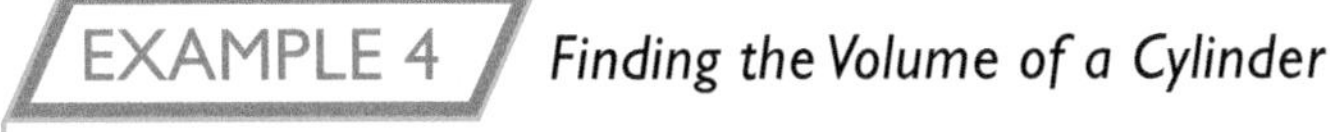

EXAMPLE 4 *Finding the Volume of a Cylinder*

Find the volume of the cylinder in **Figure 4.53**.

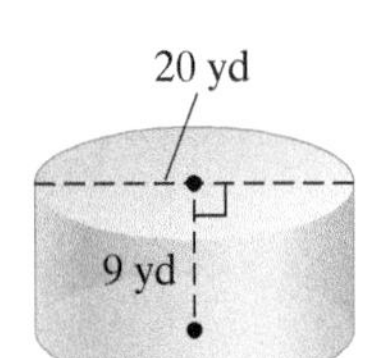

FIGURE 4.53

SOLUTION

In order to find the cylinder's volume, we need both its radius and its height. Because the diameter is 20 yards, the radius is half this length, or 10 yards. The height of the cylinder is given to be 9 yards. Thus, $r = 10$ and $h = 9$. Now we apply the formula for the volume of a cylinder.

$$V = \pi r^2 h = \pi(10 \text{ yd})^2 \cdot 9 \text{ yd} = 900\pi \text{ yd}^3 \approx 2827 \text{ yd}^3$$

The volume of the cylinder is approximately 2827 cubic yards.

CHECK POINT 4 Find the volume, to the nearest cubic inch, of a cylinder with a diameter of 8 inches and a height of 6 inches.

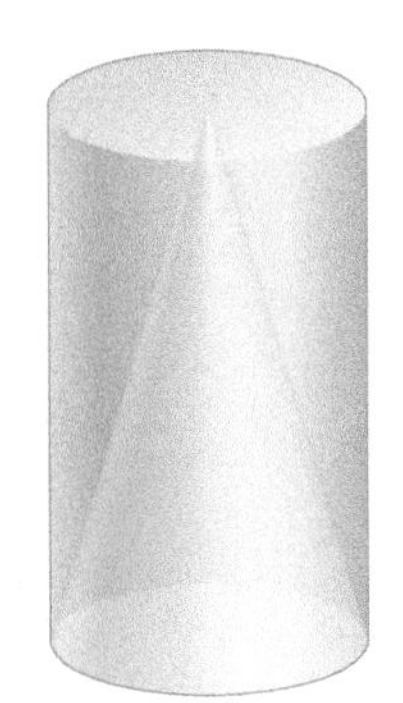

FIGURE 4.54

Figure 4.54 shows a **right circular cone** inside a cylinder, sharing the same circular base as the cylinder. The height of the cone, the perpendicular distance from the top to the circular base, is the same as that of the cylinder. Three such cones can occupy the same amount of space as the cylinder. Therefore, the formula for the volume of the cone is $\frac{1}{3}$ the volume of the cylinder.

VOLUME OF A CONE

The volume, V, of a right circular cone that has height h and radius r is given by the formula

$$V = \frac{1}{3}\pi r^2 h.$$

Cone

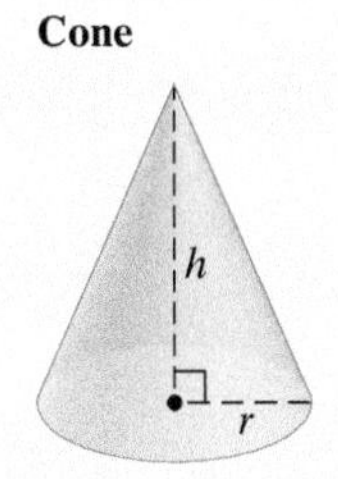

EXAMPLE 5 *Finding the Volume of a Cone*

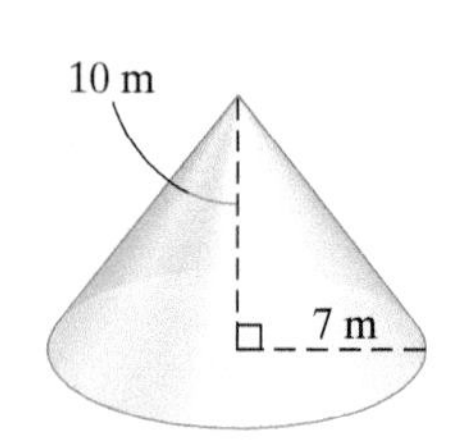

FIGURE 4.55

Find the volume of the cone in **Figure 4.55.**

SOLUTION

The radius of the cone is 7 meters and the height is 10 meters. Thus, $r = 7$ and $h = 10$. Now we apply the formula for the volume of a cone.

$$V = \frac{1}{3}\pi r^2 h = \frac{1}{3}\pi(7 \text{ m})^2 \cdot 10 \text{ m} = \frac{490\pi}{3} \text{ m}^3 \approx 513 \text{ m}^3$$

The volume of the cone is approximately 513 cubic meters.

CHECK POINT 5 Find the volume, to the nearest cubic inch, of a cone with a radius of 4 inches and a height of 6 inches.

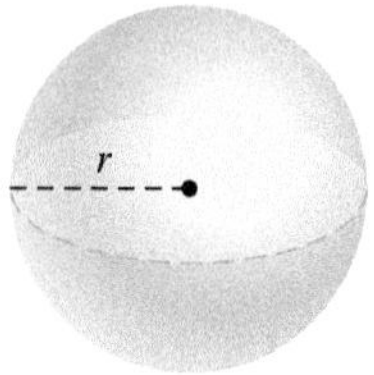

FIGURE 4.56

Figure 4.56 shows a *sphere*. Its shape may remind you of a basketball. The Earth is not a perfect sphere, but it's close. A **sphere** is the set of points in space equally distant from a given point, its **center**. Any line segment from the center to a point on the sphere is a **radius** of the sphere. The word *radius* is also used to refer to the length of this line segment. A sphere's volume can be found by using π and its radius.

VOLUME OF A SPHERE

The volume, V, of a sphere of radius r is given by the formula

$$V = \frac{4}{3}\pi r^3.$$

Sphere

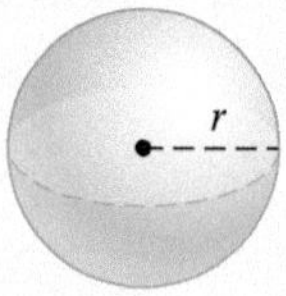

EXAMPLE 6 *Applying Volume Formulas*

An ice cream cone is 5 inches deep and has a radius of 1 inch. A spherical scoop of ice cream also has a radius of 1 inch. (See **Figure 4.57.**) If the ice cream melts into the cone, will it overflow?

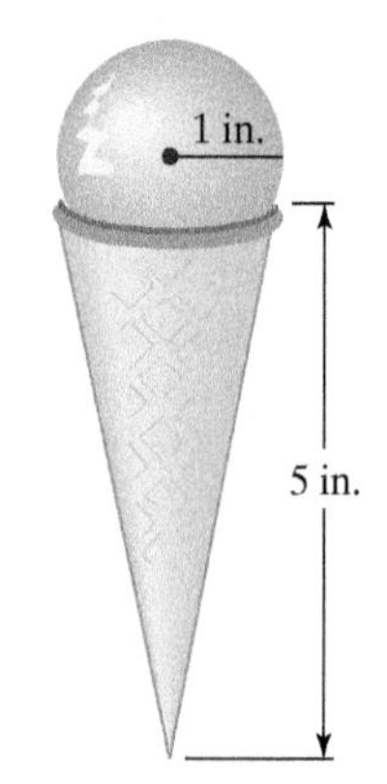

FIGURE 4.57

SOLUTION

The ice cream will overflow if the volume of the ice cream, a sphere, is greater than the volume of the cone. Find the volume of each.

$$V_{\text{cone}} = \frac{1}{3}\pi r^2 h = \frac{1}{3}\pi(1 \text{ in.})^2 \cdot 5 \text{ in.} = \frac{5\pi}{3} \text{ in.}^3 \approx 5 \text{ in.}^3$$

$$V_{\text{sphere}} = \frac{4}{3}\pi r^3 = \frac{4}{3}\pi(1 \text{ in.})^3 = \frac{4\pi}{3} \text{ in.}^3 \approx 4 \text{ in.}^3$$

The volume of the spherical scoop of ice cream is less than the volume of the cone, so there will be no overflow.

CHECK POINT 6 A basketball has a radius of 4.5 inches. If the ball is filled with 350 cubic inches of air, is this enough air to fill it completely?

2 Compute the surface area of a three-dimensional figure.

Surface Area

In addition to volume, we can also measure the area of the outer surface of a three-dimensional object, called its **surface area**. Like area, surface area is measured in square units. For example, the surface area of the rectangular solid in **Figure 4.58** is the sum of the areas of the six outside rectangles of the solid.

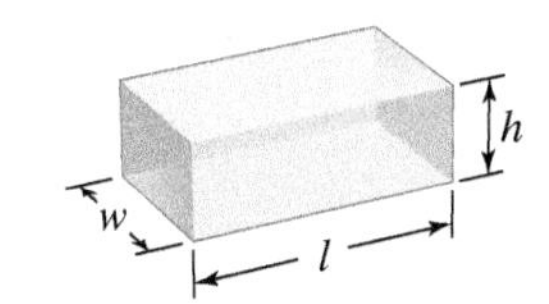

FIGURE 4.58

$$\text{Surface Area} = \underbrace{lw + lw}_{\text{Areas of top and bottom rectangles}} + \underbrace{lh + lh}_{\text{Areas of front and back rectangles}} + \underbrace{wh + wh}_{\text{Areas of rectangles on left and right sides}}$$

$$= 2lw + 2lh + 2wh$$

Formulas for the surface area, abbreviated SA, of three-dimensional figures are given in **Table 4.4**.

Table 10.4 Common Formulas for Surface Area

Cube	Rectangular Solid	Circular Cylinder
$SA = 6s^2$	$SA = 2lw + 2lh + 2wh$	$SA = 2\pi r^2 + 2\pi rh$

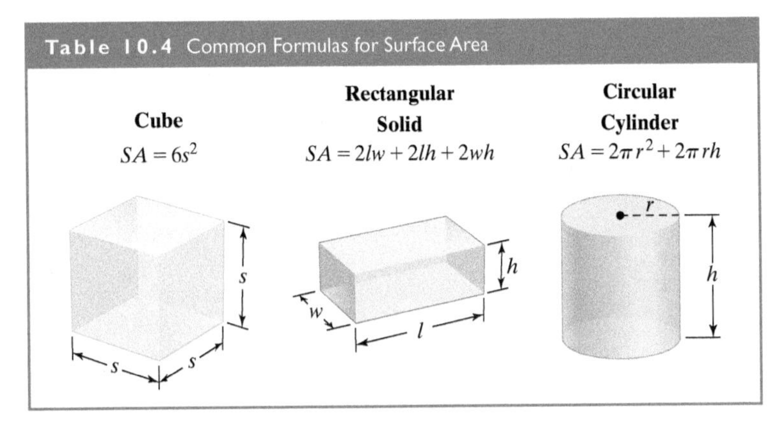

EXAMPLE 7 *Finding the Surface Area of a Solid*

Find the surface area of the rectangular solid in **Figure 4.59**.

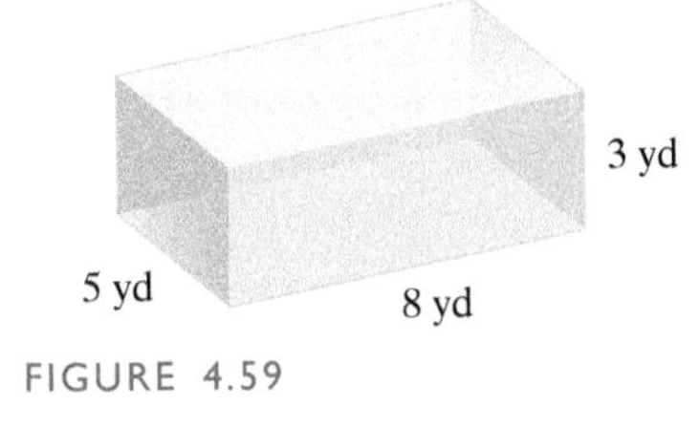

FIGURE 4.59

SOLUTION

As shown in the figure, the length is 8 yards, the width is 5 yards, and the height is 3 yards. Thus, $l = 8$, $w = 5$, and $h = 3$.

$$\begin{aligned} SA &= 2lw + 2lh + 2wh \\ &= 2 \cdot 8 \text{ yd} \cdot 5 \text{ yd} + 2 \cdot 8 \text{ yd} \cdot 3 \text{ yd} + 2 \cdot 5 \text{ yd} \cdot 3 \text{ yd} \\ &= 80 \text{ yd}^2 + 48 \text{ yd}^2 + 30 \text{ yd}^2 = 158 \text{ yd}^2 \end{aligned}$$

The surface area is 158 square yards.

CHECK POINT 7 If the length, width, and height shown in **Figure 4.59** are each doubled, find the surface area of the resulting rectangular solid.

Concept and Vocabulary Check

Fill in each blank so that the resulting statement is true.

1. The volume, V, of a rectangular solid with length l, width w, and height h is given by the formula ________.
2. The volume, V, of a cube with an edge that measures s linear units is given by the formula ________.
3. A solid figure bounded by polygons is called a/an ________.
4. The volume, V, of a pyramid with base area B and height h is given by the formula ________.
5. The volume, V, of a right circular cylinder with height h and radius r is given by the formula ________.
6. The volume, V, of a right circular cone with height h and radius r is given by the formula ________.
7. The volume, V, of a sphere of radius r is given by the formula ________.

In Exercises 8–14, determine whether each statement is true or false. If the statement is false, make the necessary change(s) to produce a true statement.

8. A cube is a rectangular solid with the same length, width, and height. ______

9. A cube is an example of a polyhedron. ______

10. The volume of a pyramid is $\frac{1}{2}$ the volume of a rectangular solid having the same base and the same height. ______

11. Some three-dimensional figures are not polyhedrons. ______

12. A sphere is the set of points in space equally distant from its center. ______

13. Surface area refers to the area of the outer surface of a three-dimensional object. ______

14. The surface area, SA, of a rectangular solid with length l, width w, and height h is given by the formula $SA = lw + lh + wh$. ______

Exercise Set 4.5

Practice Exercises

In Exercises 1–20, find the volume of each figure. If necessary, express answers in terms of π and then round to the nearest whole number.

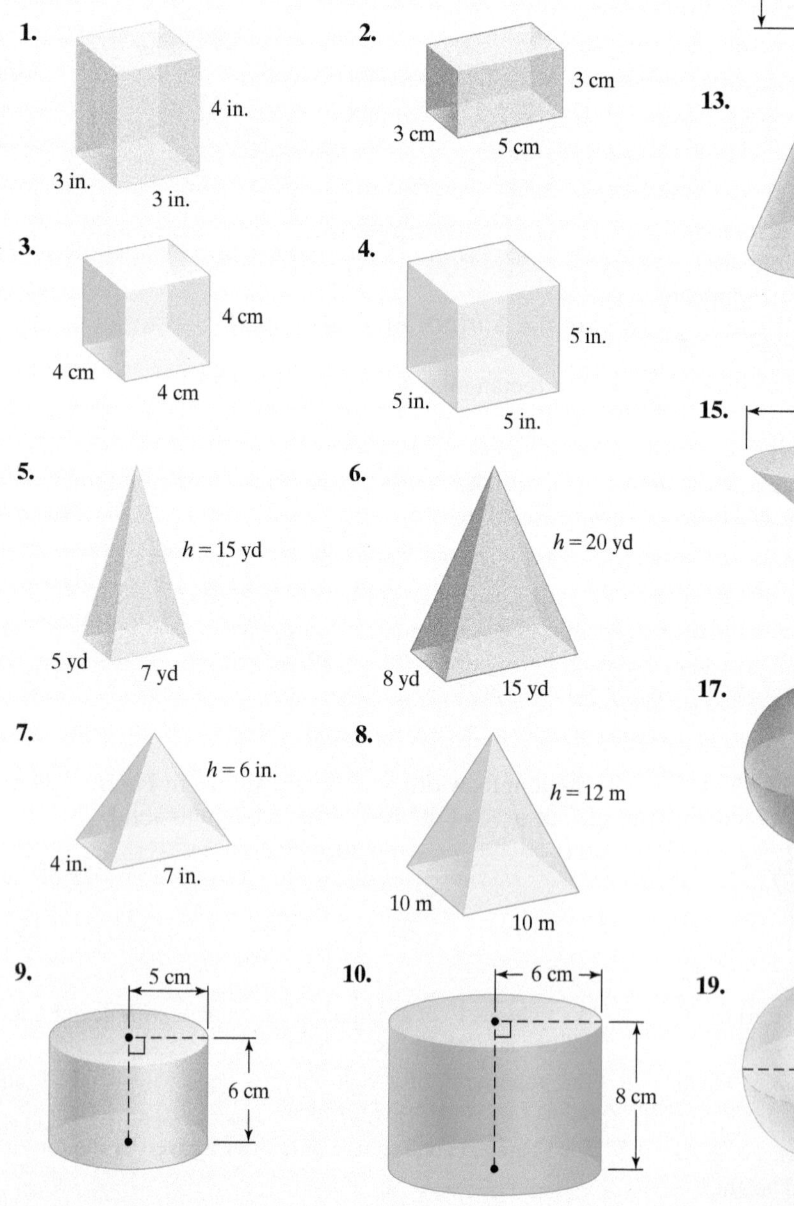

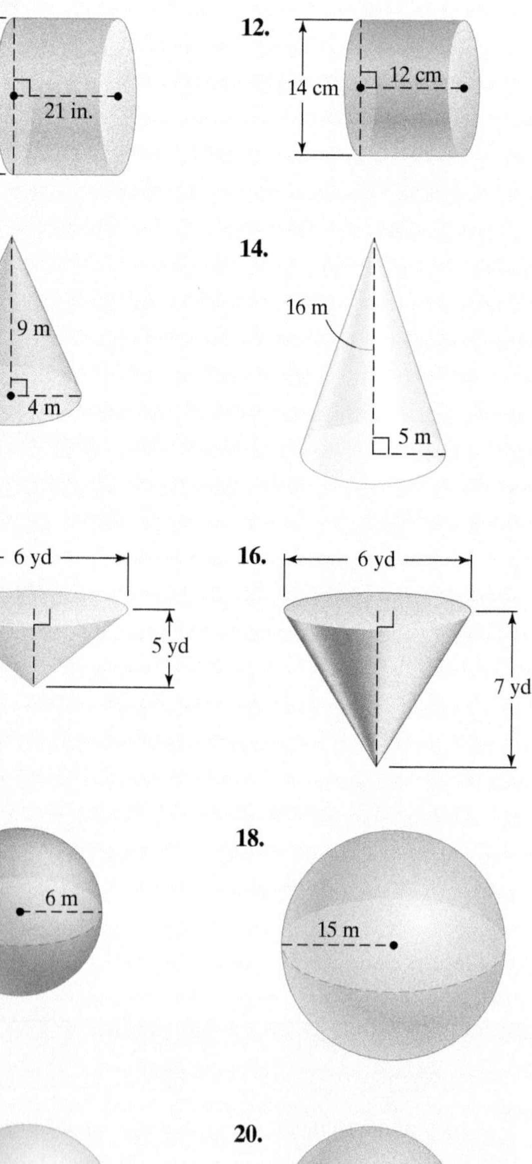

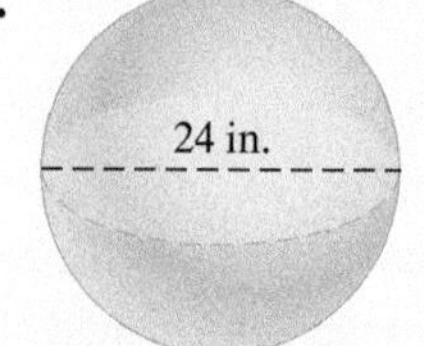

In Exercises 21–24, find the surface area of each figure.

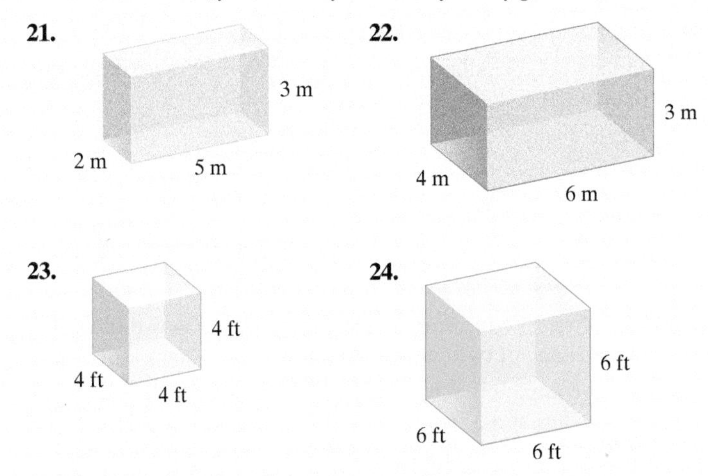

In Exercises 25–30, use two formulas for volume to find the volume of each figure. Express answers in terms of π and then round to the nearest whole number.

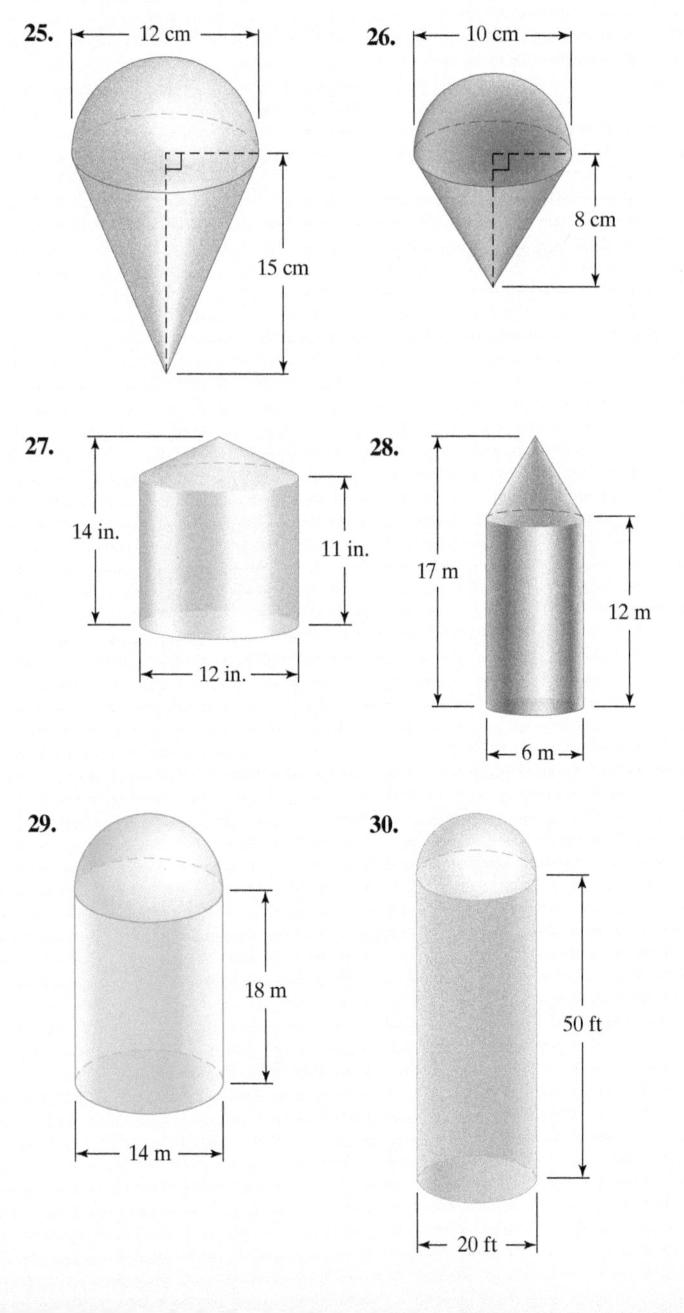

Practice Plus

31. Find the surface area and the volume of the figure shown.

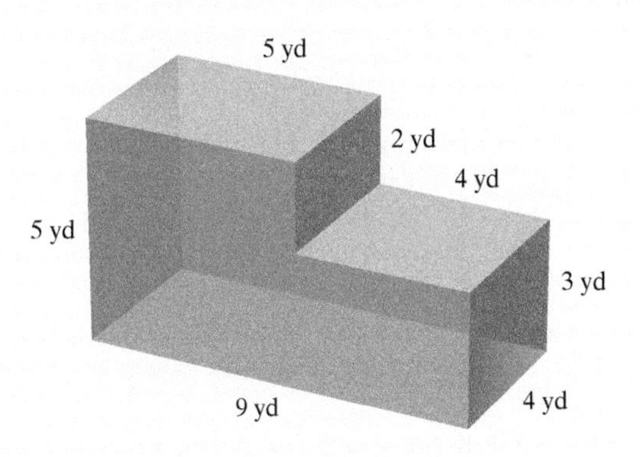

32. Find the surface area and the volume of the cement block in the figure shown.

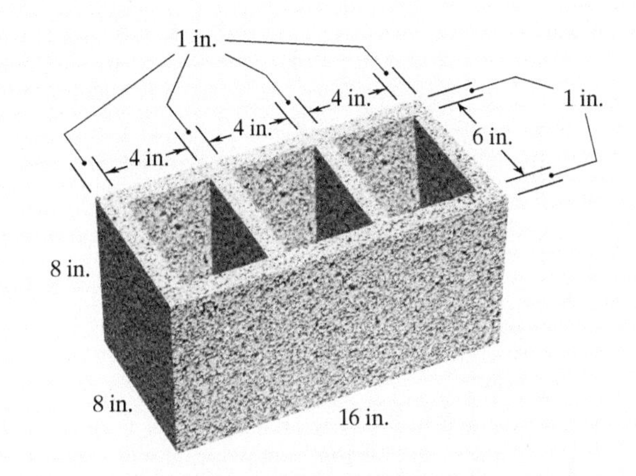

33. Find the surface area of the figure shown.

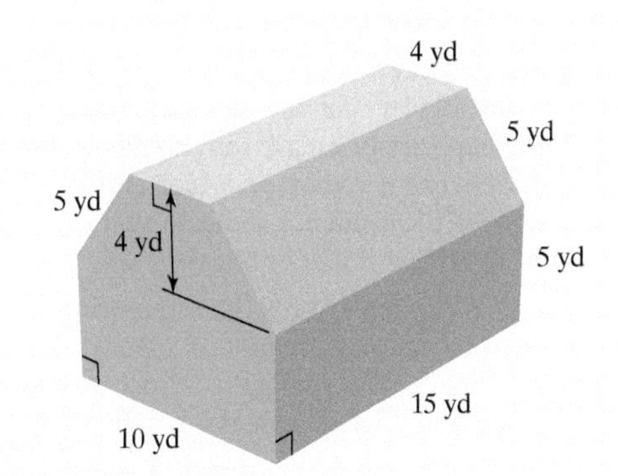

34. A machine produces open boxes using square sheets of metal measuring 12 inches on each side. The machine cuts equal-sized squares whose sides measure 2 inches from each corner. Then it shapes the metal into an open box by turning up the sides. Find the volume of the box.

35. Find the ratio, reduced to lowest terms, of the volume of a sphere with a radius of 3 inches to the volume of a sphere with a radius of 6 inches.

36. Find the ratio, reduced to lowest terms, of the volume of a sphere with a radius of 3 inches to the volume of a sphere with a radius of 9 inches.

37. A cylinder with radius 3 inches and height 4 inches has its radius tripled. How many times greater is the volume of the larger cylinder than the smaller cylinder?

38. A cylinder with radius 2 inches and height 3 inches has its radius quadrupled. How many times greater is the volume of the larger cylinder than the smaller cylinder?

Application Exercises

39. A building contractor is to dig a foundation 12 feet long, 9 feet wide, and 6 feet deep for a toll booth. The contractor pays $85 per load for trucks to remove the dirt. Each truck holds 6 cubic yards. What is the cost to the contractor to have all the dirt hauled away?

40. What is the cost of concrete for a walkway that is 15 feet long, 8 feet wide, and 9 inches deep if the concrete costs $30 per cubic yard?

41. A furnace is designed to heat 10,000 cubic feet. Will this furnace be adequate for a 1400-square-foot house with a 9-foot ceiling?

42. A water reservoir is shaped like a rectangular solid with a base that is 50 yards by 30 yards, and a vertical height of 20 yards. At the start of a three-month period of no rain, the reservoir was completely full. At the end of this period, the height of the water was down to 6 yards. How much water was used in the three-month period?

43. The Great Pyramid outside Cairo, Egypt, has a square base measuring 756 feet on a side and a height of 480 feet.

a. What is the volume of the Great Pyramid, in cubic yards?

b. The stones used to build the Great Pyramid were limestone blocks with an average volume of 1.5 cubic yards. How many of these blocks were needed to construct the Great Pyramid?

44. Although the Eiffel Tower in Paris is not a solid pyramid, its shape approximates that of a pyramid with a square base measuring 120 feet on a side and a height of 980 feet. If it were a solid pyramid, what would be the Eiffel Tower's volume, in cubic yards?

45. You are about to sue your contractor who promised to install a water tank that holds 500 gallons of water. You know that 500 gallons is the capacity of a tank that holds 67 cubic feet. The cylindrical tank has a radius of 3 feet and a height of 2 feet 4 inches. Does the evidence indicate you can win the case against the contractor if it goes to court?

46. Two cylindrical cans of soup sell for the same price. One can has a diameter of 6 inches and a height of 5 inches. The other has a diameter of 5 inches and a height of 6 inches. Which can contains more soup and, therefore, is the better buy?

47. A circular backyard pool has a diameter of 24 feet and is 4 feet deep. One cubic foot of water has a capacity of approximately 7.48 gallons. If water costs $2 per thousand gallons, how much, to the nearest dollar, will it cost to fill the pool?

48. The tunnel under the English Channel that connects England and France is the world's longest tunnel. There are actually three separate tunnels built side by side. Each is a half-cylinder that is 50,000 meters long and 4 meters high. How many cubic meters of dirt had to be removed to build the tunnel?

Writing in Mathematics

49. Explain the following analogy:

In terms of formulas used to compute volume, a pyramid is to a rectangular solid just as a cone is to a cylinder.

50. Explain why a cylinder is not a polyhedron.

Critical Thinking Exercises

Make Sense? *In Exercises 51–54, determine whether each statement makes sense or does not make sense, and explain your reasoning.*

51. The physical education department ordered new basketballs in the shape of right circular cylinders.

52. When completely full, a cylindrical soup can with a diameter of 3 inches and a height of 4 inches holds more soup than a cylindrical can with a diameter of 4 inches and a height of 3 inches.

53. I found the volume of a rectangular solid in cubic inches and then divided by 12 to convert the volume to cubic feet.

54. Because a cylinder is a solid figure, I use cubic units to express its surface area.

55. What happens to the volume of a sphere if its radius is doubled?

56. A scale model of a car is constructed so that its length, width, and height are each $\frac{1}{10}$ the length, width, and height of the actual car. By how many times does the volume of the car exceed its scale model?

In Exercises 57–58, find the volume of the darkly shaded region. If necessary, round to the nearest whole number.

57. **58.**

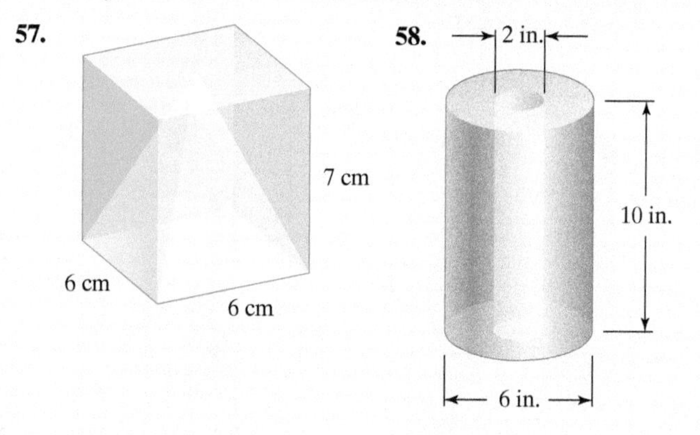

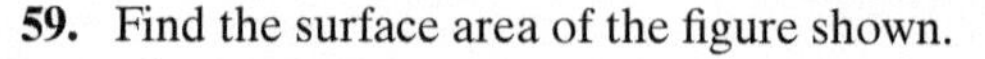

59. Find the surface area of the figure shown.

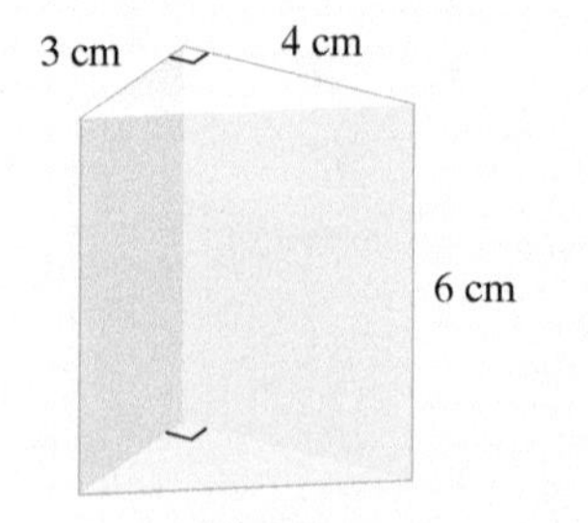

Chapter Summary, Review, and Test

SUMMARY – DEFINITIONS AND CONCEPTS

4.1 Points, Lines, Planes, and Angles

SUMMARY – DEFINITIONS AND CONCEPTS	EXAMPLES
a. Line AB ($\overleftrightarrow{AB}$ or $\overleftrightarrow{BA}$), half-line AB ($\overset{\circ\!\longrightarrow}{AB}$), ray AB ($\overrightarrow{AB}$), and line segment AB ($\overline{AB}$ or $\overline{BA}$) are represented in Figure 4.2 on page 120.	
b. Angles are measured in degrees. A degree, $1°$, is $\frac{1}{360}$ of a complete rotation. Acute angles measure less than $90°$, right angles $90°$, obtuse angles more than $90°$ but less than $180°$, and straight angles $180°$.	Ex. 1, p. 121
c. Complementary angles are two angles whose measures have a sum of $90°$. Supplementary angles are two angles whose measures have a sum of $180°$.	Ex. 2, p. 122; Ex. 3, p. 123
d. Vertical angles have the same measure.	Ex. 4, p. 123
e. If parallel lines are intersected by a transversal, alternate interior angles, alternate exterior angles, and corresponding angles have the same measure.	Ex. 5, p. 125

4.2 Triangles

SUMMARY – DEFINITIONS AND CONCEPTS	EXAMPLES
a. The sum of the measures of the three angles of any triangle is $180°$.	Ex. 1, p. 130; Ex. 2, p. 130
b. Triangles can be classified by angles (acute, right, obtuse) or by sides (isosceles, equilateral, scalene). See the box on page 131.	
c. Similar triangles have the same shape, but not necessarily the same size. Corresponding angles have the same measure and corresponding sides are proportional. If the measures of two angles of one triangle are equal to those of two angles of a second triangle, then the two triangles are similar.	Ex. 3, p. 132; Ex. 4, p. 133
d. The Pythagorean Theorem: The sum of the squares of the lengths of the legs of a right triangle equals the square of the length of the hypotenuse.	Ex. 5, p. 134; Ex. 6, p. 134

4.3 Polygons, Perimeter, and Tessellations

SUMMARY – DEFINITIONS AND CONCEPTS	EXAMPLES
a. A polygon is a closed geometric figure in a plane formed by three or more line segments. Names of some polygons, given in Table 4.2 on page 141, include triangles (three sides), quadrilaterals (four sides), pentagons (five sides), hexagons (six sides), heptagons (seven sides), and octagons (eight sides). A regular polygon is one whose sides are all the same length and whose angles all have the same measure. The perimeter of a polygon is the sum of the lengths of its sides.	Ex. 1, p. 142
b. Types of quadrilaterals, including the parallelogram, rhombus, rectangle, square, and trapezoid, and their characteristics, are given in Table 4.3 on page 141.	
c. The sum of the measures of the angles of an n-sided polygon is $(n - 2)180°$. If the n-sided polygon is a regular polygon, then each angle measures $\frac{(n-2)180°}{n}$.	Ex. 2, p. 143
d. A tessellation is a pattern consisting of the repeated use of the same geometric figures to completely cover a plane, leaving no gaps and having no overlaps. The angle requirement for the formation of a tessellation is that the sum of the measures of the angles at each vertex must be $360°$.	Ex. 3, p. 145

4.4 Area and Circumference

SUMMARY – DEFINITIONS AND CONCEPTS	EXAMPLES
a. Formulas for Area Rectangle: $A = lw$; Square: $A = s^2$; Parallelogram: $A = bh$; Triangle: $A = \frac{1}{2}bh$; Trapezoid: $A = \frac{1}{2}h(a + b)$	Ex. 1, p. 149; Ex. 2, p. 150; Ex. 3, p. 151; Ex. 4, p. 152; Ex. 5, p. 153
b. Circles Circumference: $C = 2\pi r$ or $C = \pi d$ Area: $A = \pi r^2$	Ex. 6, p. 154; Ex. 7, p. 154; Ex. 8, p. 155

4.5 Volume and Surface Area

a. Formulas for Volume Rectangular Solid: $V = lwh$; Cube: $V = s^3$; Pyramid: $V = \frac{1}{3}Bh$; Cylinder: $V = \pi r^2 h$; Cone: $V = \frac{1}{3}\pi r^2 h$ Sphere: $V = \frac{4}{3}\pi r^3$	Ex. 1, p. 161; Ex. 2, p. 161; Ex. 3, p. 162; Ex. 4, p. 163; Ex. 5, p. 164; Ex. 6, p. 164
b. Formulas for surface area are given in Table 4.4 on page 165.	Ex. 7, p. 165

Review Exercises

4.1

In the figure shown, lines l and m are parallel. In Exercises 1–7, match each term with the numbered angle or angles in the figure.

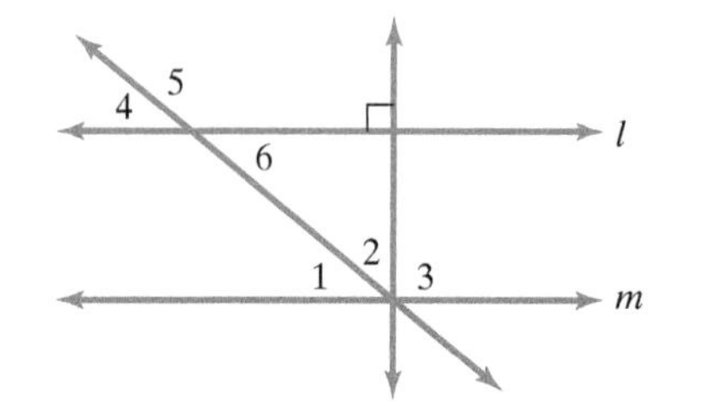

1. right angle

2. obtuse angle

3. vertical angles

4. alternate interior angles

5. corresponding angles

6. the complement of ∡1

7. the supplement of ∡6

In Exercises 8–9, find the measure of the angle in which a question mark with a degree symbol appears.

8.

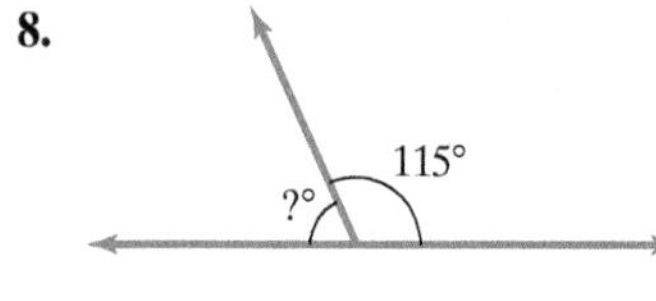

9.

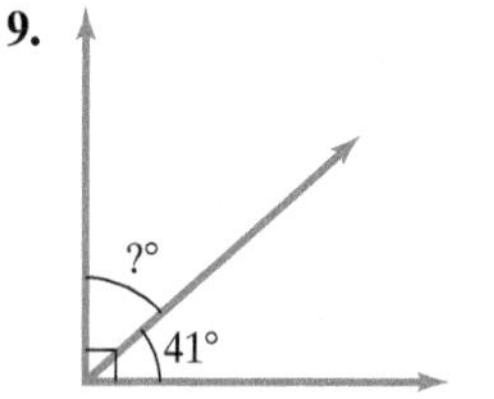
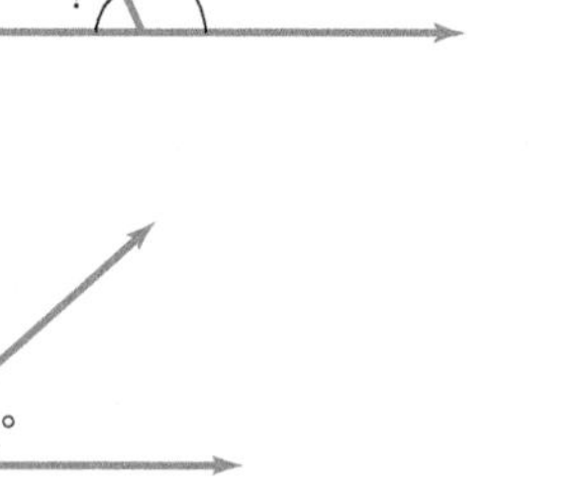

10. If an angle measures 73°, find the measure of its complement.

11. If an angle measures 46°, find the measure of its supplement.

12. In the figure shown, find the measures of angles 1, 2, and 3.

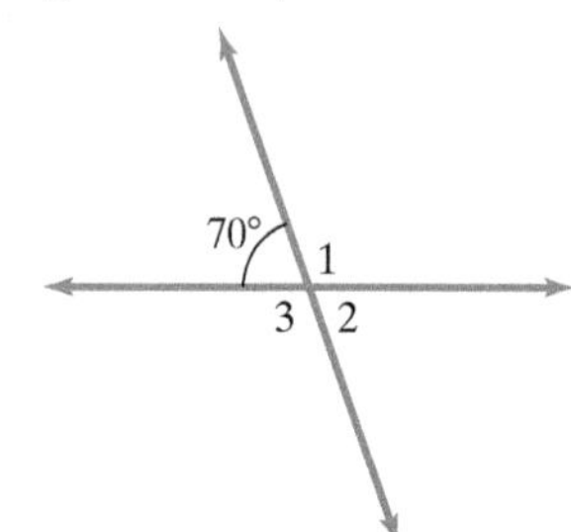

13. In the figure shown, two parallel lines are intersected by a transversal. One of the angle measures is given. Find the measure of each of the other seven angles.

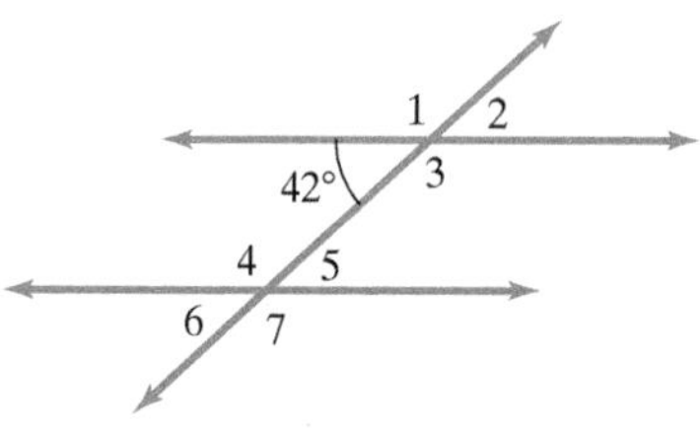

4.2

In Exercises 14–15, find the measure of angle A for the triangle shown.

14. **15.**

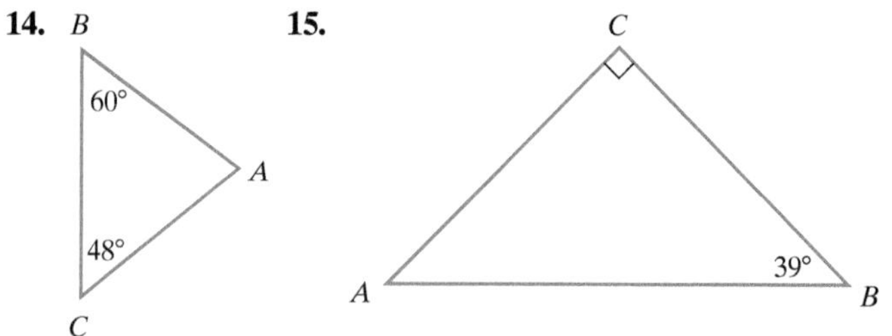

16. Find the measures of angles 1 through 5 in the figure shown.

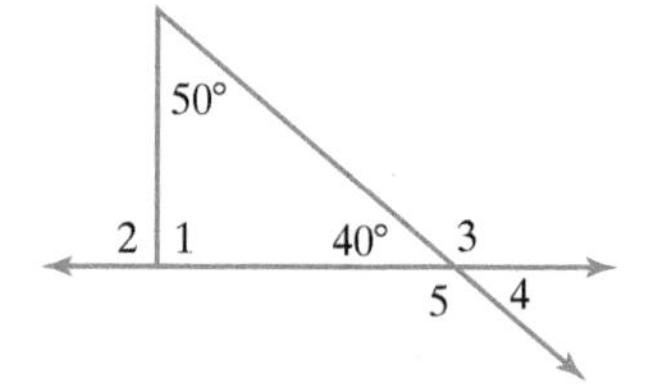

17. In the figure shown, lines l and m are parallel. Find the measure of each numbered angle.

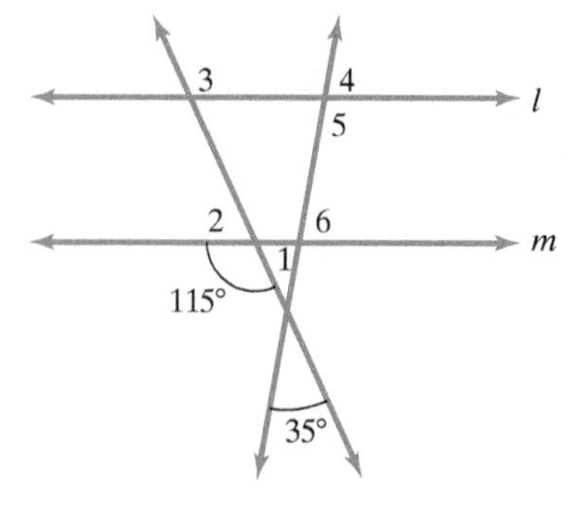

In Exercises 18–19, use similar triangles and the fact that corresponding sides are proportional to find the length of each side marked with an x.

18.

19.

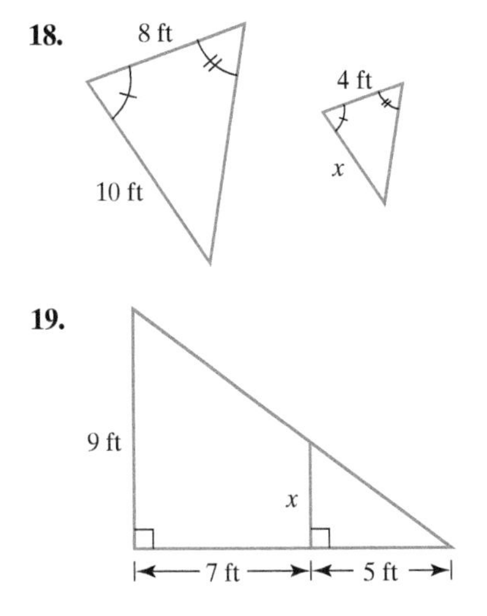

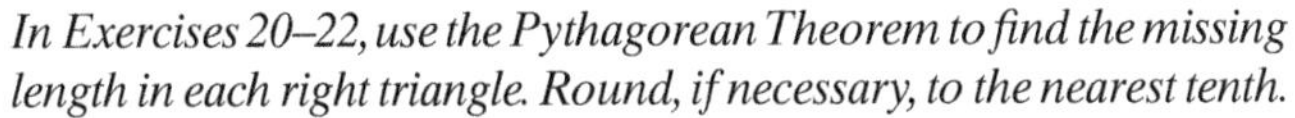

In Exercises 20–22, use the Pythagorean Theorem to find the missing length in each right triangle. Round, if necessary, to the nearest tenth.

20.

21.

22.

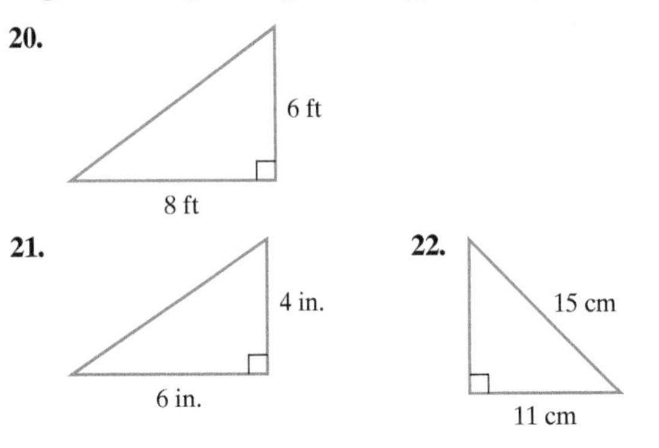

23. Find the height of the lamppost in the figure.

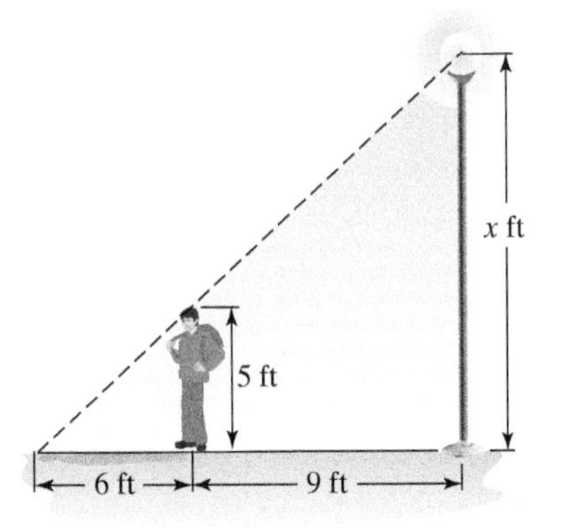

24. How far away from the building in the figure shown is the bottom of the ladder?

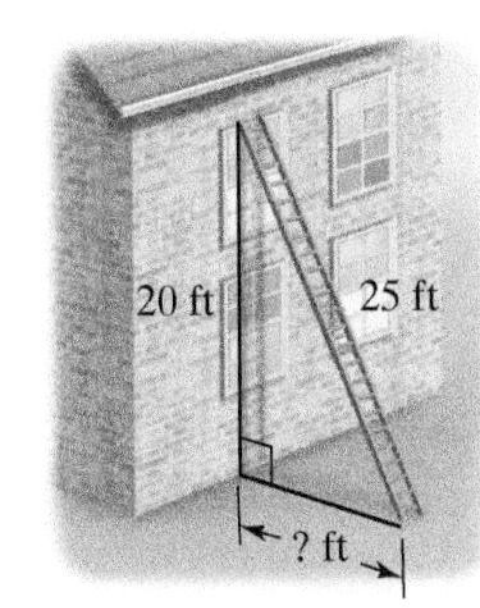

25. A vertical pole is to be supported by three wires. Each wire is 13 yards long and is anchored 5 yards from the base of the pole. How far up the pole will the wires be attached?

4.3

26. Write the names of all quadrilaterals that always have four right angles.

27. Write the names of all quadrilaterals with four sides always having the same measure.

28. Write the names of all quadrilaterals that do not always have four angles with the same measure.

In Exercises 29–31, find the perimeter of the figure shown. Express the perimeter using the same unit of measure that appears in the figure.

29.

30.

31.

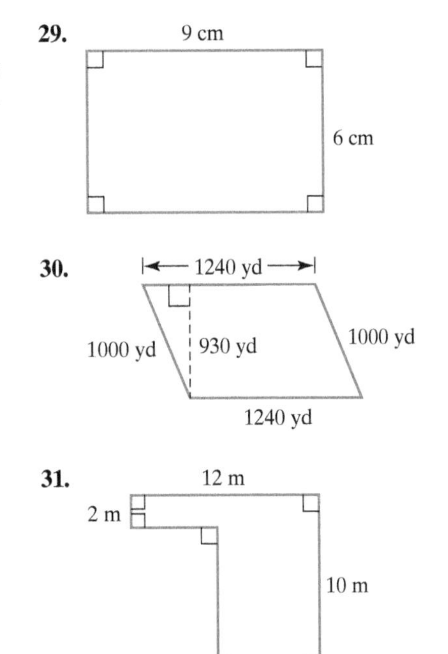

32. Find the sum of the measures of the angles of a 12-sided polygon.

33. Find the sum of the measures of the angles of an octagon.

34. The figure shown is a regular polygon. Find the measures of angle 1 and angle 2.

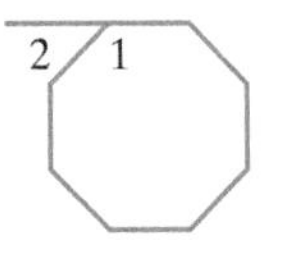

35. A carpenter is installing a baseboard around a room that has a length of 35 feet and a width of 15 feet. The room has four doorways and each doorway is 3 feet wide. If no baseboard is to be put across the doorways and the cost of the baseboard is $1.50 per foot, what is the cost of installing the baseboard around the room?

36. Use the following tessellation to solve this exercise.

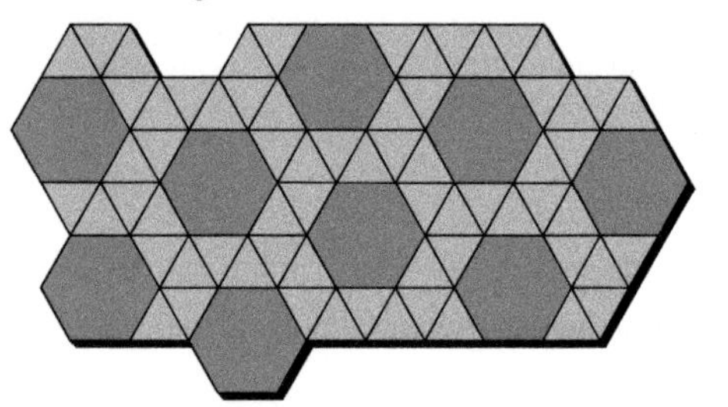

a. Name the types of regular polygons that surround each vertex.
b. Determine the number of angles that come together at each vertex, as well as the measures of these angles.
c. Use the angle measures from part (b) to explain why the tessellation is possible.

37. Can a tessellation be created using only regular hexagons? Explain your answer.

4.4

In Exercises 38–41, find the area of each figure.

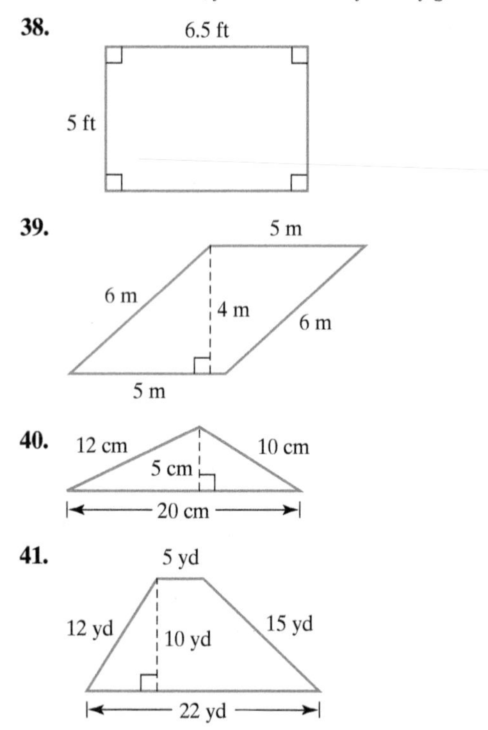

42. Find the circumference and the area of a circle with a diameter of 20 meters. Express answers in terms of π and then round to the nearest tenth.

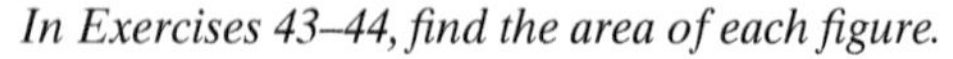

In Exercises 43–44, find the area of each figure.

43.

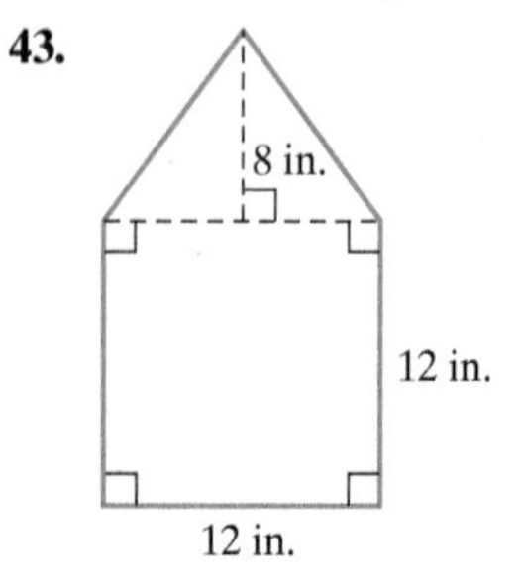

44.

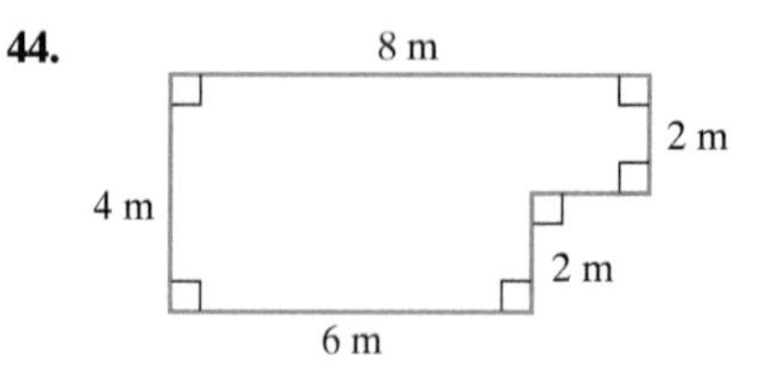

In Exercises 45–46, find the area of each shaded region. Where necessary, express answers in terms of π and then round to the nearest tenth.

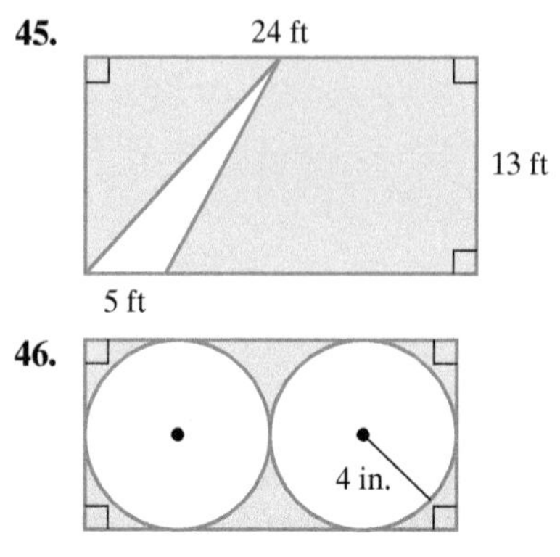

47. What will it cost to carpet a rectangular floor measuring 15 feet by 21 feet if the carpet costs \$22.50 per square yard?

48. What will it cost to cover a rectangular floor measuring 40 feet by 50 feet with square tiles that measure 2 feet on each side if a package of 10 tiles costs \$13?

49. How much fencing, to the nearest whole yard, is needed to enclose a circular garden that measures 10 yards across?

4.5

In Exercises 50–54, find the volume of each figure. Where necessary, express answers in terms of π and then round to the nearest whole number.

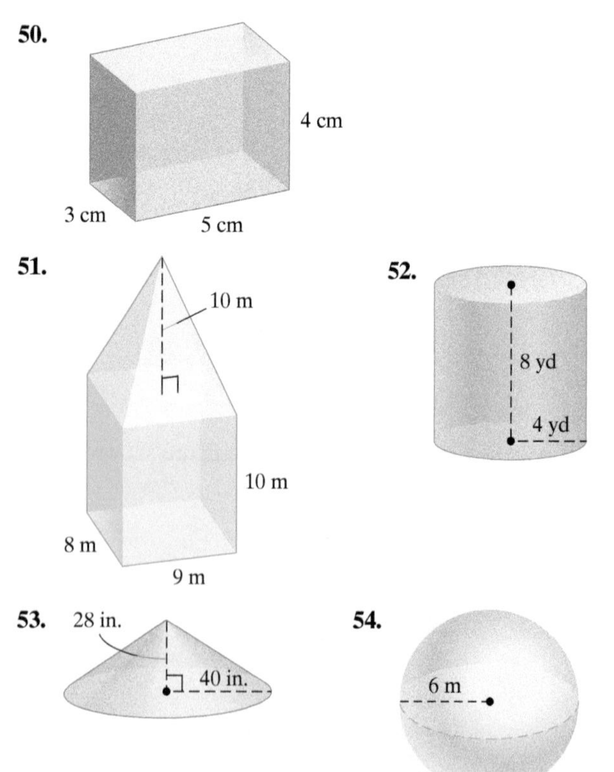

55. Find the surface area of the figure shown.

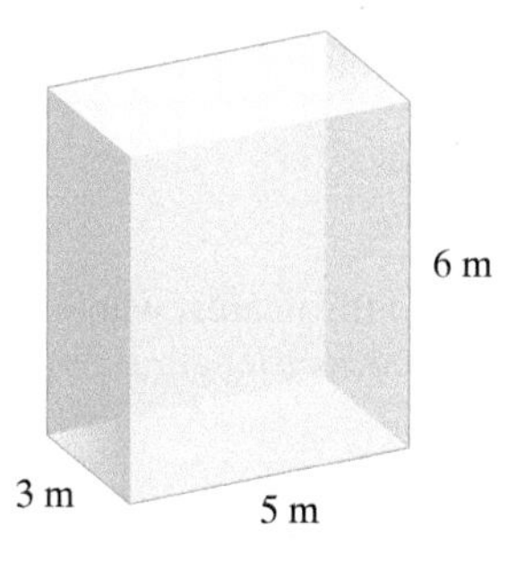

56. A train is being loaded with shipping boxes. Each box is 8 meters long, 4 meters wide, and 3 meters high. If there are 50 shipping boxes, how much space is needed?

57. An Egyptian pyramid has a square base measuring 145 meters on each side. If the height of the pyramid is 93 meters, find its volume.

58. What is the cost of concrete for a walkway that is 27 feet long, 4 feet wide, and 6 inches deep if the concrete is $40 per cubic yard?

Chapter 4 Test

1. If an angle measures 54°, find the measure of its complement and supplement.

In Exercises 2–4, use the figure shown to find the measure of angle 1.

2.

3.

4.

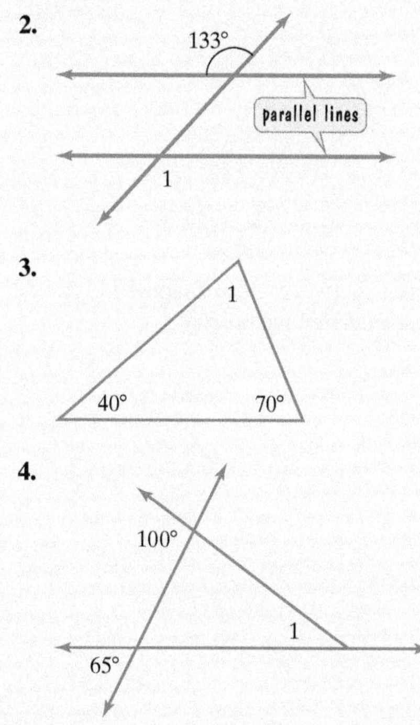

5. The triangles in the figure are similar. Find the length of the side marked with an x.

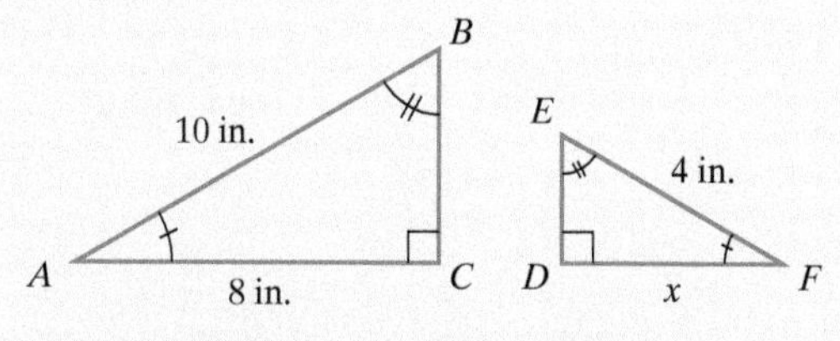

6. A vertical pole is to be supported by three wires. Each wire is 26 feet long and is anchored 24 feet from the base of the pole. How far up the pole should the wires be attached?

7. Find the sum of the measures of the angles of a ten-sided polygon.

8. Find the perimeter of the figure shown.

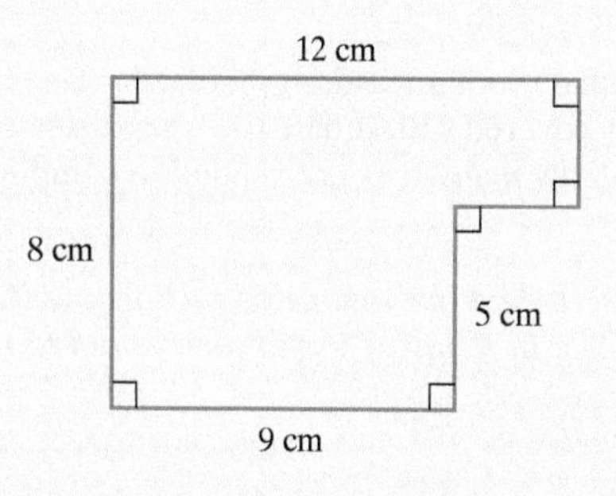

9. Which one of the following names a quadrilateral in which the sides that meet at each vertex have the same measure?
a. rectangle **b.** parallelogram
c. trapezoid **d.** rhombus

10. Use the following tessellation to solve this exercise.

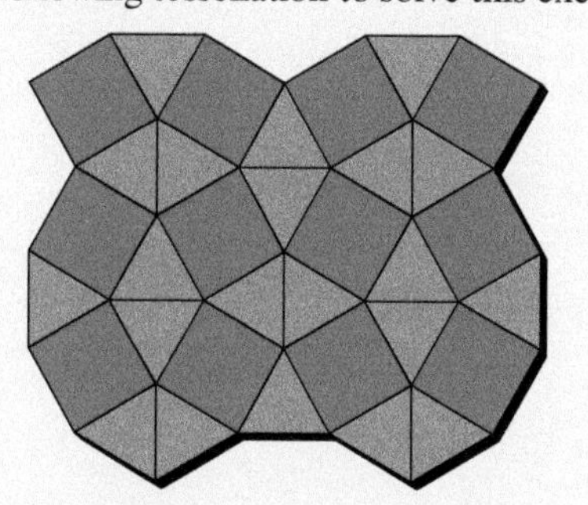

a. Name the types of regular polygons that surround each vertex.
b. Determine the number of angles that come together at each vertex, as well as the measures of these angles.
c. Use the angle measures from part (b) to explain why the tessellation is possible.

In Exercises 11–12, find the area of each figure.

11.

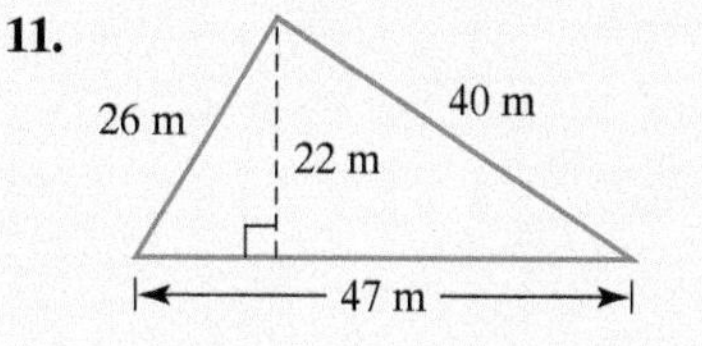

12.

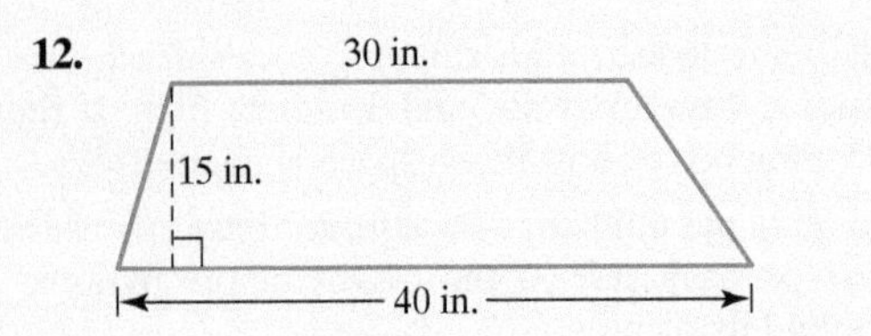

13. The right triangle shown has one leg of length 5 centimeters and a hypotenuse of length 13 centimeters.

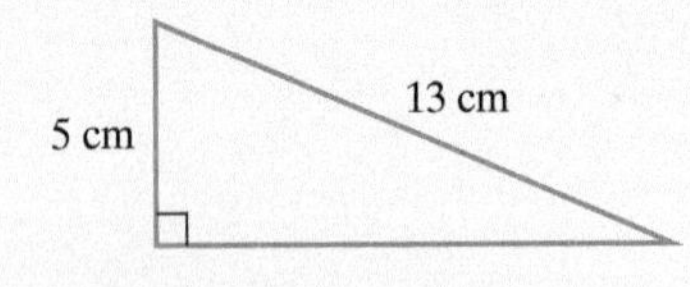

a. Find the length of the other leg.
b. What is the perimeter of the triangle?
c. What is the area of the triangle?

14. Find the circumference and area of a circle with a diameter of 40 meters. Express answers in terms of π and then round to the nearest tenth.

15. A rectangular floor measuring 8 feet by 6 feet is to be completely covered with square tiles measuring 8 inches on each side. How many tiles are needed to completely cover the floor?

In Exercises 16–18, find the volume of each figure. If necessary, express the answer in terms of π and then round to the nearest whole number.

16.

17.

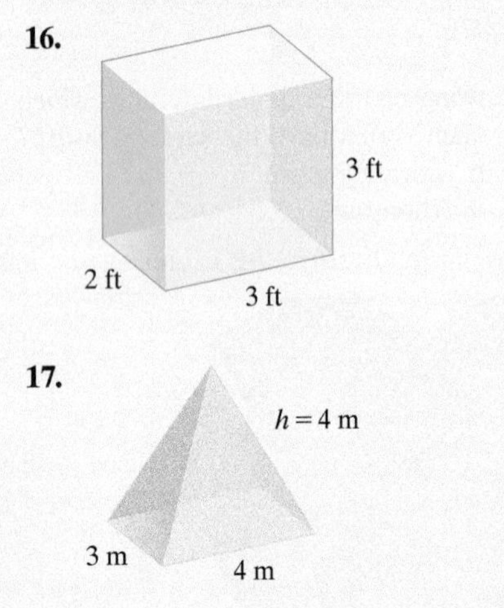

18.

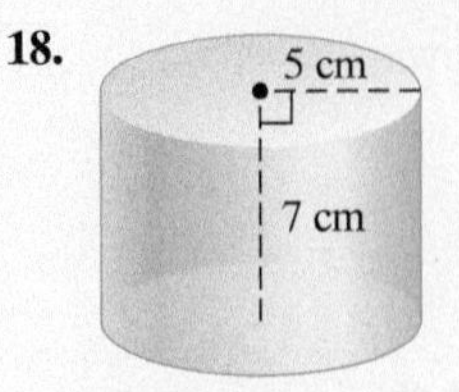

19. Find the measure, to the nearest whole number, of the side of the right triangle whose length is designated by c.

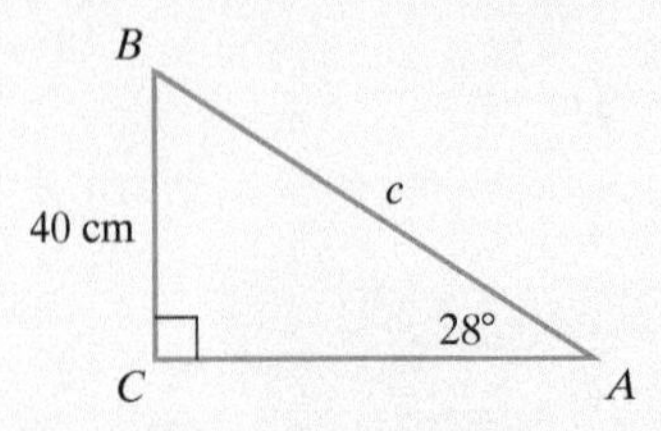

20. At a certain time of day, the angle of elevation of the sun is 34°. If a building casts a shadow measuring 104 feet, find the height of the building to the nearest foot.

21. Determine if the graph shown is traversable. If it is, describe a path that will traverse it.

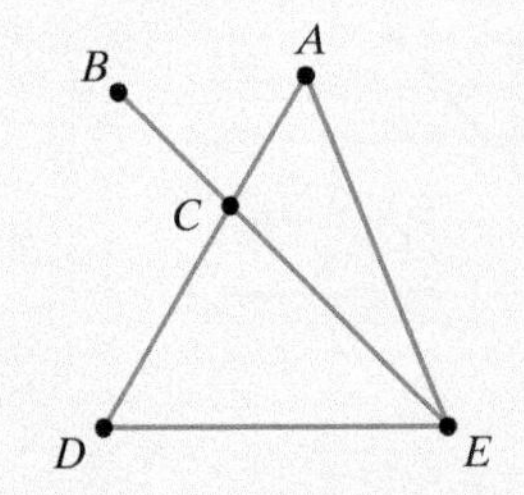

22. Describe a difference between the shapes of fractal geometry and those of Euclidean geometry.

Statistics

Objective	Sample Problems		For help, go to page
When you finish this chapter, you will be able to:			
1. Read bar graphs, line graphs, and circle graphs.	Trades Management From the bar graph below,		178
	(a) Determine the number of frames assembled by the Tuesday day shift.	________	
	(b) Calculate the percent decrease in output from the Monday day shift to the Monday night shift.	________	

Weekly Frame Assembly

Number of Frames: 0, 10, 20, 30, 40, 50, 60, 70, 80, 90, 100

Day / Night

Monday, Tuesday, Wednesday, Thursday, Friday

Day of Week

Monthly Paint Jobs at Autobrite

Number of Jobs: 0, 10, 20, 30, 40, 50, 60, 70

January, February, March, April, May, June

Month

Problems (c) and (d) refer to the line graph above,		186
(c) Determine the maximum number of paint jobs and the month during which it occurred.	________	
(d) Calculate the percent increase in the number of paint jobs from January to February.	________	
(e) The average job for ABC Plumbing generates \$227.50. Use the circle graph on the next page to calculate what portion of this amount is spent on advertising.	________	190

Name ______________________

Date ______________________

Course/Section ______________________

Objective	Sample Problems	For help, go to page

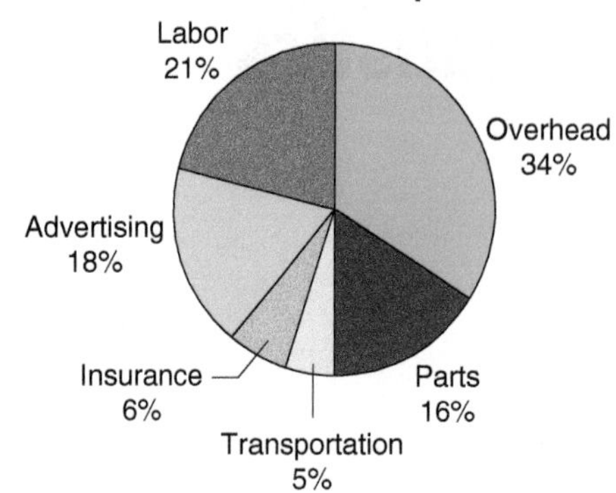

2. Draw bar graphs, line graphs, and circle graphs from tables of data.

Work Output	Day
150	Mon
360	Tues
435	Wed
375	Thurs
180	Fri

Trades Management For the data in the table, draw:

(a) A bar graph. 182
(b) A line graph. 189
(c) A circle graph. 191

3. Calculate measures of central tendency: mean.

Find the mean, for the following set of lengths. All measurements are in meters.

12.7 16.2 15.5 13.9 13.2 17.1 15.5 204

(Answers to these preview problems are given in the Appendix.)

If you cannot work one or more of the preview problems, turn to the page indicated after the problem. Those who wish to master this material with the greatest success should turn to Section 5-1 and begin work there.

Statistics

Working with the flood of information available to us today is a major problem for scientists, technicians, business and finance personnel, and those in management positions. We need ways to organize and analyze numerical data in order to make it meaningful and useful. **Statistics** is a branch of mathematics that provides us with the tools we need to do this. In this chapter, you will learn the basics of how to prepare and read statistical graphs, calculate some statistical measures, and use these to help analyze data. This chapter features many examples of how people in **trades management** apply statistics, including the following:

- Analyzing a graph of monthly tire sales (Section 5-1, Example 6)
- Reading a graph showing energy consumption of gas appliances (Exercises 5-1, A-2)
- Plotting a graph of auto sales data (Exercises 5-1, B-8)
- Analyzing sales trends to make purchasing decisions

5-1 Reading and Constructing Graphs

Note In discussing statistics, we often use the word *data*. The word *data* refers to a collection of measurement numbers that describe some specific characteristic of an object or person or a group of objects or people. ●

Reading Bar Graphs

Graphs allow us to transform a collection of measurement numbers into a visual form that is useful, simplified, and brief. Every graph tells a story that you need to be able to read.

A **bar graph** is used to display and compare the sizes of different but related quantities. The lengths of the bars are meant to convey a general sense of magnitude but not necessarily precise numerical quantities. The bars are usually arranged in either ascending or descending order of magnitude. On a **vertical bar graph**, the bars are oriented vertically, and their labels appear underneath them along the **horizontal axis**. The numerical scale appears along the left **vertical axis**. By aligning the top of a bar horizontally with this scale, we can estimate the numerical value of the quantity represented by the bar.

EXAMPLE 1 **Allied Health** The following vertical bar graph shows the average annual health-care cost per person in six different countries in 2010.

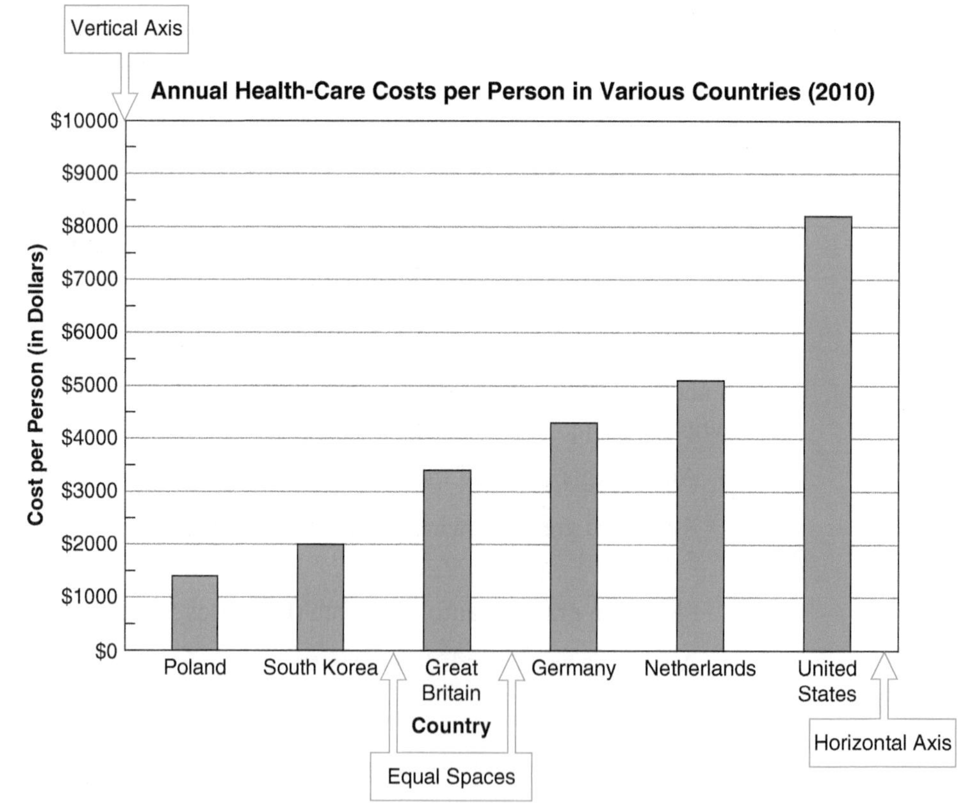

(*Source:* OECD Health Data 2012)

The countries being compared are listed, equally spaced, along the horizontal axis. The cost, in dollars, is shown along the vertical axis. The numbers are listed in thousand-dollar increments, and tick marks halfway between the numbers represent \$500, \$1500, \$2500, and so on. Horizontal lines are drawn across the graph at the thousand-dollar intervals. This scale allows the reader to estimate the annual cost to about the nearest hundred dollars. For example,

- The average cost of health care during 2010 in South Korea was about $2000 per person because the top of the South Korea bar coincides exactly with the $2000 line.
- The top of the bar representing Poland is just below the $1500 tick mark, so we can estimate that Poland's 2010 health-care cost was about $1400 per person.

We can also use the graph to make some rough calculations. For example, suppose we wish to know the *total* cost of health care in the United States during 2010. From the graph, we can estimate the cost per person to be about $8200. The average population of the United States in 2010 was about 309,000,000. Multiplying these two numbers and rounding to two significant digits, we can conclude that the total cost of health care in the United States in 2010 was approximately $2,500,000,000,000, or $2.5 trillion.

Your Turn **Allied Health** Use the graph in Example 1 to answer the following questions:

(a) What was the average cost of health care per person in Germany in 2010, to the nearest hundred dollars?

(b) By what percent did the cost per person in the Netherlands exceed that of Great Britain?

Answers (a) $4300 (b) 50%

On a horizontal bar graph, the bars are oriented horizontally, the category labels are listed along the left vertical axis, and the numerical scale is on the horizontal axis.

EXAMPLE 2 **Automotive Trades** The following bar graph compares the approximate costs of driving seven different fuel-efficient cars over a distance of 25 miles.

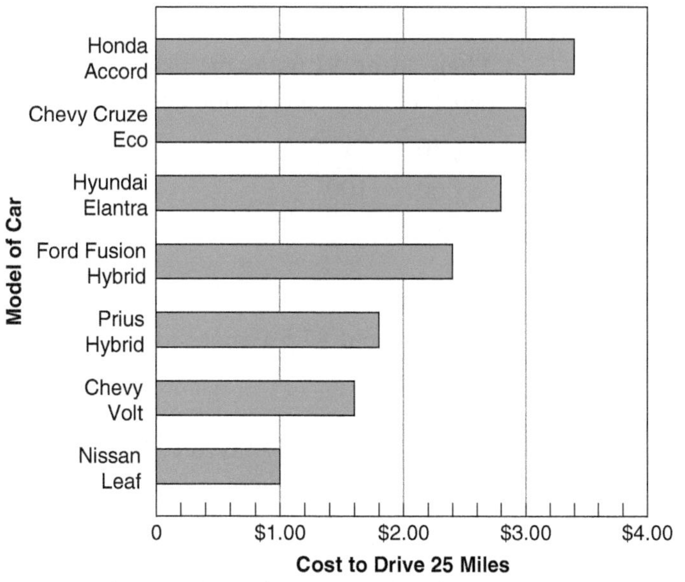

(*Source:* Environmental Protection Agency, Union of Concerned Scientists)

This is a horizontal bar graph. The different car models are listed on the vertical axis, and the numerical scale is on the horizontal axis. Labels are placed on the numerical scale at one-dollar increments, but each tick mark represents a $0.20

increment. Therefore, we can estimate that a Prius hybrid costs about \$1.80 to drive 25 miles, while a Ford Fusion hybrid costs \$2.40. We can calculate the approximate cost to drive a Hyundai Elantra for 5000 miles using a proportion, as follows:

$$\frac{5000}{25} = \frac{x}{\$2.80}$$

$$25x = \$14{,}000$$

$$x = \$560$$

Your Turn **Automotive Trades** Use the graph in Example 2 to answer the following questions:

(a) How much does it cost to drive the Nissan Leaf a distance of 25 miles?

(b) How much more would it cost to drive the Honda Accord 1000 miles compared to a Nissan Leaf?

(c) By what percent does the cost of driving a Chevy Cruze Eco exceed that of a Chevy Volt?

Solutions (a) \$1.00

(b) **First,** subtract to find the cost difference for driving 25 miles:

$$\$3.40 - \$1.00 = \$2.40$$

Then, use a proportion to calculate the cost difference for 1000 miles:

$$\frac{1000}{25} = \frac{x}{\$2.40}$$

$$25x = \$2400$$

$$x = \$96$$

It costs approximately \$96 more to drive a Honda Accord 1000 miles than it does to drive a Nissan Leaf.

(c) **First,** subtract to find the difference in the 25-miles costs of the two models:

$$\$3.00 - \$1.60 = \$1.40$$

Then, using \$1.60 as the base and \$1.40 as the amount of increase, set up a percent change proportion and solve:

$$\frac{\$1.40}{\$1.60} = \frac{x}{100}$$

$$\$1.60x = \$140$$

$$x = 87.5\%$$

It costs about 87.5% more to drive a Chevy Cruze Eco than it does to drive a Chevy Volt.

If the quantity being displayed consists of two or more parts, we can split each bar into sections using different colors or shading to show the magnitude of each part.

EXAMPLE 3 **Automotive Trades** The following sectioned bar graph compares the average cost per gallon of gas in nine different countries during the spring of 2013. The lighter, lower section of each bar shows the portion of each price represented by taxes. The scale of the graph allows us to estimate the costs to the nearest 25 cents. For example, a gallon of gas in New Zealand had an average price of about \$6.75, of which about \$1.25 represented taxes.

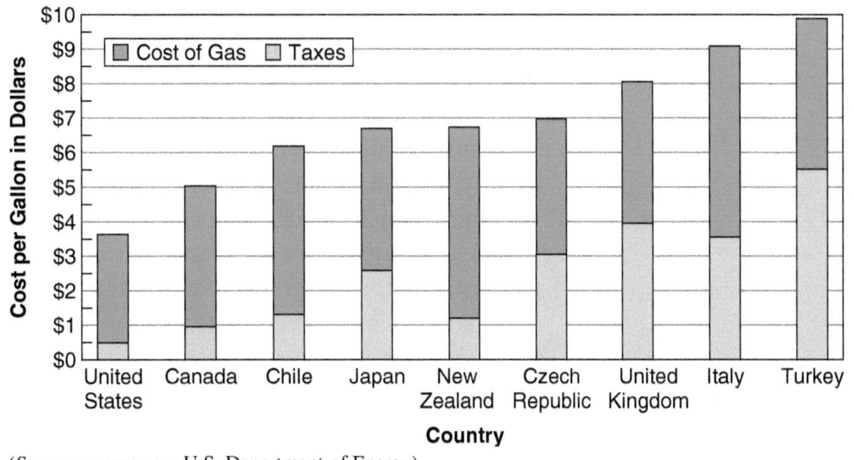

(*Sources:* energy.eu, U.S. Department of Energy)

Your Turn **Automotive Trades** Use the graph in Example 3 to answer the following questions. Estimate the costs per gallon to the nearest $0.25.

(a) What was the total cost for a gallon of gas in Canada?

(b) In the United Kingdom, what was the dollar amount per gallon represented by taxes?

(c) In Italy, what percent of the total cost per gallon was represented by taxes?

(d) How much more did it cost to fill up a 16-gallon tank in Turkey than it did in the United States?

(e) By what percent did the total cost of a gallon of gas in the Czech Republic exceed the cost in Chile?

Answers (a) $5.00 (b) $4.00 (c) 39% (d) about $100 (e) 12%

A **multiple bar graph** allows us to show side-by-side comparisons of related quantities on the same graph.

EXAMPLE 4 **Allied Health** The following horizontal double-bar graph shows the amounts of fat and protein per ounce for four different types of nuts. Both are measured in grams.

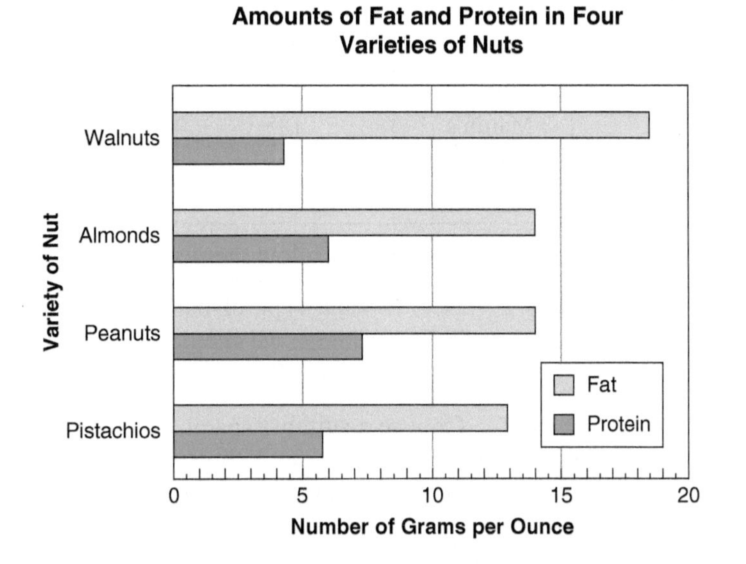

The main purpose of the graph is to compare the relative amounts of fat and protein contained in each type of nut. For example, we can see that walnuts contain the largest amount of fat per ounce and the smallest amount of protein per ounce. The scale also allows us to estimate the actual amounts of fat and protein to about the nearest 0.25 grams. For example, we can estimate that one ounce of almonds contains about 14 grams of fat, while one ounce of pistachios contains about 5.75 grams of protein. Finally, we can use these approximate numbers to perform various calculations. For example, if we ate four ounces of almonds, we would be consuming approximately (4 oz) × (14 g/oz), or 56 grams, of fat. If we wanted to eat enough pistachios to give us 20 grams of protein, we would divide 20 grams by 5.75 grams per ounce and find that we would need to eat about 3.5 ounces of pistachios.

Your Turn **Allied Health** Use the graph in Example 4 to answer the following questions:

(a) Which nut contains the least amount of fat per ounce?

(b) Which nut contains the most amount of protein per ounce?

(c) How many grams of fat are contained in six ounces of peanuts?

(d) How many ounces of almonds do we need to eat in order to consume 60 grams of protein?

Solutions

(a) Pistachios

(b) Peanuts

(c) $(6 \text{ oz})(14 \text{ g/oz}) = 84 \text{ g}$

(d) $(60 \text{ g}) \div (6 \text{ g/oz}) = 10 \text{ oz}$

Drawing Bar Graphs

Usually, a bar graph is created not from mathematical theory or abstractions, but from a set of measurement numbers.

EXAMPLE 5 **Retail Merchandising** Suppose you want to display the following data in a bar graph showing sales of DVD players and televisions in five stores.

Quarterly Sales of DVD Players and TVs in Five Stores

Store	DVD Players	Televisions
Ace	140	65
Wilson's	172	130
Martin's	185	200
XXX	195	285
Shop-Rite	190	375

To draw a bar graph, follow these steps:

Step 1 Decide what type of bar graph to use. Because we are comparing two different items, we should use a double bar graph. The bars can be placed either horizontally or vertically. In this case let's make the bars horizontal.

Step 2 Choose a suitable spacing for the vertical (side) axis and a suitable scale for the horizontal (bottom) axis. Label each axis. When you label the vertical or side axis it should read in the normal way.

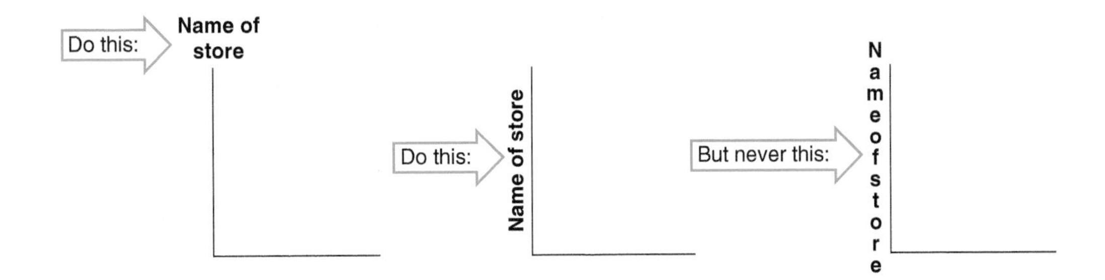

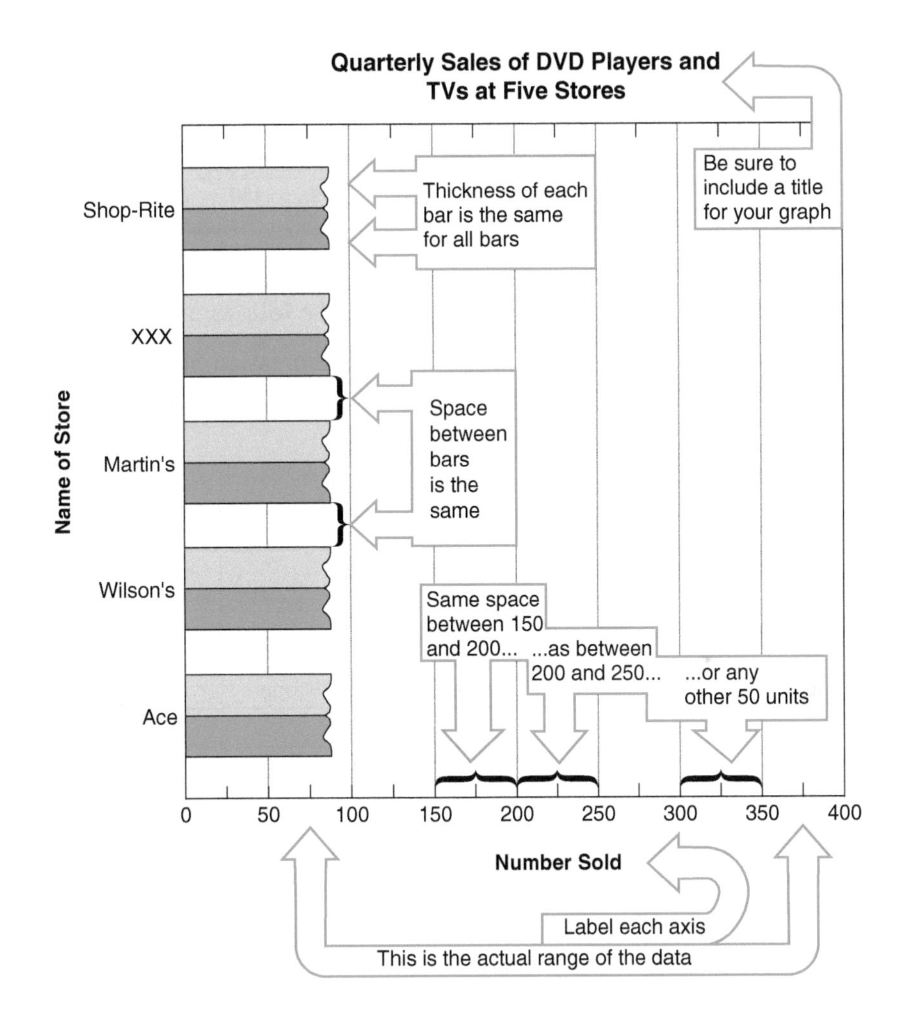

Notice that the numbers on the bottom axis are evenly spaced and end at 400, just past the highest value in the set of data. Because each bar provides a visual indication of magnitude, it is preferable to begin the numerical scale at zero.

Also notice that the stores were arranged in order of amount of sales. The biggest seller, Shop-Rite, is at the top, and the smallest seller, Ace, is at the bottom. This is not necessary, but it makes the graph easier to read.

Step 3 Use a straightedge to mark the length of each bar according to the data given. Round the numbers if necessary. Drawing your bar graph on graph paper will make the process easier.

The final bar graph will look like this:

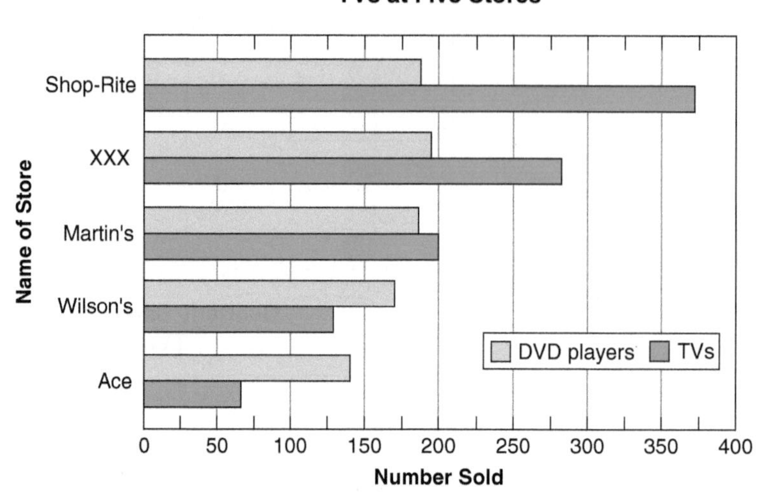

Your Turn (a) **Construction** Use the following data to make a vertical bar graph.

Average Ultimate Compression Strength of Common Materials

Material	Compression Strength (psi)
Hard bricks	12,000
Light red bricks	1,000
Portland cement	3,000
Portland concrete	1,000
Granite	19,000
Limestone and sandstone	9,000
Trap rock	20,000
Slate	14,000

(b) **General Interest** The following table shows the total enrollments and the total female enrollments at colleges and universities from 1965 to 2010, in five-year increments. Construct a bar graph of these data similar to the one in Example 3, where each bar consists of two sections, one representing female enrollment and the other representing male enrollment.

Year	Total Enrollment (in millions)	Total Female Enrollment (in millions)
1965	5.9	2.3
1970	8.6	3.5
1975	11.2	5.0
1980	12.1	6.2
1985	12.3	6.4
1990	13.8	7.5
1995	14.3	7.9
2000	15.3	8.6
2005	17.5	10.0
2010	21.0	12.0

(*Source:* National Center for Educational Statistics, U.S. Department of Education)

(c) **Transportation** The following table shows the percentage of teenagers and young adults with driver's licenses in 1983 and in 2010. Construct a double-bar graph illustrating these data. The categories along the horizontal axis will be the age groups, and for each age group there will be two bars: one for 1983 and one for 2010.

Age	1983	2010
16	46.2%	28.1%
17	68.9%	46.2%
18	80.4%	60.7%
19	87.3%	69.5%
20–24	91.8%	80.9%
25–29	95.6%	87.3%

(*Source:* Michael Sivak and Brandon Schoettle, University of Michigan)

Solutions (a)

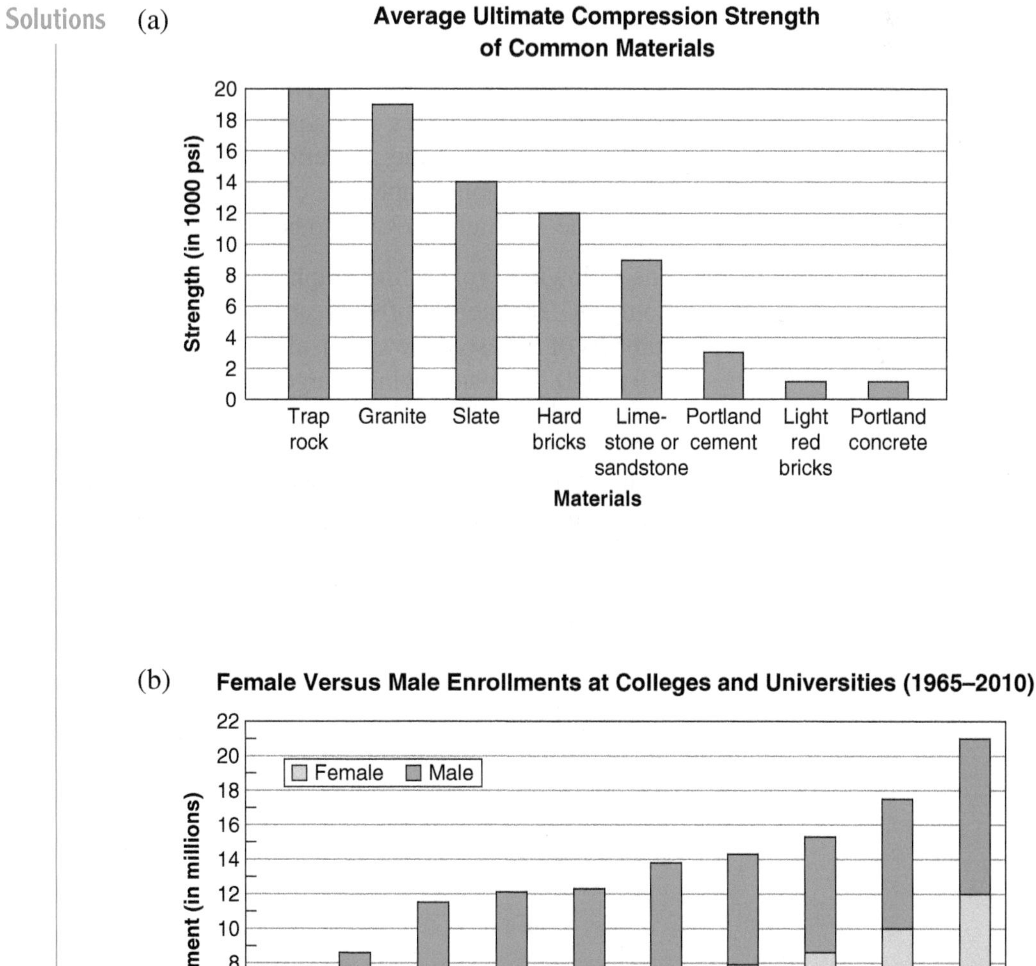

(b)

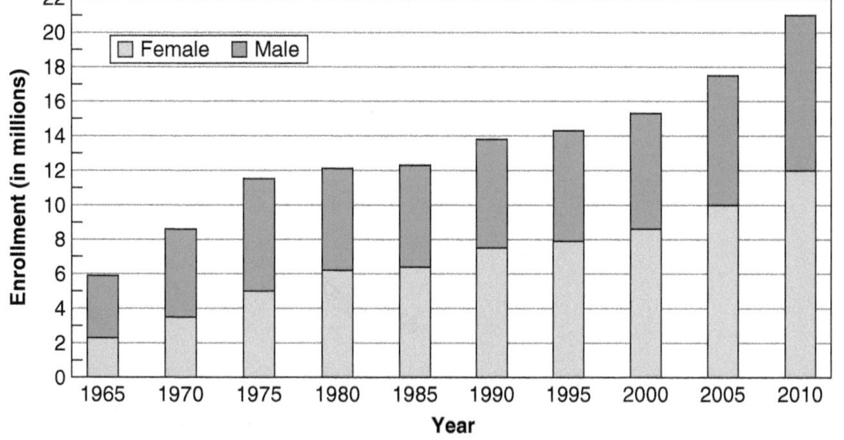

(c)

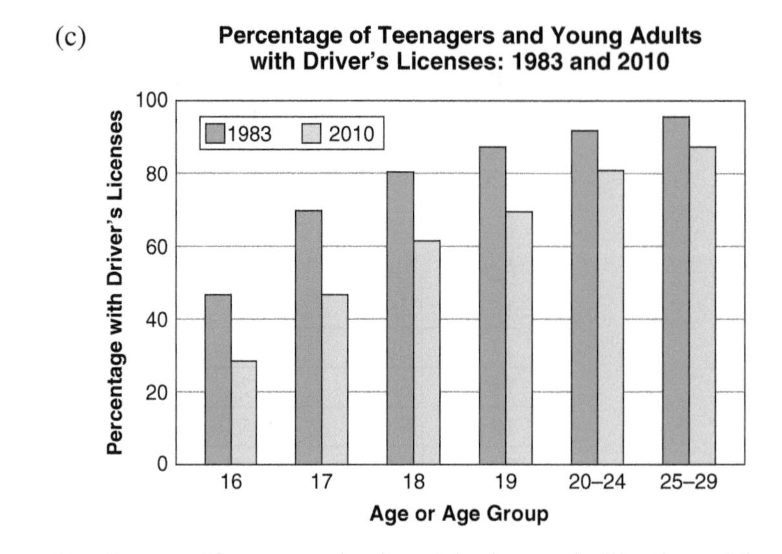

Don't worry if your graphs do not look exactly like these. The only requirement is that all of the data be displayed clearly and accurately.

A Closer Look Notice that the vertical scales in the previous graphs have units of "*thousands* of pounds per square inch" and "millions of students". They were drawn this way to save space.

Reading Line Graphs

A **line graph**, or **broken-line graph**, is a display that shows the change in a quantity, usually as it changes over a period of time. Time is always displayed along the horizontal axis, and the numerical scale is always shown on the vertical axis. Because line graphs emphasize changes and patterns over time more than they do magnitude, it is not necessary to begin the vertical axis at zero.

The following broken-line graph shows monthly sales of tires at Treadwell Tire Company. The months of the year are indicated along the horizontal axis, while the numbers of tires sold are shown along the vertical axis. The actual data ranges from 550 to 950. To avoid having a large empty space below the broken line, we begin the vertical axis at 500. Each interval represents 50 tires, and the vertical axis ends at 1000 tires, just slightly above the largest data value. Each dot represents the number of tires sold in the month that is directly below the dot, and straight line segments connect the dots to show the monthly fluctuations in sales.

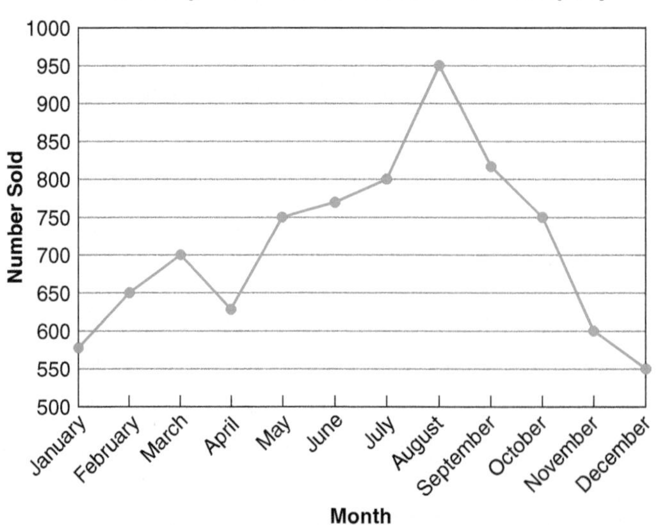

The following example illustrates how to read information from a broken-line graph.

EXAMPLE 6 **Trades Management** To find the number of tires sold in May, find May along the horizontal axis and follow the perpendicular line up to the graph. From this point, look directly across to the vertical axis and read or estimate the number sold. There were approximately 750 tires sold in May.

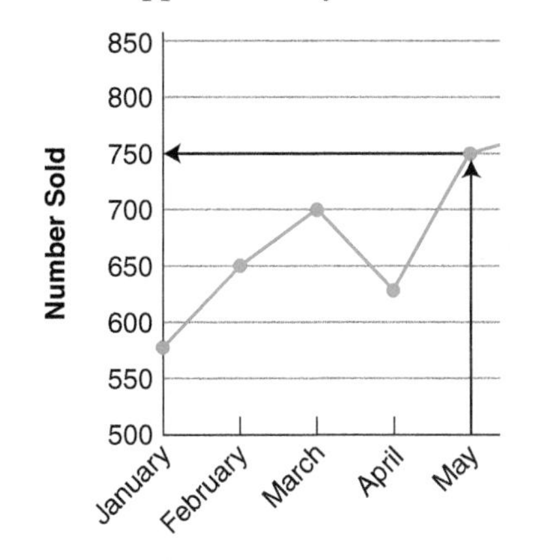

Other useful information can be gathered from the graph:

The highest monthly total was 950 in August.
The largest jump in sales occurred from July to August, with sales rising from 800 to 950 tires. To calculate the percent increase in August, set up the following proportion:

$$\frac{950 - 800}{800} = \frac{R}{100} \quad \text{or} \quad \frac{150}{800} = \frac{R}{100}$$

$$R = \frac{150 \cdot 100}{800}$$

$$= 18.75\%$$

The increase in sales from July to August was approximately 19%.

Your Turn **Trades Management** Answer the following questions about the graph of monthly tire sales.

(a) What was the lowest monthly total, and when did this occur?

(b) How many tires were sold during the first three months of the year combined?

(c) During which two consecutive months did the largest drop in sales occur? By what percent did sales decrease?

Solutions (a) Only 550 tires were sold in December.

(b) We estimate that 580 tires were sold in January, 650 in February, and 700 in March. Adding these, we get a total of 1930 for the three months.

(c) The largest drop in sales occurred from October to November, when sales decreased from 750 to 600. Calculating the percent decrease, we have

$$\frac{750 - 600}{750} = \frac{R}{100} \quad \text{or} \quad \frac{150}{750} = \frac{R}{100}$$

$$R = \frac{150 \cdot 100}{750}$$

$$= 20\%$$

Sales decreased by 20% from October to November.

If we wish to compare changes over time of two or more related quantities, we can use a multiple-line graph.

EXAMPLE 7 Life Skills The following double-line graph compares the median home prices in Duneville with those in Surf City. The graph covers the 13-month period from January 2012 through February 2013.

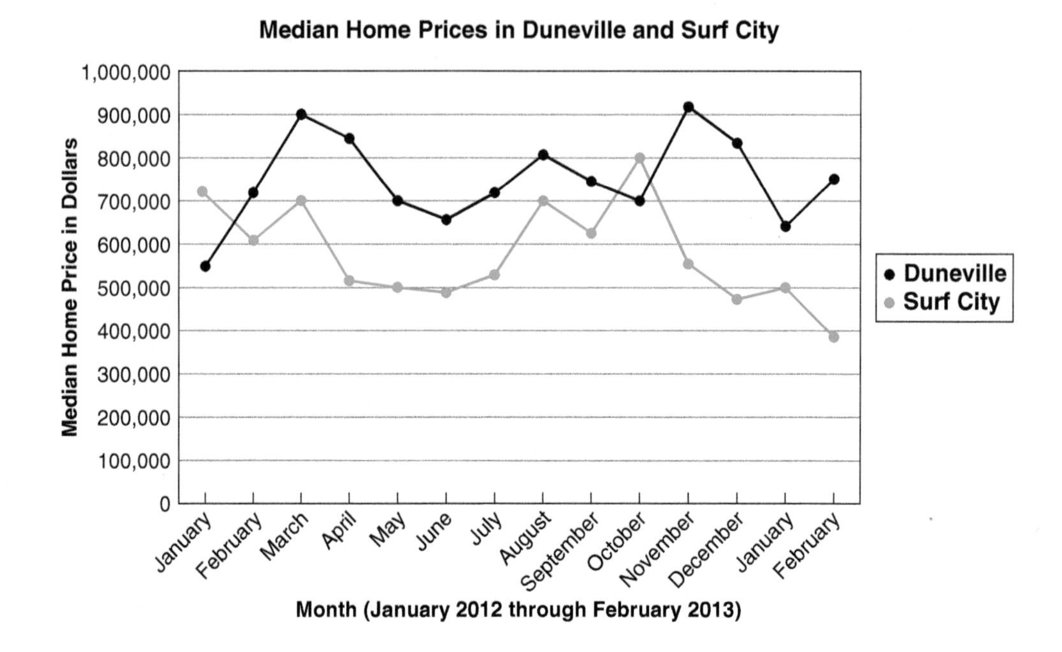

Here are some observations that we can make from the graph:

- The highest median home price in Surf City was about \$800,000, in October 2012.
- The lowest median home price in Duneville was about \$550,000, in January 2012.
- The steepest decline in Surf City's median home price occurred between October and November 2012, when it dropped from \$800,000 to \$550,000. The percent decrease from the previous month can be calculated as follows:

$$\frac{\$800{,}000 - \$550{,}000}{\$800{,}000} = \frac{x}{100}$$

$$\frac{\$250{,}000}{\$800{,}000} = \frac{x}{100}$$

$$\text{or} \quad \frac{25}{80} = \frac{x}{100}$$

$$80x = 2500$$

$$x \approx 31\%$$

Your Turn Life Skills Use the graph in Example 7 to answer the following questions:

(a) What was the lowest median price in Surf City and when did it occur?

(b) What was the highest median price in Duneville and when did it occur?

(c) In which months did Duneville's median home price increase from the previous month while Surf City's median price decreased?

(d) By what percent did Duneville's median price increase from January 2012 to January 2013?

Answers
(a) Just under $400,000 in February 2013
(b) Just over $900,000 in November 2012
(c) February 2012, November 2012, and February 2013
(d) Approximately 18%

Drawing Line Graphs

Constructing a broken-line graph is similar to drawing a bar graph. If possible, begin with data arranged in a table. Then follow the steps shown in the next example.

EXAMPLE 8

Manufacturing The following table shows the average unit production cost for an electronic component during the years 2008–2013.

Year	Production Costs (per unit)
2008	$5.16
2009	$5.33
2010	$5.04
2011	$5.57
2012	$6.55
2013	$6.94

Step 1 Draw and label the axes. According to convention, time is plotted on the horizontal axis. In this case, production cost is placed on the vertical axis. Space the years equally on the horizontal axis, placing them directly on a graph line and not between lines. Choose a suitable scale for the vertical axis. In this case, each graph line represents an interval of $0.20. Notice that we begin the vertical axis at $5.00 to avoid a large gap at the bottom of the graph. Be sure to title the graph.

Step 2 For each pair of numbers, locate the year on the horizontal scale and the cost for that year on the vertical scale. Imagine a line extended up from the year and another line extended horizontally from the cost. Place a dot where these two lines intersect.

From the table, the cost in 2009 is $5.33.

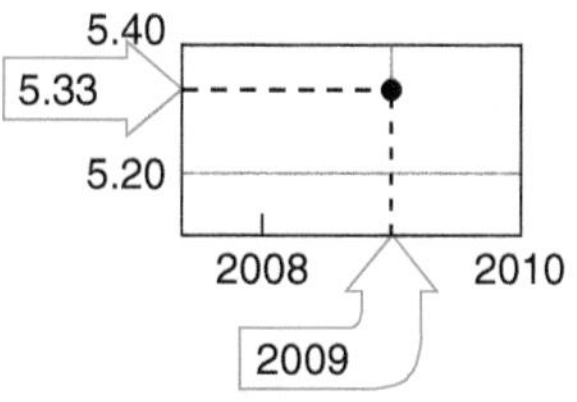

Step 3 After all the number pairs have been placed on the graph, connect adjacent points with straight-line segments.

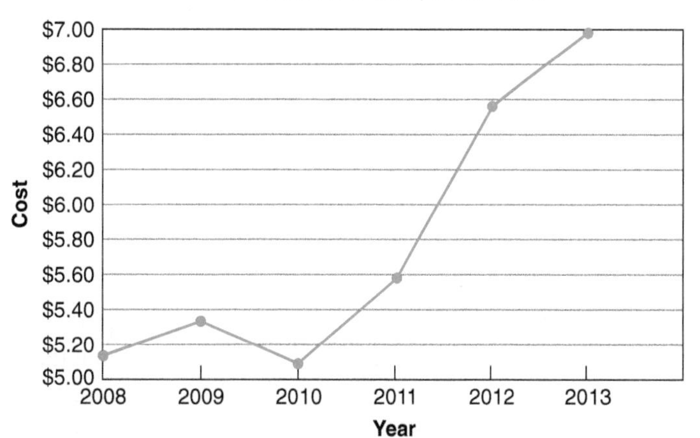

Your Turn **Manufacturing** Plot the following data on the graph in the previous example to create a double-line graph.

Year	Shipping Cost (per unit)
2008	$5.30
2009	$5.61
2010	$6.05
2011	$6.20
2012	$6.40
2013	$6.50

Solution

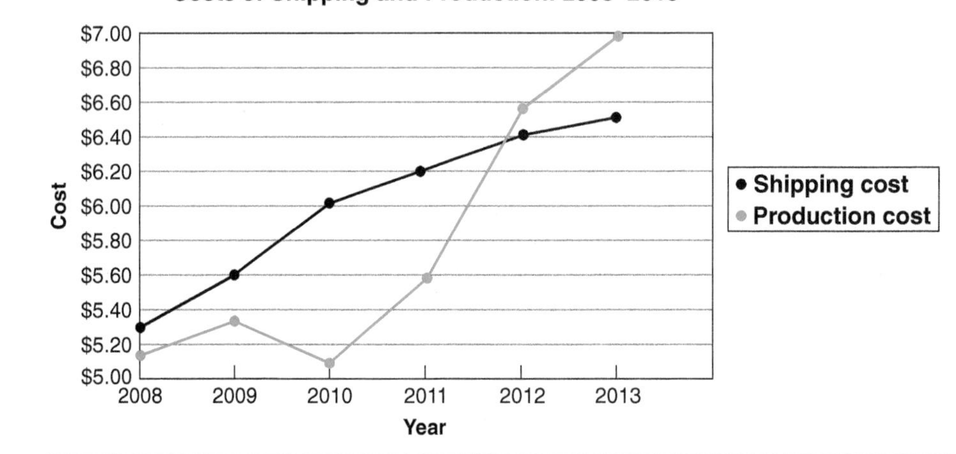

Reading Circle Graphs

A **circle graph**, or **pie chart**, is used to show what percent of the whole of some quantity is represented by its separate parts.

EXAMPLE 9

Welding The following circle graph gives the distribution of questions contained on a comprehensive welding exam. The area of the circle represents the entire exam, and the wedge-shaped sectors represent the percentage of questions in each part of the exam. The percents on the sectors add up to 100%.

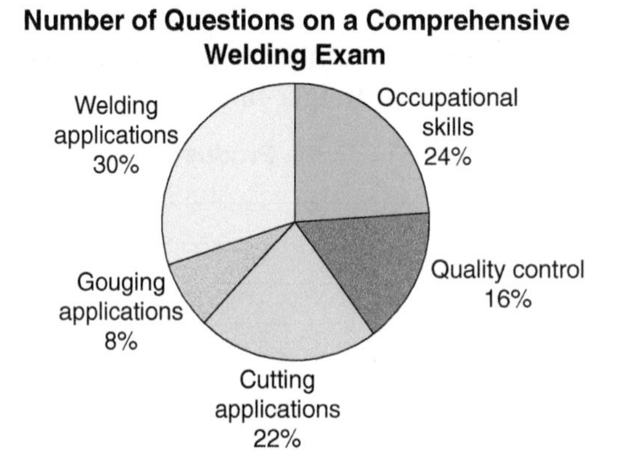

The size of each sector is proportional to the percent it represents. If we wanted to know which topic was asked about the most, we could visually pick out the largest sector, welding applications, or compare the percents shown to reach the same conclusion.

We can also use the percents on the graph to calculate additional information. For example, suppose we know that there are 150 questions on the exam, and we want to know exactly how many questions deal with occupational skills. From the graph, we see that 24% of the questions relate to occupational skills, so we find 24% of 150 as follows:

$$\frac{S}{150} = \frac{24}{100}$$

$$S = \frac{24 \cdot 150}{100}$$

$$= 36$$

There are 36 questions relating to occupational skills.

Your Turn **Welding** Use the graph from Example 9 to answer the following questions.

(a) What percent of the exam dealt with cutting?

(b) Which question topic was asked about least?

(c) If there were 125 questions on the exam, how many questions would deal with quality control?

Solutions (a) 22% (b) Gouging

(c) From the graph, we see that 16% of the questions deal with quality control. Using a proportion, we can calculate 16% of 125 as follows:

$$\frac{Q}{125} = \frac{16}{100}$$

$$Q = \frac{16 \cdot 125}{100}$$

$$= 20$$

There would be 20 questions on quality control.

Constructing Circle Graphs If the data to be used for a circle graph is given in percent form, determine the number of degrees for each sector using the quick calculation method explained in Chapter 2. Convert each percent to a decimal and multiply by 360°.

EXAMPLE 10 **Automotive Trades** In a survey of automotive tasks, the following data were found to represent a typical work week.

Transmission	65%
Tune-up	15%
Front-end	10%
Diagnostics	5%
Exhaust	5%

Extend the table to show the calculations for the angles for each sector.

Transmission	65%	65% of 360° $= 0.65 \times 360° = 234°$
Tune-up	15%	15% of 360° $= 0.15 \times 360° = 54°$
Front-end	10%	10% of 360° $= 0.10 \times 360° = 36°$
Diagnostic	5%	5% of 360° $= 0.05 \times 360° = 18°$
Exhaust	5%	5% of 360° $= 0.05 \times 360° = 18°$

Sum = 100%

Round to the nearest degree

Note The sum of the angles should be 360° most of the time, but it may be a degree off due to rounding.

Finally, using a protractor, mark off the sectors and complete the circle graph. Notice that each sector is labeled with a category name and its percent.

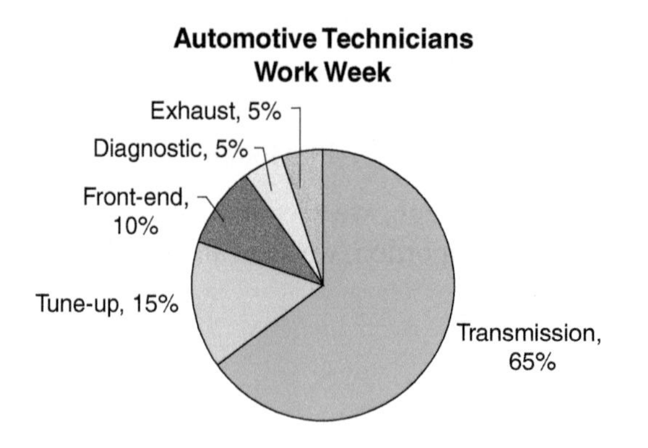

If the data for a circle graph are not given in percent form, first convert the data to percents and then convert the percents to degrees.

EXAMPLE 11 **Trades Management** The Zapp Electric Company produces novelty electrical toys. The company has a very top-heavy compensation plan. The chief executive officer is paid $175,000 yearly; the vice president for finance, $70,000; a shop supervisor, $55,000; and 10 hourly workers, $25,000 each. Draw a circle graph of this situation.

It is helpful to organize our information in a table such as this:

Employee	Compensation	Percent	Angle
CEO	$175,000		
VP	70,000		
Supervisor	55,000		
10 hourly workers	250,000		

Sum = $550,000

First, find the sum of the compensations.

$\$175{,}000 + 70{,}000 + 55{,}000 + 250{,}000 = \$550{,}000$

Second, use this sum as the base to calculate the percents needed. Because all of the compensations end in three zeros, these may be dropped when setting up the proportions.

$$\frac{175}{550} = \frac{C}{100} \qquad \frac{70}{550} = \frac{V}{100} \qquad \frac{55}{550} = \frac{S}{100} \qquad \frac{250}{550} = \frac{E}{100}$$

$$C \approx 32\% \qquad V \approx 13\% \qquad S = 10\% \qquad E \approx 45\%$$

Third, use the percent values to calculate the angles in the last column.

$$(0.32)(360°) \approx 115° \qquad (0.13)(360°) \approx 47°$$

$$(0.10)(360°) = 36° \qquad (0.45)(360°) = 162°$$

The completed table:

Employee	Compensation	Percent	Angle
CEO	$175,000	32%	115°
VP	70,000	13%	47°
Supervisor	55,000	10%	36°
10 hourly workers	250,000	45%	162°
	Sum = $550,000	Sum = 100%	Sum = 360°

Finally, use the angles in the last column to draw the circle graph. Label each sector as shown.

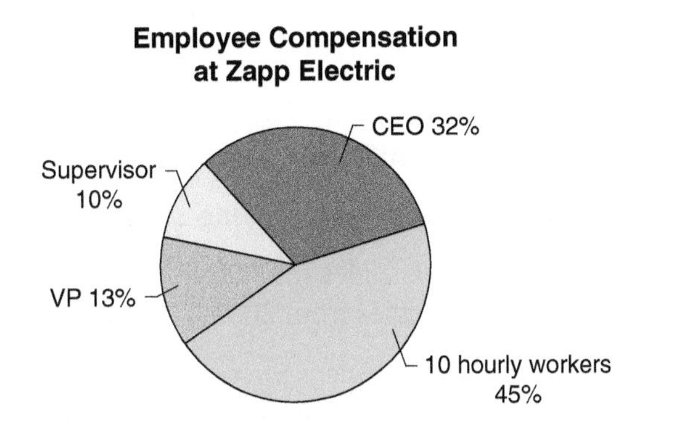

Your Turn **Plumbing** Jane the plumber keeps a record of the number of trips she makes to answer emergency calls. A summary of her records looks like this:

Trip Length	Number of Trips
Less than 5 miles	152
5–9 miles	25
10–19 miles	49
20–49 miles	18
50 or more miles	10

Calculate the percents and the angles for each category, and plot Jane's data in a circle graph.

Solution The completed table shows the percents and angles for each category:

Trip Length	Number of Trips	Percent	Angle
Less than 5 miles	152	60%	216°
5–9 miles	25	10%	36°
10–19 miles	49	19%	68°
20–49 miles	18	7%	25°
50+ miles	10	4%	14°
	254	100%	359°

Because of rounding, the percents will not always sum to exactly 100% and the angles will not always sum to exactly 360°. In this case, the angles added up to 359°. This will not noticeably affect the appearance of the graph.

The circle graph is shown here.

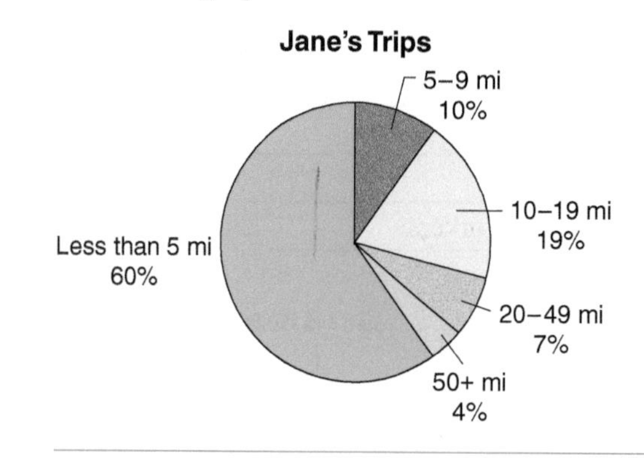

Now turn to Exercises 5-1 for more practice in reading and constructing bar graphs, line graphs, and circle graphs.

Exercises 5-1 Reading and Constructing Graphs

A. Answer the questions following each graph.

1. **Automotive Trades** The following bar graph shows the annual U.S. sales of hybrid vehicles from 2003–2011. Study the graph and answer the questions below.

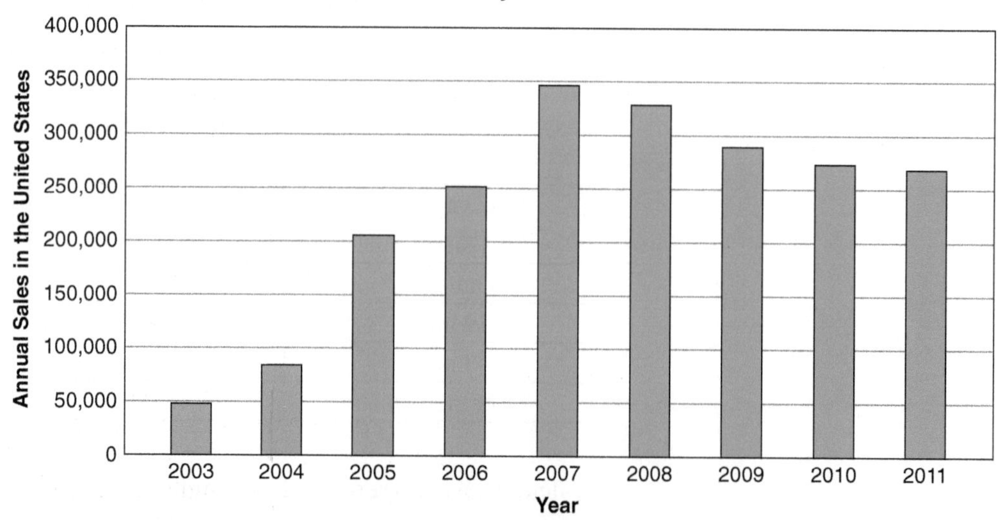

(*Source:* Green Car Congress)

(a) During which year did the largest increase in hybrid sales occur?

(b) During which year did the largest decrease in hybrid sales occur?

(c) Approximately how many hybrid vehicles were sold in 2008?

(d) How many more hybrid vehicles were sold in 2006 than in 2003? (Estimate your answer to the nearest hundred thousand.)

(e) By what percent did sales increase from 2004 to 2007? (Round to the nearest hundred percent.)

(f) By what percent did sales decrease from 2007 to 2011? (Round to the nearest percent.)

2. Trades Management The following graph shows the hourly energy consumption of eight different appliances. Study the graph and answer the questions that follow.

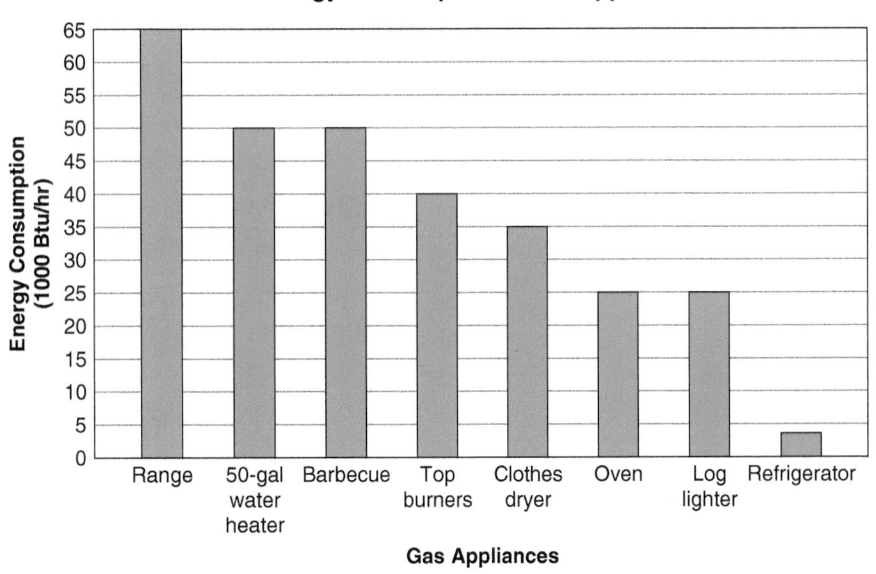

(a) Which appliance uses the most energy in an hour?

(b) Which appliance uses the least energy in an hour?

(c) How many Btu/hr does a gas barbecue use?

(d) How many Btu/*day* (24 hr) would a 50-gal water heater use?

(e) Is there any difference between the energy consumption of the range and that of the top burners plus oven?

(f) How many Btus are used by a log lighter in 15 min?

(g) What is the difference in energy consumption between a 50-gal water heater and a clothes dryer?

3. HVAC The following double-bar graph represents the energy efficiency ratio (EER) and seasonal energy efficiency ratio (SEER) for different models of residential air conditioners. The EER is the measure of the instantaneous energy efficiency of the cooling equipment in an air conditioner. The SEER is the measure of the energy efficiency of the equipment over the entire cooling season. Both efficiency ratios are given in British thermal units per watt-hour (Btu/Wh).

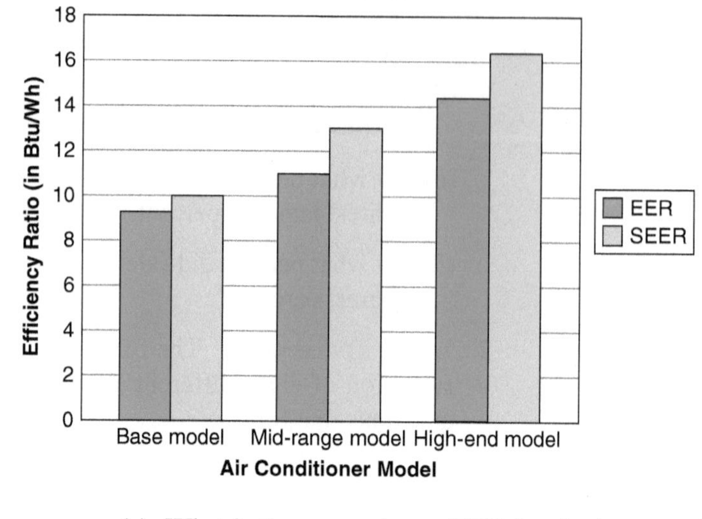

(a) What is the approximate EER for the base model?

(b) Which model has a SEER of about 13?

(c) Calculate the percent increase in SEER from the base model to the high-end model.

(d) Calculate the percent increase in the EER from the base model to the mid-range model.

4. **Police Science** The following bar graph represents crime statistics over a three-year period.

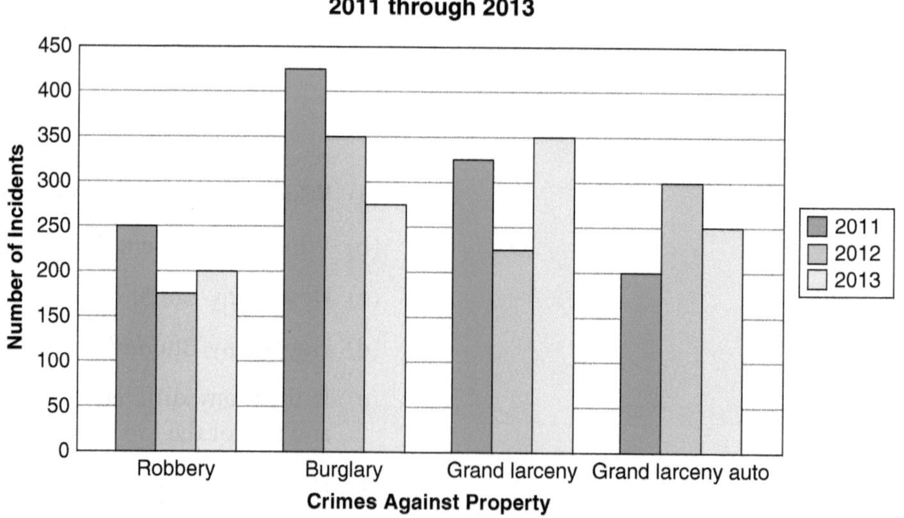

(a) Over which two years did the number of incidents of grand larceny increase?

(b) Which two crimes had the highest number of occurrences in 2012?

(c) Which two crimes had the highest number of occurrences in 2011?

(d) In which category are crimes decreasing?

(e) Which crime had the lowest number of incidents in 2011? In 2013?

(f) What was the approximate total number of incidents in 2012?

(g) By what percent did grand larceny auto increase between 2011 and 2012?

5. **Allied Health** When Dr. Friedrich began working at the Zizyx County Hospital in 2004, his goal was to improve the quality and quantity of bone marrow transplants performed at the hospital. The number of successful bone marrow transplants performed at the Zizyx County Hospital from 2004 through 2013 is illustrated in the following broken-line graph.

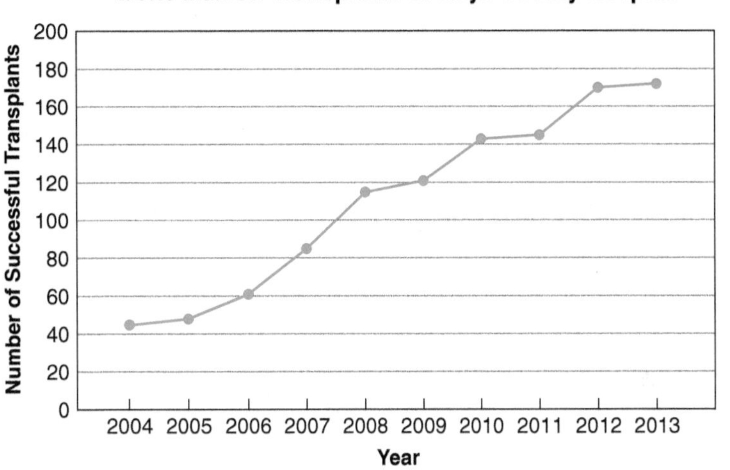

(a) Approximately how many successful bone marrow transplants were performed in 2004?

(b) Approximately how many successful bone marrow transplants were performed in 2013?

(c) By about what percent did the number of successful bone marrow transplants increase in the five-year period from 2008 to 2013?

(d) If the bone marrow transplant program increases at the same rate as it did from 2008 to 2013, how many successful bone marrow transplants can the Zizyx County Hospital expect to perform in 2018?

6. **Automotive Trades** The following line graph shows how the average fuel economy of a selected group of automobiles varies according to the speed of the vehicle.

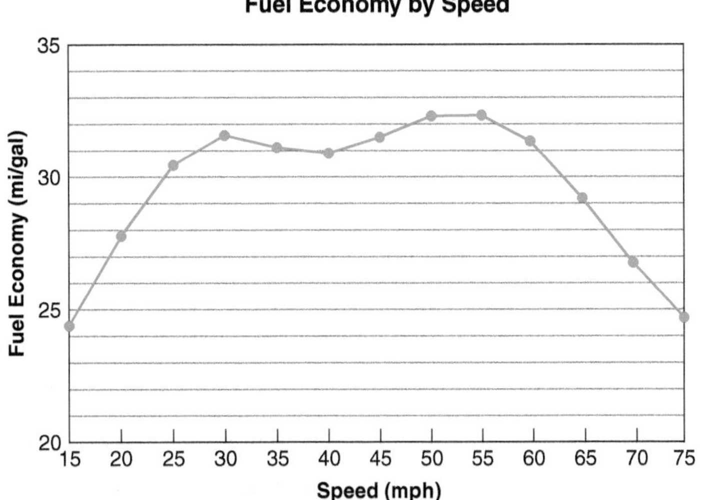

(a) At what speed is fuel economy the best? The worst?

(b) What is the fuel economy at 65 mph? At 40 mph?

(c) At what speed is the fuel economy 29 mi/gal?

(d) After which two speeds does fuel economy begin to decrease?

7. **Construction** The following double-line graph compares the number of existing home sales to the number of homes for sale (inventory) at the end of the year in the United States from 1991 through 2011. Note that the vertical scale is in thousands—meaning that 5000, for example, actually means 5,000,000. Study the graph and answer the questions that follow.

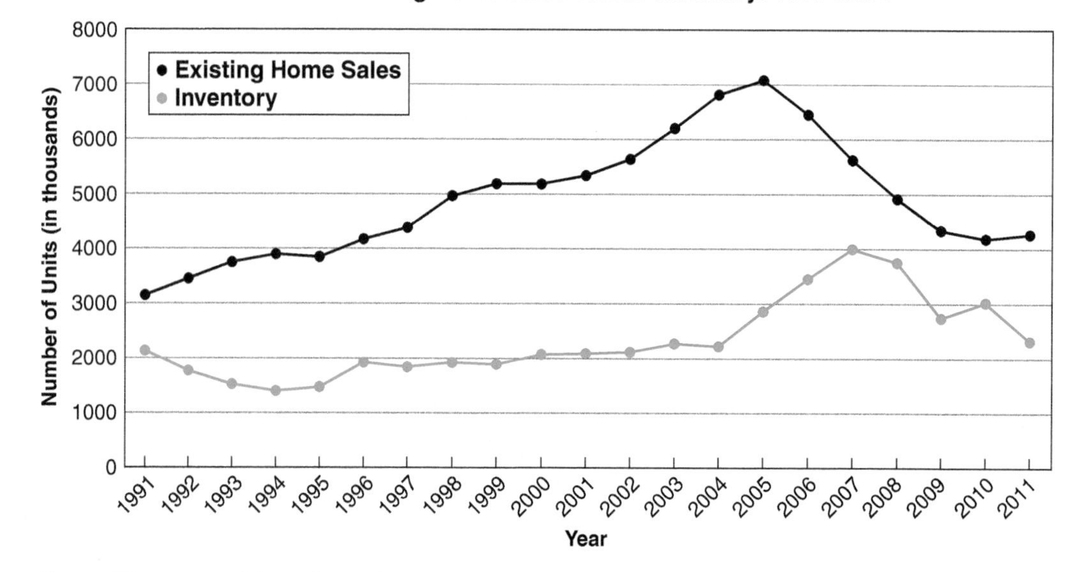

(*Source:* National Association of Realtors)

(a) In what year did the biggest drop in home sales occur? By approximately how many units did sales drop?

(b) Identify at least two years when the number of sales and the inventory both increased.

(c) In what year were home sales at their lowest level? In what year were home sales at their highest level?

(d) Based on your answer to part (c), how many more units were sold in the highest-selling year than in the lowest-selling year?

(e) By approximately what percent did the inventory increase between 2004 and 2007?

(f) By approximately what percent did home sales drop between 2005 and 2010?

8. **General Interest** Study the circle graph at the top of page 199 and answer the questions that follow.

(a) Which are the largest two continents on the earth?

(b) Which two are the smallest?

(c) Which continent covers 12% of the earth?

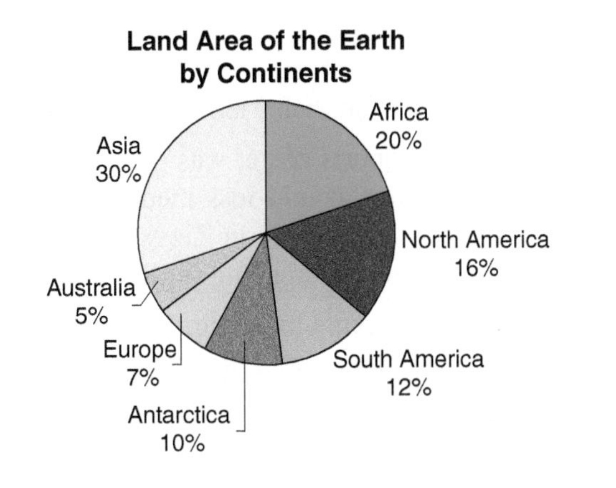

9. Life Skills Study this circle graph and answer the questions that follow.

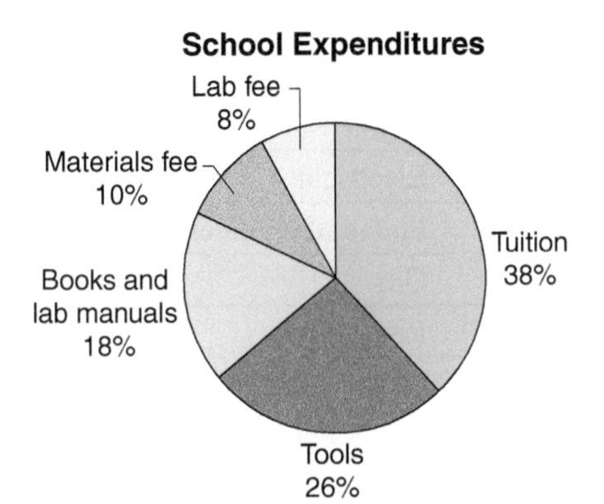

(a) Which category represents the largest expenditure?

(b) Which category represents the smallest expenditure?

(c) If a student spent a total of \$2500, how much of this went toward tools and lab fees combined?

(d) If a student spent \$300 on materials, how much would she spend on books and lab manuals?

10. Allied Health An assistant at a pharmaceutical company summarized the use of anti-obesity drugs in Zizyx County. Based on a survey of local pharmacies, the assistant estimated the percent of patients using each of the most common weight-loss medications, and presented the results in a circle graph.

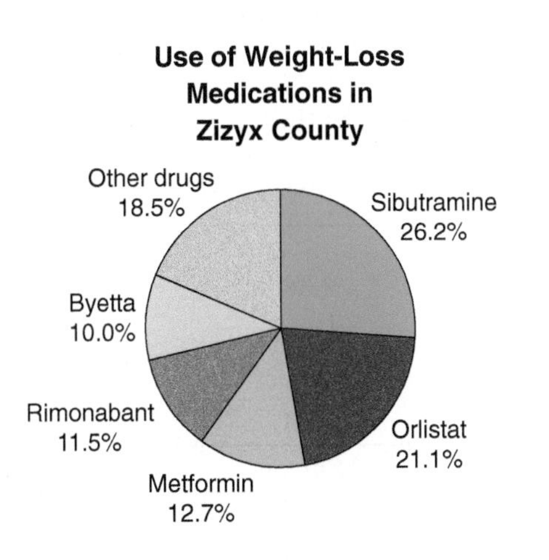

(a) What is the most commonly used weight-loss medication Zizyx County?

(b) If a total of 2780 people in Zizyx County take weight-loss medication, how many of these are taking Sibutramine? How many more people take Orlistat than Metformin?

(c) After a sports center was opened in Zizyx County, the number of people taking weight-loss medications [see part (b)] decreased by 43%. How many people in Zizyx County were taking weight-loss medications after the opening of the sports center?

(d) If the percents in the circle graph remained the same after the opening of the sports center, how many patients were still taking Byetta?

B. From the following data, construct the type of graph indicated.

1. **Fire Protection** Plot the following data as a bar graph.

Causes of Fires in District 12

Cause of Fire	Number of Fires
Appliance	6
Arson	8
Electrical	18
Flammable materials	7
Gas	2
Lightning	2
Motor vehicle	10
Unknown	9

2. **Transportation** The following table lists the total carbon emissions per person for various forms of transportation for a round-trip from Los Angeles to San Francisco. Construct a bar graph of these data.

Form of Transportation	Carbon Emissions (pounds)
Flying: smaller, newer plane	300
Flying: larger, older plane	406
Driving alone (car with 47 mi/gal)	273
Driving alone (car with 25 mi/gal)	527
Driving alone (car with 16 mi/gal)	793
Carpooling (2 people, car with 25 mi/gal)	263
Train	284

(*Source:* Terra Pass)

3. **Metalworking** Draw a bar graph from the following information. (*Hint:* Use multiples of 5 on the vertical axis.)

Linear Thermal Expansion Coefficients for Materials

Material	Coefficient (in parts per million per °C)
Aluminum	23
Copper	17
Gold	14
Silicon	3
Concrete	12
Brass	19
Lead	29

4. **Trades Management** Plot the following data as a bar graph.

Radish Tool and Dye Worker Experience

Length of Service	Number of Workers
20 years or more	9
15–19	7
10–14	14
5–9	20
1–4	33
Less than 1 year	5

5. **Construction** Plot the following data as a double-bar graph.

Sales of Construction Material: CASH IS US

Year	Wood (× $1000)	Masonry (×$1000)
2008	$289	$131
2009	$325	$33
2010	$296	$106
2011	$288	$92
2012	$307	$94
2013	$412	$89

6. **General Interest** The following table shows the total annual costs of tuition, room, and board for full-time undergraduate students at both public and private colleges and universities. The costs are shown in ten-year increments beginning in 1980–1981, and they are given in terms of 2011 dollars. Construct a double-bar graph comparing these costs. (*Hint:* Round each amount to the nearest $500 before drawing the graph.)

Year	Public Institutions	Private Institutions
1980–1981	$2373	$5470
1990–1991	$4757	$12,910
2000–2001	$7586	$21,373
2010–2011	$13,564	$32,026

7. **Automotive Trades** The following table shows the average U.S. prices per gallon of both regular gasoline and diesel fuel from 2003 through 2012. (The prices are quoted for November of each year.) Construct a double-bar graph illustrating these prices.

Year	Cost of Regular Gasoline	Cost of Diesel Fuel
2003	$1.49	$1.48
2004	$1.99	$2.21
2005	$2.34	$2.70
2006	$2.18	$2.51
2007	$3.01	$3.30
2008	$2.45	$3.09
2009	$2.68	$2.81
2010	$2.76	$3.07
2011	$3.37	$3.89
2012	$3.41	$4.01

8. **Trades Management** The following table shows the monthly breakdown of sales of new cars, new trucks, and used vehicles at a particular auto dealership over the first six months of the year. Construct a bar graph like the one in Example 3. (*Hint:* In this case, each bar should be divided into *three* sections.)

Month	New Cars	New Trucks	Used Vehicles
January	38	18	22
February	32	12	20
March	30	16	28
April	24	10	19
May	28	11	21
June	33	15	18

9. **Business and Finance** Plot a broken-line graph for these data.

Earnings per Share ($) XYZ Co.

Year	Earnings per Share
2005	$0.7
2006	$0.5
2007	$1.5
2008	$3.0
2009	$3.2
2010	$1.8
2011	$2.5
2012	$2.4
2013	$3.5

10. **General Interest** The following data show the world production of biofuels (in millions of gallons) from 2002 through 2011. Use these data to construct a broken-line graph.

Year	Production (million gallons)	Year	Production (million gallons)
2002	383	2007	2775
2003	510	2008	4132
2004	614	2009	4699
2005	945	2010	4893
2006	1710	2011	5651

11. **Fire Protection** The following data show the number of total acres burned in wildfires in the United States from 2002 through 2011. The numbers have been rounded to the nearest hundred thousand. Plot a broken-line graph of these data.

Year	Acres Burned	Year	Acres Burned
2002	7,200,000	2007	9,300,000
2003	4,000,000	2008	5,300,000
2004	8,100,000	2009	5,900,000
2005	8,700,000	2010	3,400,000
2006	9,900,000	2011	8,700,000

Source: National Interagency Fire Center

12. **Electrical Trades** Use the following data to plot a broken-line graph.

Total Capacity of Solar Water and Space Heating Installations in the United States

Year	Capacity (thermal megawatts)	Year	Capacity (thermal megawatts)
2000	25	2006	87
2001	17	2007	110
2002	35	2008	133
2003	36	2009	150
2004	33	2010	158
2005	46		

13. **Hydrology** The following table shows the daily evaporation and usage totals, in acre-feet, during a summer week at Bradbury Dam. Use these data to construct a double broken-line graph.

Day	Daily Evaporation (in acre-ft)	Daily Usage (in acre-ft)
Monday	62.3	108.7
Tuesday	58.2	130.2
Wednesday	51.5	117.9
Thursday	58.6	126.5
Friday	67.3	130.5
Saturday	67.3	130.2
Sunday	62.8	128.0

14. **Business and Finance** Plot a double broken-line graph for these data.

Actual and Projected Sales, IMD Corp. (× $1000)

Month	Actual	Projected
January	$10	$45
February	$18	$50
March	$12	$47
April	$22	$50
May	$40	$65
June	$39	$71
July	$50	$76
August	$42	$75
September	$35	$55
October	$37	$60
November	$41	$50
December	$44	$87

15. **Electrical Engineering** Plot the following data as a circle graph.

California's In-State Sources of Electricity

Source	Percent	Source	Percent
Renewable	14.6%	Natural gas	53.4%
Nuclear	15.7%	Large hydroelectric	14.6%
Coal	1.7%		

16. **Business and Finance** Plot a circle graph using these data.

Revenue for MEGA-CASH Construction Co., 2013 ($ billions)

First Quarter	Second Quarter	Third Quarter	Fourth Quarter
5.5	7.0	6.5	3.0

17. **Aviation** An aircraft mechanic spends 12.5% of a 40-hr week working on aircraft airframes, 37.5% of the week on landing gear, 43.75% of the week on power plants, and 6.25% of the week on avionics. Plot a circle graph using this information.

18. **General Interest** Recent surveys have shown that college graduates are still paying off loans years and even decades after graduation. The following table shows the percent of graduates still in debt by age group. Make a circle graph of these data.

Age Group	Percent of Total Graduates in Debt
Under 30	39%
30 to 39	27%
40 to 49	15%
50 to 59	12%
60+ or unknown	7%

(*Source:* Federal Reserve Bank of New York)

Check your answers to the odd-numbered problems in the Appendix, then turn to Section 5-2 to learn about measures of central tendency.

6

Statistics

SOME RANDOM STATISTICAL FACTOIDS:

- 28% of liberals have insomnia, compared with 16% of conservatives. (*Mother Jones*)
- 17% of American workers would reveal company secrets for money, and 8% have done it already. (Monster.com)
- 31% of American adults find giving up their smartphone for a day more difficult than giving up their significant other. (Microsoft)
- Between the ages of 18 and 24, 73% of Americans have used text messages to send suggestive pictures, compared with 55% ages 25–29, 52% ages 30–34, 42% ages 35–44, 26% ages 45–54, 10% ages 55–64, and 7% ages 65 and older. (*Time*)
- 49% of Americans cite a "lot" of stress at age 22, compared with 45% at 42, 35% at 58, 29% at 62, and 20% by 70. (*Proceedings of the National Academy of Sciences*)
- 34% of American adults believe in ghosts. (AP/Ipsos)
- Unwillingness to eat sushi correlates nearly perfectly with disapproval of marriage equality. (Pew Research Center)

Statisticians collect numerical data from subgroups of populations to find out everything imaginable about the population as a whole, including whom they favor in an election, what they watch on TV, how much money they make, or what worries them. Comedians and statisticians joke that 62.38% of all statistics are made up on the spot. Because statisticians both record and influence our behavior, it is important to distinguish between good and bad methods for collecting, presenting, and interpreting data.

Here's where you'll find these applications:

Throughout this chapter, you will gain an understanding of where data come from and how these numbers are used to make decisions. We'll return to the bizarre sushi/marriage equality correlation in Exercises 5 and 35 of Exercise Set 6.6.

6.1 Sampling, Frequency Distributions, and Graphs

WHAT AM I SUPPOSED TO LEARN?

After you have read this section, you should be able to:

1. Describe the population whose properties are to be analyzed.
2. Select an appropriate sampling technique.
3. Organize and present data.
4. Identify deceptions in visual displays of data.

*M*A*S*H* took place in the early 1950s, during the Korean War. By the final episode, the show had lasted four times as long as the Korean War.

AT THE END OF THE twentieth century, there were 94 million households in the United States with television sets. The television program viewed by the greatest percentage of such households in that century was the final episode of *M*A*S*H*. Over 50 million American households watched this program.

Numerical information, such as the information about the top three TV shows of the twentieth century, shown in **Table 6.1**, is called **data**. The word **statistics** is often used when referring to data. However, statistics has a second meaning: Statistics is also a method for collecting, organizing, analyzing, and interpreting data, as well as drawing conclusions based on the data. This methodology divides statistics into two main areas. **Descriptive statistics** is concerned with collecting, organizing, summarizing, and presenting data. **Inferential statistics** has to do with making generalizations about and drawing conclusions from the data collected.

TABLE 6.1 TV Programs with the Greatest U.S. Audience Viewing Percentage of the Twentieth Century

Program	Total Households	Viewing Percentage
1. *M*A*S*H* Feb. 28, 1983	50,150,000	60.2%
2. *Dallas* Nov. 21, 1980	41,470,000	53.3%
3. *Roots Part 8* Jan. 30, 1977	36,380,000	51.1%

Source: Nielsen Media Research

1 Describe the population whose properties are to be analyzed.

Populations and Samples

Consider the set of all American TV households. Such a set is called the *population*. In general, a **population** is the set containing all the people or objects whose properties are to be described and analyzed by the data collector.

The population of American TV households is huge. At the time of the *M*A*S*H* conclusion, there were nearly 84 million such households. Did over 50 million American TV households really watch the final episode of *M*A*S*H*? A friendly phone call to each household ("So, how are you? What's new? Watch any good television last night? If so, what?") is, of course, absurd. A **sample**, which is a subset or subgroup of the population, is needed. In this case, it would be appropriate to have a sample of a few thousand TV households to draw conclusions about the population of all TV households.

Blitzer Bonus

A Sampling Fiasco

In 1936, the *Literary Digest* mailed out over ten million ballots to voters throughout the country. The results poured in, and the magazine predicted a landslide victory for Republican Alf Landon over Democrat Franklin Roosevelt. However, the prediction of the *Literary Digest* was wrong. Why? The mailing lists the editors used included people from their own subscriber list, directories of automobile owners, and telephone books. As a result, its sample was anything but random. It excluded most of the poor, who were unlikely to subscribe to the *Literary Digest,* or to own a car or telephone in the heart of the Depression. Prosperous people in 1936 were more likely to be Republican than the poor. Thus, although the sample was massive, it included a higher percentage of affluent individuals than the population as a whole did. A victim of both the Depression and the 1936 sampling fiasco, the *Literary Digest* folded in 1937.

EXAMPLE 1 *Populations and Samples*

A group of hotel owners in a large city decide to conduct a survey among citizens of the city to discover their opinions about casino gambling.

a. Describe the population.

b. One of the hotel owners suggests obtaining a sample by surveying all the people at six of the largest nightclubs in the city on a Saturday night. Each person will be asked to express his or her opinion on casino gambling. Does this seem like a good idea?

SOLUTION

a. The population is the set containing all the citizens of the city.

b. Questioning people at six of the city's largest nightclubs is a terrible idea. The nightclub subset is probably more likely to have a positive attitude toward casino gambling than the population of all the city's citizens.

CHECK POINT 1 A city government wants to conduct a survey among the city's homeless to discover their opinions about required residence in city shelters from midnight until 6 A.M.

a. Describe the population.

b. A city commissioner suggests obtaining a sample by surveying all the homeless people at the city's largest shelter on a Sunday night. Does this seem like a good idea? Explain your answer.

Random Sampling

There is a way to use a small sample to make generalizations about a large population: Guarantee that every member of the population has an equal chance to be selected for the sample. Surveying people at six of the city's largest nightclubs does not provide this guarantee. Unless it can be established that all citizens of the city frequent these clubs, which seems unlikely, this sampling scheme does not permit each citizen an equal chance of selection.

RANDOM SAMPLES

A **random sample** is a sample obtained in such a way that every element in the population has an equal chance of being selected for the sample.

Suppose that you are elated with the quality of one of your courses. Although it's an auditorium section with 120 students, you feel that the professor is lecturing right to you. During a wonderful lecture, you look around the auditorium to see if any of the other students are sharing your enthusiasm. Based on body language, it's hard to tell. You really want to know the opinion of the population of 120 students taking this course. You think about asking students to grade the course on an A to F scale, anticipating a unanimous A. You cannot survey everyone. Eureka! Suddenly you have an idea on how to take a sample. Place cards numbered from 1 through 120, one number per card, in a box. Because the course has assigned seating by number, each numbered card corresponds to a student in the class. Reach in and randomly select six cards. Each card, and therefore each student, has an equal chance of being selected. Then use the opinions about the course from the six randomly selected students to generalize about the course opinion for the entire 120-student population.

2 Select an appropriate sampling technique.

Your idea is precisely how random samples are obtained. In random sampling, each element in the population must be identified and assigned a number. The numbers are generally assigned in order. The way to sample from the larger numbered population is to generate random numbers using a computer or calculator. Each numbered element from the population that corresponds to one of the generated random numbers is selected for the sample.

Call-in polls on radio and television are not reliable because those polled do not represent the larger population. A person who calls in is likely to have feelings about an issue that are consistent with the politics of the show's host. For a poll to be accurate, the sample must be chosen randomly from the larger population. The A. C. Nielsen Company uses a random sample of approximately 5000 TV households to measure the percentage of households tuned in to a television program.

EXAMPLE 2 *Selecting an Appropriate Sampling Technique*

We return to the hotel owners in the large city who are interested in how the city's citizens feel about casino gambling. Which of the following would be the most appropriate way to select a random sample?

a. Randomly survey people who live in the oceanfront condominiums in the city.

b. Survey the first 200 people whose names appear in the city's telephone directory.

c. Randomly select neighborhoods of the city and then randomly survey people within the selected neighborhoods.

SOLUTION

Keep in mind that the population is the set containing all the city's citizens. A random sample must give each citizen an equal chance of being selected.

a. Randomly selecting people who live in the city's oceanfront condominiums is not a good idea. Many hotels lie along the oceanfront, and the oceanfront property owners might object to the traffic and noise as a result of casino gambling. Furthermore, this sample does not give each citizen of the city an equal chance of being selected.

b. If the hotel owners survey the first 200 names in the city's telephone directory, all citizens do not have an equal chance of selection. For example, individuals whose last name begins with a letter toward the end of the alphabet have no chance of being selected.

c. Randomly selecting neighborhoods of the city and then randomly surveying people within the selected neighborhoods is an appropriate technique. Using this method, each citizen has an equal chance of being selected.

In summary, given the three options, the sampling technique in part (c) is the most appropriate.

Surveys and polls involve data from a sample of some population. Regardless of the sampling technique used, the sample should exhibit characteristics typical of those possessed by the target population. This type of sample is called a **representative sample**.

CHECK POINT 2 Explain why the sampling technique described in Check Point 1(b) on page 207 is not a random sample. Then describe an appropriate way to select a random sample of the city's homeless.

Blitzer Bonus

The United States Census

A census is a survey that attempts to include the entire population. The U.S. Constitution requires a census of the American population every ten years. When the Founding Fathers invented American democracy, they realized that if you are going to have government by the people, you need to know who and where they are. Nowadays about $400 billion per year in federal aid is distributed based on the Census numbers, for everything from jobs to bridges to schools. For every 100 people not counted, states and communities could lose as much as $130,000 annually, or $1300 per person each year, so this really matters.

Although the Census generates volumes of statistics, its main purpose is to give the government block-by-block population figures. The U.S. Census is not foolproof. The 1990 Census missed 1.6% of the American population, including an estimated 4.4% of the African-American population, largely in inner cities. Only 67% of households responded to the 2000 Census, even after door-to-door canvassing. About 6.4 million people were missed and 3.1 million were counted twice. Although the 2010 Census was one of the shortest forms in history, counting each person was not an easy task, particularly with concerns about immigration status and privacy of data.

Of course, there would be more than $400 billion to spread around if it didn't cost so much to count us in the first place: about $15 billion for the 2010 Census. That included $338 million for ads in 28 languages, a Census-sponsored NASCAR entry, and $2.5 million for a Super Bowl ad. The ads were meant to boost the response rate, since any household that did not mail back its form got visited by a Census worker, another pricey item. In all, the cost of the 2010 Census worked out to appoximately $49 per person.

3 Organize and present data.

Frequency Distributions

After data have been collected from a sample of the population, the next task facing the statistician is to present the data in a condensed and manageable form. In this way, the data can be more easily interpreted.

Suppose, for example, that researchers are interested in determining the age at which adolescent males show the greatest rate of physical growth. A random sample of 35 ten-year-old boys is measured for height and then remeasured each year until they reach 18. The age of maximum yearly growth for each subject is as follows:

12, 14, 13, 14, 16, 14, 14, 17, 13, 10, 13, 18, 12, 15, 14, 15, 15, 14, 14, 13, 15, 16, 15, 12, 13, 16, 11, 15, 12, 13, 12, 11, 13, 14, 14.

A piece of data is called a **data item**. This list of data has 35 data items. Some of the data items are identical. Two of the data items are 11 and 11. Thus, we can say that the **data value** 11 occurs twice. Similarly, because five of the data items are 12, 12, 12, 12, and 12, the data value 12 occurs five times.

Collected data can be presented using a **frequency distribution**. Such a distribution consists of two columns. The data values are listed in one column. Numerical data are generally listed from smallest to largest. The adjacent column is labeled **frequency** and indicates the number of times each value occurs.

EXAMPLE 3 *Constructing a Frequency Distribution*

Construct a frequency distribution for the data of the age of maximum yearly growth for 35 boys:

12, 14, 13, 14, 16, 14, 14, 17, 13, 10, 13, 18, 12, 15, 14, 15, 15, 14, 14, 13, 15, 16, 15, 12, 13, 16, 11, 15, 12, 13, 12, 11, 13, 14, 14.

SOLUTION

It is difficult to determine trends in the data above in their current format. Perhaps we can make sense of the data by organizing them into a frequency distribution. Let us create two columns. One lists all possible data values, from smallest (10) to largest (18). The other column indicates the number of times the value occurs in the sample. The frequency distribution is shown in **Table 6.2**.

The frequency distribution indicates that one subject had maximum growth at age 10, two at age 11, five at age 12, seven at age 13, and so on. The maximum growth for most of the subjects occurred between the ages of 12 and 15. Nine boys experienced maximum growth at age 14, more than at any other age within the sample. The sum of the frequencies, 35, is equal to the original number of data items.

The trend shown by the frequency distribution in **Table 6.2** indicates that the number of boys who attain their maximum yearly growth at a given age increases until age 14 and decreases after that. This trend is not evident in the data in their original format.

TABLE 6.2 A Frequency Distribution for a Boy's Age of Maximum Yearly Growth

Age of Maximum Growth	Number of Boys (Frequency)
10	1
11	2
12	5
13	7
14	9
15	6
16	3
17	1
18	1
Total:	$n = 35$

35 is the sum of the frequencies.

CHECK POINT 3 Construct a frequency distribution for the data showing final course grades for students in a precalculus course, listed alphabetically by student name in a grade book:

F, A, B, B, C, C, B, C, A, A, C, C, D, C, B, D, C, C, B, C.

A frequency distribution that lists all possible data items can be quite cumbersome when there are many such items. For example, consider the following data items. These are statistics test scores for a class of 40 students.

82	47	75	64	57	82	63	93
76	68	84	54	88	77	79	80
94	92	94	80	94	66	81	67
75	73	66	87	76	45	43	56
57	74	50	78	71	84	59	76

It's difficult to determine how well the group did when the grades are displayed like this. Because there are so many data items, one way to organize these data so that the results are more meaningful is to arrange the grades into groups, or **classes**, based on something that interests us. Many grading systems assign an A to grades in the 90–100 class, B to grades in the 80–89 class, C to grades in the 70–79 class, and so on. These classes provide one way to organize the data.

Looking at the 40 statistics test scores, we see that they range from a low of 43 to a high of 94. We can use classes that run from 40 through 49, 50 through 59, 60 through 69, and so on up to 90 through 99, to organize the scores. In Example 4, we go through the data and tally each item into the appropriate class. This method for organizing data is called a **grouped frequency distribution**.

EXAMPLE 4 *Constructing a Grouped Frequency Distribution*

Use the classes 40–49, 50–59, 60–69, 70–79, 80–89, and 90–99 to construct a grouped frequency distribution for the 40 test scores on the previous page.

SOLUTION

We use the 40 given scores and tally the number of scores in each class.

Tallying Statistics Test Scores

Test Scores (Class)	Tally	Number of Students (Frequency)
40–49	|||	3
50–59	~~||||~~ |	6
60–69	~~||||~~ |	6
70–79	~~||||~~ ~~||||~~ |	11
80–89	~~||||~~ ||||	9
90–99	~~||||~~	5

The second score in the list, 47, is shown as the first tally in this row.

The first score in the list, 82, is shown as the first tally in this row.

TABLE 6.3 A Grouped Frequency Distribution for Statistics Test Scores

Class	Frequency
40–49	3
50–59	6
60–69	6
70–79	11
80–89	9
90–99	5
Total:	$n = 40$

40, the sum of the frequencies, is the number of data items.

Omitting the tally column results in the grouped frequency distribution in **Table 6.3**. The distribution shows that the greatest frequency of students scored in the 70–79 class. The number of students decreases in classes that contain successively lower and higher scores. The sum of the frequencies, 40, is equal to the original number of data items.

The leftmost number in each class of a grouped frequency distribution is called the **lower class limit**. For example, in **Table 6.3**, the lower limit of the first class is 40 and the lower limit of the third class is 60. The rightmost number in each class is called the **upper class limit**. In **Table 6.3**, 49 and 69 are the upper limits for the first and third classes, respectively. Notice that if we take the difference between any two consecutive lower class limits, we get the same number:

$$50 - 40 = 10,\ 60 - 50 = 10,\ 70 - 60 = 10,\ 80 - 70 = 10,\ 90 - 80 = 10.$$

The number 10 is called the **class width**.

When setting up class limits, each class, with the possible exception of the first or last, should have the same width. Because each data item must fall into exactly one class, it is sometimes helpful to vary the width of the first or last class to allow for items that fall far above or below most of the data.

CHECK POINT 4 Use the classes in **Table 6.3** to construct a grouped frequency distribution for the following 37 exam scores:

73	58	68	75	94	79	96	79
87	83	89	52	99	97	89	58
95	77	75	81	75	73	73	62
69	76	77	71	50	57	41	98
77	71	69	90	75.			

TABLE 6.2 A Frequency Distribution for a Boy's Age of Maximum Yearly Growth

Age of Maximum Growth	Number of Boys (Frequency)
10	1
11	2
12	5
13	7
14	9
15	6
16	3
17	1
18	1
Total:	$n = 35$

35 is the sum of the frequencies.

Histograms and Frequency Polygons

Take a second look at the frequency distribution for the age of a boy's maximum yearly growth in **Table 6.2**. A bar graph with bars that touch can be used to visually display the data. Such a graph is called a **histogram.** **Figure 6.1** illustrates a histogram that was constructed using the frequency distribution in **Table 6.2**. A series of rectangles whose heights represent the frequencies are placed next to each other. For example, the height of the bar for the data value 10, shown in **Figure 6.1**, is 1. This corresponds to the frequency for 10 given in **Table 6.2**. The higher the bar, the more frequent the age. The break along the horizontal axis, symbolized by ⺈, eliminates listing the ages 1 through 9.

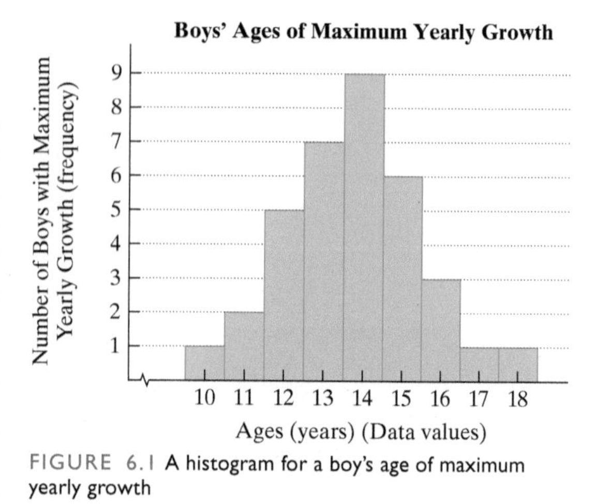

FIGURE 6.1 A histogram for a boy's age of maximum yearly growth

A line graph called a **frequency polygon** can also be used to visually convey the information shown in **Figure 6.1**. The axes are labeled just like those in a histogram. Thus, the horizontal axis shows data values and the vertical axis shows frequencies. Once a histogram has been constructed, it's fairly easy to draw a frequency polygon. **Figure 6.2** shows a histogram with a dot at the top of each rectangle at its midpoint. Connect each of these midpoints with a straight line. To complete the frequency polygon at both ends, the lines should be drawn down to touch the horizontal axis. The completed frequency polygon is shown in **Figure 6.3**.

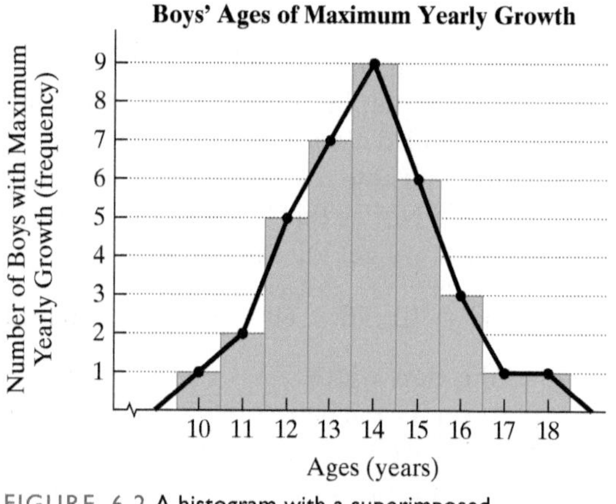

FIGURE 6.2 A histogram with a superimposed frequency polygon

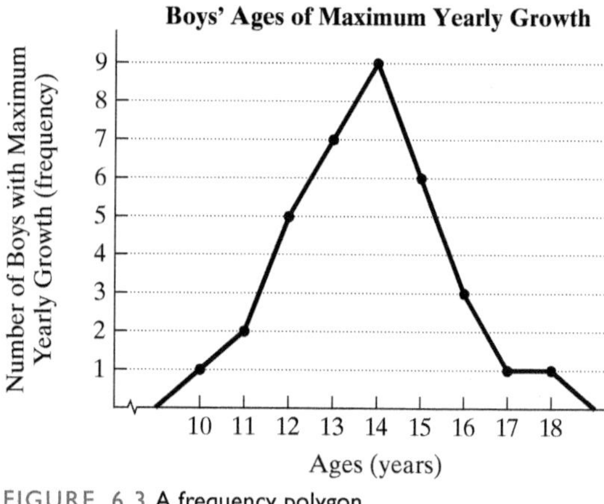

FIGURE 6.3 A frequency polygon

Stem-and-Leaf Plots

A unique way of displaying data uses a tool called a **stem-and-leaf plot**. Example 5 illustrates how we sort the data, revealing the same visual impression created by a histogram.

EXAMPLE 5 *Constructing a Stem-and-Leaf Plot*

Use the data showing statistics test scores for 40 students to construct a stem-and-leaf plot:

82	47	75	64	57	82	63	93
76	68	84	54	88	77	79	80
94	92	94	80	94	66	81	67
75	73	66	87	76	45	43	56
57	74	50	78	71	84	59	76.

SOLUTION

The plot is constructed by separating each data item into two parts. The first part is the *stem*. The **stem** consists of the tens digit. For example, the stem for the score of 82 is 8. The second part is the *leaf*. The **leaf** consists of the units digit for a given value. For the score of 82, the leaf is 2. The possible stems for the 40 scores are 4, 5, 6, 7, 8, and 9, entered in the left column of the plot.

Begin by entering each data item in the first row:

82 47 75 64 57 82 63 93.

Entering 82:

Stems	Leaves
4	
5	
6	
7	
8	2
9	

Adding 47:

Stems	Leaves
4	7
5	
6	
7	
8	2
9	

Adding 75:

Stems	Leaves
4	7
5	
6	
7	5
8	2
9	

Adding 64:

Stems	Leaves
4	7
5	
6	4
7	5
8	2
9	

Adding 57:

Stems	Leaves
4	7
5	7
6	4
7	5
8	2
9	

Adding 82:

Stems	Leaves
4	7
5	7
6	4
7	5
8	22
9	

Adding 63:

Stems	Leaves
4	7
5	7
6	43
7	5
8	22
9	

Adding 93:

Stems	Leaves
4	7
5	7
6	43
7	5
8	22
9	3

We continue in this manner and enter all the data items. **Figure 6.4** shows the completed stem-and-leaf plot. If you turn the page so that the left margin is on the bottom and facing you, the visual impression created by the enclosed leaves is the same as that created by a histogram. An advantage over the histogram is that the stem-and-leaf plot preserves exact data items. The enclosed leaves extend farthest to the right when the stem is 7. This shows that the greatest frequency of students scored in the 70s.

A Stem-and-Leaf Plot for 40 Test Scores

Tens digit — Units digit

Stems	Leaves
4	7 5 3
5	7 4 6 7 0 9
6	4 3 8 6 7 6
7	5 6 7 9 5 3 6 4 8 1 6
8	2 2 4 8 0 0 1 7 4
9	3 4 2 4 4

FIGURE 6.4 A stem-and-leaf plot displaying 40 test scores

CHECK POINT 5 Construct a stem-and-leaf plot for the data in Check Point 4 on page 211.

4 Identify deceptions in visual displays of data.

Deceptions in Visual Displays of Data

Benjamin Disraeli, Queen Victoria's prime minister, stated that there are "lies, damned lies, and statistics." The problem is not that statistics lie, but rather that liars use statistics. Graphs can be used to distort the underlying data, making it difficult for the viewer to learn the truth. One potential source of misunderstanding is the scale on the vertical axis used to draw the graph. This scale is important because it lets a researcher "inflate" or "deflate" a trend. For example, both graphs in **Figure 6.5** present identical data for the percentage of people in the United States living below the poverty level from 2001 through 2005. The graph on the left stretches the scale on the vertical axis to create an overall impression of a poverty rate increasing rapidly over time. The graph on the right compresses the scale on the vertical axis to create an impression of a poverty rate that is slowly increasing, and beginning to level off, over time.

Percentage of People in the United States Living below the Poverty Level, 2001–2005

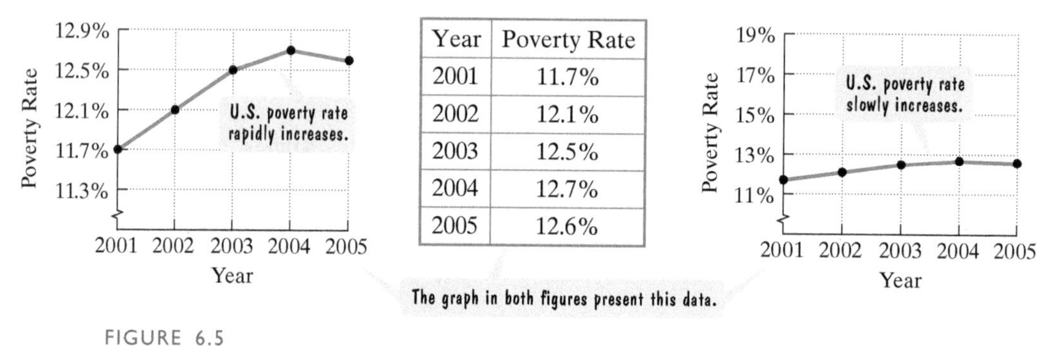

Year	Poverty Rate
2001	11.7%
2002	12.1%
2003	12.5%
2004	12.7%
2005	12.6%

FIGURE 6.5
Source: U.S. Census Bureau

There is another problem with the data in **Figure 6.5**. Look at **Table 6.4** that shows the poverty rate from 2001 through 2011. Depending on the time frame chosen, the data can be interpreted in various ways. Carefully choosing a time frame can help represent data trends in the most positive or negative light.

TABLE 6.4 U.S. Poverty Rate from 2001 to 2011

Year	Poverty Rate
2001	11.7%
2002	12.1%
2003	12.5%
2004	12.7%
2005	12.6%
2006	12.3%
2007	12.5%
2008	13.2%
2009	14.3%
2010	15.1%
2011	15.0%

THINGS TO WATCH FOR IN VISUAL DISPLAYS OF DATA

1. Is there a title that explains what is being displayed?
2. Are numbers lined up with tick marks on the vertical axis that clearly indicate the scale? Has the scale been varied to create a more or less dramatic impression than shown by the actual data?
3. Do too many design and cosmetic effects draw attention from or distort the data?
4. Has the wrong impression been created about how the data are changing because equally spaced time intervals are not used on the horizontal axis? Furthermore, has a time interval been chosen that allows the data to be interpreted in various ways?
5. Are bar sizes scaled proportionately in terms of the data they represent?
6. Is there a source that indicates where the data in the display came from? Do the data come from an entire population or a sample? Was a random sample used and, if so, are there possible differences between what is displayed in the graph and what is occurring in the entire population? (We'll discuss these margins of error in Section 6.4.) Who is presenting the visual display, and does that person have a special case to make for or against the trend shown by the graph?

Table 6.5 contains two examples of misleading visual displays.

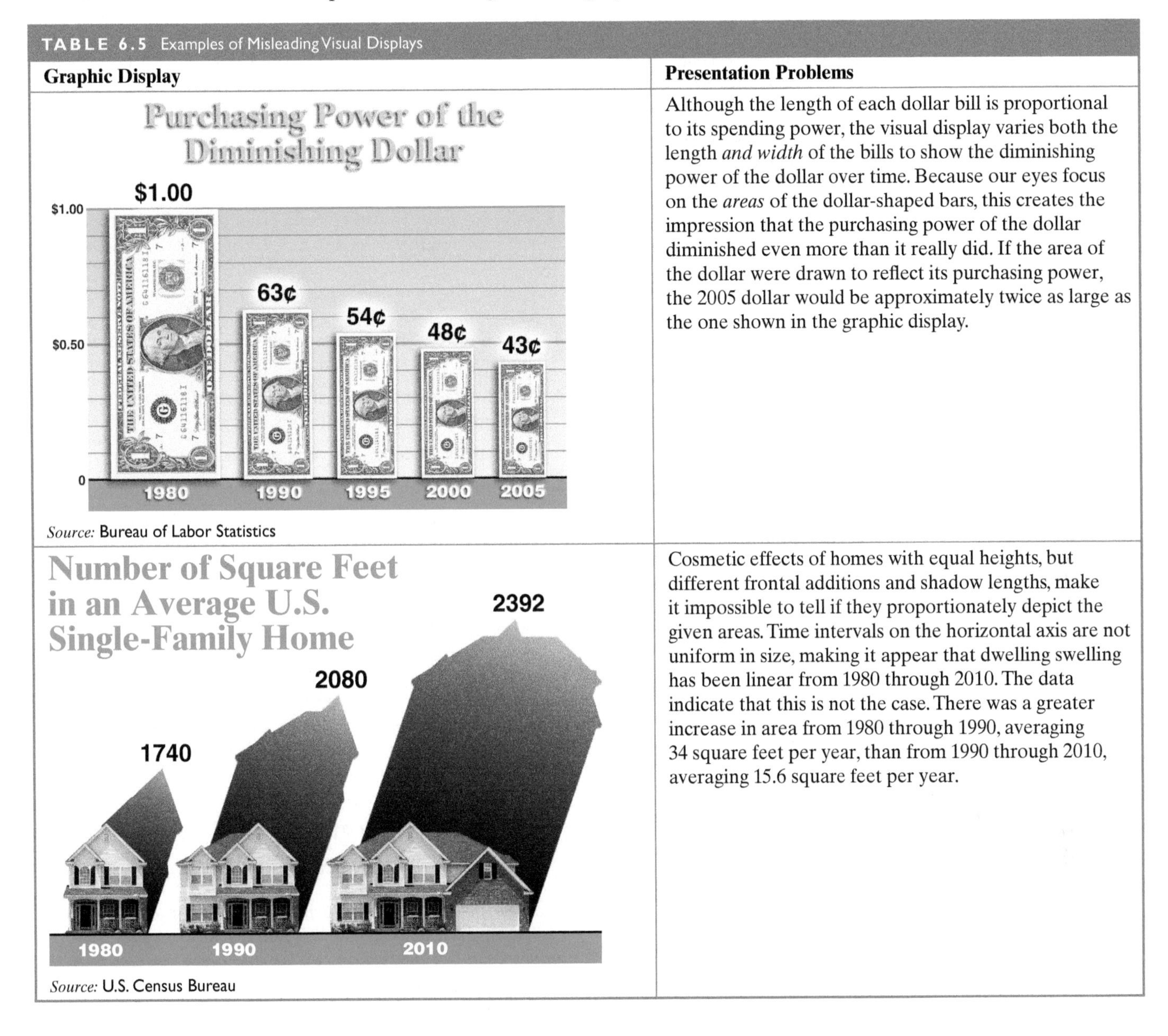

TABLE 6.5 Examples of Misleading Visual Displays

Graphic Display	Presentation Problems
Purchasing Power of the Diminishing Dollar $1.00 (1980), 63¢ (1990), 54¢ (1995), 48¢ (2000), 43¢ (2005) Vertical axis: 0, $0.50, $1.00 *Source:* Bureau of Labor Statistics	Although the length of each dollar bill is proportional to its spending power, the visual display varies both the length *and width* of the bills to show the diminishing power of the dollar over time. Because our eyes focus on the *areas* of the dollar-shaped bars, this creates the impression that the purchasing power of the dollar diminished even more than it really did. If the area of the dollar were drawn to reflect its purchasing power, the 2005 dollar would be approximately twice as large as the one shown in the graphic display.
Number of Square Feet in an Average U.S. Single-Family Home 1740 (1980), 2080 (1990), 2392 (2010) *Source:* U.S. Census Bureau	Cosmetic effects of homes with equal heights, but different frontal additions and shadow lengths, make it impossible to tell if they proportionately depict the given areas. Time intervals on the horizontal axis are not uniform in size, making it appear that dwelling swelling has been linear from 1980 through 2010. The data indicate that this is not the case. There was a greater increase in area from 1980 through 1990, averaging 34 square feet per year, than from 1990 through 2010, averaging 15.6 square feet per year.

Concept and Vocabulary Check

Fill in each blank so that the resulting statement is true.

1. A sample obtained in such a way that every member of the population has an equal chance of being selected is called a/an __________ sample.

2. If data values are listed in one column and the adjacent column indicates the number of times each value occurs, the data presentation is called a/an __________________.

3. If the data presentation in Exercise 2 is varied by organizing the data into classes, the data presentation is called a/an ______________________. If one class in such a distribution is 80–89, the lower class limit is __________ and the upper class limit is __________.

4. Data can be displayed using a bar graph with bars that touch each other. This visual presentation of the data is called a/an __________. The heights of the bars represent the __________ of the data values.

5. If the midpoints of the tops of the bars for the data presentation in Exercise 4 are connected with straight lines, the resulting line graph is a data presentation called a/an ______________. To complete such a graph at both ends, the lines are drawn down to touch the ____________.

6. A data presentation that separates each data item into two parts is called a/an ______________.

In Exercises 7–10, determine whether each statement is true or false. If the statement is false, make the necessary change(s) to produce a true statement.

7. A sample is the set of all the people or objects whose properties are to be described and analyzed by the data collector. ______

8. A call-in poll on radio or television is not reliable because the sample is not chosen randomly from a larger population. ______

9. One disadvantage of a stem-and-leaf plot is that it does not display the data items. ______

10. A deception in the visual display of data can result by stretching or compressing the scale on a graph's vertical axis. ______

Exercise Set 6.1

Practice and Application Exercises

1. The government of a large city needs to determine whether the city's residents will support the construction of a new jail. The government decides to conduct a survey of a sample of the city's residents. Which one of the following procedures would be most appropriate for obtaining a sample of the city's residents?
   - **a.** Survey a random sample of the employees and inmates at the old jail.
   - **b.** Survey every fifth person who walks into City Hall on a given day.
   - **c.** Survey a random sample of persons within each geographic region of the city.
   - **d.** Survey the first 200 people listed in the city's telephone directory.

2. The city council of a large city needs to know whether its residents will support the building of three new schools. The council decides to conduct a survey of a sample of the city's residents. Which procedure would be most appropriate for obtaining a sample of the city's residents?
   - **a.** Survey a random sample of teachers who live in the city.
   - **b.** Survey 100 individuals who are randomly selected from a list of all people living in the state in which the city in question is located.
   - **c.** Survey a random sample of persons within each neighborhood of the city.
   - **d.** Survey every tenth person who enters City Hall on a randomly selected day.

A questionnaire was given to students in an introductory statistics class during the first week of the course. One question asked, "How stressed have you been in the last $2\frac{1}{2}$ weeks, on a scale of 0 to 10, with 0 being not at all stressed and 10 being as stressed as possible?" The students' responses are shown in the frequency distribution. Use this frequency distribution to solve Exercises 3–6.

Stress Rating	Frequency
0	2
1	1
2	3
3	12
4	16
5	18

Stress Rating	Frequency
6	13
7	31
8	26
9	15
10	14

Source: Journal of Personality and Social Psychology, 69, 1102–1112

3. Which stress rating describes the greatest number of students? How many students responded with this rating?

4. Which stress rating describes the least number of students? How many responded with this rating?

5. How many students were involved in this study?

6. How many students had a stress rating of 8 or more?

7. A random sample of 30 college students is selected. Each student is asked how much time he or she spent on homework during the previous week. The following times (in hours) are obtained:

   16, 24, 18, 21, 18, 16, 18, 17, 15, 21, 19, 17, 17, 16, 19, 18, 15, 15, 20, 17, 15, 17, 24, 19, 16, 20, 16, 19, 18, 17.

   Construct a frequency distribution for the data.

8. A random sample of 30 male college students is selected. Each student is asked his height (to the nearest inch). The heights are as follows:

   72, 70, 68, 72, 71, 71, 71, 69, 73, 71, 73, 75, 66, 67, 75, 74, 73, 71, 72, 67, 72, 68, 67, 71, 73, 71, 72, 70, 73, 70.

   Construct a frequency distribution for the data.

A college professor had students keep a diary of their social interactions for a week. Excluding family and work situations, the number of social interactions of ten minutes or longer over the week is shown in the following grouped frequency distribution. Use this information to solve Exercises 9–16.

Number of Social Interactions	Frequency
0–4	12
5–9	16
10–14	16
15–19	16
20–24	10
25–29	11
30–34	4
35–39	3
40–44	3
45–49	3

Source: Society for Personality and Social Psychology

9. Identify the lower class limit for each class.

10. Identify the upper class limit for each class.

11. What is the class width?

12. How many students were involved in this study?

13. How many students had at least 30 social interactions for the week?

14. How many students had at most 14 social interactions for the week?

15. Among the classes with the greatest frequency, which class has the least number of social interactions?

16. Among the classes with the smallest frequency, which class has the least number of social interactions?

17. As of 2011, the following are the ages, in chronological order, at which U.S. presidents were inaugurated:

57, 61, 57, 57, 58, 57, 61, 54, 68, 51, 49, 64, 50, 48, 65, 52, 56, 46, 54, 49, 50, 47, 55, 55, 54, 42, 51, 56, 55, 51, 54, 51, 60, 62, 43, 55, 56, 61, 52, 69, 64, 46, 54, 47.

Source: Time Almanac

Construct a grouped frequency distribution for the data. Use 41–45 for the first class and use the same width for each subsequent class.

18. The IQ scores of 70 students enrolled in a liberal arts course at a college are as follows:

102, 100, 103, 86, 120, 117, 111, 101, 93, 97, 99, 95, 95, 104, 104, 105, 106, 109, 109, 89, 94, 95, 99, 99, 103, 104, 105, 109, 110, 114, 124, 123, 118, 117, 116, 110, 114, 114, 96, 99, 103, 103, 104, 107, 107, 110, 111, 112, 113, 117, 115, 116, 100, 104, 102, 94, 93, 93, 96, 96, 111, 116, 107, 109, 105, 106, 97, 106, 107, 108.

Construct a grouped frequency distribution for the data. Use 85–89 for the first class and use the same width for each subsequent class.

19. Construct a histogram and a frequency polygon for the data involving stress ratings in Exercises 3–6.

20. Construct a histogram and a frequency polygon for the data in Exercise 7.

21. Construct a histogram and a frequency polygon for the data in Exercise 8.

The histogram shows the distribution of starting salaries (rounded to the nearest thousand dollars) for college graduates based on a random sample of recent graduates.

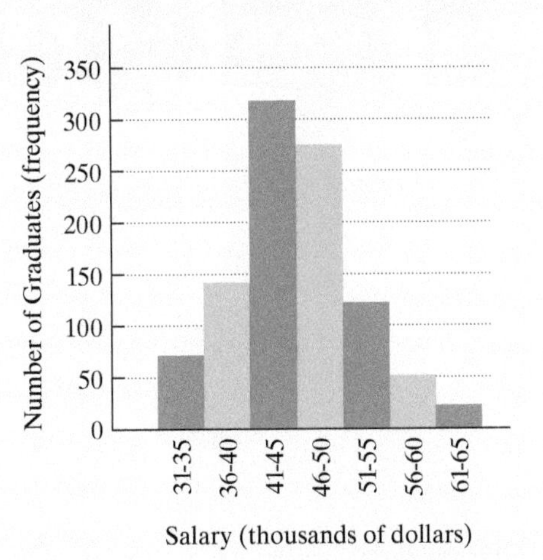

In Exercises 22–25, determine whether each statement is true or false according to the graph at the bottom of the previous column.

22. The graph is based on a sample of approximately 500 recent college graduates.

23. More college graduates had starting salaries in the \$51,000–\$55,000 range than in the \$36,000–\$40,000 range.

24. If the sample is truly representative, then for a group of 400 college graduates, we can expect about 28 of them to have starting salaries in the \$31,000–\$35,000 range.

25. The percentage of starting salaries falling above those shown by any rectangular bar is equal to the percentage of starting salaries falling below that bar.

The frequency polygon shows a distribution of IQ scores.

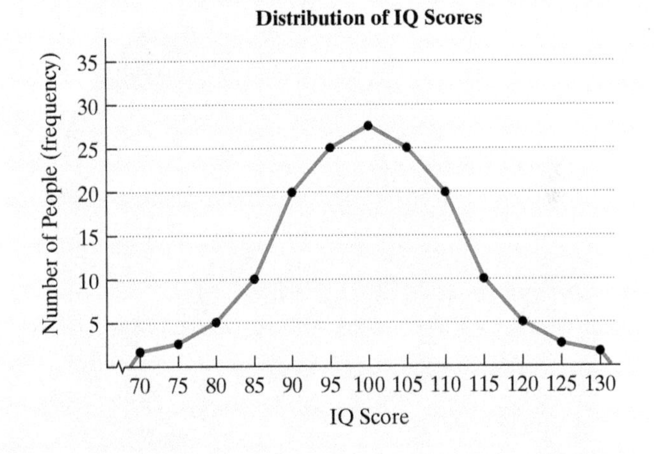

In Exercises 26–29, determine whether each statement is true or false according to the graph.

26. The graph is based on a sample of approximately 50 people.

27. More people had an IQ score of 100 than any other IQ score, and as the deviation from 100 increases or decreases, the scores fall off in a symmetrical manner.

28. More people had an IQ score of 110 than a score of 90.

29. The percentage of scores above any IQ score is equal to the percentage of scores below that score.

30. Construct a stem-and-leaf plot for the data in Exercise 17 showing the ages at which U.S. presidents were inaugurated.

31. A random sample of 40 college professors is selected from all professors at a university. The following list gives their ages:

63, 48, 42, 42, 38, 59, 41, 44, 45, 28, 54, 62, 51, 44, 63, 66, 59, 46, 51, 28, 37, 66, 42, 40, 30, 31, 48, 32, 29, 42, 63, 37, 36, 47, 25, 34, 49, 30, 35, 50.

Construct a stem-and-leaf plot for the data. What does the shape of the display reveal about the ages of the professors?

32. In "Ages of Oscar-Winning Best Actors and Actresses" (*Mathematics Teacher* magazine) by Richard Brown and Gretchen Davis, the stem-and-leaf plots shown on the right compare the ages of 30 actors and 30 actresses at the time they won the award.

a. What is the age of the youngest actor to win an Oscar?

b. What is the age difference between the oldest and the youngest actress to win an Oscar?

c. What is the oldest age shared by two actors to win an Oscar?

d. What differences do you observe between the two stem-and-leaf plots? What explanations can you offer for these differences?

Actors	Stems	Actresses
	2	146667
98753221	3	00113344455778
88776543322100	4	11129
6651	5	
210	6	011
6	7	4
	8	0

In Exercises 33–37, describe what is misleading in each visual display of data.

33. **World Population, in Billions**

1 2 3 4 5 6 7 8 9

1804 1927 1960 1974 1987 1999 2012 2026 2043

Source: U.S. Census Bureau

34. **Book Title Output in the United States**

114,487 147,120 171,061 190,078 172,000

2001 2002 2003 2004 2005

Source: R. R. Bowker

35. **Percentage of the World's Computers in Use, by Country**

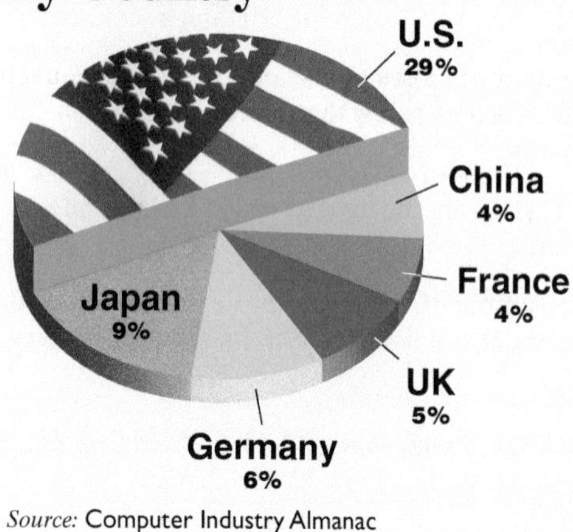

Source: Computer Industry Almanac

36. **Percentage of U.S. Households Watching ABC, CBS, and NBC in Prime Time**

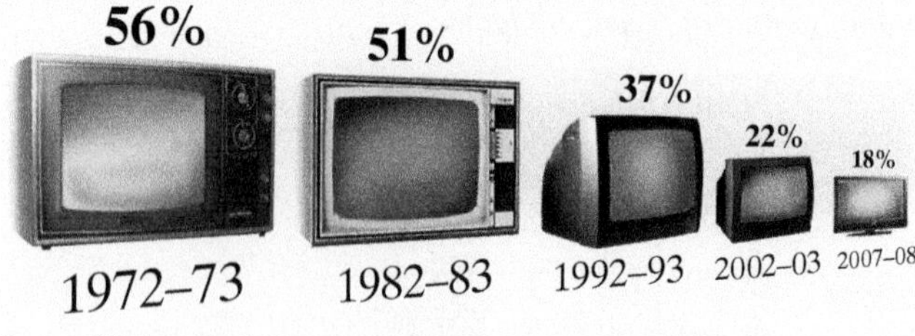

Source: Nielsen Media Research

37.

Writing in Mathematics

38. What is a population? What is a sample?

39. Describe what is meant by a random sample.

40. Suppose you are interested in whether or not the students at your college would favor a grading system in which students may receive final grades of A+, A, A−, B+, B, B−,C+, C, C−, and so on. Describe how you might obtain a random sample of 100 students from the entire student population.

41. For Exercise 40, would questioning every fifth student as he or she is leaving the campus library until 100 students are interviewed be a good way to obtain a random sample? Explain your answer.

42. What is a frequency distribution?

43. What is a histogram?

44. What is a frequency polygon?

45. Describe how to construct a frequency polygon from a histogram.

46. Describe how to construct a stem-and-leaf plot from a set of data.

47. Describe two ways that graphs can be misleading.

Critical Thinking Exercises

Make Sense? *In Exercises 48–51, determine whether each statement makes sense or does not make sense, and explain your reasoning.*

48. The death rate from this new strain of flu is catastrophic because 25% of the people hospitalized with the disease have died.

49. The following graph indicates that for the period from 2000 through 2010, the percentage of female college freshmen describing their health as "above average" has rapidly decreased.

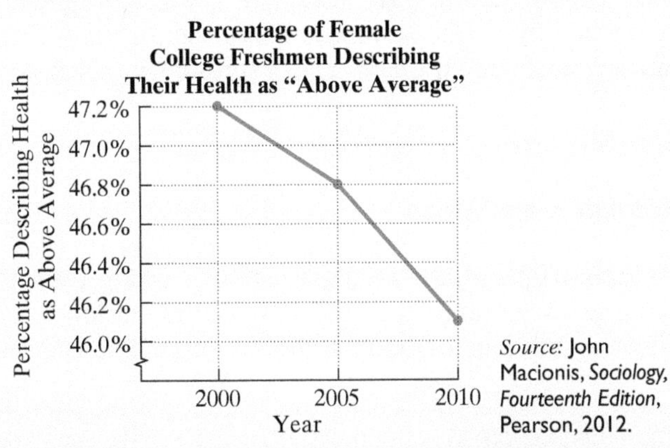

50. A public radio station needs to survey its contributors to determine their programming interests, so they should select a random sample of 100 of their largest contributors.

51. Improperly worded questions can steer respondents toward answers that are not their own.

52. Construct a grouped frequency distribution for the following data, showing the length, in miles, of the 25 longest rivers in the United States. Use five classes that have the same width.

2540	2340	1980	1900	1900
1460	1450	1420	1310	1290
1280	1240	1040	990	926
906	886	862	800	774
743	724	692	659	649

Source: U.S. Department of the Interior

Group Exercises

53. The classic book on distortion using statistics is *How to Lie with Statistics* by Darrell Huff. This activity is designed for five people. Each person should select two chapters from Huff's book and then present to the class the common methods of statistical manipulation and distortion that Huff discusses.

54. Each group member should find one example of a graph that presents data with integrity and one example of a graph that is misleading. Use newspapers, magazines, the Internet, books, and so forth. Once graphs have been collected, each member should share his or her graphs with the entire group. Be sure to explain why one graph depicts data in a forthright manner and how the other graph misleads the viewer.

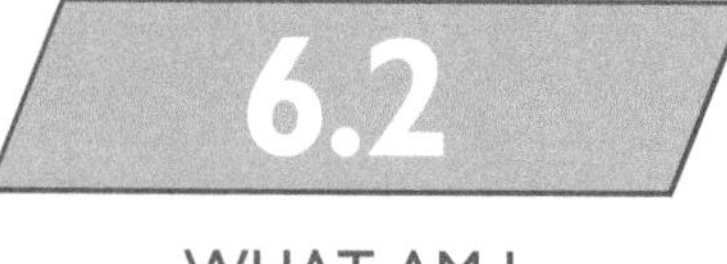

WHAT AM I SUPPOSED TO LEARN?

After you have read this section, you should be able to:

1. Determine the mean for a data set.
2. Determine the median for a data set.
3. Determine the mode for a data set.
4. Determine the midrange for a data set.

Measures of Central Tendency

DURING A LIFETIME, AMERICANS AVERAGE TWO WEEKS KISSING.
But wait, there's more:

- 130: The average number of "Friends" for a Facebook user
- 12: The average number of cars an American owns during a lifetime
- 300: The average number of times a 6-year-old child laughs each day
- 550: The average number of hairs in the human eyebrow
- 28: The average number of years in the lifespan of a citizen during the Roman Empire
- 6,000,000: The average number of dust mites living in a U.S. bed.

Source: *Listomania*, Harper Design

These numbers represent what is "average" or "typical" in a variety of situations. In statistics, such values are known as **measures of central tendency** because they are generally located toward the center of a distribution. Four such measures are discussed in this section: the mean, the median, the mode, and the midrange. Each measure of central tendency is calculated in a different way. Thus, it is better to use a specific term (mean, median, mode, or midrange) than to use the generic descriptive term "average."

1 Determine the mean for a data set.

The Mean

By far the most commonly used measure of central tendency is the *mean*. The **mean** is obtained by adding all the data items and then dividing the sum by the number of items. The Greek letter sigma, Σ, called a **symbol of summation**, is used to indicate the sum of data items. The notation Σx, read "the sum of x," means to add all the data items in a given data set. We can use this symbol to give a formula for calculating the mean.

THE MEAN

The **mean** is the sum of the data items divided by the number of items.

$$\text{Mean} = \frac{\Sigma x}{n},$$

where Σx represents the sum of all the data items and n represents the number of items.

The mean of a sample is symbolized by $\bar{x}$ (read "x bar"), while the mean of an entire population is symbolized by μ (the lowercase Greek letter *mu*). Unless otherwise indicated, the data sets throughout this chapter represent samples, so we will use $\bar{x}$ for the mean: $\bar{x} = \frac{\Sigma x}{n}$.

EXAMPLE 1 *Calculating the Mean*

Table 6.6 at the top of the next page shows the ten highest-earning TV actors and the ten highest-earning TV actresses for the 2010–2011 television season. Find the mean earnings, in millions of dollars, for the ten highest-earning actors.

Blitzer Bonus

Using Means to Compare How the U.S. Measures Up

- Mean Life Expectancy

78	82
U.S.	ITALY

- Mean Cost of an Angiogram

\$798	\$35
U.S.	CANADA

- Mean Number of Hours of TV Watched Daily

2.7	2.8
U.S.	ENGLAND

- Mean Number of Working Hours per Week

35.1	27.8
U.S.	GERMANY

- Mean Size of a Steak Served at Restaurants

13 ounces	8 ounces
U.S.	ENGLAND

Source: Time, USA Today

TABLE 6.6 Highest-Earning TV Actors and Actresses, 2010–2011

Actor	Earnings (millions of dollars)	Actress	Earnings (millions of dollars)
Charlie Sheen	\$40	Eva Longoria	\$13
Ray Romano	\$20	Tina Fey	\$13
Steve Carell	\$15	Marcia Cross	\$10
Mark Harmon	\$13	Mariska Hargitay	\$10
Jon Cryer	\$11	Marg Helgenberger	\$10
Laurence Fishburne	\$11	Teri Hatcher	\$9
Patrick Dempsey	\$10	Felicity Huffman	\$9
Simon Baker	\$9	Courteney Cox	\$7
Hugh Laurie	\$9	Ellen Pompeo	\$7
Chris Meloni	\$9	Julianna Margulies	\$7

Source: Forbes

SOLUTION

We find the mean, $\bar{x}$, by adding the earnings for the actors and dividing this sum by 10, the number of data items.

$$\bar{x} = \frac{\sum x}{n} = \frac{40 + 20 + 15 + 13 + 11 + 11 + 10 + 9 + 9 + 9}{10} = \frac{147}{10} = 14.7$$

The mean earnings of the ten highest-earning actors is \$14.7 million.

One and only one mean can be calculated for any group of numerical data. The mean may or may not be one of the actual data items. In Example 1, the mean was 14.7, although no data item is 14.7.

CHECK POINT 1 Use **Table 6.6** to find the mean earnings, $\bar{x}$, in millions of dollars, for the ten highest-earning actresses.

In Example 1, some of the data items were identical. We can use multiplication when computing the sum for these identical items.

$$\bar{x} = \frac{40 + 20 + 15 + 13 + 11 + 11 + 10 + 9 + 9 + 9}{10}$$

$$= \frac{40 \cdot 1 + 20 \cdot 1 + 15 \cdot 1 + 13 \cdot 1 + 11 \cdot 2 + 10 \cdot 1 + 9 \cdot 3}{10}$$

The data value 11 has a frequency of 2.
The data value 9 has a frequency of 3.

When many data values occur more than once and a frequency distribution is used to organize the data, we can use the following formula to calculate the mean:

CALCULATING THE MEAN FOR A FREQUENCY DISTRIBUTION

$$\text{Mean} = \bar{x} = \frac{\Sigma xf}{n},$$

where

x represents a data value.
f represents the frequency of that data value.
Σxf represents the sum of all the products obtained by multiplying each data value by its frequency.
n represents the *total frequency* of the distribution.

TABLE 6.7 Students' Stress-Level Ratings

Stress Rating x	Frequency f
0	2
1	1
2	3
3	12
4	16
5	18
6	13
7	31
8	26
9	15
10	14

Source: Journal of Personality and Social Psychology, 69, 1102–1112

EXAMPLE 2 *Calculating the Mean for a Frequency Distribution*

In the previous Exercise Set, we mentioned a questionnaire given to students in an introductory statistics class during the first week of the course. One question asked, "How stressed have you been in the last $2\frac{1}{2}$ weeks, on a scale of 0 to 10, with 0 being not at all stressed and 10 being as stressed as possible?" **Table 6.7** shows the students' responses. Use this frequency distribution to find the mean of the stress-level ratings.

SOLUTION

We use the formula for the mean, $\bar{x}$:

$$\bar{x} = \frac{\Sigma xf}{n}.$$

First, we must find xf, obtained by multiplying each data value, x, by its frequency, f. Then, we need to find the sum of these products, Σxf. We can use the frequency distribution to organize these computations. Add a third column in which each data value is multiplied by its frequency. This column, shown on the right, is headed xf. Then, find the sum of the values, Σxf, in this column.

x	f	xf
0	2	$0 \cdot 2 = 0$
1	1	$1 \cdot 1 = 1$
2	3	$2 \cdot 3 = 6$
3	12	$3 \cdot 12 = 36$
4	16	$4 \cdot 16 = 64$
5	18	$5 \cdot 18 = 90$
6	13	$6 \cdot 13 = 78$
7	31	$7 \cdot 31 = 217$
8	26	$8 \cdot 26 = 208$
9	15	$9 \cdot 15 = 135$
10	14	$10 \cdot 14 = 140$
Totals:	$n = 151$	$\Sigma xf = 975$

This value, the sum of the numbers in the second column, is the total frequency of the distribution.

Σxf is the sum of the numbers in the third column.

Now, substitute these values into the formula for the mean, $\bar{x}$. Remember that n is the *total frequency* of the distribution, or 151.

$$\bar{x} = \frac{\Sigma xf}{n} = \frac{975}{151} \approx 6.46$$

The mean of the 0 to 10 stress-level ratings is approximately 6.46. Notice that the mean is greater than 5, the middle of the 0 to 10 scale.

CHECK POINT 2 Find the mean, $\bar{x}$, for the data items in the frequency distribution. (In order to save space, we've written the frequency distribution horizontally.)

Score, x	30	33	40	50
Frequency, f	3	4	4	1

2 Determine the median for a data set.

The Median

The *median* age in the United States is 37.2. The oldest state by median age is Maine (42.7) and the youngest state is Utah (29.2). To find these values, researchers begin with appropriate random samples. The data items—that is, the ages—are arranged from youngest to oldest. The median age is the data item in the middle of each set of ranked, or ordered, data.

THE MEDIAN

To find the **median** of a group of data items,

1. Arrange the data items in order, from smallest to largest.
2. If the number of data items is odd, the median is the data item in the middle of the list.
3. If the number of data items is even, the median is the mean of the two middle data items.

EXAMPLE 3 *Finding the Median*

Find the median for each of the following groups of data:

a. 84, 90, 98, 95, 88

b. 68, 74, 7, 13, 15, 25, 28, 59, 34, 47.

SOLUTION

a. Arrange the data items in order, from smallest to largest. The number of data items in the list, five, is odd. Thus, the median is the middle number.

84, 88, 90, 95, 98

Middle data item

The median is 90. Notice that two data items lie above 90 and two data items lie below 90.

b. Arrange the data items in order, from smallest to largest. The number of data items in the list, ten, is even. Thus, the median is the mean of the two middle data items.

7, 13, 15, 25, 28, 34, 47, 59, 68, 74

Middle data items are 28 and 34.

$$\text{Median} = \frac{28 + 34}{2} = \frac{62}{2} = 31$$

The median is 31. Five data items lie above 31 and five data items lie below 31.

7 13 15 25 28 | 34 47 59 68 74

Five data items lie below 31. Five data items lie above 31.

Median is 31.

GREAT QUESTION!

What exactly does the median do with the data?

The median splits the data items down the middle, like the median strip in a road.

CHECK POINT 3 Find the median for each of the following groups of data:

a. 28, 42, 40, 25, 35

b. 72, 61, 85, 93, 79, 87.

If a relatively long list of data items is arranged in order, it may be difficult to identify the item or items in the middle. In cases like this, the median can be found by determining its position in the list of items.

GREAT QUESTION!

Does the formula

$$\frac{n+1}{2}$$

give the value of the median?

No. The formula gives the *position* of the median, and not the actual value of the median. When finding the median, be sure to first arrange the data items in order from smallest to largest.

POSITION OF THE MEDIAN

If n data items are arranged in order, from smallest to largest, the median is the value in the

$$\frac{n+1}{2}$$

position.

EXAMPLE 4 Finding the Median Using the Position Formula

Table 6.8 gives the nine longest words in the English language. Find the median number of letters for the nine longest words.

TABLE 6.8 The Nine Longest Words in the English Language

Word	Number of Letters
Pneumonoultramicroscopicsilicovolcanoconiosis A lung disease caused by breathing in volcanic dust	45
Supercalifragilisticexpialidocious Meaning "wonderful", from song of this title in the movie *Mary Poppins*	34
Floccinaucinihilipilification Meaning "the action or habit of estimating as worthless"	29
Trinitrophenylmethylnitramine A chemical compound used as a detonator in shells	29
Antidisestablishmentarianism Meaning "opposition to the disestablishment of the Church of England"	28
Electroencephalographically Relating to brain waves	27
Microspectrophotometrically Relating to the measurement of light waves	27
Immunoelectrophoretically Relating to measurement of immunoglobulin	25
Spectroheliokinematograph A 1930s' device for monitoring and filming solar activity	25

Source: Chris Cole, rec.puzzles archive

SOLUTION

We begin by listing the data items from smallest to largest.

25, 25, 27, 27, 28, 29, 29, 34, 45

There are nine data items, so $n = 9$. The median is the value in the

$$\frac{n+1}{2} \text{ position} = \frac{9+1}{2} \text{ position} = \frac{10}{2} \text{ position} = \text{fifth position.}$$

We find the median by selecting the data item in the fifth position.

Position 3 Position 4

25, 25, 27, 27, 28, 29, 29, 34, 45

Position 1 Position 2 Position 5

The median is 28. Notice that four data items lie above 28 and four data items lie below it. The median number of letters for the nine longest words in the English language is 28.

CHECK POINT 4 Find the median for the following group of data items:

1, 2, 2, 2, 3, 3, 3, 3, 3, 5, 6, 7, 7, 10, 11, 13, 19, 24, 26.

TABLE 6.9 Hours and Minutes per Day Spent Sleeping and Eating in Selected Countries

Country	Sleeping	Eating
France	8:50	2:15
U.S.	8:38	1:14
Spain	8:34	1:46
New Zealand	8:33	2:10
Australia	8:32	1:29
Turkey	8:32	1:29
Canada	8:29	1:09
Poland	8:28	1:34
Finland	8:27	1:21
Belgium	8:25	1:49
United Kingdom	8:23	1:25
Mexico	8:21	1:06
Italy	8:18	1:54
Germany	8:12	1:45
Sweden	8:06	1:34
Norway	8:03	1:22
Japan	7:50	1:57
S. Korea	7:49	1:36

Source: Organization for Economic Cooperation and Development

EXAMPLE 5 *Finding the Median Using the Position Formula*

Table 6.9 gives the mean number of hours and minutes per day spent sleeping and eating in 18 selected countries. Find the median number of hours and minutes per day spent sleeping for these countries.

SOLUTION

Reading from the bottom to the top of **Table 6.9**, the data items for sleeping appear from smallest to largest. There are 18 data items, so $n = 18$. The median is the value in the

$$\frac{n+1}{2}\text{ position} = \frac{18+1}{2}\text{ position} = \frac{19}{2}\text{ position} = 9.5\text{ position}.$$

This means that the median is the mean of the data items in positions 9 and 10.

Position 3 Position 4 Position 7 Position 8

7:49, 7:50, 8:03, 8:06, 8:12, 8:18, 8:21, 8:23, 8:25, 8:27, 8:28, 8:29, 8:32, 8:32, 8:33, 8:34, 8:38, 8:50

Position 1 Position 2 Position 5 Position 6 Position 9 Position 10

$$\text{Median} = \frac{8{:}25 + 8{:}27}{2} = \frac{16{:}52}{2} = 8{:}26$$

The median number of hours per day spent sleeping for the 18 countries is 8 hours, 26 minutes.

CHECK POINT 5 Arrange the data items for eating in **Table 6.9** from smallest to largest. Then find the median number of hours and minutes per day spent eating for the 18 countries.

When individual data items are listed from smallest to largest, you can find the median by identifying the item or items in the middle or by using the $\frac{n+1}{2}$ formula for its position. However, the formula for the position of the median is more useful when data items are organized in a frequency distribution.

EXAMPLE 6 *Finding the Median for a Frequency Distribution*

The frequency distribution for the stress-level ratings of 151 students is repeated below using a horizontal format. Find the median stress-level rating.

Stress rating / Number of college students

x	0	1	2	3	4	5	6	7	8	9	10
f	2	1	3	12	16	18	13	31	26	15	14

Total: $n = 151$

SOLUTION

There are 151 data items, so $n = 151$. The median is the value in the

$$\frac{n+1}{2} \text{ position} = \frac{151+1}{2} \text{ position} = \frac{152}{2} \text{ position} = 76\text{th position.}$$

We find the median by selecting the data item in the 76th position. The frequency distribution indicates that the data items begin with

$$0, 0, 1, 2, 2, 2, \ldots.$$

We can write the data items all out and then select the median, the 76th data item. A more efficient way to proceed is to count down the frequency column in the distribution until we identify the 76th data item:

x	f	We count down the frequency column.
0	2	1, 2
1	1	3
2	3	4, 5, 6
3	12	7, 8, 9, 10, 11, 12, 13, 14, 15, 16, 17, 18
4	16	19, 20, 21, 22, 23, 24, 25, 26, 27, 28, 29, 30, 31, 32, 33, 34
5	18	35, 36, 37, 38, 39, 40, 41, 42, 43, 44, 45, 46, 47, 48, 49, 50, 51, 52
6	13	53, 54, 55, 56, 57, 58, 59, 60, 61, 62, 63, 64, 65
7	31	66, 67, 68, 69, 70, 71, 72, 73, 74, 75, 76
8	26	
9	15	
10	14	

Stop counting. We've reached the 76th data item.

The 76th data item is 7. The median stress-level rating is 7.

CHECK POINT 6 Find the median for the following frequency distribution.

Age at presidential inauguration / Number of U.S. presidents assuming office in the 20th century with the given age

x	42	43	46	51	52	54	55	56	60	61	64	69
f	1	1	1	3	1	2	2	2	1	2	1	1

Statisticians generally use the median, rather than the mean, when reporting income. Why? Our next example will help to answer this question.

EXAMPLE 7 *Comparing the Median and the Mean*

Five employees in the assembly section of a television manufacturing company earn salaries of $19,700, $20,400, $21,500, $22,600, and $23,000 annually. The section manager has an annual salary of $95,000.

a. Find the median annual salary for the six people.

b. Find the mean annual salary for the six people.

SOLUTION

a. To compute the median, first arrange the salaries in order:

$19,700, $20,400, $21,500, $22,600, $23,000, $95,000.

Because the list contains an even number of data items, six, the median is the mean of the two middle items.

$$\text{Median} = \frac{\$21{,}500 + \$22{,}600}{2} = \frac{\$44{,}100}{2} = \$22{,}050$$

The median annual salary is $22,050.

b. We find the mean annual salary by adding the six annual salaries and dividing by 6.

$$\text{Mean} = \frac{\$19{,}700 + \$20{,}400 + \$21{,}500 + \$22{,}600 + \$23{,}000 + \$95{,}000}{6}$$

$$= \frac{\$202{,}200}{6} = \$33{,}700$$

The mean annual salary is $33,700.

In Example 7, the median annual salary is $22,050 and the mean annual salary is $33,700. Why such a big difference between these two measures of central tendency? The relatively high annual salary of the section manager, $95,000, pulls the mean salary to a value considerably higher than the median salary. When one or more data items are much greater than the other items, these extreme values can greatly influence the mean. In cases like this, the median is often more representative of the data.

This is why the median, rather than the mean, is used to summarize the incomes, by gender and race, shown in **Figure 6.6**. Because no one can earn less than $0, the distribution of income must come to an end at $0 for each of these eight groups. By contrast, there is no upper limit on income on the high side. In the United States, the wealthiest 20% of the population earn about 50% of the total income. The relatively few people with very high annual incomes tend to pull the mean income to a value considerably greater than the median income. Reporting mean incomes in **Figure 6.6** would inflate the numbers shown, making them nonrepresentative of the millions of workers in each of the eight groups.

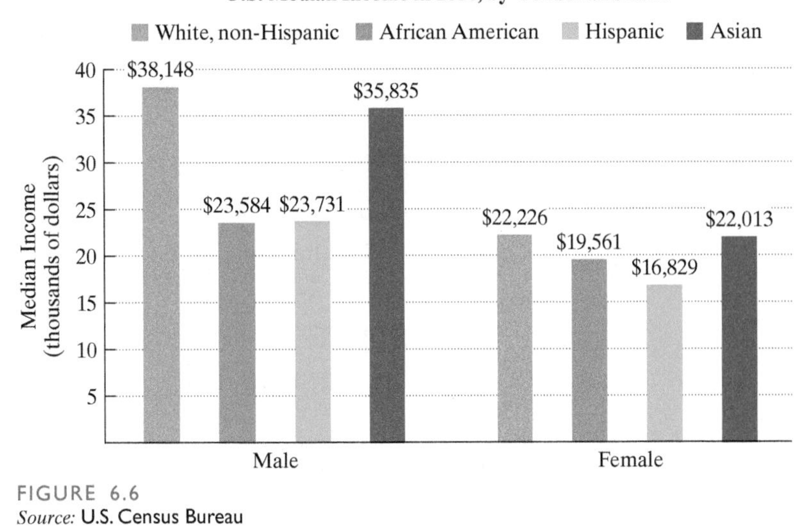

FIGURE 6.6
Source: U.S. Census Bureau

CHECK POINT 7 **Table 6.10** shows the net worth, in millions of 2010 dollars, for ten U.S. presidents from Kennedy through Obama.

TABLE 6.10 Net Worth for Ten U.S. Presidents

President	Net Worth (millions of dollars)
Kennedy	\$1000 (i.e. \$1 billion)
Johnson	\$98
Nixon	\$15
Ford	\$7
Carter	\$7
Reagan	\$13
Bush	\$23
Clinton	\$38
Bush	\$20
Obama	\$5

Source: Time

a. Find the mean net worth, in millions of dollars, for the ten presidents.
b. Find the median net worth, in millions of dollars, for the ten presidents.
c. Describe why one of the measures of central tendency is greater than the other.

3 Determine the mode for a data set.

The Mode

Let's take one final look at the frequency distribution for the stress-level ratings of 151 college students.

Stress rating

Number of college students

x	0	1	2	3	4	5	6	7	8	9	10
f	2	1	3	12	16	18	13	31	26	15	14

7 is the stress rating with the greatest frequency.

The data value that occurs most often in this distribution is 7, the stress rating for 31 of the 151 students. We call 7 the *mode* of this distribution.

THE MODE

The **mode** is the data value that occurs most often in a data set. If more than one data value has the highest frequency, then each of these data values is a mode. If there is no data value that occurs most often, then the data set has no mode.

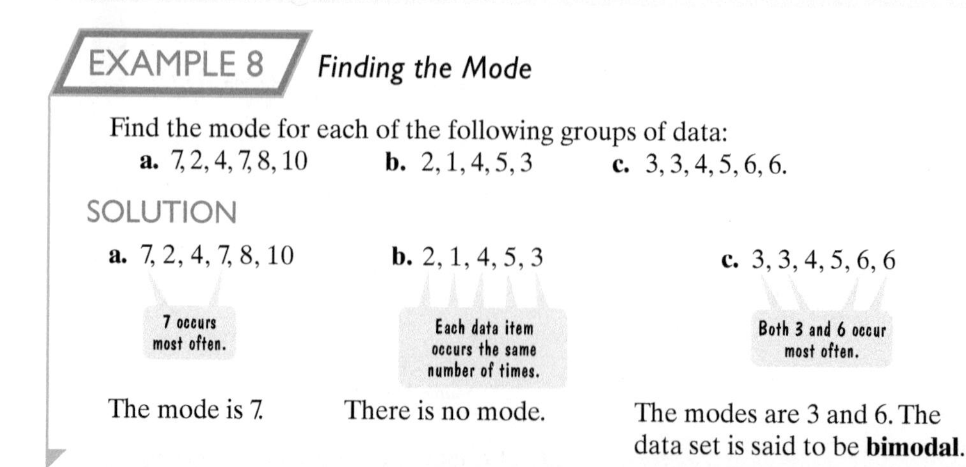

EXAMPLE 8 *Finding the Mode*

Find the mode for each of the following groups of data:
a. 7, 2, 4, 7, 8, 10 **b.** 2, 1, 4, 5, 3 **c.** 3, 3, 4, 5, 6, 6.

SOLUTION

a. 7, 2, 4, 7, 8, 10

7 occurs most often.

The mode is 7.

b. 2, 1, 4, 5, 3

Each data item occurs the same number of times.

There is no mode.

c. 3, 3, 4, 5, 6, 6

Both 3 and 6 occur most often.

The modes are 3 and 6. The data set is said to be **bimodal**.

CHECK POINT 8 Find the mode for each of the following groups of data:

a. 3, 8, 5, 8, 9, 10

b. 3, 8, 5, 8, 9, 3

c. 3, 8, 5, 6, 9, 10.

4 Determine the midrange for a data set.

TABLE 6.11 Ten Hottest U.S. Cities

City	Mean Temperature
Key West, FL	77.8°
Miami, FL	75.9°
West Palm Beach, FL	74.7°
Fort Myers, FL	74.4°
Yuma, AZ	74.2°
Brownsville, TX	73.8°
Phoenix, AZ	72.6°
Vero Beach, FL	72.4°
Orlando, FL	72.3°
Tampa, FL	72.3°

Source: National Oceanic and Atmospheric Administration

The Midrange

Table 6.11 shows the ten hottest cities in the United States. Because temperature is constantly changing, you might wonder how the mean temperatures shown in the table are obtained.

First, we need to find a representative daily temperature. This is obtained by adding the lowest and highest temperatures for the day and then dividing this sum by 2. Next, we take the representative daily temperatures for all 365 days, add them, and divide the sum by 365. These are the mean temperatures that appear in **Table 6.11**.

Representative daily temperature,

$$\frac{\text{lowest daily temperature} + \text{highest daily temperature}}{2},$$

is an example of a measure of central tendency called the *midrange*.

THE MIDRANGE

The **midrange** is found by adding the lowest and highest data values and dividing the sum by 2.

$$\text{Midrange} = \frac{\text{lowest data value} + \text{highest data value}}{2}$$

EXAMPLE 9 *Finding the Midrange*

Newsweek magazine examined factors that affect women's lives, including justice, health, education, economics, and politics. Using these five factors, the magazine graded each of 165 countries on a scale from 0 to 100. The 12 best places to be a woman and the 12 worst places to be a woman are shown in **Table 6.12**.

TABLE 6.12 Women in the World

Best Places to Be a Woman		Worst Places to Be a Woman	
Country	**Score**	**Country**	**Score**
Iceland	100.0	Chad	0.0
Canada	99.6	Afghanistan	2.0
Sweden	99.2	Yemen	12.1
Denmark	95.3	Democratic Republic of the Congo	13.6
Finland	92.8	Mali	17.6
Switzerland	91.9	Solomon Islands	20.8
Norway	91.3	Niger	21.2
United States	89.8	Pakistan	21.4
Australia	88.2	Ethiopia	23.7
Netherlands	87.7	Sudan	26.1
New Zealand	87.2	Guinea	28.5
France	87.2	Sierra Leone	29.0

Source: Newsweek

Find the midrange score among the 12 best countries to be a woman.

SOLUTION

Refer to **Table 6.12** on the previous page.

$$\text{Midrange} = \frac{\text{best place with the lowest score} + \text{best place with the highest score}}{2}$$

$$= \frac{87.2 + 100.0}{2} = \frac{187.2}{2} = 93.6$$

The midrange score among the 12 best countries to be a woman is 93.6.

We can find the mean score among the 12 best countries to be a woman by adding up the 12 scores and then dividing the sum by 12. By doing so, we can determine that the mean score is approximately 92.5. It is much faster to calculate the midrange, which is often used as an estimate for the mean.

CHECK POINT 9 Use **Table 6.12** on the previous page to find the midrange score among the 12 worst countries to be a woman.

EXAMPLE 10 *Finding the Four Measures of Central Tendency*

Suppose your six exam grades in a course are

52, 69, 75, 86, 86, and 92.

Compute your final course grade (90–100 = A, 80–89 = B, 70–79 = C, 60–69 = D, below 60 = F) using the

a. mean. **b.** median. **c.** mode. **d.** midrange.

SOLUTION

a. The mean is the sum of the data items divided by the number of items, 6.

$$\text{Mean} = \frac{52 + 69 + 75 + 86 + 86 + 92}{6} = \frac{460}{6} \approx 76.67$$

Using the mean, your final course grade is C.

b. The six data items, 52, 69, 75, 86, 86, and 92, are arranged in order. Because the number of data items is even, the median is the mean of the two middle items.

$$\text{Median} = \frac{75 + 86}{2} = \frac{161}{2} = 80.5$$

Using the median, your final course grade is B.

c. The mode is the data value that occurs most frequently. Because 86 occurs most often, the mode is 86. Using the mode, your final course grade is B.

d. The midrange is the mean of the lowest and highest data values.

$$\text{Midrange} = \frac{52 + 92}{2} = \frac{144}{2} = 72$$

Using the midrange, your final course grade is C.

CHECK POINT 10 *Consumer Reports* magazine gave the following data for the number of calories in a meat hot dog for each of 17 brands:

173, 191, 182, 190, 172, 147, 146, 138, 175, 136, 179, 153, 107, 195, 135, 140, 138.

Find the mean, median, mode, and midrange for the number of calories in a meat hot dog for the 17 brands. If necessary, round answers to the nearest tenth of a calorie.

Concept and Vocabulary Check

Fill in each blank so that the resulting statement is true.

1. $\frac{\Sigma x}{n}$, the sum of all the data items divided by the number of data items, is the measure of central tendency called the ________.
2. The measure of central tendency that is the data item in the middle of ranked, or ordered, data is called the ________.
3. If n data items are arranged in order, from smallest to largest, the data item in the middle is the value in ________ position.
4. A data value that occurs most often in a data set is the measure of central tendency called the ________.
5. The measure of central tendency that is found by adding the lowest and highest data values and dividing the sum by 2 is called the ________.

In Exercises 6–9, determine whether each statement is true or false. If the statement is false, make the necessary change(s) to produce a true statement.

6. Numbers representing what is average or typical about a data set are called measures of central tendency. ______
7. When finding the mean, it is necessary to arrange the data items in order. ______
8. If one or more data items are much greater than the other items, the mean, rather than the median, is more representative of the data. ______
9. A data set can contain more than one median, or no median at all. ______

Exercise Set 6.2

Practice Exercises

In Exercises 1–8, find the mean for each group of data items.

1. 7, 4, 3, 2, 8, 5, 1, 3
2. 11, 6, 4, 0, 2, 1, 12, 0, 0
3. 91, 95, 99, 97, 93, 95
4. 100, 100, 90, 30, 70, 100
5. 100, 40, 70, 40, 60
6. 1, 3, 5, 10, 8, 5, 6, 8
7. 1.6, 3.8, 5.0, 2.7, 4.2, 4.2, 3.2, 4.7, 3.6, 2.5, 2.5
8. 1.4, 2.1, 1.6, 3.0, 1.4, 2.2, 1.4, 9.0, 9.0, 1.8

In Exercises 9–12, find the mean for the data items in the given frequency distribution.

9.

Score x	Frequency f
1	1
2	3
3	4
4	4
5	6
6	5
7	3
8	2

10.

Score x	Frequency f
1	2
2	4
3	5
4	7
5	6
6	4
7	3

11.

Score x	Frequency f
1	1
2	1
3	2
4	5
5	7
6	9
7	8
8	6
9	4
10	3

12.

Score x	Frequency f
1	3
2	4
3	6
4	8
5	9
6	7
7	5
8	2
9	1
10	1

In Exercises 13–20, find the median for each group of data items.

13. 7, 4, 3, 2, 8, 5, 1, 3
14. 11, 6, 4, 0, 2, 1, 12, 0, 0
15. 91, 95, 99, 97, 93, 95
16. 100, 100, 90, 30, 70, 100
17. 100, 40, 70, 40, 60
18. 1, 3, 5, 10, 8, 5, 6, 8
19. 1.6, 3.8, 5.0, 2.7, 4.2, 4.2, 3.2, 4.7, 3.6, 2.5, 2.5
20. 1.4, 2.1, 1.6, 3.0, 1.4, 2.2, 1.4, 9.0, 9.0, 1.8

Find the median for the data items in the frequency distribution in

21. Exercise 9.
22. Exercise 10.
23. Exercise 11.
24. Exercise 12.

In Exercises 25–32, find the mode for each group of data items. If there is no mode, so state.

25. 7, 4, 3, 2, 8, 5, 1, 3
26. 11, 6, 4, 0, 2, 1, 12, 0, 0
27. 91, 95, 99, 97, 93, 95
28. 100, 100, 90, 30, 70, 100
29. 100, 40, 70, 40, 60
30. 1, 3, 5, 10, 8, 5, 6, 8
31. 1.6, 3.8, 5.0, 2.7, 4.2, 4.2, 3.2, 4.7, 3.6, 2.5, 2.5
32. 1.4, 2.1, 1.6, 3.0, 1.4, 2.2, 1.4, 9.0, 9.0, 1.8

Find the mode for the data items in the frequency distribution in

33. Exercise 9.
34. Exercise 10.
35. Exercise 11.
36. Exercise 12.

In Exercises 37–44, find the midrange for each group of data items.

37. 7, 4, 3, 2, 8, 5, 1, 3
38. 11, 6, 4, 0, 2, 1, 12, 0, 0
39. 91, 95, 99, 97, 93, 95
40. 100, 100, 90, 30, 70, 100
41. 100, 40, 70, 40, 60
42. 1, 3, 5, 10, 8, 5, 6, 8
43. 1.6, 3.8, 5.0, 2.7, 4.2, 4.2, 3.2, 4.7, 3.6, 2.5, 2.5
44. 1.4, 2.1, 1.6, 3.0, 1.4, 2.2, 1.4, 9.0, 9.0, 1.8

Find the midrange for the data items in the frequency distribution in

45. Exercise 9.
46. Exercise 10.
47. Exercise 11.
48. Exercise 12.

Practice Plus

In Exercises 49–54, use each display of data items to find the mean, median, mode, and midrange.

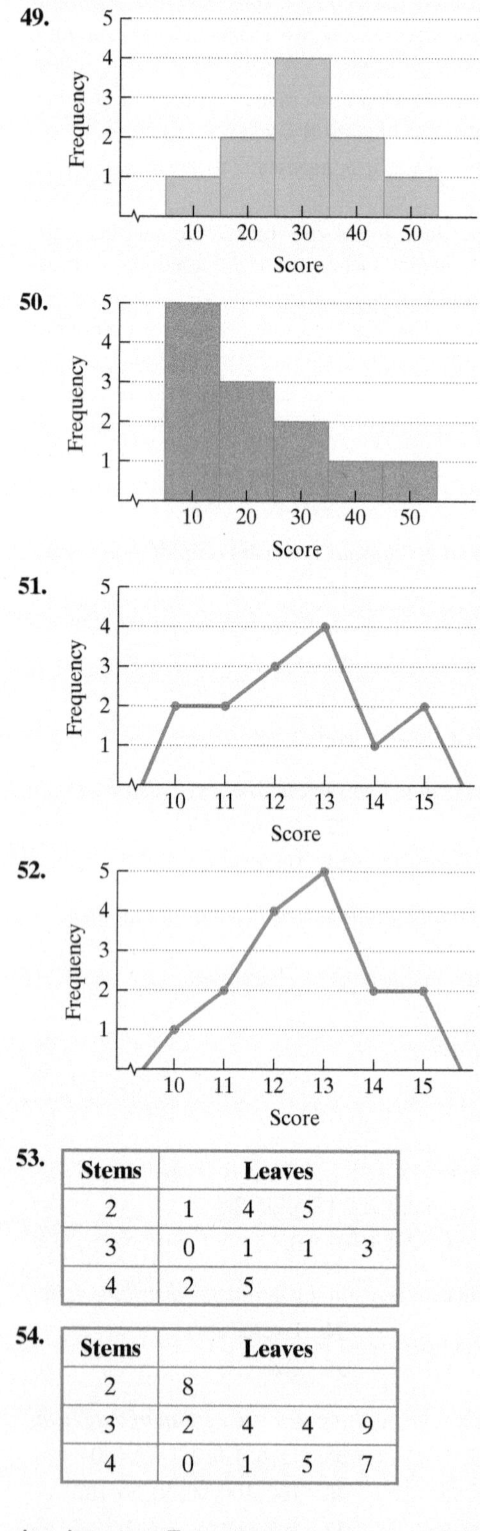

53.

Stems	Leaves			
2	1	4	5	
3	0	1	1	3
4	2	5		

54.

Stems	Leaves			
2	8			
3	2	4	4	9
4	0	1	5	7

Application Exercises

Exercises 55–57 present data on a variety of topics. For each data set described in boldface, find the

a. *mean.* **b.** *median.*

c. *mode (or state that there is no mode).*

d. *midrange.*

55. Top Cities with New College Graduates

Metro Area	Number of Recent College Graduates Who Moved to the Area from 2000–2011 (thousands)
New York	200
Chicago	97
Washington, D.C.	92
Los Angeles	92
San Francisco	64
Houston	51
Boston	51
Dallas-Fort Worth	50
Philadelphia	49
Denver	37
Seattle	34
Minneapolis-St. Paul	32
San Jose	27

Source: USA Today

56. Net Worth for the First 13 U.S. Presidents

President	Net Worth (millions of 2010 dollars)
Washington	\$525
Adams	\$19
Jefferson	\$212
Madison	\$101
Monroe	\$27
Adams	\$21
Jackson	\$119
Van Buren	\$26
Harrison	\$5
Tyler	\$51
Polk	\$10
Taylor	\$6
Fillmore	\$4

Source: Time

57. Number of Social Interactions of College Students In Exercise Set 6.1, we presented a grouped frequency distribution showing the number of social interactions of ten minutes or longer over a one-week period for a group of college students. (These interactions excluded family and work situations.) Use the frequency distribution shown to solve this exercise. (This distribution was obtained by replacing the classes in the grouped frequency distribution previously shown with the midpoints of the classes.)

Social interactions in a week → x; Number of college students → f

x	2	7	12	17	22	27	32	37	42	47
f	12	16	16	16	10	11	4	3	3	3

The weights (to the nearest five pounds) of 40 randomly selected male college students are organized in a histogram with a superimposed frequency polygon. Use the graph to answer Exercises 58–61.

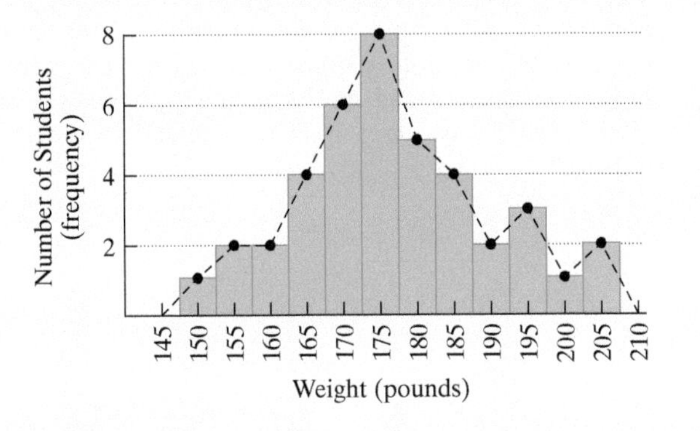

58. Find the mean weight.

59. Find the median weight.

60. Find the modal weight.

61. Find the midrange weight.

62. An advertisement for a speed-reading course claimed that the "average" reading speed for people completing the course was 1000 words per minute. Shown below are the actual data for the reading speeds per minute for a sample of 24 people who completed the course.

1000	900	800	1000	900	850
650	1000	1050	800	1000	850
700	750	800	850	900	950
600	1100	950	700	750	650

a. Find the mean, median, mode, and midrange. (If you prefer, first organize the data in a frequency distribution.)

b. Which measure of central tendency was given in the advertisement?

c. Which measure of central tendency is the best indicator of the "average" reading speed in this situation? Explain your answer.

63. In one common system for finding a grade-point average, or GPA,

$$A = 4, B = 3, C = 2, D = 1, F = 0.$$

The GPA is calculated by multiplying the number of credit hours for a course and the number assigned to each grade, and then adding these products. Then divide this sum by the total number of credit hours. Because each course grade is weighted according to the number of credits of the course, GPA is called a *weighted mean*. Calculate the GPA for this transcript:

Sociology: 3 cr. A; Biology: 3.5 cr. C; Music: 1 cr. B; Math: 4 cr. B; English: 3 cr. C.

Writing in Mathematics

64. What is the mean and how is it obtained?

65. What is the median and how is it obtained?

66. What is the mode and how is it obtained?

67. What is the midrange and how is it obtained?

68. The "average" income in the United States can be given by the mean or the median.

a. Which measure would be used in anti-U.S. propaganda? Explain your answer.

b. Which measure would be used in pro-U.S. propaganda? Explain your answer.

69. In a class of 40 students, 21 have examination scores of 77%. Which measure or measures of central tendency can you immediately determine? Explain your answer.

70. You read an article that states, "Of the 411 players in the National Basketball Association, only 138 make more than the average salary of \$3.12 million." Is \$3.12 million the mean or the median salary? Explain your answer.

71. A student's parents promise to pay for next semester's tuition if an A average is earned in chemistry. With examination grades of 97%, 97%, 75%, 70%, and 55%, the student reports that an A average has been earned. Which measure of central tendency is the student reporting as the average? How is this student misrepresenting the course performance with statistics?

72. According to the National Oceanic and Atmospheric Administration, the coldest city in the United States is International Falls, Minnesota, with a mean Fahrenheit temperature of 36.8°. Explain how this mean is obtained.

Critical Thinking Exercises

Make Sense? *In Exercises 73–76, determine whether each statement makes sense or does not make sense, and explain your reasoning.*

73. I'm working with a data set for which neither the mean nor the median is one of the data items.

74. I made a distribution of the heights of the 12 players on our basketball team. Because one player is much taller than the others, the team's median height is greater than its mean height.

75. Although the data set 1, 1, 2, 3, 3, 3, 4, 4 has a number of repeated items, there is only one mode.

76. If professors use the same test scores for a particular student and calculate measures of central tendency correctly, they will always agree on the student's final course grade.

77. Give an example of a set of six examination grades (from 0 to 100) with each of the following characteristics:

a. The mean and the median have the same value, but the mode has a different value.

b. The mean and the mode have the same value, but the median has a different value.

c. The mean is greater than the median.

d. The mode is greater than the mean.

e. The mean, median, and mode have the same value.

f. The mean and mode have values of 72.

78. On an examination given to 30 students, no student scored below the mean. Describe how this occurred.

Group Exercises

79. Select a characteristic, such as shoe size or height, for which each member of the group can provide a number. Choose a characteristic of genuine interest to the group. For this characteristic, organize the data collected into a frequency distribution and a graph. Compute the mean, median, mode, and midrange. Discuss any differences among these values. What happens if the group is divided (men and women, or people under a certain age and people over a certain age) and these measures of central tendency are computed for each of the subgroups? Attempt to use measures of central tendency to discover something interesting about the entire group or the subgroups.

80. A book on spotting bad statistics and learning to think critically about these influential numbers is *Damn Lies and Statistics* by Joel Best (University of California Press, 2001). This activity is designed for six people. Each person should select one chapter from Best's book. The group report should include examples of the use, misuse, and abuse of statistical information. Explain exactly how and why bad statistics emerge, spread, and come to shape policy debates. What specific ways does Best recommend to detect bad statistics?

WHAT AM I SUPPOSED TO LEARN?

After you have read this section, you should be able to:

1 Determine the range for a data set.

2 Determine the standard deviation for a data set.

Measures of Dispersion

WHEN YOU THINK OF HOUSTON, TEXAS, AND Honolulu, Hawaii, do balmy temperatures come to mind? Both cities have a mean temperature of 75°. However, the mean temperature does not tell the whole story. The temperature in Houston differs seasonally from a low of about 40° in January to a high of close to 100° in July and August. By contrast, Honolulu's temperature varies less throughout the year, usually ranging between 60° and 90°.

Measures of dispersion are used to describe the spread of data items in a data set. Two of the most common measures of dispersion, the *range* and the *standard deviation,* are discussed in this section.

1 Determine the range for a data set.

The Range

A quick but rough measure of dispersion is the **range**, the difference between the highest and lowest data values in a data set. For example, if Houston's hottest annual temperature is 103° and its coldest annual temperature is 33°, the range in temperature is

$$103° - 33°, \quad \text{or} \quad 70°.$$

If Honolulu's hottest day is 89° and its coldest day 61°, the range in temperature is

$$89° - 61°, \quad \text{or} \quad 28°.$$

THE RANGE

The **range**, the difference between the highest and lowest data values in a data set, indicates the total spread of the data.

$$\text{Range} = \text{highest data value} - \text{lowest data value}$$

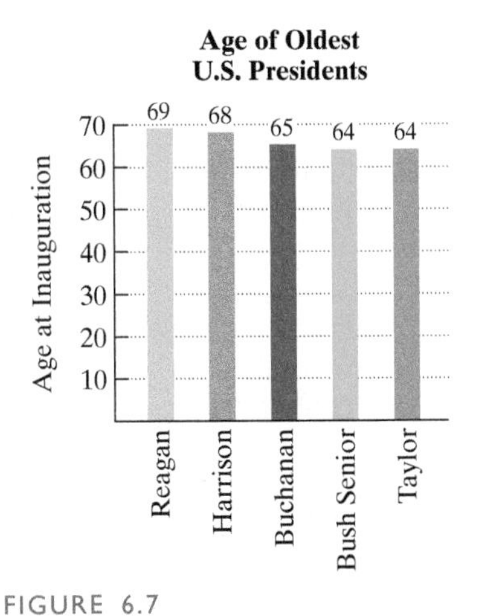

FIGURE 6.7
Source: Internet Public Library

EXAMPLE 1 Computing the Range

Figure 6.7 shows the age of the five oldest U.S presidents at the start of their first term. Find the age range for the five oldest presidents.

SOLUTION

$$\text{Range} = \text{highest data value} - \text{lowest data value}$$
$$= 69 - 64 = 5$$

The range is 5 years.

CHECK POINT 1 Find the range for the following group of data items:

4, 2, 11, 7.

The Standard Deviation

A second measure of dispersion, and one that is dependent on *all* of the data items, is called the **standard deviation**. The standard deviation is found by determining how much each data item differs from the mean.

In order to compute the standard deviation, it is necessary to find by how much each data item deviates from the mean. First compute the mean, $\bar{x}$. Then subtract the mean from each data item, $x - \bar{x}$. Example 2 shows how this is done. In Example 3, we will use this skill to actually find the standard deviation.

EXAMPLE 2 Preparing to Find the Standard Deviation; Finding Deviations from the Mean

Find the deviations from the mean for the five data items 69, 68, 65, 64, and 64, shown in **Figure 6.7**.

SOLUTION

First, calculate the mean, $\bar{x}$.

$$\bar{x} = \frac{\Sigma x}{n} = \frac{69 + 68 + 65 + 64 + 64}{5} = \frac{330}{5} = 66$$

The mean age for the five oldest U.S. presidents is 66 years. Now, let's find by how much each of the five data items in **Figure 6.7** differs from 66, the mean. For Reagan, who was 69 at the start of his first term, the computation is shown as follows:

$$\text{Deviation from mean} = \text{data item} - \text{mean}$$
$$= x - \bar{x}$$
$$= 69 - 66 = 3.$$

This indicates that Reagan's inaugural age exceeds the mean by three years.

The computation for Buchanan, who was 65 at the start of his first term, is given by

$$\text{Deviation from mean} = \text{data item} - \text{mean}$$
$$= x - \bar{x}$$
$$= 65 - 66 = -1.$$

This indicates that Buchanan's inaugural age is one year below the mean.

The deviations from the mean for each of the five given data items are shown in **Table 6.13**.

TABLE 6.13 Deviations from the Mean

Data item x	Deviation: data item − mean $x - \bar{x}$
69	$69 - 66 = 3$
68	$68 - 66 = 2$
65	$65 - 66 = -1$
64	$64 - 66 = -2$
64	$64 - 66 = -2$

CHECK POINT 2 Compute the mean for the following group of data items:

$$2, 4, 7, 11.$$

Then find the deviations from the mean for the four data items. Organize your work in table form just like **Table 6.13**. Keep track of these computations. You will be using them in Check Point 3.

TABLE 6.13 (repeated)
Deviations from the Mean

Data item x	Deviation: data item − mean $x - \bar{x}$
69	69 − 66 = 3
68	68 − 66 = 2
65	65 − 66 = −1
64	64 − 66 = −2
64	64 − 66 = −2

The sum of the deviations from the mean for a set of data is always zero: $\Sigma(x - \bar{x}) = 0$. For the deviations from the mean shown in **Table 6.13**,

$$3 + 2 + (-1) + (-2) + (-2) = 5 + (-5) = 0.$$

This shows that we cannot find a measure of dispersion by finding the mean of the deviations, because this value is always zero. However, a kind of average of the deviations from the mean, called the **standard deviation**, can be computed. We do so by squaring each deviation and later introducing a square root in the computation. Here are the details on how to find the standard deviation for a set of data:

2 Determine the standard deviation for a data set.

COMPUTING THE STANDARD DEVIATION FOR A DATA SET

1. Find the mean of the data items.
2. Find the deviation of each data item from the mean:
$$\text{data item} - \text{mean}.$$
3. Square each deviation:
$$(\text{data item} - \text{mean})^2.$$
4. Sum the squared deviations:
$$\Sigma(\text{data item} - \text{mean})^2.$$
5. Divide the sum in step 4 by $n - 1$, where n represents the number of data items:
$$\frac{\Sigma(\text{data item} - \text{mean})^2}{n - 1}.$$
6. Take the square root of the quotient in step 5. This value is the standard deviation for the data set.
$$\text{Standard deviation} = \sqrt{\frac{\Sigma(\text{data item} - \text{mean})^2}{n - 1}}$$

The standard deviation of a sample is symbolized by s, while the standard deviation of an entire population is symbolized by σ (the lowercase Greek letter *sigma*). Unless otherwise indicated, data sets represent samples, so we will use s for the standard deviation:

$$s = \sqrt{\frac{\Sigma(x - \bar{x})^2}{n - 1}}.$$

The computation of the standard deviation can be organized using a table with three columns:

Data item x	Deviation: $x - \bar{x}$ Data item − mean	(Deviation)^2: $(x - \bar{x})^2$ (Data item − mean)^2

In Example 2, we worked out the first two columns of such a table. Let's continue working with the data for the ages of the five oldest U.S. presidents and compute the standard deviation.

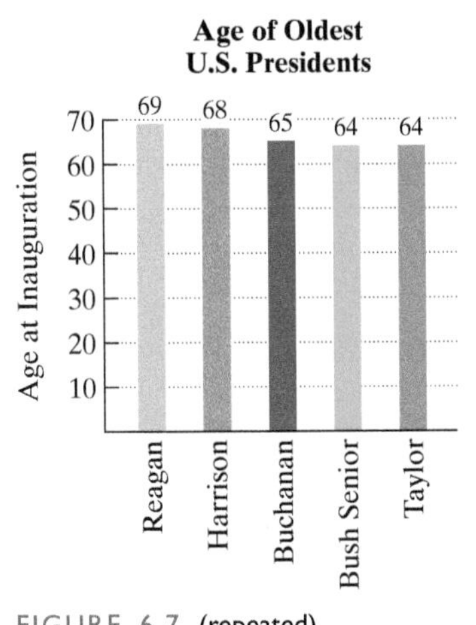

FIGURE 6.7 (repeated)

EXAMPLE 3 Computing the Standard Deviation

Figure 6.7, showing the age of the five oldest U.S. presidents at the start of their first term, is repeated in the margin. Find the standard deviation for the ages of the five presidents.

SOLUTION

Step 1 Find the mean. From our work in Example 2, the mean is 66: $\bar{x} = 66$.

Step 2 Find the deviation of each data item from the mean: data item − mean or $x - \bar{x}$. This, too, was done in Example 2 for each of the five data items.

Step 3 Square each deviation: (data item − mean)^2 or $(x - \bar{x})^2$. We square each of the numbers in the (data item − mean) column, shown in **Table 6.14.** Notice that squaring the difference always results in a nonnegative number.

TABLE 6.14 Computing the Standard Deviation

Data item x	Deviation: data item − mean $x - \bar{x}$	(Deviation)^2: (data item − mean)^2 $(x - \bar{x})^2$
69	$69 - 66 = 3$	$3^2 = 3 \cdot 3 = 9$
68	$68 - 66 = 2$	$2^2 = 2 \cdot 2 = 4$
65	$65 - 66 = -1$	$(-1)^2 = (-1) \cdot (-1) = 1$
64	$64 - 66 = -2$	$(-2)^2 = (-2) \cdot (-2) = 4$
64	$64 - 66 = -2$	$(-2)^2 = (-2) \cdot (-2) = 4$
Totals:	$\Sigma(x - \bar{x}) = 0$	$\Sigma(x - \bar{x})^2 = 22$

The sum of the deviations for a set of data is always zero.

Adding the five numbers in the third column gives the sum of the squared deviations: Σ(data item − mean)^2.

Step 4 Sum the squared deviations: Σ(data item − mean)^2. This step is shown in **Table 6.14.** The squares in the third column were added, resulting in a sum of 22: $\Sigma(x - \bar{x})^2 = 22$.

Step 5 Divide the sum in step 4 by $n - 1$, where n represents the number of data items. The number of data items is 5 so we divide by 4.

$$\frac{\Sigma(x - \bar{x})^2}{n - 1} = \frac{\Sigma(\text{data item} - \text{mean})^2}{n - 1} = \frac{22}{5 - 1} = \frac{22}{4} = 5.5$$

Step 6 The standard deviation, s, is the square root of the quotient in step 5.

$$s = \sqrt{\frac{\Sigma(x - \bar{x})^2}{n - 1}} = \sqrt{\frac{\Sigma(\text{data item} - \text{mean})^2}{n - 1}} = \sqrt{5.5} \approx 2.35$$

The standard deviation for the five oldest U.S. presidents is approximately 2.35 years.

TECHNOLOGY

Almost all scientific and graphing calculators compute the standard deviation of a set of data. Using the data items in Example 3,

69, 68, 65, 64, 64,

the keystrokes for obtaining the standard deviation on many scientific calculators are as follows:

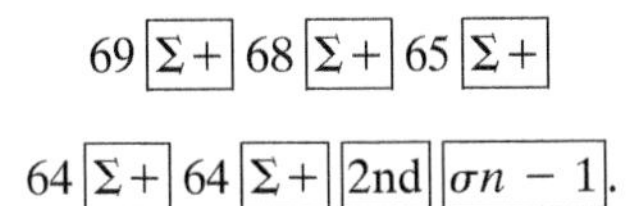

Graphing calculators require that you specify if data items are from an entire population or a sample of the population.

CHECK POINT 3 Find the standard deviation for the group of data items in Check Point 2 on page 236. Round to two decimal places.

Example 4 illustrates that as the spread of data items increases, the standard deviation gets larger.

EXAMPLE 4 *Computing the Standard Deviation*

Find the standard deviation of the data items in each of the samples shown below.

Sample A	**Sample B**
17, 18, 19, 20, 21, 22, 23	5, 10, 15, 20, 25, 30, 35

SOLUTION

Begin by finding the mean for each sample.

Sample A:

$$\text{Mean} = \frac{17 + 18 + 19 + 20 + 21 + 22 + 23}{7} = \frac{140}{7} = 20$$

Sample B:

$$\text{Mean} = \frac{5 + 10 + 15 + 20 + 25 + 30 + 35}{7} = \frac{140}{7} = 20$$

Although both samples have the same mean, the data items in sample B are more spread out. Thus, we would expect sample B to have the greater standard deviation. The computation of the standard deviation requires that we find $\Sigma(\text{data item} - \text{mean})^2$, shown in **Table 6.15.**

TABLE 6.15 Computing Standard Deviations for Two Samples

Sample A		
Data item x	Deviation: data item − mean $x - \bar{x}$	(Deviation)^2: (data item − mean)^2 $(x - \bar{x})^2$
17	$17 - 20 = -3$	$(-3)^2 = 9$
18	$18 - 20 = -2$	$(-2)^2 = 4$
19	$19 - 20 = -1$	$(-1)^2 = 1$
20	$20 - 20 = 0$	$0^2 = 0$
21	$21 - 20 = 1$	$1^2 = 1$
22	$22 - 20 = 2$	$2^2 = 4$
23	$23 - 20 = 3$	$3^2 = 9$
Totals:		$\Sigma(x - \bar{x})^2 = 28$

Sample B		
Data item x	Deviation: data item − mean $x - \bar{x}$	(Deviation)^2: (data item − mean)^2 $(x - \bar{x})$
5	$5 - 20 = -15$	$(-15)^2 = 225$
10	$10 - 20 = -10$	$(-10)^2 = 100$
15	$15 - 20 = -5$	$(-5)^2 = 25$
20	$20 - 20 = 0$	$0^2 = 0$
25	$25 - 20 = 5$	$5^2 = 25$
30	$30 - 20 = 10$	$10^2 = 100$
35	$35 - 20 = 15$	$15^2 = 225$
		$\Sigma(x - \bar{x})^2 = 700$

Each sample contains seven data items, so we compute the standard deviation by dividing the sums in **Table 6.15**, 28 and 700, by $7 - 1$, or 6. Then we take the square root of each quotient.

$$\text{Standard deviation} = \sqrt{\frac{\Sigma(x - \bar{x})^2}{n - 1}} = \sqrt{\frac{\Sigma(\text{data item} - \text{mean})^2}{n - 1}}$$

Sample A:

$$\text{Standard deviation} = \sqrt{\frac{28}{6}} \approx 2.16$$

Sample B:

$$\text{Standard deviation} = \sqrt{\frac{700}{6}} \approx 10.80$$

Sample A has a standard deviation of approximately 2.16 and sample B has a standard deviation of approximately 10.80. The data in sample B are more spread out than those in sample A.

CHECK POINT 4 Find the standard deviation of the data items in each of the samples shown below. Round to two decimal places.

Sample A: 73, 75, 77, 79, 81, 83

Sample B: 40, 44, 92, 94, 98, 100

Figure 6.8 illustrates four sets of data items organized in histograms. From left to right, the data items are

Figure 6.8(a): 4, 4, 4, 4, 4, 4, 4

Figure 6.8(b): 3, 3, 4, 4, 4, 5, 5

Figure 6.8(c): 3, 3, 3, 4, 5, 5, 5

Figure 6.8(d): 1, 1, 1, 4, 7, 7, 7.

Each data set has a mean of 4. However, as the spread of the data items increases, the standard deviation gets larger. Observe that when all the data items are the same, the standard deviation is 0.

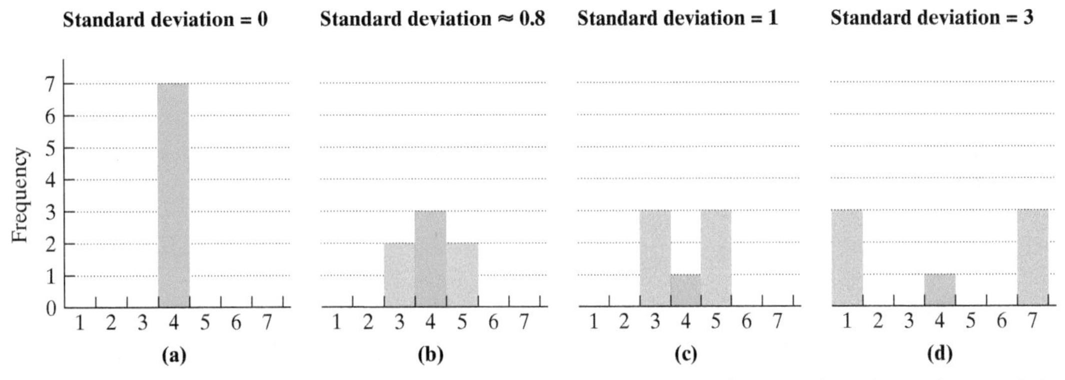

FIGURE 6.8 The standard deviation gets larger with increased dispersion among data items. In each case, the mean is 4.

EXAMPLE 5 *Interpreting Standard Deviation*

Two fifth-grade classes have nearly identical mean scores on an aptitude test, but one class has a standard deviation three times that of the other. All other factors being equal, which class is easier to teach, and why?

SOLUTION

The class with the smaller standard deviation is easier to teach because there is less variation among student aptitudes. Course work can be aimed at the average student without too much concern that the work will be too easy for some or too difficult for others. By contrast, the class with greater dispersion poses a greater challenge. By teaching to the average student, the students whose scores are significantly above the mean will be bored; students whose scores are significantly below the mean will be confused.

CHECK POINT 5 Shown below are the means and standard deviations of the yearly returns on two investments from 1926 through 2004.

Investment	Mean Yearly Return	Standard Deviation
Small-Company Stocks	17.5%	33.3%
Large-Company Stocks	12.4%	20.4%

Source: Summary Statistics of Annual Total Returns 1926 to 2004 Yearbook, Ibbotson Associates, Chicago

a. Use the means to determine which investment provided the greater yearly return.

b. Use the standard deviations to determine which investment had the greater risk. Explain your answer.

Concept and Vocabulary Check

Fill in each blank so that the resulting statement is true.

1. The difference between the highest and lowest data values in a data set is called the ____________.
2. The formula

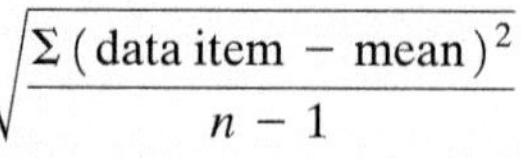

$$\sqrt{\frac{\Sigma(\text{data item} - \text{mean})^2}{n-1}}$$

gives the value of the ____________ for a data set.

In Exercises 3–5, determine whether each statement is true or false. If the statement is false, make the necessary change(s) to produce a true statement.

3. Measures of dispersion are used to describe the spread of data items in a data set. ______
4. The sum of the deviations from the mean for a data set is always zero. ______
5. Measures of dispersion get smaller as the spread of data items increases. ______

Exercise Set 6.3

Practice Exercises

In Exercises 1–6, find the range for each group of data items.

1. 1, 2, 3, 4, 5
2. 16, 17, 18, 19, 20
3. 7, 9, 9, 15
4. 11, 13, 14, 15, 17
5. 3, 3, 4, 4, 5, 5
6. 3, 3, 3, 4, 5, 5, 5

In Exercises 7–10, a group of data items and their mean are given.

a. *Find the deviation from the mean for each of the data items.*

b. *Find the sum of the deviations in part (a).*

7. 3, 5, 7, 12, 18, 27; Mean = 12
8. 84, 88, 90, 95, 98; Mean = 91
9. 29, 38, 48, 49, 53, 77; Mean = 49
10. 60, 60, 62, 65, 65, 65, 66, 67, 70, 70; Mean = 65

In Exercises 11–16, find a. the mean; b. the deviation from the mean for each data item; and c. the sum of the deviations in part (b).

11. 85, 95, 90, 85, 100
12. 94, 62, 88, 85, 91
13. 146, 153, 155, 160, 161
14. 150, 132, 144, 122
15. 2.25, 3.50, 2.75, 3.10, 1.90
16. 0.35, 0.37, 0.41, 0.39, 0.43

In Exercises 17–26, find the standard deviation for each group of data items. Round answers to two decimal places.

17. 1, 2, 3, 4, 5
18. 16, 17, 18, 19, 20
19. 7, 9, 9, 15
20. 11, 13, 14, 15, 17
21. 3, 3, 4, 4, 5, 5
22. 3, 3, 3, 4, 5, 5, 5
23. 1, 1, 1, 4, 7, 7, 7
24. 6, 6, 6, 6, 7, 7, 7, 4, 8, 3
25. 9, 5, 9, 5, 9, 5, 9, 5
26. 6, 10, 6, 10, 6, 10, 6, 10

In Exercises 27–28, compute the mean, range, and standard deviation for the data items in each of the three samples. Then describe one way in which the samples are alike and one way in which they are different.

27. Sample A: 6, 8, 10, 12, 14, 16, 18
    Sample B: 6, 7, 8, 12, 16, 17, 18
    Sample C: 6, 6, 6, 12, 18, 18, 18
28. Sample A: 8, 10, 12, 14, 16, 18, 20
    Sample B: 8, 9, 10, 14, 18, 19, 20
    Sample C: 8, 8, 8, 14, 20, 20, 20

Practice Plus

In Exercises 29–36, use each display of data items to find the standard deviation. Where necessary, round answers to two decimal places.

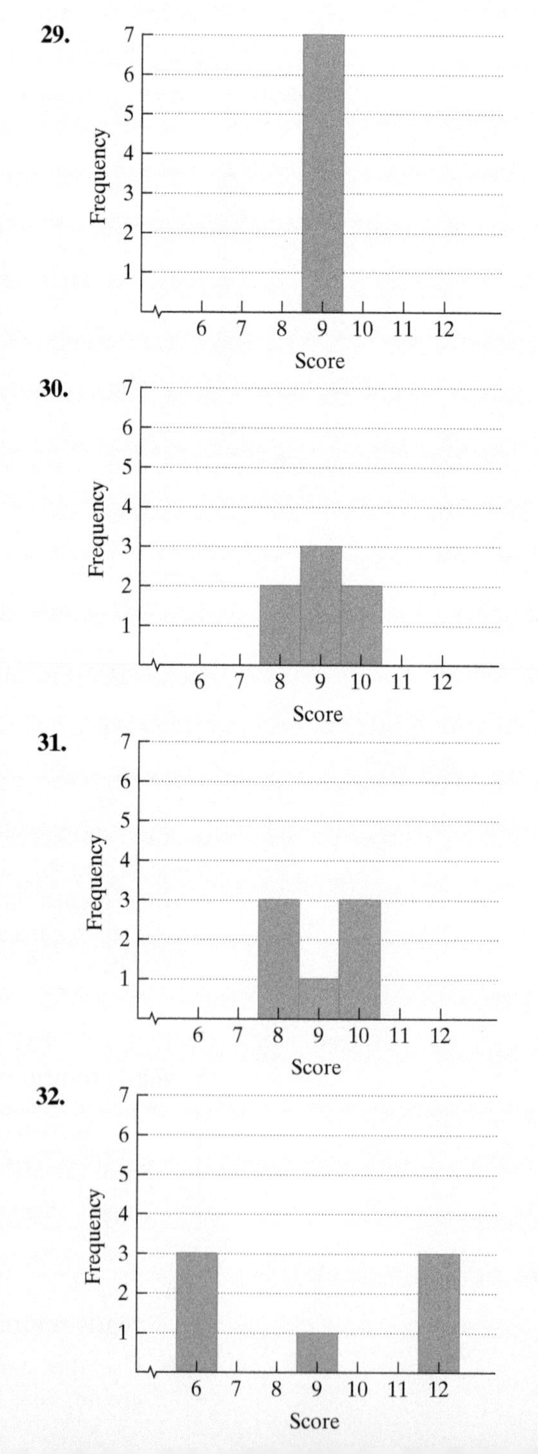

33.

Stems	Leaves
0	5
1	0 5
2	0 5

34.

Stems	Leaves
0	4 8
1	2 6
2	0

35.

Stems	Leaves
1	8 9 9 8 7 8
2	0 1 0 2

36.

Stems	Leaves
1	3 5 3 8 3 4
2	3 0 0 4

Application Exercises

37. The data sets give the number of platinum albums for the five male artists and the five female artists in the United States with the most platinum albums. (Platinum albums sell one million units or more.)

MALE ARTISTS WITH THE MOST PLATINUM ALBUMS

Artist	Platinum Albums
Garth Brooks	145
Elvis Presley	104
Billy Joel	80
Michael Jackson	71
Elton John	65

FEMALE ARTISTS WITH THE MOST PLATINUM ALBUMS

Artist	Platinum Albums
Mariah Carey	64
Madonna	63
Barbra Streisand	61
Whitney Houston	54
Celine Dion	48

Source: RIAA

a. Without calculating, which data set has the greater mean number of platinum albums? Explain your answer.

b. Verify your conjecture from part (a) by calculating the mean number of platinum albums for each data set.

c. Without calculating, which data set has the greater standard deviation? Explain your answer.

d. Verify your conjecture from part (c) by calculating the standard deviation for each data set. Round answers to two decimal places.

38. The data sets give the ages of the first six U.S. presidents and the last six U.S. presidents (through Barack Obama).

AGE OF FIRST SIX U.S. PRESIDENTS AT INAUGURATION

President	Age
Washington	57
J. Adams	61
Jefferson	57
Madison	57
Monroe	58
J. Q. Adams	57

AGE OF LAST SIX U.S. PRESIDENTS AT INAUGURATION

President	Age
Carter	52
Reagan	69
G. H. W. Bush	64
Clinton	46
G. W. Bush	54
Obama	47

Source: *Time Almanac*

a. Without calculating, which set has the greater standard deviation? Explain your answer.

b. Verify your conjecture from part (b) by calculating the standard deviation for each data set. Round answers to two decimal places.

Writing in Mathematics

39. Describe how to find the range of a data set.

40. Describe why the range might not be the best measure of dispersion.

41. Describe how the standard deviation is computed.

42. Describe what the standard deviation reveals about a data set.

43. If a set of test scores has a standard deviation of zero, what does this mean about the scores?

44. Two classes took a statistics test. Both classes had a mean score of 73. The scores of class A had a standard deviation of 5 and those of class B had a standard deviation of 10. Discuss the difference between the two classes' performance on the test.

45. A sample of cereals indicates a mean potassium content per serving of 93 milligrams and a standard deviation of 2 milligrams. Write a description of what this means for a person who knows nothing about statistics.

46. Over a one-month period, stock A had a mean daily closing price of 124.7 and a standard deviation of 12.5. By contrast, stock B had a mean daily closing price of 78.2 and a standard deviation of 6.1. Which stock was more volatile? Explain your answer.

Critical Thinking Exercises

Make Sense? *In Exercises 47–50, determine whether each statement makes sense or does not make sense, and explain your reasoning.*

47. The mean can be misleading if you don't know the spread of data items.

48. The standard deviation for the weights of college students is greater than the standard deviation for the weights of 3-year-old children.

49. I'm working with data sets with different means and the same standard deviation.

50. I'm working with data sets with the same mean and different standard deviations.

51. Describe a situation in which a relatively large standard deviation is desirable.

52. If a set of test scores has a large range but a small standard deviation, describe what this means about students' performance on the test.

53. Use the data 1, 2, 3, 5, 6, 7. Without actually computing the standard deviation, which of the following best approximates the standard deviation?

a. 2 **b.** 6 **c.** 10 **d.** 20

54. Use the data 0, 1, 3, 4, 4, 6. Add 2 to each of the numbers. How does this affect the mean? How does this affect the standard deviation?

Group Exercises

55. As a follow-up to Group Exercise 79 on page 234, the group should reassemble and compute the standard deviation for each data set whose mean you previously determined. Does the standard deviation tell you anything new or interesting about the entire group or subgroups that you did not discover during the previous group activity?

56. Group members should consult a current almanac or the Internet and select intriguing data. The group's function is to use statistics to tell a story. Once "intriguing" data are identified, as a group

a. Summarize the data. Use words, frequency distributions, and graphic displays.

b. Compute measures of central tendency and dispersion, using these statistics to discuss the data.

The Normal Distribution

WHAT AM I SUPPOSED TO LEARN?

After you have read this section, you should be able to:

1 Recognize characteristics of normal distributions.
2 Understand the 68–95–99.7 Rule.
3 Find scores at a specified standard deviation from the mean.
4 Use the 68–95–99.7 Rule.
5 Convert a data item to a z-score.
6 Understand percentiles and quartiles.
7 Use and interpret margins of error.
8 Recognize distributions that are not normal.

1 Recognize characteristics of normal distributions.

OUR HEIGHTS ARE ON THE RISE! IN ONE million B.C., the mean height for men was 4 feet 6 inches. The mean height for women was 4 feet 2 inches. Because of improved diets and medical care, the mean height for men is now 5 feet 10 inches and for women it is 5 feet 5 inches. Mean adult heights are expected to plateau by 2050.

Mean Adult Heights

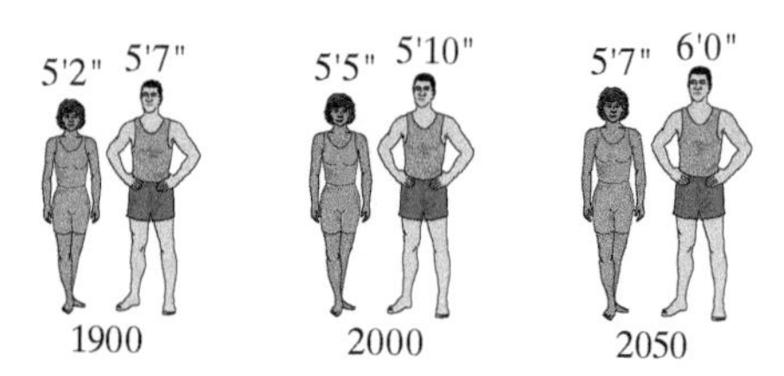

Source: National Center for Health Statistics

Suppose that a researcher selects a random sample of 100 adult men, measures their heights, and constructs a histogram for the data. The graph is shown in **Figure 6.9(a)** below. **Figure 6.9(b)** and **(c)** illustrate what happens as the sample size increases. In **Figure 6.9(c)**, if you were to fold the graph down the middle, the left side would fit the right side. As we move out from the middle, the heights of the bars are the same to the left and right. Such a histogram is called **symmetric**. As the sample size increases, so does the graph's symmetry. If it were possible to measure the heights of all adult males, the entire population, the histogram would approach what is called the **normal distribution**, shown in **Figure 6.9(d)**. This distribution is also called the **bell curve** or the **Gaussian distribution**, named for the German mathematician Carl Friedrich Gauss (1777–1855).

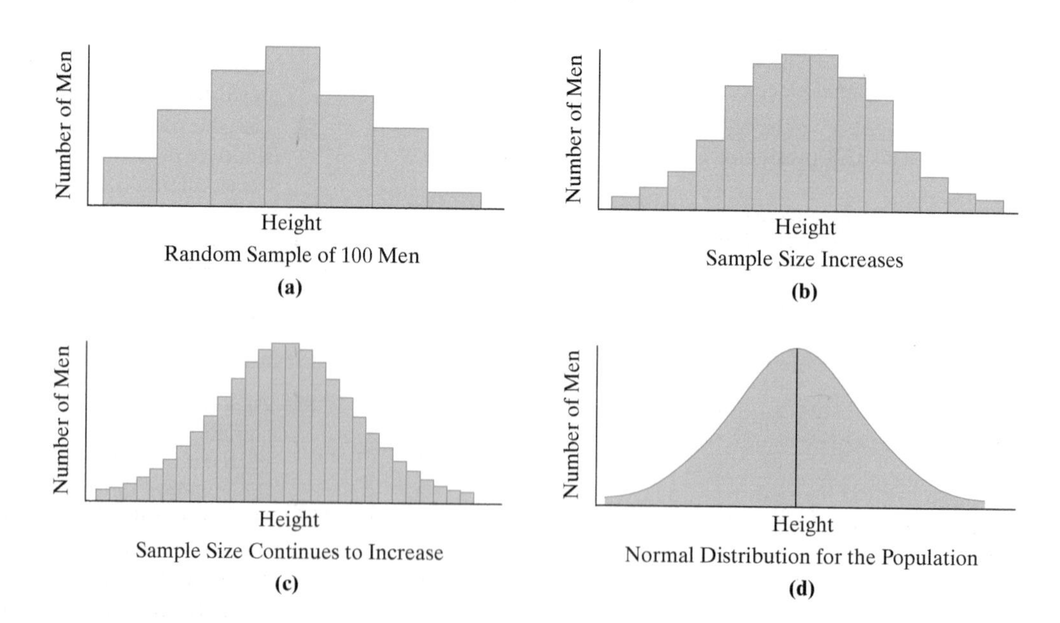

FIGURE 6.9 Heights of adult males

Figure 6.9(d) illustrates that the normal distribution is bell shaped and symmetric about a vertical line through its center. Furthermore, **the mean, median, and mode of a normal distribution are all equal** and located at the center of the distribution.

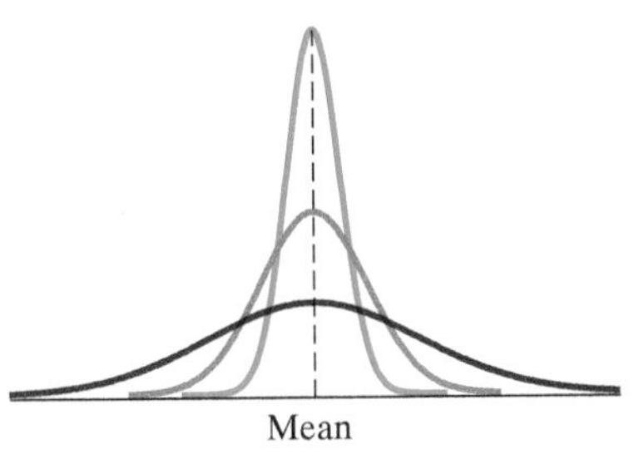

FIGURE 6.10

The shape of the normal distribution depends on the mean and the standard deviation. **Figure 6.10** illustrates three normal distributions with the same mean, but different standard deviations. As the standard deviation increases, the distribution becomes more dispersed, or spread out, but retains its symmetric bell shape.

The normal distribution provides a wonderful model for all kinds of phenomena because many sets of data items closely resemble this population distribution. Examples include heights and weights of adult males, intelligence quotients, SAT scores, prices paid for a new car model, and life spans of light bulbs. In these distributions, the data items tend to cluster around the mean. The more an item differs from the mean, the less likely it is to occur.

The normal distribution is used to make predictions about an entire population using data from a sample. In this section, we focus on the characteristics and applications of the normal distribution.

2 Understand the 68–95–99.7 Rule.

The Standard Deviation and z-Scores in Normal Distributions

The standard deviation plays a crucial role in the normal distribution, summarized by the **68–95–99.7 Rule**. This rule is illustrated in **Figure 6.11**.

THE 68–95–99.7 RULE FOR THE NORMAL DISTRIBUTION

1. Approximately 68% of the data items fall within 1 standard deviation of the mean (in both directions).
2. Approximately 95% of the data items fall within 2 standard deviations of the mean.
3. Approximately 99.7% of the data items fall within 3 standard deviations of the mean.

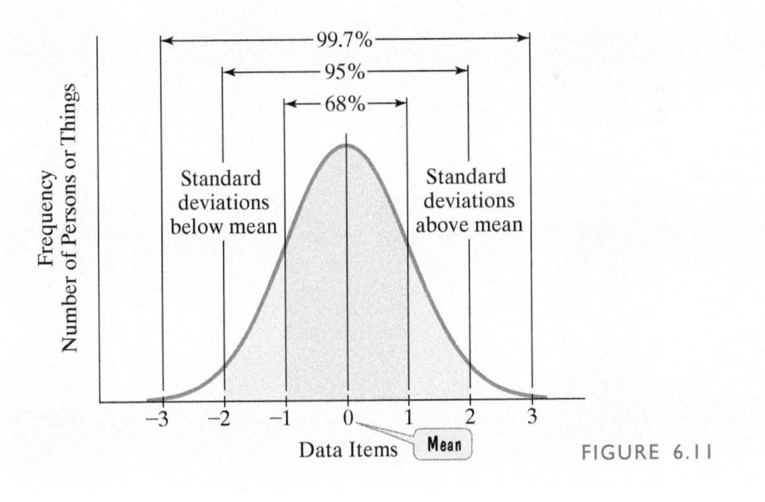

FIGURE 6.11

Blitzer Bonus

Well-Worn Steps and the Normal Distribution

These ancient steps each take on the shape of a normal distribution when the picture is viewed upside down. The center of each step is more worn than the outer edges. The greatest number of people have walked in the center, making this the mean, median, and mode for where people have walked.

Figure 6.11 illustrates that a very small percentage of the data in a normal distribution lies more than 3 standard deviations above or below the mean. As we move from the mean, the curve falls rapidly, and then more and more gradually, toward the horizontal axis. The tails of the curve approach, but never touch, the horizontal axis, although they are quite close to the axis at 3 standard deviations from the mean. The range of the normal distribution is infinite. No matter how far out from the mean we move, there is always the probability (although very small) of a data item occurring even farther out.

3 Find scores at a specified standard deviation from the mean.

Finding Scores at a Specified Standard Deviation from the Mean

Male adult heights in North America are approximately normally distributed with a mean of 70 inches and a standard deviation of 4 inches. Find the height that is

a. 2 standard deviations above the mean.

b. 3 standard deviations below the mean.

SOLUTION

a. First, let us find the height that is 2 standard deviations above the mean.

$$\text{Height} = \text{mean} + 2 \cdot \text{standard deviation}$$
$$= 70 + 2 \cdot 4 = 70 + 8 = 78$$

A height of 78 inches is 2 standard deviations above the mean.

b. Next, let us find the height that is 3 standard deviations below the mean.

$$\text{Height} = \text{mean} - 3 \cdot \text{standard deviation}$$
$$= 70 - 3 \cdot 4 = 70 - 12 = 58$$

A height of 58 inches is 3 standard deviations below the mean.

The distribution of male adult heights in North America is illustrated as a normal distribution in **Figure 6.12**.

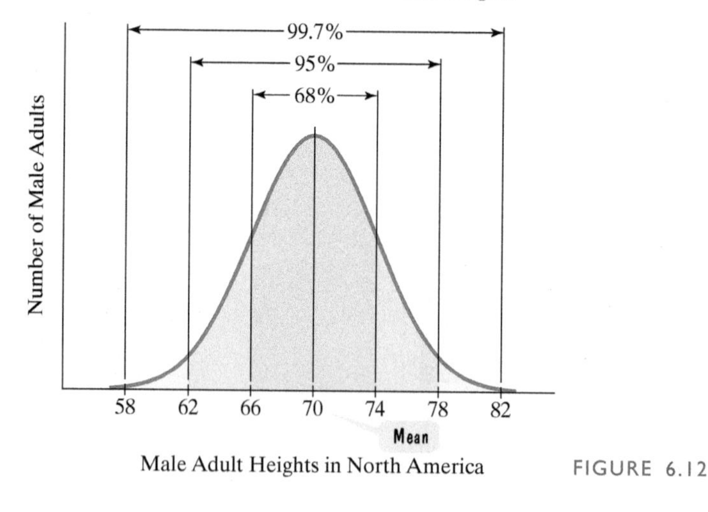

FIGURE 6.12

CHECK POINT 1 Female adult heights in North America are approximately normally distributed with a mean of 65 inches and a standard deviation of 3.5 inches. Find the height that is

a. 3 standard deviations above the mean.

b. 2 standard deviations below the mean.

4 Use the 68–95–99.7 Rule.

EXAMPLE 2 *Using the 68–95–99.7 Rule*

Use the distribution of male adult heights in **Figure 6.12** on the previous page to find the percentage of men in North America with heights

a. between 66 inches and 74 inches. **b.** between 70 inches and 74 inches.

c. above 78 inches.

SOLUTION

a. The 68–95–99.7 Rule states that approximately 68% of the data items fall within 1 standard deviation, 4, of the mean, 70.

$$\text{mean} - 1 \cdot \text{standard deviation} = 70 - 1 \cdot 4 = 70 - 4 = 66$$
$$\text{mean} + 1 \cdot \text{standard deviation} = 70 + 1 \cdot 4 = 70 + 4 = 74$$

Figure 6.12 shows that 68% of male adults have heights between 66 inches and 74 inches.

b. The percentage of men with heights between 70 inches and 74 inches is not given directly in **Figure 6.12**. Because of the distribution's symmetry, the percentage with heights between 66 inches and 70 inches is the same as the percentage with heights between 70 and 74 inches. **Figure 6.13** indicates that 68% have heights between 66 inches and 74 inches. Thus, half of 68%, or 34%, of men have heights between 70 inches and 74 inches.

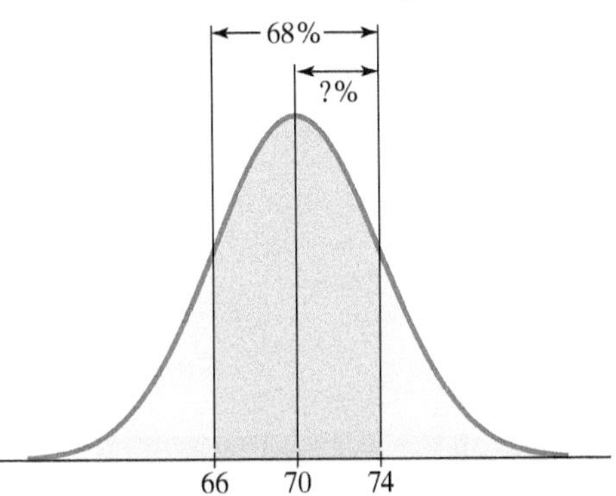

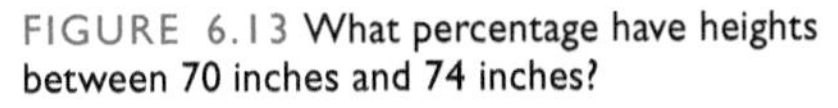
FIGURE 6.13 What percentage have heights between 70 inches and 74 inches?

c. The percentage of men with heights above 78 inches is not given directly in **Figure 6.12**. A height of 78 inches is 2 standard deviations, $2 \cdot 4$, or 8 inches, above the mean, 70 inches. The 68–95–99.7 Rule states that approximately 95% of the data items fall within 2 standard deviations of the mean. Thus, approximately 100% − 95%, or 5%, of the data items are farther than 2 standard deviations from the mean. The 5% of the data items are represented by the two shaded green regions in **Figure 6.14**. Because of the distribution's symmetry, half of 5%, or 2.5%, of the data items are more than 2 standard deviations above the mean. This means that 2.5% of men have heights above 78 inches.

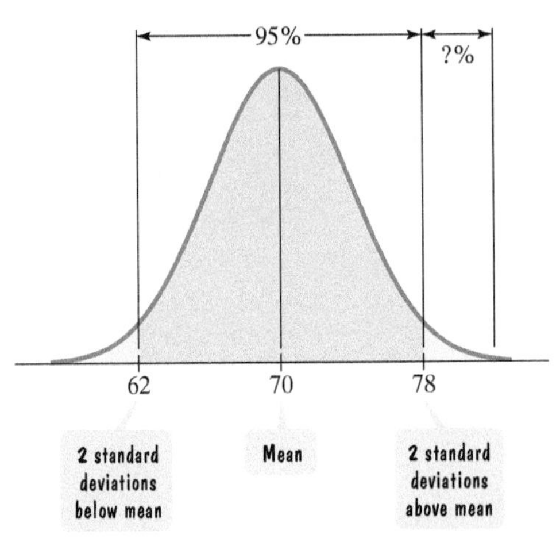

FIGURE 6.14 What percentage have heights above 78 inches?

CHECK POINT 2 Use the distribution of male adult heights in North America in **Figure 6.12** to find the percentage of men with heights

a. between 62 inches and 78 inches.

b. between 70 inches and 78 inches. **c.** above 74 inches.

Because the normal distribution of male adult heights in North America has a mean of 70 inches and a standard deviation of 4 inches, a height of 78 inches lies 2 standard deviations above the mean. In a normal distribution, a **z-score** describes how many standard deviations a particular data item lies above or below the mean. Thus, the z-score for the data item 78 is 2.

The following formula can be used to express a data item in a normal distribution as a z-score:

5 Convert a data item to a z-score.

COMPUTING z-SCORES

A z-score describes how many standard deviations a data item in a normal distribution lies above or below the mean. The z-score can be obtained using

$$z\text{-score} = \frac{\text{data item} - \text{mean}}{\text{standard deviation}}.$$

Data items above the mean have positive z-scores. Data items below the mean have negative z-scores. The z-score for the mean is 0.

EXAMPLE 3 *Computing z-Scores*

The mean weight of newborn infants is 7 pounds, and the standard deviation is 0.8 pound. The weights of newborn infants are normally distributed. Find the z-score for a weight of

a. 9 pounds. **b.** 7 pounds. **c.** 6 pounds.

SOLUTION

We compute the z-score for each weight by using the z-score formula. The mean is 7 and the standard deviation is 0.8.

a. The z-score for a weight of 9 pounds, written z_9, is

$$z_9 = \frac{\text{data item} - \text{mean}}{\text{standard deviation}} = \frac{9-7}{0.8} = \frac{2}{0.8} = 2.5.$$

The z-score of a data item greater than the mean is always positive. A 9-pound infant is a chubby little tyke, with a weight that is 2.5 standard deviations above the mean.

b. The z-score for a weight of 7 pounds is

$$z_7 = \frac{\text{data item} - \text{mean}}{\text{standard deviation}} = \frac{7-7}{0.8} = \frac{0}{0.8} = 0.$$

The z-score for the mean is always 0. A 7-pound infant is right at the mean, deviating 0 pounds above or below it.

c. The z-score for a weight of 6 pounds is

$$z_6 = \frac{\text{data item} - \text{mean}}{\text{standard deviation}} = \frac{6-7}{0.8} = \frac{-1}{0.8} = -1.25.$$

The z-score of a data item less than the mean is always negative. A 6-pound infant's weight is 1.25 standard deviations below the mean.

Figure 6.15 shows the normal distribution of weights of newborn infants. The horizontal axis is labeled in terms of weights and z-scores.

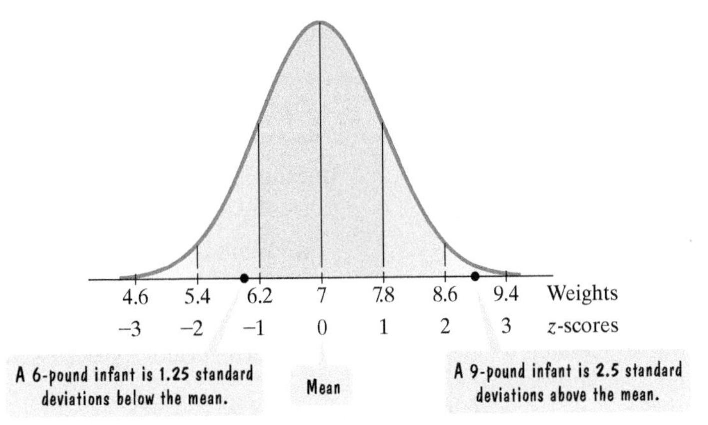

FIGURE 6.15 Infants' weights are normally distributed.

CHECK POINT 3 The length of horse pregnancies from conception to birth is normally distributed with a mean of 336 days and a standard deviation of 3 days. Find the z-score for a horse pregnancy of

a. 342 days. **b.** 336 days. **c.** 333 days.

In Example 4, we consider two normally distributed sets of test scores, in which a higher score generally indicates a better result. To compare scores on two different tests in relation to the mean on each test, we can use z-scores. The better score is the item with the greater z-score.

EXAMPLE 4 *Using and Interpreting z-Scores*

A student scores 70 on an arithmetic test and 66 on a vocabulary test. The scores for both tests are normally distributed. The arithmetic test has a mean of 60 and a standard deviation of 20. The vocabulary test has a mean of 60 and a standard deviation of 2. On which test did the student have the better score?

SOLUTION

To answer the question, we need to find the student's z-score on each test, using

$$z = \frac{\text{data item} - \text{mean}}{\text{standard deviation}}.$$

The arithmetic test has a mean of 60 and a standard deviation of 20.

$$z\text{-score for } 70 = z_{70} = \frac{70 - 60}{20} = \frac{10}{20} = 0.5$$

The vocabulary test has a mean of 60 and a standard deviation of 2.

$$z\text{-score for } 66 = z_{66} = \frac{66 - 60}{2} = \frac{6}{2} = 3$$

The arithmetic score, 70, is half a standard deviation above the mean, whereas the vocabulary score, 66, is 3 standard deviations above the mean. The student did much better than the mean on the vocabulary test.

CHECK POINT 4 The SAT (Scholastic Aptitude Test) has a mean of 500 and a standard deviation of 100. The ACT (American College Test) has a mean of 18 and a standard deviation of 6. Both tests measure the same kind of ability, with scores that are normally distributed. Suppose that you score 550 on the SAT and 24 on the ACT. On which test did you have the better score?

Blitzer Bonus

The IQ Controversy

Is intelligence something we are born with or is it a quality that can be manipulated through education? Can it be measured accurately and is IQ the way to measure it? There are no clear answers to these questions.

In a study by Carolyn Bird (*Pygmalion in the Classroom*), a group of third-grade teachers was told that they had classes of students with IQs well above the mean. These classes made incredible progress throughout the year. In reality, these were not gifted kids, but, rather, a random sample of all third-graders. It was the teachers' expectations, and not the IQs of the students, that resulted in increased performance.

EXAMPLE 5 *Understanding z-Scores*

Intelligence quotients (IQs) on the Stanford-Binet intelligence test are normally distributed with a mean of 100 and a standard deviation of 16.

a. What is the IQ corresponding to a z-score of -1.5?

b. Mensa is a group of people with high IQs whose members have z-scores of 2.05 or greater on the Stanford-Binet intelligence test. What is the IQ corresponding to a z-score of 2.05?

SOLUTION

a. We begin with the IQ corresponding to a z-score of -1.5. The negative sign in -1.5 tells us that the IQ is $1\frac{1}{2}$ standard deviations below the mean.

$$\begin{aligned} \text{IQ} &= \text{mean} - 1.5 \cdot \text{standard deviation} \\ &= 100 - 1.5(16) = 100 - 24 = 76 \end{aligned}$$

The IQ corresponding to a z-score of -1.5 is 76.

b. Next, we find the IQ corresponding to a z-score of 2.05. The positive sign implied in 2.05 tells us that the IQ is 2.05 standard deviations above the mean.

$$\begin{aligned} \text{IQ} &= \text{mean} + 2.05 \cdot \text{standard deviation} \\ &= 100 + 2.05(16) = 100 + 32.8 = 132.8 \end{aligned}$$

The IQ corresponding to a z-score of 2.05 is 132.8. (An IQ score of at least 133 is required to join Mensa.)

CHECK POINT 5 Use the information in Example 5 to find the IQ corresponding to a z-score of

a. -2.25.

b. 1.75.

6 Understand percentiles and quartiles.

Percentiles and Quartiles

A z-score measures a data item's position in a normal distribution. Another measure of a data item's position is its **percentile**. Percentiles are often associated with scores on standardized tests. If a score is in the 45th percentile, this means that 45% of the scores are less than this score. If a score is in the 95th percentile, this indicates that 95% of the scores are less than this score.

PERCENTILES

If n% of the items in a distribution are less than a particular data item, we say that the data item is in the ***n*th percentile** of the distribution.

EXAMPLE 6 *Interpreting Percentile*

The cutoff IQ score for Mensa membership, 132.8, is in the 98th percentile. What does this mean?

SOLUTION

Because 132.8 is in the 98th percentile, this means that 98% of IQ scores fall below 132.8. Caution: A score in the 98th percentile does *not* mean that 98% of the answers are correct. Nor does it mean that the score was 98%.

CHECK POINT 6 A student scored in the 75th percentile on the SAT. What does this mean?

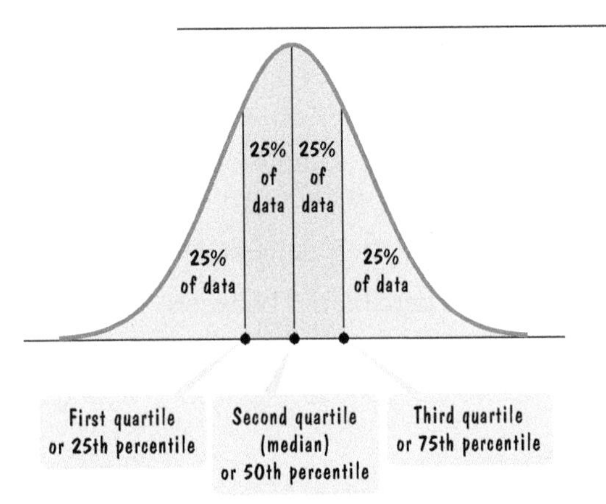

FIGURE 6.16 Quartiles

Three commonly encountered percentiles are the *quartiles*. **Quartiles** divide data sets into four equal parts. The 25th percentile is the **first quartile**: 25% of the data fall below the first quartile. The 50th percentile is the **second quartile**: 50% of the data fall below the second quartile, so the second quartile is equivalent to the median. The 75th percentile is the **third quartile**: 75% of the data fall below the third quartile. **Figure 6.16** illustrates the concept of quartiles for the normal distribution.

7 Use and interpret margins of error.

Polls and Margins of Error

What activities do you dread? Reading math textbooks with cows posing for photos on the cover? (Be kind!) No, that's not America's most-dreaded activity. In a random sample of 1000 U.S. adults, 46% of those questioned responded, "Public speaking." The problem is that this is a single random sample. Do 46% of adults in the entire U.S. population dread public speaking?

Statisticians use properties of the normal distribution to estimate the probability that a result obtained from a single sample reflects what is truly happening in the population. If you look at the results of a poll like the one shown in **Figure 6.17**, you will observe that a *margin of error* is reported. Surveys and opinion polls often give a margin of error. Let's use our understanding of the normal distribution to see how to calculate and interpret margins of error.

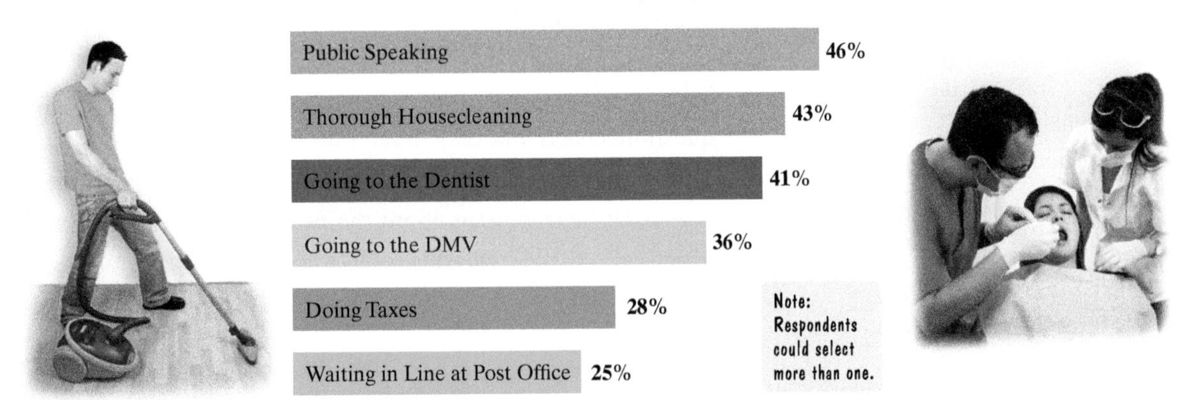

FIGURE 6.17 *Source:* TNS survey of 1000 adults, March 2010, Margin of error: ±3.2%

Note the margin of error.

Suppose that $p\%$ of the population of U.S. adults dread public speaking. Instead of taking only one random sample of 1000 adults, we repeat the process of selecting a random sample of 1000 adults hundreds of times. Then, we calculate the percentage of adults for each sample who dread public speaking. With random sampling, we expect to find the percentage in many of the samples close to $p\%$, with relatively few samples having percentages far from $p\%$. **Figure 6.18** shows that the percentages of U.S adults from the hundreds of samples can be modeled by a normal distribution. The mean of this distribution is the actual population percent, $p\%$, and is the most frequent result from the samples.

Mathematicians have shown that the standard deviation of a normal distribution of samples like the one in **Figure 6.18** is approximately $\frac{1}{2\sqrt{n}} \times 100\%$, where n is the sample size. Using the 68–95–99.7 Rule, approximately 95% of the samples have a percentage within 2 standard deviations of the true population percentage, $p\%$:

$$\text{2 standard deviations} = 2 \cdot \frac{1}{2\sqrt{n}} \times 100\% = \frac{1}{\sqrt{n}} \times 100\%.$$

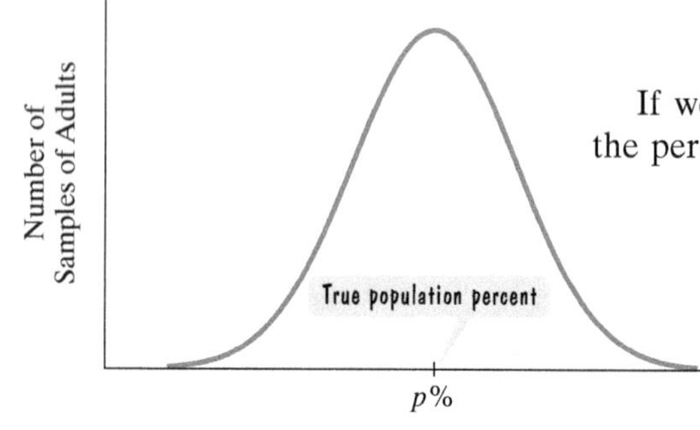

FIGURE 6.18 Percentage of U.S. adults who dread public speaking

If we use a single random sample of size n, there is a 95% probability that the percent obtained will lie within two standard deviations, or $\frac{1}{\sqrt{n}} \times 100\%$, of the true population percent. We can be 95% confident that the true population percent lies between

$$\text{the sample percent} - \frac{1}{\sqrt{n}} \times 100\%$$

and

$$\text{the sample percent} + \frac{1}{\sqrt{n}} \times 100\%.$$

We call $\pm \frac{1}{\sqrt{n}} \times 100\%$ the **margin of error.**

MARGIN OF ERROR IN A SURVEY

If a statistic is obtained from a random sample of size n, there is a 95% probability that it lies within $\frac{1}{\sqrt{n}} \times 100\%$ of the true population percent, where $\pm\frac{1}{\sqrt{n}} \times 100\%$ is called the **margin of error**.

TABLE 6.16 Activities U.S. Adults Dread

Activity	Percentage Who Dread the Activity
Public speaking	46%
Thorough house-cleaning	43%
Going to the dentist	41%
Going to the DMV	36%
Doing taxes	28%
Waiting in line at the post office	25%

Source: TNS survey of 1000 adults, March 2010,

EXAMPLE 7 *Using and Interpreting Margin of Error*

Table 6.16 shows that in a random sample of 1000 U.S adults, 46% of those questioned said that they dread public speaking.

a. Verify the margin of error that was given for this survey.

b. Write a statement about the percentage of adults in the U.S. population who dread public speaking.

SOLUTION

a. The sample size is $n = 1000$. The margin of error is

$$\pm\frac{1}{\sqrt{n}} \times 100\% = \pm\frac{1}{\sqrt{1000}} \times 100\% \approx \pm 0.032 \times 100\% = \pm 3.2\%.$$

b. There is a 95% probability that the true population percentage lies between

$$\text{the sample percent} - \frac{1}{\sqrt{n}} \times 100\% = 46\% - 3.2\% = 42.8\%$$

and

$$\text{the sample percent} + \frac{1}{\sqrt{n}} \times 100\% = 46\% + 3.2\% = 49.2\%.$$

We can be 95% confident that between 42.8% and 49.2% of all U.S adults dread public speaking.

Blitzer Bonus

A Caveat Giving a True Picture of a Poll's Accuracy

Unlike the precise calculation of a poll's margin of error, certain polling imperfections cannot be determined exactly. One problem is that people do not always respond to polls honestly and accurately. Some people are embarrassed to say "undecided," so they make up an answer. Other people may try to respond to questions in the way they think will make the pollster happy, just to be "nice." Perhaps the following caveat, applied to the poll in Example 7, would give the public a truer picture of its accuracy:

> The poll results are 42.8% to 49.2% at the 95% confidence level, but it's only under ideal conditions that we can be 95% confident that the true numbers are within 3.2% of the poll's results. The true error span is probably greater than 3.2% due to limitations that are inherent in this and every poll, but, unfortunately, this additional error amount cannot be calculated precisely. Warning: Five percent of the time—that's one time out of 20—the error will be greater than 3.2%. We remind readers of the poll that things occurring "only" 5% of the time do, indeed, happen.

We suspect that the public would tire of hearing this.

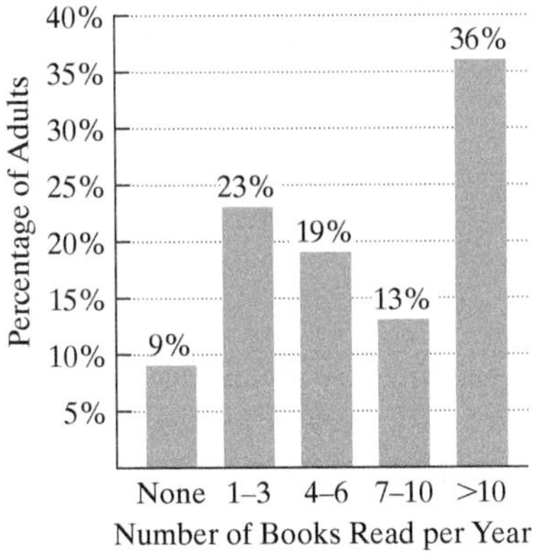

FIGURE 6.19
Source: Harris Poll of 2513 U.S. adults ages 18 and older conducted March 11 and 18, 2008

CHECK POINT 7 A Harris Poll of 2513 U.S. adults ages 18 and older asked the question

How many books do you typically read in a year?

The results of the poll are shown in **Figure 6.19**.

a. Find the margin of error for this survey. Round to the nearest tenth of a percent.

b. Write a statement about the percentage of U.S. adults who read more than ten books per year.

c. Why might some people not respond honestly and accurately to the question in this poll?

8 Recognize distributions that are not normal.

Other Kinds of Distributions

Although the normal distribution is the most important of all distributions in terms of analyzing data, not all data can be approximated by this symmetric distribution with its mean, median, and mode all having the same value.

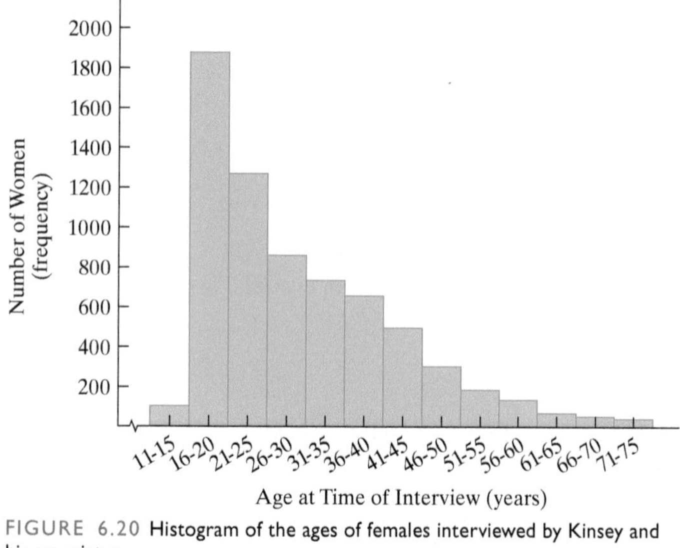

FIGURE 6.20 Histogram of the ages of females interviewed by Kinsey and his associates

The histogram in **Figure 6.20** represents the frequencies of the ages of women interviewed by Kinsey and his colleagues in their study of female sexual behavior. This distribution is not symmetric. The greatest frequency of women interviewed was in the 16–20 age range. The bars get shorter and shorter after this. The shorter bars fall on the right, indicating that relatively few older women were included in Kinsey's interviews.

In our discussion of measures of central tendency, we mentioned that the median, rather than the mean, is used to summarize income. **Figure 6.21** illustrates the population distribution of weekly earnings in the United States. There is no upper limit on weekly earnings. The relatively few people with very high weekly incomes tend to pull the mean income to a value greater than the median. The most frequent income, the mode, occurs toward the low end of the data items. The mean, median, and mode do not have the same value, and a normal distribution is not an appropriate model for describing weekly earnings in the United States.

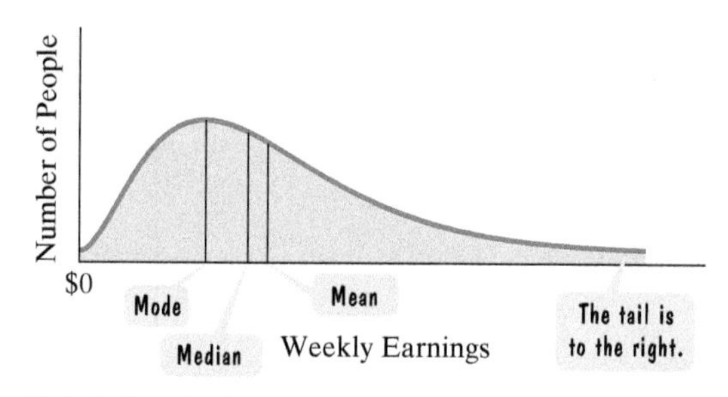

FIGURE 6.21 Skewed to the right

The distribution in **Figure 6.21** is called a *skewed distribution.* A distribution of data is **skewed** if a large number of data items are piled up at one end or the other, with a "tail" at the opposite end. In the distribution of weekly earnings in **Figure 6.21**, the tail is to the right. Such a distribution is said to be **skewed to the right**.

By contrast to the distribution of weekly earnings, the distribution in **Figure 6.22** has more data items at the high end of the scale than at the low end. The tail of this distribution is to the left. The distribution is said to be **skewed to the left**. In many colleges, an example of a distribution skewed to the left is based on the student ratings of faculty teaching performance. Most professors are given rather high ratings, while only a few are rated as terrible. These low ratings pull the value of the mean lower than the median.

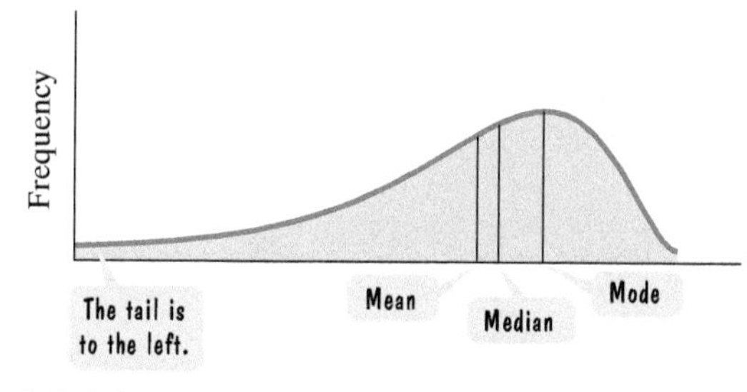

FIGURE 6.22 Skewed to the left

GREAT QUESTION!

What's the bottom line on the relationship between the mean and the median for skewed distributions?

If the data are skewed to the right, the mean is greater than the median. If the data are skewed to the left, the mean is less than the median.

Concept and Vocabulary Check

Fill in each blank so that the resulting statement is true.

1. In a normal distribution, approximately ____________% of the data items fall within 1 standard deviation of the mean, approximately ____________% of the data items fall within 2 standard deviations of the mean, and approximately ____________% of the data items fall within 3 standard deviations of the mean.

2. A z-score describes how many standard deviations a data item in a normal distribution lies above or below the ____________.

3. If n% of the items in a distribution are less than a particular data item, we say that the data item is in the nth ____________ of the distribution.

4. If a statistic is obtained from a random sample of size n, there is a 95% probability that it lies within $\frac{1}{\sqrt{n}} \times 100\%$ of the true population percent, where $\pm \frac{1}{\sqrt{n}} \times 100\%$ is called the ____________.

In Exercises 5–8, determine whether each statement is true or false. If the statement is false, make the necessary change(s) to produce a true statement.

5. The mean, median, and mode of a normal distribution are all equal. ______

6. In a normal distribution, the z-score for the mean is 0. ______

7. The z-score for a data item in a normal distribution is obtained using

$$z\text{-score} = \frac{\text{data item} - \text{standard deviation}}{\text{mean}}.$$ ______

8. A score in the 50th percentile on a standardized test is the median. ______

Exercise Set 6.4

Practice and Application Exercises

The scores on a test are normally distributed with a mean of 100 and a standard deviation of 20. In Exercises 1–10, find the score that is

1. 1 standard deviation above the mean.

2. 2 standard deviations above the mean.

3. 3 standard deviations above the mean.

4. $1\frac{1}{2}$ standard deviations above the mean.

5. $2\frac{1}{2}$ standard deviations above the mean.

6. 1 standard deviation below the mean.

7. 2 standard deviations below the mean.

8. 3 standard deviations below the mean.

9. one-half a standard deviation below the mean.

10. $2\frac{1}{2}$ standard deviations below the mean.

Not everyone pays the same price for the same model of a car. The figure illustrates a normal distribution for the prices paid for a particular model of a new car. The mean is \$17,000 and the standard deviation is \$500.

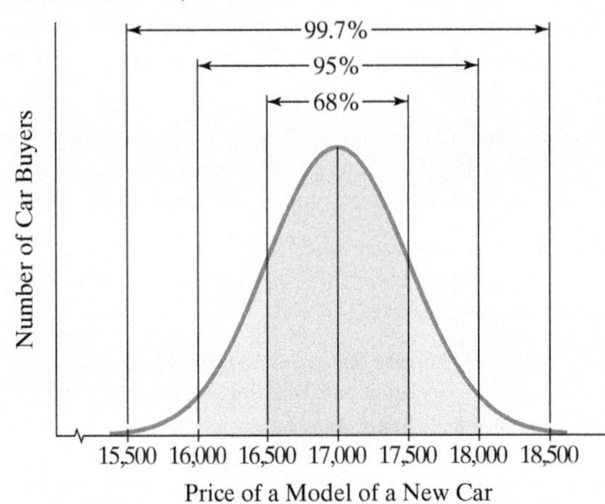

In Exercises 11–22, use the 68–95–99.7 Rule, illustrated in the figure, to find the percentage of buyers who paid

11. between \$16,500 and \$17,500.

12. between \$16,000 and \$18,000.

13. between \$17,000 and \$17,500.

14. between \$17,000 and \$18,000.

15. between \$16,000 and \$17,000.

16. between \$16,500 and \$17,000.

17. between \$15,500 and \$17,000.

18. between \$17,000 and \$18,500.

19. more than \$17,500.

20. more than \$18,000.

21. less than \$16,000.

22. less than \$16,500.

Intelligence quotients (IQs) on the Stanford-Binet intelligence test are normally distributed with a mean of 100 and a standard deviation of 16. In Exercises 23–32, use the 68–95–99.7 Rule to find the percentage of people with IQs

23. between 68 and 132.

24. between 84 and 116.

25. between 68 and 100.

26. between 84 and 100.

27. above 116.

28. above 132.

29. below 68.

30. below 84.

31. above 148.

32. below 52.

A set of data items is normally distributed with a mean of 60 and a standard deviation of 8. In Exercises 33–48, convert each data item to a z-score.

33. 68 **34.** 76 **35.** 84

36. 92 **37.** 64 **38.** 72

39. 74 **40.** 78 **41.** 60

42. 100 **43.** 52 **44.** 44

45. 48 **46.** 40 **47.** 34

48. 30

Scores on a dental anxiety scale range from 0 (no anxiety) to 20 (extreme anxiety). The scores are normally distributed with a mean of 11 and a standard deviation of 4. In Exercises 49–56, find the z-score for the given score on this dental anxiety scale.

49. 17 **50.** 18

51. 20 **52.** 12

53. 6 **54.** 8

55. 5 **56.** 1

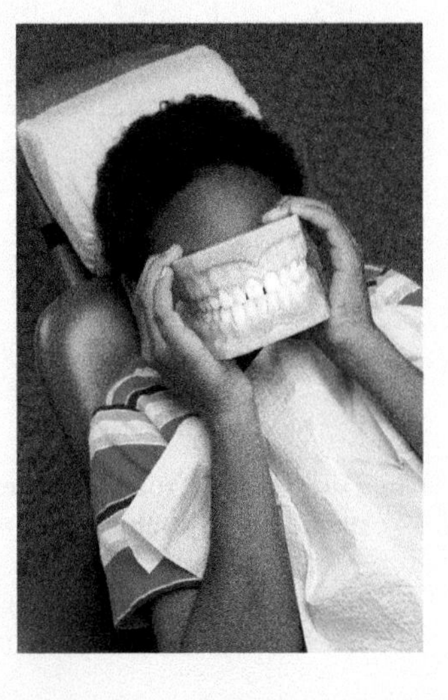

Intelligence quotients on the Stanford-Binet intelligence test are normally distributed with a mean of 100 and a standard deviation of 16. Intelligence quotients on the Wechsler intelligence test are normally distributed with a mean of 100 and a standard deviation of 15. Use this information to solve Exercises 57–58.

57. Use z-scores to determine which person has the higher IQ: an individual who scores 128 on the Stanford-Binet or an individual who scores 127 on the Wechsler.

58. Use z-scores to determine which person has the higher IQ: an individual who scores 150 on the Stanford-Binet or an individual who scores 148 on the Wechsler.

A set of data items is normally distributed with a mean of 400 and a standard deviation of 50. In Exercises 59–66, find the data item in this distribution that corresponds to the given z-score.

59. $z = 2$

60. $z = 3$

61. $z = 1.5$

62. $z = 2.5$

63. $z = -3$

64. $z = -2$

65. $z = -2.5$

66. $z = -1.5$

67. Reducing Gun Violence The data in the bar graph are from a random sample of 814 American adults. The graph shows four proposals to reduce gun violence in the United States and the percentage of surveyed adults who favored each of these proposals.

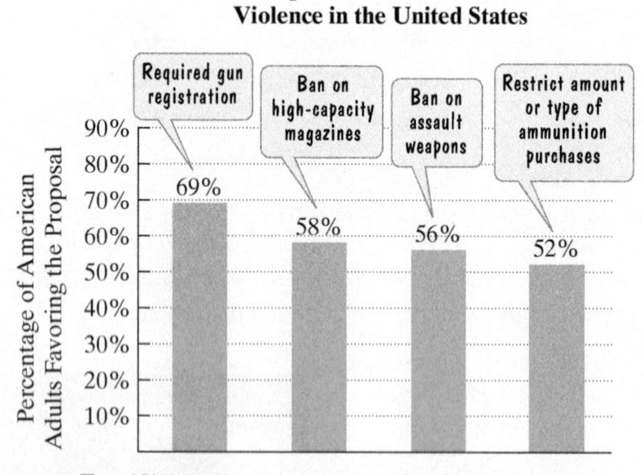

Source: Time/CNN poll using a sample of 814 American adults, January 14–15, 2013

a. Find the margin of error, to the nearest tenth of a percent, for this survey.

b. Write a statement about the percentage of adults in the U.S population who favor required gun registration to reduce gun violence.

68. How to Blow Your Job Interview The data in the bar graph at the top of the next column are from a random sample of 1910 job interviewers. The graph shows the top interviewer turnoffs and the percentage of surveyed interviewers who were offended by each of these behaviors.

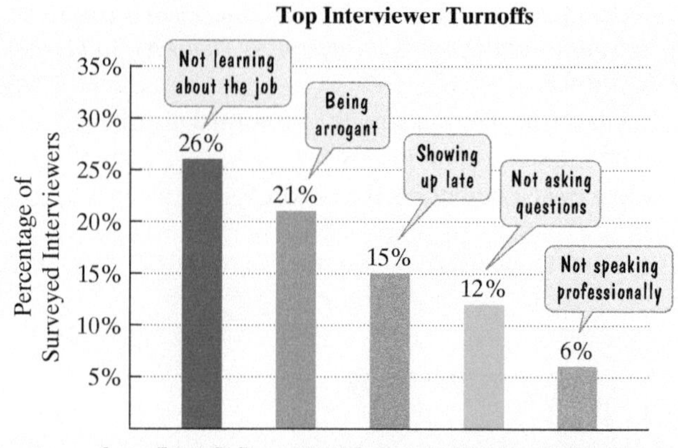

Source: Scott Erker, PhD., and Kelli Buczynski, "Are You Failing the Interview? 2009 Survey of Global Interviewing Practices and Perceptions." Development Dimensions International.

a. Find the margin of error, to the nearest tenth of a percent, for this survey.

b. Write a statement about the percentage of interviewers in the population who are turned off by a job applicant being arrogant.

69. Using a random sample of 4000 TV households, Nielsen Media Research found that 60.2% watched the final episode of *M*A*S*H*.

a. Find the margin of error in this percent.

b. Write a statement about the percentage of TV households in the population that tuned into the final episode of *M*A*S*H*.

70. Using a random sample of 4000 TV households, Nielsen Media Research found that 51.1% watched *Roots, Part 8*.

a. Find the margin of error in this percent.

b. Write a statement about the percentage of TV households in the population that tuned into *Roots, Part 8*.

71. In 1997, Nielsen Media Research increased its random sample to 5000 TV households. By how much, to the nearest tenth of a percent, did this improve the margin of error over that in Exercises 69 and 70?

72. If Nielsen Media Research were to increase its random sample from 5000 to 10,000 TV households, by how much, to the nearest tenth of a percent, would this improve the margin of error?

The histogram shows murder rates per 100,000 residents and the number of U.S. states that had these rates for a recent year. Use this histogram to solve Exercises 73–74.

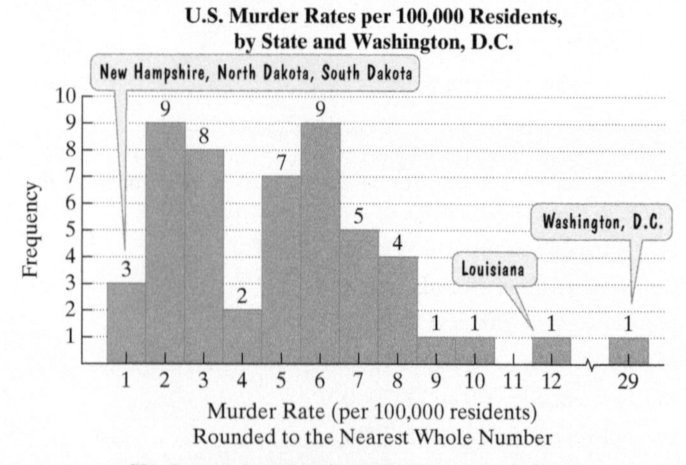

Source: FBI, *Crime in the United States*

73. a. Is the shape of this distribution best classified as normal, skewed to the right, or skewed to the left?

b. Calculate the mean murder rate per 100,000 residents for the 50 states and Washington, D.C.

c. Find the median murder rate per 100,000 residents for the 50 states and Washington, D.C.

d. Are the mean and median murder rates consistent with the shape of the distribution that you described in part (a)? Explain your answer.

e. The standard deviation for the data is approximately 4.2. If the distribution were roughly normal, what would be the z-score, rounded to one decimal place, for Washington, D.C.? Does this seem unusually high? Explain your answer.

74. a. Find the median murder rate per 100,000 residents for the 50 states and Washington, D.C.

b. Find the first quartile by determining the median of the lower half of the data. (This is the median of the items that lie below the median that you found in part (a).)

c. Find the third quartile by determining the median of the upper half of the data. (This is the median of the items that lie above the median that you found in part (a).)

d. Use the following numerical scale:

0 5 10 15 20 25 30

Murder Rate (per 100,000 residents)

Above this scale, show five points, each at the same height. (The height is arbitrary.) Each point should represent one of the following numbers:

lowest data value, first quartile, median, third quartile, highest data value.

e. A **box-and-whisker plot** consists of a rectangular box extending from the first quartile to the third quartile, with a dashed line representing the median, and line segments (or whiskers) extending outward from the box to the lowest and highest data values:

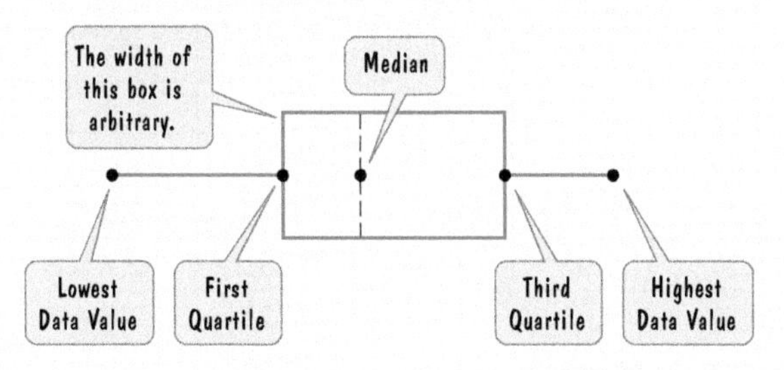

Use your graph from part (d) to create a box-and-whisker plot for U.S. murder rates per 100,000 residents.

f. If one of the whiskers in a box-and-whisker plot is clearly longer, the distribution is usually skewed in the direction of the longer whisker. Based on this observation, does your box-and-whisker plot in part (e) indicate that the distribution is skewed to the right or skewed to the left?

g. Is the shape of the distribution of scores shown by the given histogram consistent with your observation in part (f)?

Writing in Mathematics

75. What is a symmetric histogram?

76. Describe the normal distribution and discuss some of its properties.

77. Describe the 68–95–99.7 Rule.

78. Describe how to determine the z-score for a data item in a normal distribution.

79. What does a z-score measure?

80. Give an example of both a commonly occurring and an infrequently occurring z-score. Explain how you arrived at these examples.

81. Describe when a z-score is negative.

82. If you score in the 83rd percentile, what does this mean?

83. If your weight is in the third quartile, what does this mean?

84. Two students have scores with the same percentile, but for different administrations of the SAT. Does this mean that the students have the same score on the SAT? Explain your answer.

85. Give an example of a phenomenon that is normally distributed. Explain why. (Try to be creative and not use one of the distributions discussed in this section.) Estimate what the mean and the standard deviation might be and describe how you determined these estimates.

86. Give an example of a phenomenon that is not normally distributed and explain why.

Critical Thinking Exercises

Make Sense? *In Exercises 87–90, determine whether each statement makes sense or does not make sense, and explain your reasoning.*

87. The heights of the men on our college basketball team are normally distributed with a mean of 6 feet 3 inches and a standard deviation of 1 foot 2 inches.

88. I scored in the 50th percentile on a standardized test, so my score is the median.

89. A poll administered to a random sample of 1150 voters shows 51% in favor of candidate A, so I'm 95% confident that candidate A will win the election.

90. My math teacher gave a very difficult exam for which the distribution of scores was skewed to the right.

Group Exercise

91. For this activity, group members will conduct interviews with a random sample of students on campus. Each student is to be asked, "What is the worst thing about being a student?" One response should be recorded for each student.

a. Each member should interview enough students so that there are at least 50 randomly selected students in the sample.

b. After all responses have been recorded, the group should organize the four most common answers. For each answer, compute the percentage of students in the sample who felt that this is the worst thing about being a student.

c. Find the margin of error for your survey.

d. For each of the four most common answers, write a statement about the percentage of all students on your campus who feel that this is the worst thing about being a student.

WHAT AM I SUPPOSED TO LEARN?

After you have read this section, you should be able to:

1 Solve applied problems involving normal distributions.

Problem Solving with the Normal Distribution

WE HAVE SEEN THAT MALE HEIGHTS IN NORTH AMERICA ARE approximately normally distributed with a mean of 70 inches and a standard deviation of 4 inches. Suppose we are interested in the percentage of men with heights below 80 inches:

$$z_{80} = \frac{\text{data item} - \text{mean}}{\text{standard deviation}} = \frac{80 - 70}{4} = \frac{10}{4} = 2.5.$$

Because this z-score is not an integer, the 68–95–99.7 Rule is not helpful in finding the percentage of data items that fall below 2.5 standard deviations of the mean. In this section, we will use a table that contains numerous z-scores and their percentiles to solve a variety of problems involving the normal distribution.

1 Solve applied problems involving normal distributions.

Problem Solving Using z-Scores and Percentiles

Table 6.17 gives a percentile interpretation for z-scores.

TABLE 6.17 z-Scores and Percentiles

z-Score	Percentile	z-Score	Percentile	z-Score	Percentile	z-Score	Percentile
−4.0	0.003	−1.0	15.87	0.0	50.00	1.1	86.43
−3.5	0.02	−0.95	17.11	0.05	51.99	1.2	88.49
−3.0	0.13	−0.90	18.41	0.10	53.98	1.3	90.32
−2.9	0.19	−0.85	19.77	0.15	55.96	1.4	91.92
−2.8	0.26	−0.80	21.19	0.20	57.93	1.5	93.32
−2.7	0.35	−0.75	22.66	0.25	59.87	1.6	94.52
−2.6	0.47	−0.70	24.20	0.30	61.79	1.7	95.54
−2.5	0.62	−0.65	25.78	0.35	63.68	1.8	96.41
−2.4	0.82	−0.60	27.43	0.40	65.54	1.9	97.13
−2.3	1.07	−0.55	29.12	0.45	67.36	2.0	97.72
−2.2	1.39	−0.50	30.85	0.50	69.15	2.1	98.21
−2.1	1.79	−0.45	32.64	0.55	70.88	2.2	98.61
−2.0	2.28	−0.40	34.46	0.60	72.57	2.3	98.93
−1.9	2.87	−0.35	36.32	0.65	74.22	2.4	99.18
−1.8	3.59	−0.30	38.21	0.70	75.80	2.5	99.38
−1.7	4.46	−0.25	40.13	0.75	77.34	2.6	99.53
−1.6	5.48	−0.20	42.07	0.80	78.81	2.7	99.65
−1.5	6.68	−0.15	44.04	0.85	80.23	2.8	99.74
−1.4	8.08	−0.10	46.02	0.90	81.59	2.9	99.81
−1.3	9.68	−0.05	48.01	0.95	82.89	3.0	99.87
−1.2	11.51	0.0	50.00	1.0	84.13	3.5	99.98
−1.1	13.57					4.0	99.997

TWO ENTRIES FROM TABLE 6.17

z-Score	Percentile
2.5	99.38
0.0	50.00

The portion of the table in the margin indicates that the corresponding percentile for a z-score of 2.5 is 99.38. This tells us that 99.38% of North American men have heights that are less than 80 inches, or $z = 2.5$.

In a normal distribution, the mean, median, and mode all have a corresponding z-score of 0. **Table 6.17** shows that the percentile for a z-score of 0 is 50.00. Thus,

50% of the data items in a normal distribution are less than the mean, median, and mode. Consequently, 50% of the data items are greater than or equal to the mean, median, and mode.

Table 6.17 can be used to find the percentage of data items that are less than any data item in a normal distribution. Begin by converting the data item to a z-score. Then, use the table to find the percentile for this z-score. This percentile is the percentage of data items that are less than the data item in question.

EXAMPLE 1 *Finding the Percentage of Data Items Less Than a Given Data Item*

According to the Department of Health and Education, cholesterol levels are normally distributed. For men between 18 and 24 years, the mean is 178.1 (measured in milligrams per 100 milliliters) and the standard deviation is 40.7. What percentage of men in this age range have a cholesterol level less than 239.15?

SOLUTION

If you are familiar with your own cholesterol level, you probably recognize that a level of 239.15 is fairly high for a young man. Because of this, we would expect most young men to have a level less than 239.15. Let's see if this is so. **Table 6.17** requires that we use z-scores. We compute the z-score for a 239.15 cholesterol level by using the z-score formula.

$$z_{239.15} = \frac{\text{data item} - \text{mean}}{\text{standard deviation}} = \frac{239.15 - 178.1}{40.7} = \frac{61.05}{40.7} = 1.5$$

A PORTION OF TABLE 6.17

z-Score	Percentile
1.4	91.92
1.5	93.32
1.6	94.52

A man between 18 and 24 with a 239.15 cholesterol level is 1.5 standard deviations above the mean, illustrated in **Figure 6.23(a)**. The question mark indicates that we must find the percentage of men with a cholesterol level less than $z = 1.5$, the z-score for a 239.15 cholesterol level. **Table 6.17** gives this percentage as a percentile. Find 1.5 in the z-score column in the right portion of the table. The percentile given to the right of 1.5 is 93.32. Thus, 93.32% of men between 18 and 24 have a cholesterol level less than 239.15, shown in **Figure 6.23(b)**.

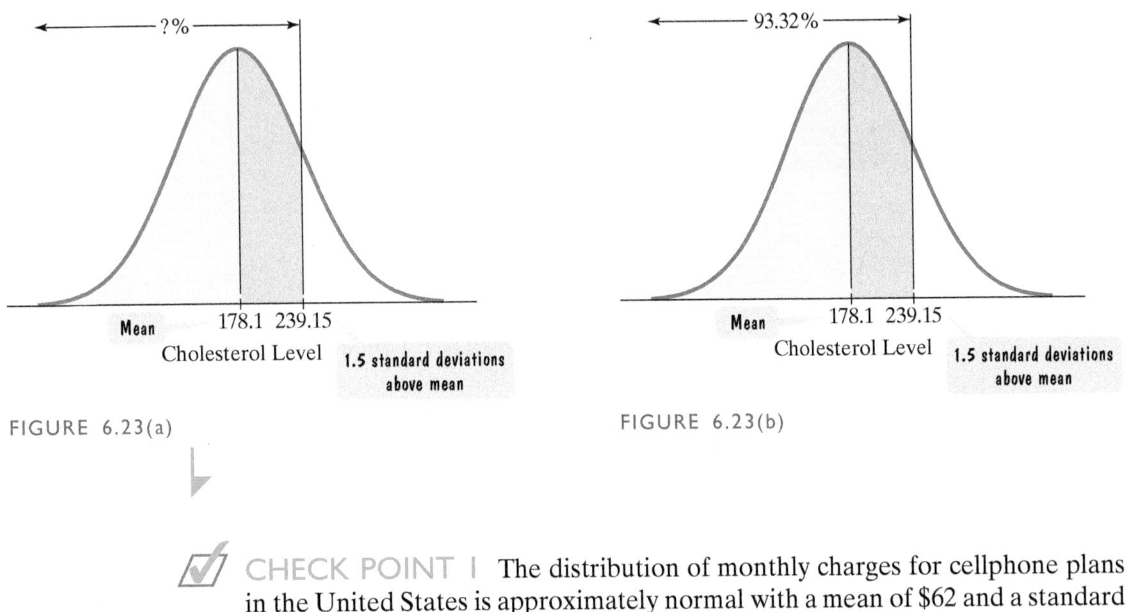

FIGURE 6.23(a)

FIGURE 6.23(b)

CHECK POINT 1 The distribution of monthly charges for cellphone plans in the United States is approximately normal with a mean of \$62 and a standard deviation of \$18. What percentage of plans have charges that are less than \$83.60?

The normal distribution accounts for all data items, meaning 100% of the scores. This means that **Table 6.17** can also be used to find the percentage of data items that are greater than any data item in a normal distribution. Use the percentile in the table to determine the percentage of data items less than the data item in question. Then subtract this percentage from 100% to find the percentage of data items greater than the item in question. In using this technique, we will treat the phrases "greater than" and "greater than or equal to" as equivalent.

EXAMPLE 2 *Finding the Percentage of Data Items Greater Than a Given Data Item*

Lengths of pregnancies of women are normally distributed with a mean of 266 days and a standard deviation of 16 days. What percentage of children are born from pregnancies lasting more than 274 days?

SOLUTION

A PORTION OF TABLE 6.17

z-Score	Percentile
0.45	67.36
0.50	69.15
0.55	70.88

Table 6.17 requires that we use z-scores. We compute the z-score for a 274-day pregnancy by using the z-score formula.

$$z_{274} = \frac{\text{data item} - \text{mean}}{\text{standard deviation}} = \frac{274 - 266}{16} = \frac{8}{16} = 0.5$$

A 274-day pregnancy is 0.5 standard deviation above the mean. **Table 6.17** gives the percentile corresponding to 0.50 as 69.15. This means that 69.15% of pregnancies last less than 274 days, illustrated in **Figure 6.24.** We must find the percentage of pregnancies lasting more than 274 days by subtracting 69.15% from 100%.

$$100\% - 69.15\% = 30.85\%$$

Thus, 30.85% of children are born from pregnancies lasting more than 274 days.

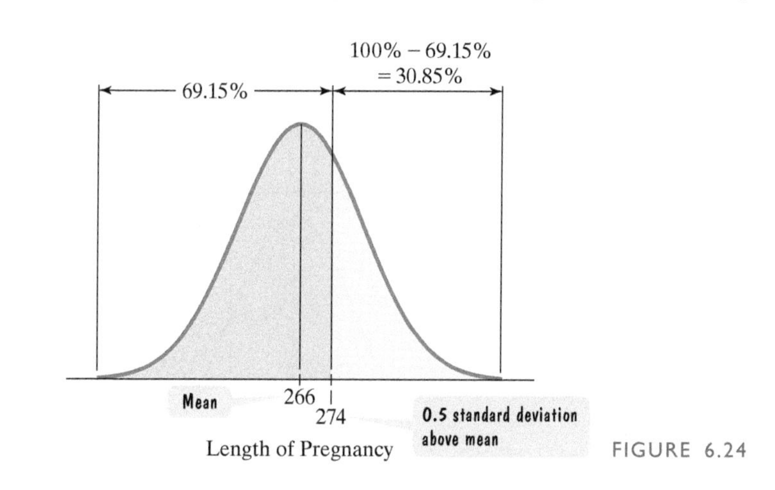

FIGURE 6.24

CHECK POINT 2 Female adult heights in North America are approximately normally distributed with a mean of 65 inches and a standard deviation of 3.5 inches. What percentage of North American women have heights that exceed 69.9 inches?

We have seen how **Table 6.17** is used to find the percentage of data items that are less than or greater than any given item. The table can also be used to find the percentage of data items *between* two given items. Because the percentile for each item is the percentage of data items less than the given item, the percentage of data between the two given items is found by subtracting the lesser percent from the greater percent. This is illustrated in **Figure 6.25.**

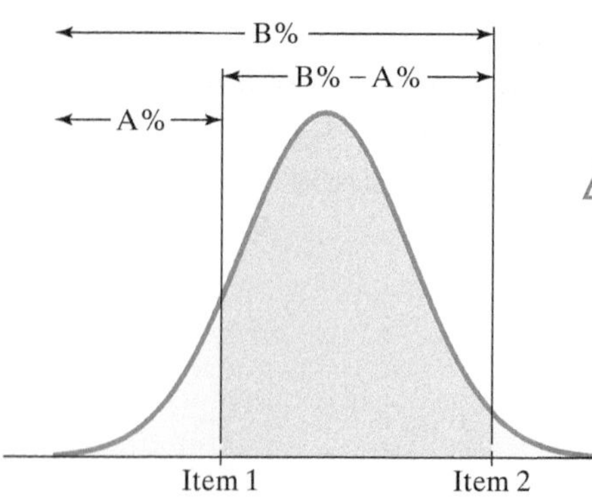

FIGURE 6.25 The percentile for data item 1 is A. The percentile for data item 2 is B. The percentage of data items between item 1 and item 2 is B% − A%.

FINDING THE PERCENTAGE OF DATA ITEMS BETWEEN TWO GIVEN ITEMS IN A NORMAL DISTRIBUTION

1. Convert each given data item to a z-score:

$$z = \frac{\text{data item} - \text{mean}}{\text{standard deviation}}.$$

2. Use **Table 6.17** to find the percentile corresponding to each z-score in step 1.
3. Subtract the lesser percentile from the greater percentile and attach a % sign.

EXAMPLE 3 *Finding the Percentage of Data Items between Two Given Data Items*

A PORTION OF TABLE 6.17

z-Score	Percentile
−0.55	29.12
−0.50	30.85
−0.45	32.64

A PORTION OF TABLE 6.17

z-Score	Percentile
2.4	99.18
2.5	99.38
2.6	99.53

The amount of time that self-employed Americans work each week is normally distributed with a mean of 44.6 hours and a standard deviation of 14.4 hours. What percentage of self-employed individuals in the United States work between 37.4 and 80.6 hours per week?

SOLUTION

Step 1 Convert each given data item to a z-score.

$$z_{37.4} = \frac{\text{data item} - \text{mean}}{\text{standard deviation}} = \frac{37.4 - 44.6}{14.4} = \frac{-7.2}{14.4} = -0.5$$

$$z_{80.6} = \frac{\text{data item} - \text{mean}}{\text{standard deviation}} = \frac{80.6 - 44.6}{14.4} = \frac{36}{14.4} = 2.5$$

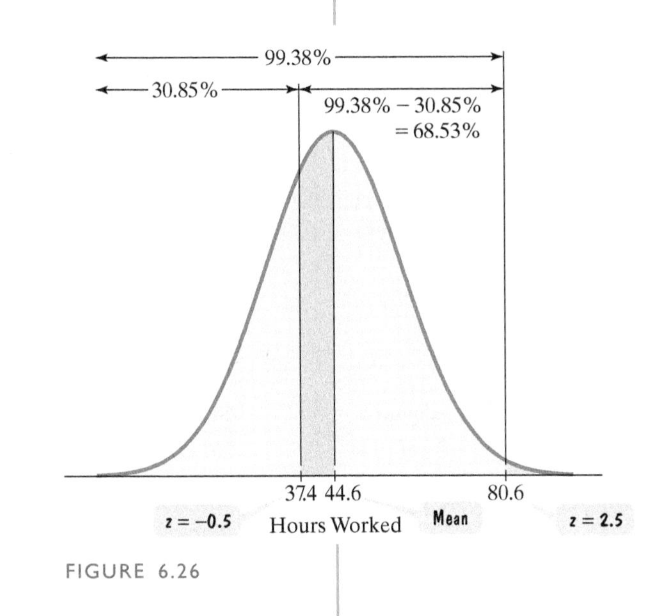

FIGURE 6.26

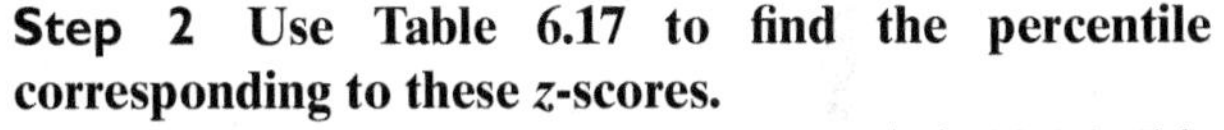

Step 2 Use Table 6.17 to find the percentile corresponding to these z-scores. The percentile given to the right of −0.50 is 30.85. This means that 30.85% of self-employed Americans work less than 37.4 hours per week.

Table 6.17 also gives the percentile corresponding to $z = 2.5$. Find 2.5 in the z-score column in the far-right portion of the table. The percentile given to the right of 2.5 is 99.38. This means that 99.38% of self-employed Americans work less than 80.6 hours per week.

Step 3 Subtract the lesser percentile from the greater percentile and attach a % sign. Subtracting percentiles, we obtain

$$99.38 - 30.85 = 68.53.$$

Thus, 68.53% of self-employed Americans work between 37.4 and 80.6 hours per week. The solution is illustrated in **Figure 6.26**.

CHECK POINT 3 The distribution for the life of refrigerators is approximately normal with a mean of 14 years and a standard deviation of 2.5 years. What percentage of refrigerators have lives between 11 years and 18 years?

Our work in Examples 1 through 3 is summarized as follows:

COMPUTING PERCENTAGE OF DATA ITEMS FOR NORMAL DISTRIBUTIONS

Description of Percentage	Graph	Computation of Percentage
Percentage of data items less than a given data item with $z = b$	0 b	Use the table percentile for $z = b$ and add a % sign.
Percentage of data items greater than a given data item with $z = a$	a 0	Subtract the table percentile for $z = a$ from 100 and add a % sign.
Percentage of data items between two given data items with $z = a$ and $z = b$	a 0 b	Subtract the table percentile for $z = a$ from the table percentile for $z = b$ and add a % sign.

Concept and Vocabulary Check

Use the information shown below to fill in each blank so that the resulting statement is true.

-1.2 0 2.3

z-Score	Percentile
−1.2	11.51
2.3	98.93

1. The percentage of scores less than $z = 2.3$ is ________.
2. The percentage of scores greater than $z = 2.3$ is ________.
3. The percentage of scores greater than $z = -1.2$ is ________.
4. The percentage of scores between $z = -1.2$ and $z = 2.3$ is ________.
5. True or False: The 68–95–99.7 Rule cannot be used if z-scores are not integers. ______

Exercise Set 6.5

Practice and Application Exercises

Use **Table 6.17** *on page 256 to solve Exercises 1–16.*

In Exercises 1–8, find the percentage of data items in a normal distribution that lie **a.** *below and* **b.** *above the given z-score.*

1. $z = 0.6$
2. $z = 0.8$
3. $z = 1.2$
4. $z = 1.4$
5. $z = -0.7$
6. $z = -0.4$
7. $z = -1.2$
8. $z = -1.8$

In Exercises 9–16, find the percentage of data items in a normal distribution that lie between

9. $z = 0.2$ and $z = 1.4$.
10. $z = 0.3$ and $z = 2.1$.
11. $z = 1$ and $z = 3$.
12. $z = 2$ and $z = 3$.
13. $z = -1.5$ and $z = 1.5$.
14. $z = -1.2$ and $z = 1.2$.
15. $z = -2$ and $z = -0.5$.
16. $z = -2.2$ and $z = -0.3$.

Systolic blood pressure readings are normally distributed with a mean of 121 and a standard deviation of 15. (A reading above 140 is considered to be high blood pressure.) In Exercises 17–26, begin by converting any given blood pressure reading or readings into z-scores. Then use **Table 6.17** *on page 256 to find the percentage of people with blood pressure readings*

17. below 142.
18. below 148.
19. above 130.
20. above 133.
21. above 103.
22. above 100.
23. between 142 and 154.
24. between 145 and 157.
25. between 112 and 130.
26. between 109 and 133.

The weights for 12-month-old baby boys are normally distributed with a mean of 22.5 pounds and a standard deviation of 2.2 pounds. In Exercises 27–30, use **Table 6.17** *on page 256 to find the percentage of 12-month-old baby boys who weigh*

27. more than 25.8 pounds.

28. more than 23.6 pounds.

29. between 19.2 and 21.4 pounds.

30. between 18.1 and 19.2 pounds.

Practice Plus

The table shows selected ages of licensed drivers in the United States and the corresponding percentiles.

AGES OF U.S. DRIVERS

Age	Percentile
75	98
65	88
55	77
45	60
35	37
25	14
20	5

Source: Department of Transportation

In Exercises 31–36, use the information given by the table to find the percentage of U.S. drivers who are

31. younger than 55.

32. younger than 45.

33. at least 25.

34. at least 35.

35. at least 65 and younger than 75.

36. at least 20 and younger than 65.

Writing in Mathematics

37. Explain when it is necessary to use a table showing z-scores and percentiles rather than the 68–95–99.7 Rule to determine the percentage of data items less than a given data item.

38. Explain how to use a table showing z-scores and percentiles to determine the percentage of data items between two z-scores.

Critical Thinking Exercises

Make Sense? *In Exercises 39–42, determine whether each statement makes sense or does not make sense, and explain your reasoning.*

39. I'm using a table showing z-scores and percentiles that has positive percentiles corresponding to positive z-scores and negative percentiles corresponding to negative z-scores.

40. My table showing z-scores and percentiles displays the percentage of data items less than a given value of z.

41. My table showing z-scores and percentiles does not display the percentage of data items greater than a given value of z.

42. I can use a table showing z-scores and percentiles to verify the three approximate numbers given by the 68–95–99.7 Rule.

43. Find two z-scores so that 40% of the data in the distribution lies between them. (More than one answer is possible.)

44. A woman insists that she will never marry a man as short or shorter than she, knowing that only one man in 400 falls into this category. Assuming a mean height of 69 inches for men with a standard deviation of 2.5 inches (and a normal distribution), approximately how tall is the woman?

45. The placement test for a college has scores that are normally distributed with a mean of 500 and a standard deviation of 100. If the college accepts only the top 10% of examinees, what is the cutoff score on the test for admission?

6.6 Scatter Plots, Correlation, and Regression Lines

WHAT AM I SUPPOSED TO LEARN?

After you have read this section, you should be able to:

1. Make a scatter plot for a table of data items.
2. Interpret information given in a scatter plot.
3. Compute the correlation coefficient.
4. Write the equation of the regression line.
5. Use a sample's correlation coefficient to determine whether there is a correlation in the population.

THESE PHOTOS OF PRESIDENTIAL PUFFING INDICATE that the White House was not always a no-smoking zone. According to *Cigar Aficionado*, nearly half of U.S. presidents have had a nicotine habit, from cigarettes to pipes to cigars. Franklin Roosevelt's stylish way with a cigarette holder was part of his mystique. Although Dwight Eisenhower quit his wartime four-pack-a-day habit before taking office, smoking in the residence was still common, with ashtrays on the tables at state dinners and free cigarettes for guests. In 1993, Hillary Clinton banned smoking in the White House, although Bill Clinton's cigars later made a sordid cameo in the Lewinsky scandal. Barack Obama quit smoking before entering the White House, but had "fallen off the wagon occasionally" as he admitted in a *Meet the Press* interview.

Changing attitudes toward smoking, both inside and outside the White House, date back to 1964 and an equation in two variables. To understand the mathematics behind this turning point in public health, we need to explore situations involving data collected on two variables.

Up to this point in the chapter, we have studied situations in which data sets involve a single variable, such as height, weight, cholesterol level, and length of pregnancies. By contrast, the 1964 study involved data collected on two variables from 11 countries—annual cigarette consumption for each adult male and deaths per million males from lung cancer. In this section, we consider situations in which there are two data items for each randomly selected person or thing. Our interest is in determining whether or not there is a relationship between the two variables and, if so, the strength of that relationship.

Make a scatter plot for a table of data items.

Scatter Plots and Correlation

Is there a relationship between education and prejudice? With increased education, does a person's level of prejudice tend to decrease? Notice that we are interested in two quantities—years of education and level of prejudice. For each person in our sample, we will record the number of years of school completed and the score on a test measuring prejudice. Higher scores on this 1-to-10 test indicate greater prejudice. Using x to represent years of education and y to represent scores on a test measuring prejudice, **Table 6.18** shows these two quantities for a random sample of ten people.

TABLE 6.18 Recording Two Quantities in a Sample of Ten People

Respondent	A	B	C	D	E	F	G	H	I	J
Years of education (x)	12	5	14	13	8	10	16	11	12	4
Score on prejudice test (y)	1	7	2	3	5	4	1	2	3	10

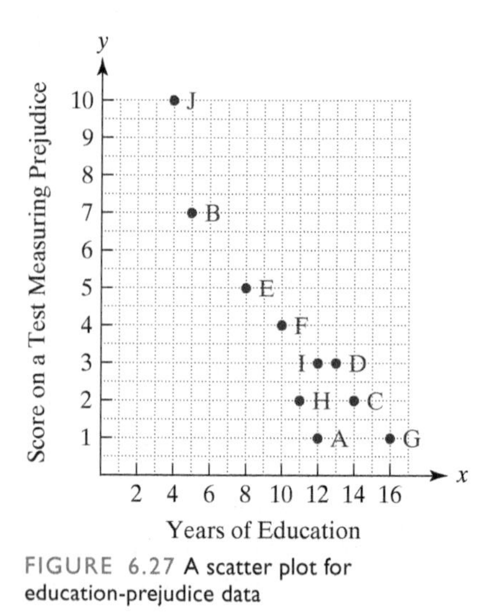

FIGURE 6.27 A scatter plot for education-prejudice data

When two data items are collected for every person or object in a sample, the data items can be visually displayed using a *scatter plot*. A **scatter plot** is a collection of data points, one data point per person or object. We can make a scatter plot of the data in **Table 6.18** by drawing a horizontal axis to represent years of education and a vertical axis to represent scores on a test measuring prejudice. We then represent each of the ten respondents with a single point on the graph. For example, the dot for respondent A is located to represent 12 years of education on the horizontal axis and 1 on the prejudice test on the vertical axis. Plotting each of the ten pieces of data in a rectangular coordinate system results in the scatter plot shown in **Figure 6.27**.

A scatter plot like the one in **Figure 6.27** can be used to determine whether two quantities are related. If there is a clear relationship, the quantities are said to be **correlated**. The scatter plot shows a downward trend among the data points, although there are a few exceptions. People with increased education tend to have a lower score on the test measuring prejudice. **Correlation** is used to determine if there is a relationship between two variables and, if so, the strength and direction of that relationship.

Correlation and Causal Connections

Correlations can often be seen when data items are displayed on a scatter plot. Although the scatter plot in **Figure 6.27** indicates a correlation between education and prejudice, we cannot conclude that increased education causes a person's level of prejudice to decrease. There are at least three possible explanations:

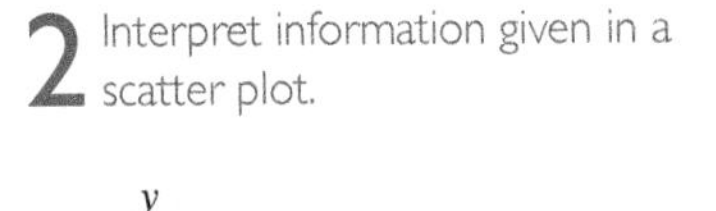

1. The correlation between increased education and decreased prejudice is simply a coincidence.
2. Education usually involves classrooms with a variety of different kinds of people. Increased exposure to diversity in the classroom setting, which accompanies increased levels of education, might be an underlying cause for decreased prejudice.
3. Education, the process of acquiring knowledge, requires people to look at new ideas and see things in different ways. Thus, education causes one to be more tolerant and less prejudiced.

Establishing that one thing causes another is extremely difficult, even if there is a strong correlation between these things. For example, as the air temperature increases, there is an increase in the number of people stung by jellyfish at the beach. This does not mean that an increase in air temperature causes more people to be stung. It might mean that because it is hotter, more people go into the water. With an increased number of swimmers, more people are likely to be stung. In short, correlation is not necessarily causation.

2 Interpret information given in a scatter plot.

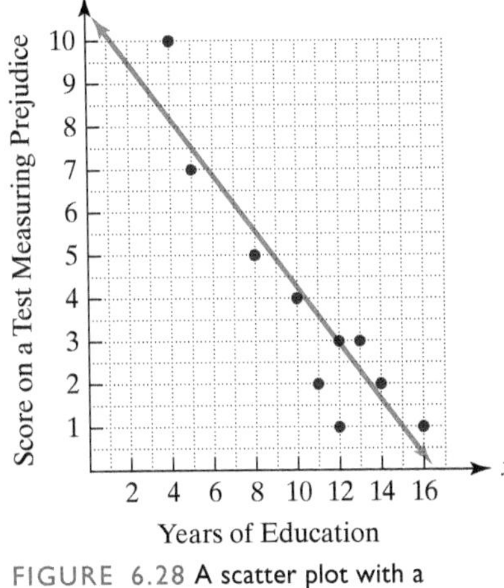

FIGURE 6.28 A scatter plot with a regression line

Regression Lines and Correlation Coefficients

Figure 6.28 shows the scatter plot for the education-prejudice data. Also shown is a straight line that seems to approximately "fit" the data points. Most of the data points lie either near or on this line. A line that best fits the data points in a scatter plot is called a **regression line**. The regression line is the particular line in which the spread of the data points around it is as small as possible.

A measure that is used to describe the strength and direction of a relationship between variables whose data points lie on or near a line is called the **correlation coefficient,** designated by r. **Figure 6.29** shows scatter plots and correlation coefficients. Variables are **positively correlated** if they tend to increase or decrease together, as in **Figure 6.29(a)**, **(b)**, and **(c)**. By contrast, variables are **negatively correlated** if one variable tends to decrease while the other increases, as in **Figure 6.29(e)**, **(f)**, and **(g)**. **Figure 6.29** illustrates that a correlation coefficient, r, is a number between -1 and 1, inclusive. **Figure 6.29(a)** shows a value of 1. This indicates a **perfect positive correlation** in which all points in the scatter plot lie precisely on the regression line that rises from left to right. **Figure 6.29(g)** shows a value of -1. This indicates a **perfect negative correlation** in which all points in the scatter plot lie precisely on the regression line that falls from left to right.

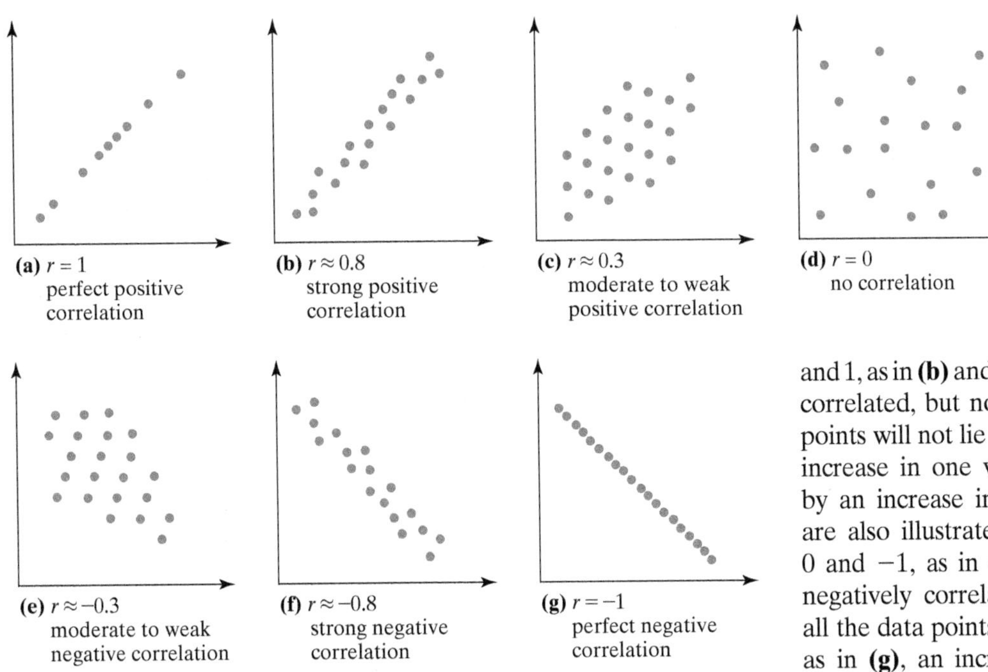

FIGURE 6.29 Scatter plots and correlation coefficients

Take another look at **Figure 6.29**. If r is between 0 and 1, as in **(b)** and **(c)**, the two variables are positively correlated, but not perfectly. Although all the data points will not lie on the regression line, as in **(a)**, an increase in one variable tends to be accompanied by an increase in the other. Negative correlations are also illustrated in **Figure 6.29**. If r is between 0 and -1, as in **(e)** and **(f)**, the two variables are negatively correlated, but not perfectly. Although all the data points will not lie on the regression line, as in **(g)**, an increase in one variable tends to be accompanied by a decrease in the other.

Blitzer Bonus

Beneficial Uses of Correlation Coefficients

- A Florida study showed a high positive correlation between the number of powerboats and the number of manatee deaths. Many of these deaths were seen to be caused by boats' propellers gashing into the manatees' bodies. Based on this study, Florida set up coastal sanctuaries where powerboats are prohibited so that these large gentle mammals that float just below the water's surface could thrive.
- Researchers studied how psychiatric patients readjusted to their community after their release from a mental hospital. A moderate positive correlation ($r = 0.38$) was found between patients' attractiveness and their postdischarge social adjustment. The better-looking patients were better off. The researchers suggested that physical attractiveness plays a role in patients' readjustment to community living because good-looking people tend to be treated better by others than homely people are.

EXAMPLE 1 *Interpreting a Correlation Coefficient*

In a 1971 study involving 232 subjects, researchers found a relationship between the subjects' level of stress and how often they became ill. The correlation coefficient in this study was 0.32. Does this indicate a strong relationship between stress and illness?

SOLUTION

The correlation coefficient $r = 0.32$ means that as stress increases, frequency of illness also tends to increase. However, 0.32 is only a moderate correlation, illustrated in **Figure 6.29(c)** on the previous page. There is not, based on this study, a strong relationship between stress and illness. In this study, the relationship is somewhat weak.

CHECK POINT 1 In a 1996 study involving obesity in mothers and daughters, researchers found a relationship between a high body-mass index for the girls and their mothers. (Body-mass index is a measure of weight relative to height. People with a high body-mass index are overweight or obese.) The correlation coefficient in this study was 0.51. Does this indicate a weak relationship between the body-mass index of daughters and the body-mass index of their mothers?

How to Obtain the Correlation Coefficient and the Equation of the Regression Line

The easiest way to find the correlation coefficient and the equation of the regression line is to use a graphing or statistical calculator. Graphing calculators have statistical menus that enable you to enter the x and y data items for the variables. Based on this information, you can instruct the calculator to display a scatter plot, the equation of the regression line, and the correlation coefficient.

We can also compute the correlation coefficient and the equation of the regression line by hand using formulas. First, we compute the correlation coefficient.

COMPUTING THE CORRELATION COEFFICIENT BY HAND

The following formula is used to calculate the correlation coefficient, r:

$$r = \frac{n(\Sigma xy) - (\Sigma x)(\Sigma y)}{\sqrt{n(\Sigma x^2) - (\Sigma x)^2}\sqrt{n(\Sigma y^2) - (\Sigma y)^2}}.$$

In the formula,

n = the number of data points, (x, y)
Σx = the sum of the x-values
Σy = the sum of the y-values
Σxy = the sum of the product of x and y in each pair
Σx^2 = the sum of the squares of the x-values
Σy^2 = the sum of the squares of the y-values
$(\Sigma x)^2$ = the square of the sum of the x-values
$(\Sigma y)^2$ = the square of the sum of the y-values

When computing the correlation coefficient by hand, organize your work in five columns:

x	y	xy	x^2	y^2

Find the sum of the numbers in each column. Then, substitute these values into the formula for r. Example 2 illustrates computing the correlation coefficient for the education-prejudice test data.

3 Compute the correlation coefficient.

EXAMPLE 2 *Computing the Correlation Coefficient*

Shown below are the data involving the number of years of school, x, completed by ten randomly selected people and their scores on a test measuring prejudice, y. Recall that higher scores on the measure of prejudice (1 to 10) indicate greater levels of prejudice. Determine the correlation coefficient between years of education and scores on a prejudice test.

Respondent	**A**	**B**	**C**	**D**	**E**	**F**	**G**	**H**	**I**	**J**
Years of education (x)	12	5	14	13	8	10	16	11	12	4
Score on prejudice test (y)	1	7	2	3	5	4	1	2	3	10

SOLUTION

As suggested, organize the work in five columns.

x	y	xy	x^2	y^2
12	1	12	144	1
5	7	35	25	49
14	2	28	196	4
13	3	39	169	9
8	5	40	64	25
10	4	40	100	16
16	1	16	256	1
11	2	22	121	4
12	3	36	144	9
4	10	40	16	100
$\Sigma x = 105$	$\Sigma y = 38$	$\Sigma xy = 308$	$\Sigma x^2 = 1235$	$\Sigma y^2 = 218$
Add all values in the x-column.	Add all values in the y-column.	Add all values in the xy-column.	Add all values in the x^2-column.	Add all values in the y^2-column.

We use these five sums to calculate the correlation coefficient.

Another value in the formula for r that we have not yet determined is n, the number of data points (x, y). Because there are ten items in the x-column and ten items in the y-column, the number of data points (x, y) is ten. Thus, $n = 10$.

In order to calculate r, we also need to find the square of the sum of the x-values and the y-values:

$$(\Sigma x)^2 = (105)^2 = 11{,}025 \quad \text{and} \quad (\Sigma y)^2 = (38)^2 = 1444.$$

TECHNOLOGY

Graphing Calculators, Scatter Plots, and Regression Lines

You can use a graphing calculator to display a scatter plot and the regression line. After entering the x and y data items for years of education and scores on a prejudice test, the calculator shows the scatter plot of the data and the regression line.

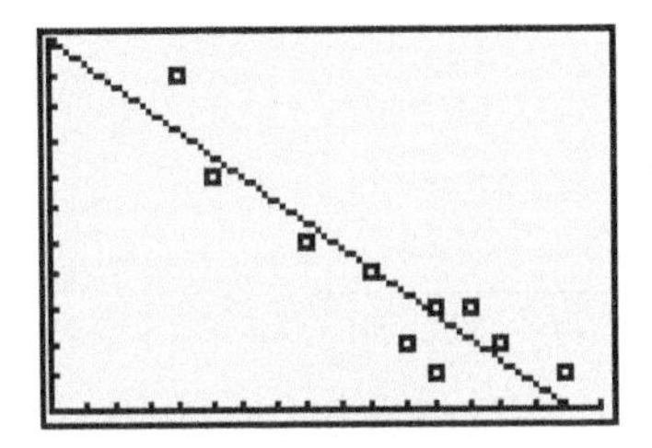

Also displayed below is the regression line's equation and the correlation coefficient, r. The slope shown below is approximately -0.69. The negative slope reinforces the fact that there is a negative correlation between the variables in Example 2.

We are ready to determine the value for r. We use the sums obtained on the previous page, with $n = 10$

$$r = \frac{n(\Sigma xy) - (\Sigma x)(\Sigma y)}{\sqrt{n(\Sigma x^2) - (\Sigma x)^2}\sqrt{n(\Sigma y^2) - (\Sigma y)^2}}$$

$$= \frac{10(308) - 105(38)}{\sqrt{10(1235) - 11{,}025}\sqrt{10(218) - 1444}}$$

$$= \frac{-910}{\sqrt{1325}\sqrt{736}}$$

$$\approx -0.92$$

The value for r, approximately -0.92, is fairly close to -1 and indicates a strong negative correlation. This means that the more education a person has, the less prejudiced that person is (based on scores on the test measuring levels of prejudice).

CHECK POINT 2 The points in the scatter plot in **Figure 6.30** show the number of firearms per 100 persons and the number of deaths per 100,000 persons for the ten industrialized countries with the highest death rates. Use the data displayed by the voice balloons to determine the correlation coefficient between these variables. Round to two decimal places. What does the correlation coefficient indicate about the strength and direction of the relationship between firearms per 100 persons and deaths per 100,000 persons?

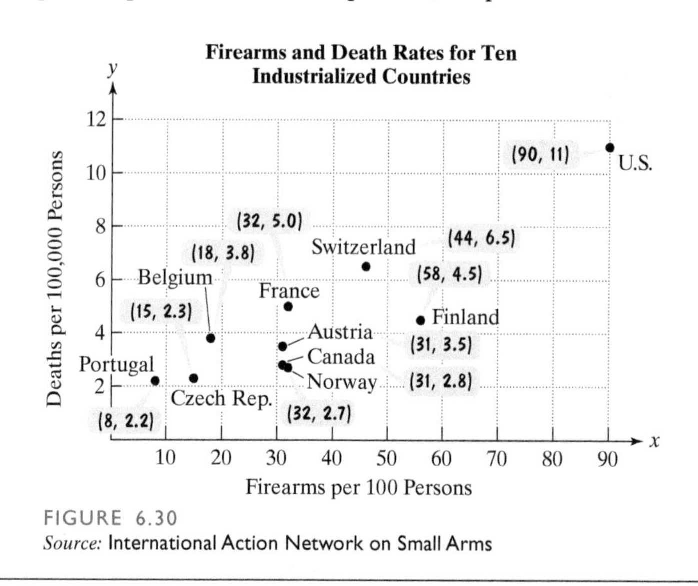

FIGURE 6.30
Source: International Action Network on Small Arms

Once we have determined that two variables are related, we can use the equation of the regression line to determine the exact relationship. Here is the formula for writing the equation of the line that best fits the data:

4 Write the equation of the regression line.

WRITING THE EQUATION OF THE REGRESSION LINE BY HAND

The equation of the regression line is

$$y = mx + b,$$

where

$$m = \frac{n(\Sigma xy) - (\Sigma x)(\Sigma y)}{n(\Sigma x^2) - (\Sigma x)^2} \quad \text{and} \quad b = \frac{\Sigma y - m(\Sigma x)}{n}.$$

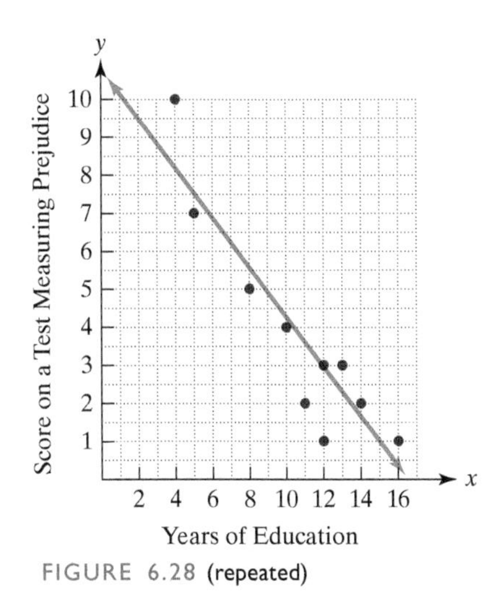

FIGURE 6.28 (repeated)

Why is $b \approx 11.05$ in Example 3, but $b \approx 11.01$ in the Technology box on page 265?

In Example 3, we rounded the value of m when we calculated b. The value of b on the calculator screen on page 265 is more accurate.

EXAMPLE 3 *Writing the Equation of the Regression Line*

a. Shown, again, in **Figure 6.28** is the scatter plot and the regression line for the data in Example 2. Use the data to find the equation of the regression line that relates years of education and scores on a prejudice test.

b. Approximately what score on the test can be anticipated by a person with nine years of education?

SOLUTION

a. We use the sums obtained in Example 2. We begin by computing m.

$$m = \frac{n(\Sigma xy) - (\Sigma x)(\Sigma y)}{n(\Sigma x^2) - (\Sigma x)^2} = \frac{10(308) - 105(38)}{10(1235) - (105)^2} = \frac{-910}{1325} \approx -0.69$$

With a negative correlation coefficient, it makes sense that the slope of the regression line is negative. This line falls from left to right, indicating a negative correlation.

Now, we find the y-intercept, b.

$$b = \frac{\Sigma y - m(\Sigma x)}{n} = \frac{38 - (-0.69)(105)}{10} = \frac{110.45}{10} \approx 11.05$$

Using $m \approx -0.69$ and $b \approx 11.05$, the equation of the regression line, $y = mx + b$, is

$$y = -0.69x + 11.05,$$

where x represents the number of years of education and y represents the score on the prejudice test.

b. To anticipate the score on the prejudice test for a person with nine years of education, substitute 9 for x in the regression line's equation.

$$y = -0.69x + 11.05$$
$$y = -0.69(9) + 11.05 = 4.84$$

A person with nine years of education is anticipated to have a score close to 5 on the prejudice test.

CHECK POINT 3 Use the data in **Figure 6.30** of Check Point 2 on page 266 to find the equation of the regression line. Round m and b to one decimal place. Then use the equation to project the number of deaths per 100,000 persons in a country with 80 firearms per 100 persons.

5 Use a sample's correlation coefficient to determine whether there is a correlation in the population.

The Level of Significance of r

In Example 2, we found a strong negative correlation between education and prejudice, computing the correlation coefficient, r, to be -0.92. However, the sample size ($n = 10$) was relatively small. With such a small sample, can we truly conclude that a correlation exists in the population? Or could it be that education and prejudice are not related? Perhaps the results we obtained were simply due to sampling error and chance.

Mathematicians have identified values to determine whether r, the correlation coefficient for a sample, can be attributed to a relationship between variables in the population. These values are shown in the second and third columns of

TABLE 6.19 Values for Determining Correlations in a Population

n	$\alpha = 0.05$	$\alpha = 0.01$
4	0.950	0.990
5	0.878	0.959
6	0.811	0.917
7	0.754	0.875
8	0.707	0.834
9	0.666	0.798
10	0.632	0.765
11	0.602	0.735
12	0.576	0.708
13	0.553	0.684
14	0.532	0.661
15	0.514	0.641
16	0.497	0.623
17	0.482	0.606
18	0.468	0.590
19	0.456	0.575
20	0.444	0.561
22	0.423	0.537
27	0.381	0.487
32	0.349	0.449
37	0.325	0.418
42	0.304	0.393
47	0.288	0.372
52	0.273	0.354
62	0.250	0.325
72	0.232	0.302
82	0.217	0.283
92	0.205	0.267
102	0.195	0.254

The larger the sample size, n, the smaller is the value of r needed for a correlation in the population.

Table 6.19. They depend on the sample size, n, listed in the left column. If $|r|$, the absolute value of the correlation coefficient computed for the sample, is greater than the value given in the table, a correlation exists between the variables in the population. The column headed $\alpha = 0.05$ denotes a **significance level of 5%**, meaning that there is a 0.05 probability that, when the statistician says the variables are correlated, they are actually not related in the population. The column on the right, headed $\alpha = 0.01$, denotes a **significance level of 1%**, meaning that there is a 0.01 probability that, when the statistician says the variables are correlated, they are actually not related in the population. Values in the $\alpha = 0.01$ column are greater than those in the $\alpha = 0.05$ column. Because of the possibility of sampling error, there is always a probability that when we say the variables are related, there is actually not a correlation in the population from which the sample was randomly selected.

EXAMPLE 4 *Determining a Correlation in the Population*

In Example 2, we computed $r = -0.92$ for $n = 10$. Can we conclude that there is a negative correlation between education and prejudice in the population?

SOLUTION

Begin by taking the absolute value of the calculated correlation coefficient.

$$|r| = |-0.92| = 0.92$$

Now, look to the right of $n = 10$ in **Table 6.19**. Because 0.92 is greater than both of these values (0.632 and 0.765), we may conclude that a correlation does exist between education and prejudice in the population. (There is a probability of at most 0.01 that the variables are not really correlated in the population and our results could be attributed to chance.)

Blitzer Bonus

Cigarettes and Lung Cancer

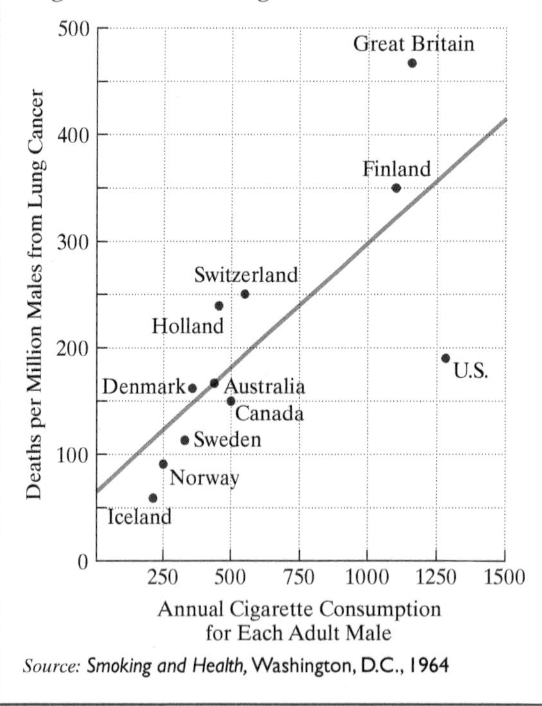

Source: Smoking and Health, Washington, D.C., 1964

This scatter plot shows a relationship between cigarette consumption among males and deaths due to lung cancer per million males. The data are from 11 countries and date back to a 1964 report by the U.S. Surgeon General. The scatter plot can be modeled by a line whose slope indicates an increasing death rate from lung cancer with increased cigarette consumption. At that time, the tobacco industry argued that in spite of this regression line, tobacco use is not the cause of cancer. Recent data do, indeed, show a causal effect between tobacco use and numerous diseases.

CHECK POINT 4 If you worked Check Point 2 correctly, you should have found that $r \approx 0.89$ for $n = 10$. Can you conclude that there is a positive correlation for all industrialized countries between firearms per 100 persons and deaths per 100,000 persons?

Concept and Vocabulary Check

Fill in each blank so that the resulting statement is true.

1. A set of points representing data is called a/an ____________.
2. The line that best fits a set of points is called a/an ____________.
3. A measure that is used to describe the strength and direction of a relationship between variables whose data points lie on or near a line is called the ________________, ranging from $r =$ ____________ to $r =$ ____________.

In Exercises 4–7, determine whether each statement is true or false. If the statement is false, make the necessary change(s) to produce a true statement.

4. If $r = 0$, there is no correlation between two variables. ______
5. If $r = 1$, changes in one variable cause changes in the other variable. ______
6. If $r = -0.1$, there is a strong negative correlation between two variables. ______
7. A significance level of 5% means that there is a 0.05 probability that when a statistician says that variables are correlated, they are actually not related in the population. ______

Exercise Set 6.6

Practice and Application Exercises

In Exercises 1–8, make a scatter plot for the given data. Use the scatter plot to describe whether or not the variables appear to be related.

1.

x	1	6	4	3	7	2
y	2	5	3	3	4	1

2.

x	2	1	6	3	4
y	4	5	10	8	9

3.

x	8	6	1	5	4	10	3
y	2	4	10	5	6	2	9

4.

x	4	5	2	1
y	1	3	5	4

5. HAMACHIPHOBIA

	Percentage Who	
Generation	**Won't Try Sushi** x	**Don't Approve of Marriage Equality** y
Millennials	42	36
Gen X	52	49
Boomers	60	59
Silent/Greatest Generation	72	66

Source: Pew Research Center

6. TREASURED CHEST: FILMS OF MATTHEW MCCONAUGHEY

Film	**Minutes Shirtless** x	**Opening Weekend Gross (millions of dollars)** y
We Are Marshall	0	6.1
EDtv	0.8	8.3
Reign of Fire	1.6	15.6
Sahara	1.8	18.1
Fool's Gold	14.6	21.6

Source: Entertainment Weekly

7. TEENAGE DRUG USE

	Percentage Who Have Used	
Country	**Marijuana** x	**Other Illegal Drugs** y
Czech Republic	22	4
Denmark	17	3
England	40	21
Finland	5	1
Ireland	37	16
Italy	19	8
Northern Ireland	23	14
Norway	6	3
Portugal	7	3
Scotland	53	31
United States	34	24

Source: De Veaux et.al., *Intro Stats,* Pearson, 2009.

8. LITERACY AND HUNGER

	Percentage Who Are	
	Literate	**Undernourished**
Country	x	y
Cuba	100	2
Egypt	71	4
Ethiopia	36	46
Grenada	96	7
Italy	98	2
Jamaica	80	9
Jordan	91	6
Pakistan	50	24
Russia	99	3
Togo	53	24
Uganda	67	19

Source: The Penguin State of the World Atlas, 2008

The scatter plot in the figure shows the relationship between the percentage of married women of child-bearing age using contraceptives and births per woman in selected countries. Use the scatter plot to determine whether each of the statements in Exercises 9–18 is true or false.

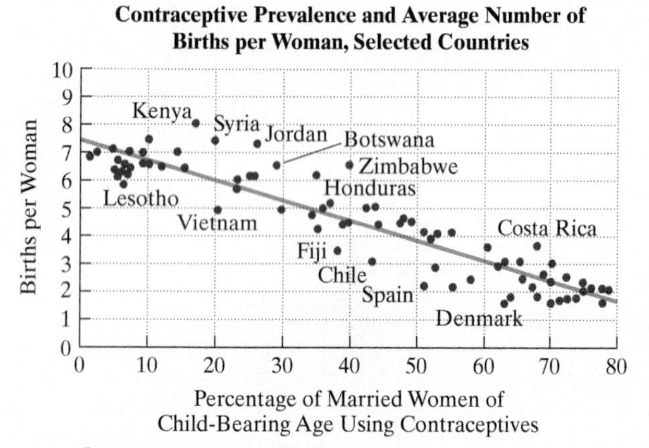

Source: Population Reference Bureau

9. There is a strong positive correlation between contraceptive use and births per woman.

10. There is no correlation between contraceptive use and births per woman.

11. There is a strong negative correlation between contraceptive use and births per woman.

12. There is a causal relationship between contraceptive use and births per woman.

13. With approximately 43% of women of child-bearing age using contraceptives, there are three births per woman in Chile.

14. With 20% of women of child-bearing age using contraceptives, there are six births per woman in Vietnam.

15. No two countries have a different number of births per woman with the same percentage of married women using contraceptives.

16. The country with the greatest number of births per woman also has the smallest percentage of women using contraceptives.

17. Most of the data points do not lie on the regression line.

18. The number of selected countries shown in the scatter plot is approximately 20.

Just as money doesn't buy happiness for individuals, the two don't necessarily go together for countries either. However, the scatter plot does show a relationship between a country's annual per capita income and the percentage of people in that country who call themselves "happy." Use the scatter plot to determine whether each of the statements in Exercises 19–26 is true or false.

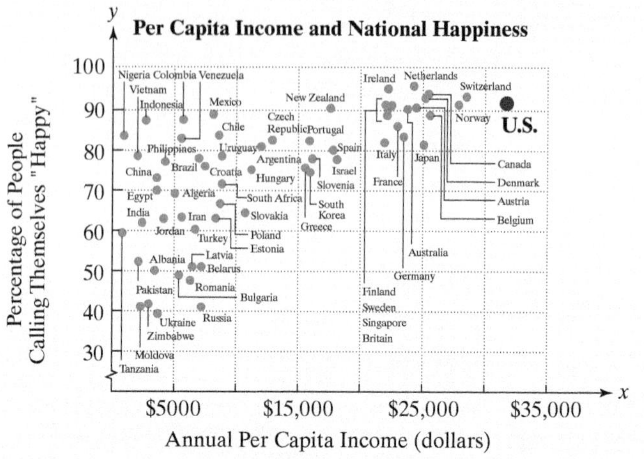

Source: Richard Layard, *Happiness: Lessons from a New Science*, Penguin, 2005

19. There is no correlation between per capita income and the percentage of people who call themselves "happy."

20. There is an almost-perfect positive correlation between per capita income and the percentage of people who call themselves "happy."

21. There is a positive correlation between per capita income and the percentage of people who call themselves "happy."

22. As per capita income decreases, the percentage of people who call themselves "happy" also tends to decrease.

23. The country with the lowest per capita income has the least percentage of people who call themselves "happy."

24. The country with the highest per capita income has the greatest percentage of people who call themselves "happy."

25. A reasonable estimate of the correlation coefficient for the data is 0.8.

26. A reasonable estimate of the correlation coefficient for the data is −0.3.

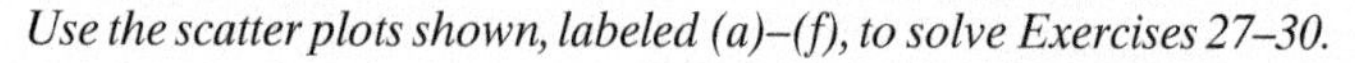

Use the scatter plots shown, labeled (a)–(f), to solve Exercises 27–30.

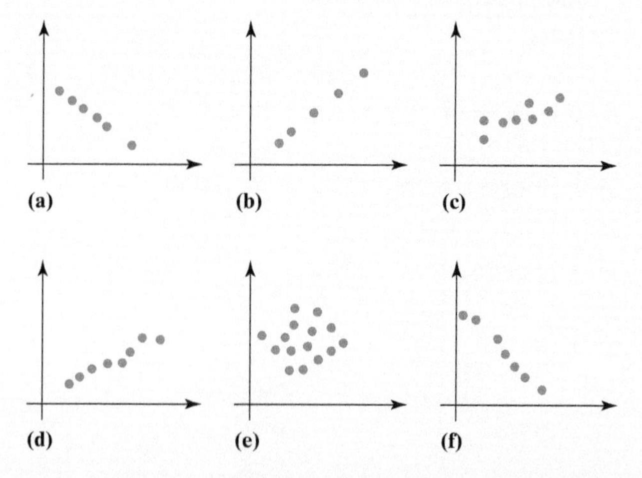

27. Which scatter plot indicates a perfect negative correlation?

28. Which scatter plot indicates a perfect positive correlation?

29. In which scatter plot is $r = 0.9$?

30. In which scatter plot is $r = 0.01$?

Compute r, the correlation coefficient, rounded to two decimal places, for the data in

31. Exercise 1.

32. Exercise 2.

33. Exercise 3.

34. Exercise 4.

35. Use the data in Exercise 5 to solve this exercise.

a. Determine the correlation coefficient, rounded to two decimal places, between the percentage of people who won't try sushi and the percentage who don't approve of marriage equality.

b. What explanations can you offer for the correlation coefficient in part (a)?

c. Find the equation of the regression line for the percentage who won't try sushi and the percentage who don't approve of marriage equality. Round m and b to two decimal places.

d. What percentage of people, to the nearest percent, can we anticipate do not approve of marriage equality in a generation where 30% won't try sushi?

36. Use the data in Exercise 6 to solve this exercise.

a. Determine the correlation coefficient, rounded to two decimal places, between the minutes Matthew McConaughey appeared shirtless in a film and the film's opening weekend gross.

b. Find the equation of the regression line for the minutes McConaughey appeared shirtless in a film and the film's opening weekend gross. Round m and b to two decimal places.

c. What opening weekend gross, to the nearest tenth of a million dollars, can we anticipate in a McConaughey film in which he appears shirtless for 20 minutes?

37. Use the data in Exercise 7 to solve this exercise.

a. Determine the correlation coefficient, rounded to two decimal places, between the percentage of teenagers who have used marijuana and the percentage who have used other drugs.

b. Find the equation of the regression line for the percentage of teenagers who have used marijuana and the percentage who have used other drugs. Round m and b to two decimal places.

c. What percentage of teenagers, to the nearest percent, can we anticipate using illegal drugs other than marijuana in a country where 10% of teenagers have used marijuana?

38. Use the data in Exercise 8 to solve this exercise.

a. Determine the correlation coefficient, rounded to two decimal places, between the percentage of people in a country who are literate and the percentage who are undernourished.

b. Find the equation of the regression line for the percentage who are literate and the percentage who are undernourished. Round m and b to two decimal places.

c. What percentage of people, to the nearest percent, can we anticipate are undernourished in a country where 60% of the people are literate?

In Exercises 39–45, the correlation coefficient, r, is given for a sample of n data points. Use the $\alpha = 0.05$ column in **Table 6.19** *on page 268 to determine whether or not we may conclude that a correlation does exist in the population. (Using the $\alpha = 0.05$ column, there is a probability of 0.05 that the variables are not really correlated in the population and our results could be attributed to chance. Ignore this possibility when concluding whether or not there is a correlation in the population.)*

39. $n = 20, r = 0.5$

40. $n = 27, r = 0.4$

41. $n = 12, r = 0.5$

42. $n = 22, r = 0.04$

43. $n = 72, r = -0.351$

44. $n = 37, r = -0.37$

45. $n = 20, r = -0.37$

46. In the 1964 study on cigarette consumption and deaths due to lung cancer (see the Blitzer Bonus on page 268), $n = 11$ and $r = 0.73$. What can you conclude using the $\alpha = 0.05$ column in **Table 6.19** on page 268?

Writing in Mathematics

47. What is a scatter plot?

48. How does a scatter plot indicate that two variables are correlated?

49. Give an example of two variables with a strong positive correlation and explain why this is so.

50. Give an example of two variables with a strong negative correlation and explain why this is so.

51. What is meant by a regression line?

52. When all points in a scatter plot fall on the regression line, what is the value of the correlation coefficient? Describe what this means.

For the pairs of quantities in Exercises 53–56, describe whether a scatter plot will show a positive correlation, a negative correlation, or no correlation. If there is a correlation, is it strong, moderate, or weak? Explain your answers.

53. Height and weight

54. Number of days absent and grade in a course

55. Height and grade in a course

56. Hours of television watched and grade in a course

57. Explain how to use the correlation coefficient for a sample to determine if there is a correlation in the population.

Critical Thinking Exercises

Make Sense? *In Exercises 58–61, determine whether each statement makes sense or does not make sense, and explain your reasoning.*

58. I found a strong positive correlation for the data in Exercise 7 relating the percentage of teenagers in various countries who have used marijuana and the percentage who have used other drugs. I concluded that using marijuana leads to the use of other drugs.

59. I found a strong negative correlation for the data in Exercise 8 relating the percentage of people in various countries who are literate and the percentage who are undernourished. I concluded that an increase in literacy causes a decrease in undernourishment.

60. I'm working with a data set for which the correlation coefficient and the slope of the regression line have opposite signs.

61. I read that there is a correlation of 0.72 between IQ scores of identical twins reared apart, so I would expect a significantly lower correlation, approximately 0.52, between IQ scores of identical twins reared together.

62. Give an example of two variables with a strong correlation, where each variable is not the cause of the other.

Technology Exercise

63. Use the linear regression feature of a graphing calculator to verify your work in any two exercises from Exercises 35–38, parts (a) and (b).

Group Exercises

64. The group should select two variables related to people on your campus that it believes have a strong positive or negative correlation. Once these variables have been determined,
    - **a.** Collect at least 30 ordered pairs of data (x, y) from a sample of people on your campus.
    - **b.** Draw a scatter plot for the data collected.
    - **c.** Does the scatter plot indicate a positive correlation, a negative correlation, or no relationship between the variables?
    - **d.** Calculate r. Does the value of r reinforce the impression conveyed by the scatter plot?
    - **e.** Find the equation of the regression line.
    - **f.** Use the regression line's equation to make a prediction about a y-value given an x-value.
    - **g.** Are the results of this project consistent with the group's original belief about the correlation between the variables, or are there some surprises in the data collected?

65. What is the opinion of students on your campus about . . .? Group members should begin by deciding on some aspect of college life around which student opinion can be polled. The poll should consist of the question, "What is your opinion of . . .?" Be sure to provide options such as excellent, good, average, poor, horrible, or a 1-to-10 scale, or possibly grades of A, B, C, D, F. Use a random sample of students on your campus and conduct the opinion survey. After collecting the data, present and interpret it using as many of the skills and techniques learned in this chapter as possible.

Chapter Summary, Review, and Test

SUMMARY – DEFINITIONS AND CONCEPTS	EXAMPLES
6.1 Sampling, Frequency Distributions, and Graphs	
a. A population is the set containing all objects whose properties are to be described and analyzed. A sample is a subset of the population.	Ex. 1, p. 207
b. Random samples are obtained in such a way that each member of the population has an equal chance of being selected.	Ex. 2, p. 208
c. Data can be organized and presented in frequency distributions, grouped frequency distributions, histograms, frequency polygons, and stem-and-leaf plots.	Ex. 3, p. 210; Ex. 4, p. 211; Figures 6.2 and 6.3, p. 212; Ex. 5, p. 212
d. The box on page 214 lists some things to watch for in visual displays of data.	Table 6.5, p. 215
6.2 Measures of Central Tendency	
a. The mean, $\bar{x}$, is the sum of the data items divided by the number of items: $\bar{x} = \frac{\Sigma x}{n}$.	Ex. 1, p. 220
b. The mean, $\bar{x}$, of a frequency distribution is computed using $\bar{x} = \frac{\Sigma xf}{n}$, where x is a data value, f is its frequency, and n is the total frequency of the distribution.	Ex. 2, p. 222
c. The median of ranked data is the item in the middle or the mean of the two middlemost items. The median is the value in the $\frac{n+1}{2}$ position in the list of ranked data.	Ex. 3, p. 223; Ex. 4, p. 224; Ex. 5, p. 225; Ex. 6, p. 226

d. When one or more data items are much greater than or much less than the other items, these extreme values greatly influence the mean, often making the median more representative of the data.	Ex. 7, p. 226
e. The mode of a data set is the value that occurs most often. If there is no such value, there is no mode. If more than one data value has the highest frequency, then each of these data values is a mode.	Ex. 8, p. 228
f. The midrange is computed using $\frac{\text{lowest data value} + \text{highest data value}}{2}$.	Ex. 9, p. 229; Ex. 10, p. 230

6.3 Measures of Dispersion

a. Range = highest data value − lowest data value	Ex. 1, p. 235
b. Standard deviation $= \sqrt{\frac{\Sigma(\text{data item} - \text{mean})^2}{n-1}}$ This is symbolized by $s = \sqrt{\frac{\Sigma(x-\bar{x})^2}{n-1}}$.	Ex. 2, p. 235; Ex. 3, p. 237; Ex. 4, p. 238
c. As the spread of data items increases, the standard deviation gets larger.	Ex. 5, p. 239

6.4 The Normal Distribution

a. The normal distribution is a theoretical distribution for the entire population. The distribution is bell shaped and symmetric about a vertical line through its center, where the mean, median, and mode are located.	
b. The 68–95–99.7 Rule Approximately 68% of the data items fall within 1 standard deviation of the mean. Approximately 95% of the data items fall within 2 standard deviations of the mean. Approximately 99.7% of the data items fall within 3 standard deviations of the mean.	Ex. 1, p. 244; Ex. 2, p. 245
c. A z-score describes how many standard deviations a data item in a normal distribution lies above or below the mean. $z\text{-score} = \frac{\text{data item} - \text{mean}}{\text{standard deviation}}$	Ex. 3, p. 246; Ex. 4, p. 247; Ex. 5, p. 248
d. If n% of the items in a distribution are less than a particular data item, that data item is in the nth percentile of the distribution. The 25th percentile is the first quartile, the 50th percentile, or the median, is the second quartile, and the 75th percentile is the third quartile.	Ex. 6, p. 249; Figure 6.16, p. 249
e. If a statistic is obtained from a random sample of size n, there is a 95% probability that it lies within $\frac{1}{\sqrt{n}} \times 100\%$ of the true population statistic. $\pm\frac{1}{\sqrt{n}} \times 100\%$ is called the margin of error.	Ex. 7, p. 250
f. A distribution of data is skewed if a large number of data items are piled up at one end or the other, with a "tail" at the opposite end.	Figure 6.21, p. 252; Figure 6.22, p. 252

6.5 Problem Solving with the Normal Distribution

a. A table showing z-scores and their percentiles can be used to find the percentage of data items less than or greater than a given data item in a normal distribution, as well as the percentage of data items between two given items. See the boxed summary on computing percentage of data items on page 260.	Ex. 1, p. 257; Ex. 2, p. 258; Ex. 3, p. 259

6.6 Scatter Plots, Correlation, and Regression Lines

a. A plot of data points is called a scatter plot. If the points lie approximately along a line, the line that best fits the data is called a regression line.	
b. A correlation coefficient, r, measures the strength and direction of a possible relationship between variables. If $r = 1$, there is a perfect positive correlation, and if $r = -1$, there is a perfect negative correlation. If $r = 0$, there is no relationship between the variables. Table 6.19 on page 268 indicates whether r denotes a correlation in the population.	Ex. 1, p. 264; Ex. 4, p. 268
c. The formula for computing the correlation coefficient, r, is given in the box on page 264. The equation of the regression line is given in the box on page 266.	Ex. 2, p. 265; Ex. 3, p. 267

Review Exercises

6.1

1. The government of a large city wants to know if its citizens will support a three-year tax increase to provide additional support to the city's community college system. The government decides to conduct a survey of the city's residents before placing a tax increase initiative on the ballot. Which one of the following is most appropriate for obtaining a sample of the city's residents?
   a. Survey a random sample of persons within each geographic region of the city.
   b. Survey a random sample of community college professors living in the city.
   c. Survey every tenth person who walks into the city's government center on two randomly selected days of the week.
   d. Survey a random sample of persons within each geographic region of the state in which the city is located.

A random sample of ten college students is selected and each student is asked how much time he or she spent on homework during the previous weekend. The following times, in hours, are obtained:

8, 10, 9, 7, 9, 8, 7, 6, 8, 7.

Use these data items to solve Exercises 2–4.

2. Construct a frequency distribution for the data.
3. Construct a histogram for the data.
4. Construct a frequency polygon for the data.

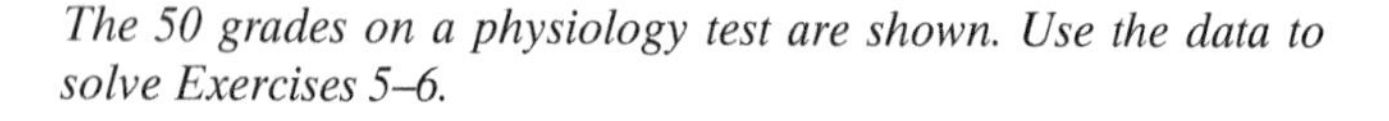

The 50 grades on a physiology test are shown. Use the data to solve Exercises 5–6.

44	24	54	81	18
34	39	63	67	60
72	36	91	47	75
57	74	87	49	86
59	14	26	41	90
13	29	13	31	68
63	35	29	70	22
95	17	50	42	27
73	11	42	31	69
56	40	31	45	51

5. Construct a grouped frequency distribution for the data. Use 0–39 for the first class, 40–49 for the second class, and make each subsequent class width the same as the second class.
6. Construct a stem-and-leaf plot for the data.

7. Describe what is misleading about the size of the barrels in the following visual display.

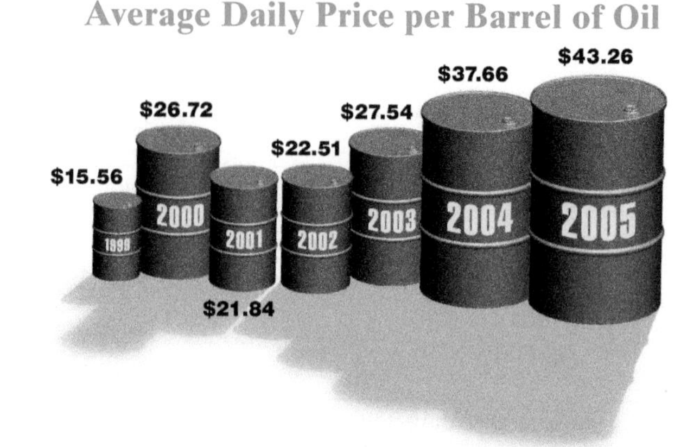

Source: U.S. Department of Energy

6.2

In Exercises 8–9, find the mean for each group of data items.

8. 84, 90, 95, 89, 98
9. 33, 27, 9, 10, 6, 7, 11, 23, 27
10. Find the mean for the data items in the given frequency distribution.

Score x	Frequency f
1	2
2	4
3	3
4	1

In Exercises 11–12, find the median for each group of data items.

11. 33, 27, 9, 10, 6, 7, 11, 23, 27
12. 28, 16, 22, 28, 34
13. Find the median for the data items in the frequency distribution in Exercise 10.

In Exercises 14–15, find the mode for each group of data items. If there is no mode, so state.

14. 33, 27, 9, 10, 6, 7, 11, 23, 27
15. 582, 585, 583, 585, 587, 587, 589
16. Find the mode for the data items in the frequency distribution in Exercise 10.

In Exercises 17–18, find the midrange for each group of data items.

17. 84, 90, 95, 88, 98
18. 33, 27, 9, 10, 6, 7, 11, 23, 27
19. Find the midrange for the data items in the frequency distribution in Exercise 10.

20. A student took seven tests in a course, scoring between 90% and 95% on three of the tests, between 80% and 89% on three of the tests, and below 40% on one of the tests. In this distribution, is the mean or the median more representative of the student's overall performance in the course? Explain your answer.

21. The data items below are the ages of U.S. presidents at the time of their first inauguration.

57 61 57 57 58 57 61 54 68 51 49 64 50 48
65 52 56 46 54 49 51 47 55 55 54 42 51 56
55 51 54 51 60 62 43 55 56 61 52 69 64 46 54 47

a. Organize the data in a frequency distribution.
b. Use the frequency distribution to find the mean age, median age, modal age, and midrange age of the presidents when they were inaugurated.

In Exercises 22–23, find the range for each group of data items.

22. 28, 34, 16, 22, 28

23. 312, 783, 219, 312, 426, 219

24. The mean for the data items 29, 9, 8, 22, 46, 51, 48, 42, 53, 42 is 35. Find **a.** the deviation from the mean for each data item and **b.** the sum of the deviations in part (a).

25. Use the data items 36, 26, 24, 90, and 74 to find **a.** the mean, **b.** the deviation from the mean for each data item, and **c.** the sum of the deviations in part (b).

In Exercises 26–27, find the standard deviation for each group of data items.

26. 3, 3, 5, 8, 10, 13

27. 20, 27, 23, 26, 28, 32, 33, 35

28. A test measuring anxiety levels is administered to a sample of ten college students with the following results. (High scores indicate high anxiety.)

10, 30, 37, 40, 43, 44, 45, 69, 86, 86

Find the mean, range, and standard deviation for the data.

29. Compute the mean and the standard deviation for each of the following data sets. Then, write a brief description of similarities and differences between the two sets based on each of your computations.

Set A: 80, 80, 80, 80 Set B: 70, 70, 90, 90

30. Describe how you would determine
a. which of the two groups, men or women, at your college has a higher mean grade point average.
b. which of the groups is more consistently close to its mean grade point average.

6.4

The scores on a test are normally distributed with a mean of 70 and a standard deviation of 8. In Exercises 31–33, find the score that is

31. 2 standard deviations above the mean.

32. $3\frac{1}{2}$ standard deviations above the mean.

33. $1\frac{1}{4}$ standard deviations below the mean.

The ages of people living in a retirement community are normally distributed with a mean age of 68 years and a standard deviation of 4 years. In Exercises 34–40, use the 68–95–99.7 Rule to find the percentage of people in the community whose ages

34. are between 64 and 72.

35. are between 60 and 76.

36. are between 68 and 72.

37. are between 56 and 80.

38. exceed 72.

39. are less than 72.

40. exceed 76.

A set of data items is normally distributed with a mean of 50 and a standard deviation of 5. In Exercises 41–45, convert each data item to a z-score.

41. 50 **42.** 60

43. 58 **44.** 35

45. 44

46. A student scores 60 on a vocabulary test and 80 on a grammar test. The data items for both tests are normally distributed. The vocabulary test has a mean of 50 and a standard deviation of 5. The grammar test has a mean of 72 and a standard deviation of 6. On which test did the student have the better score? Explain why this is so.

The number of miles that a particular brand of car tires lasts is normally distributed with a mean of 32,000 miles and a standard deviation of 4000 miles. In Exercises 47–49, find the data item in this distribution that corresponds to the given z-score.

47. $z = 1.5$

48. $z = 2.25$

49. $z = -2.5$

50. Using a random sample of 2281 American adults ages 18 and older, an Adecco survey asked respondents if they would be willing to sacrifice a percentage of their salary in order to work for an environmentally friendly company. The poll indicated that 31% of the respondents said "yes," 39% said "no," and 30% declined to answer.
a. Find the margin of error, to the nearest tenth of a percent, for this survey.
b. Write a statement about the percentage of American adults who would be willing to sacrifice a percentage of their salary in order to work for an environmentally friendly company.

51. The histogram indicates the frequencies of the number of syllables per word for 100 randomly selected words in Japanese.

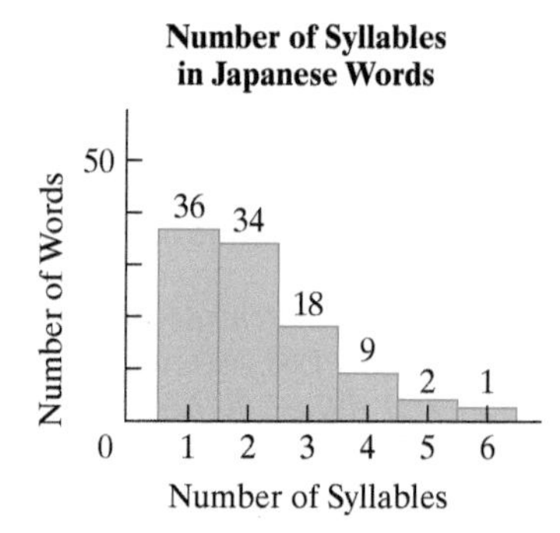

a. Is the shape of this distribution best classified as normal, skewed to the right, or skewed to the left?

b. Find the mean, median, and mode for the number of syllables in the sample of Japanese words.

c. Are the measures of central tendency from part (b) consistent with the shape of the distribution that you described in part (a)? Explain your answer.

6.5

The mean cholesterol level for all men in the United States is 200 and the standard deviation is 15. In Exercises 52–55, use **Table 6.17** *on page 256 to find the percentage of U.S. men whose cholesterol level*

52. is less than 221.

53. is greater than 173.

54. is between 173 and 221.

55. is between 164 and 182.

Use the percentiles for the weights of adult men over 40 to solve Exercises 56–58.

Weight	Percentile
235	86
227	third quartile
180	second quartile
173	first quartile

Find the percentage of men over 40 who weigh

56. less than 227 pounds.

57. more than 235 pounds.

58. between 227 and 235 pounds.

6.6

In Exercises 59–60, make a scatter plot for the given data. Use the scatter plot to describe whether or not the variables appear to be related.

59.

x	1	3	4	6	8	9
y	1	2	3	3	5	5

60.

Country	Canada	U.S.	Mexico	Brazil	Costa Rica
Life expectancy in years, x	81	78	76	72	77
Infant deaths per 1000 births, y	5.1	6.3	19.0	23.3	9.0

Denmark	China	Egypt	Pakistan	Bangla-desh	Australia	Japan	Russia
78	73	72	64	63	82	82	66
4.4	21.2	28.4	66.9	57.5	4.8	2.8	10.8

Source: U.S. Bureau of the Census International Database

The scatter plot shows the relationship between the percentage of adult females in a country who are literate and the mortality of children under five. Also shown is the regression line. Use this information to determine whether each of the statements in Exercises 61–67 is true or false.

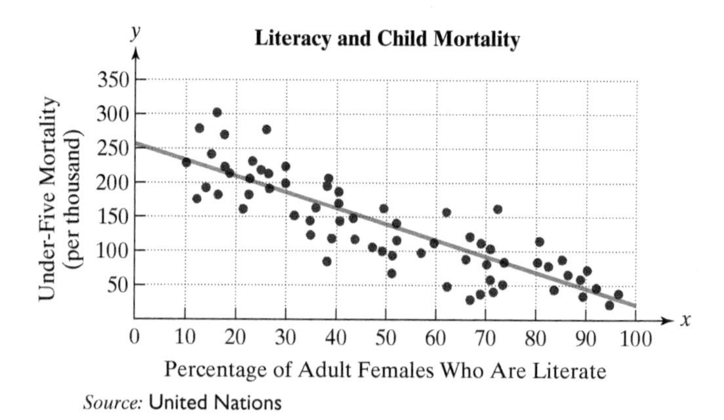

Source: United Nations

61. There is a perfect negative correlation between the percentage of adult females who are literate and under-five mortality.

62. As the percentage of adult females who are literate increases, under-five mortality tends to decrease.

63. The country with the least percentage of adult females who are literate has the greatest under-five mortality.

64. No two countries have the same percentage of adult females who are literate but different under-five mortalities.

65. There are more than 20 countries in this sample.

66. There is no correlation between the percentage of adult females who are literate and under-five mortality.

67. The country with the greatest percentage of adult females who are literate has an under-five mortality rate that is less than 50 children per thousand.

68. Which one of the following scatter plots indicates a correlation coefficient of approximately -0.9?

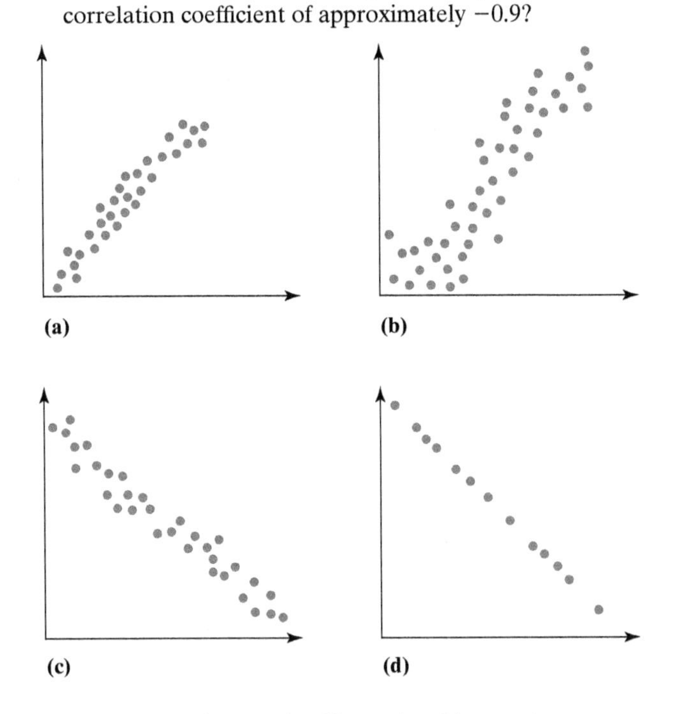

69. Use the data in Exercise 59 to solve this exercise.

a. Compute r, the correlation coefficient, rounded to the nearest thousandth.

b. Find the equation of the regression line.

70. The graph, based on Nielsen Media Research data taken from random samples of Americans at various ages, indicates that as we get older, we watch more television.

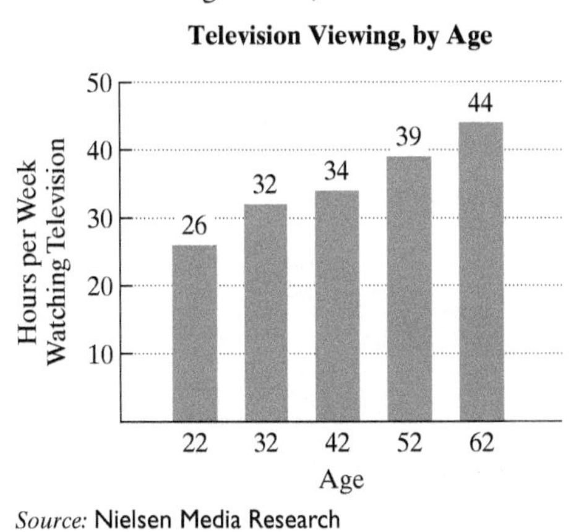

Source: Nielsen Media Research

a. Let x represent one's age and let y represent hours per week watching television. Calculate the correlation coefficient.

b. Using **Table 6.19** on page 268 and the $\alpha = 0.05$ column, determine whether there is a correlation between age and time spent watching television in the American population.

Chapter 6 Test

1. Politicians in the Florida Keys need to know if the residents of Key Largo think the amount of money charged for water is reasonable. The politicians decide to conduct a survey of a sample of Key Largo's residents. Which procedure would be most appropriate for a sample of Key Largo's residents?

a. Survey all water customers who pay their water bills at Key Largo City Hall on the third day of the month.

b. Survey a random sample of executives who work for the water company in Key Largo.

c. Survey 5000 individuals who are randomly selected from a list of all people living in Georgia and Florida.

d. Survey a random sample of persons within each neighborhood of Key Largo.

Use these scores on a ten-point quiz to solve Exercises 2–4.

8, 5, 3, 6, 5, 10, 6, 9, 4, 5, 7, 9, 7, 4, 8, 8

2. Construct a frequency distribution for the data.

3. Construct a histogram for the data.

4. Construct a frequency polygon for the data.

Use the 30 test scores listed below to solve Exercises 5–6.

79	51	67	50	78
62	89	83	73	80
88	48	60	71	79
89	63	55	93	71
41	81	46	50	61
59	50	90	75	61

5. Construct a grouped frequency distribution for the data. Use 40–49 for the first class and use the same width for each subsequent class.

6. Construct a stem-and-leaf display for the data.

7. The graph shows the percentage of students in the United States through grade 12 who were home-schooled in 1999 and 2007. What impression does the roofline in the visual display imply about what occurred in 2000 through 2006? How might this be misleading?

Source: National Center for Education Statistics

Use the six data items listed below to solve Exercises 8–11.

3, 6, 2, 1, 7, 3

8. Find the mean.
9. Find the median.
10. Find the midrange.
11. Find the standard deviation.

Use the frequency distribution shown to solve Exercises 12–14.

Score x	Frequency f
1	3
2	5
3	2
4	2

12. Find the mean.
13. Find the median.
14. Find the mode.
15. The annual salaries of four salespeople and the owner of a bookstore are

$17,500, $19,000, $22,000, $27,500, $98,500.

Is the mean or the median more representative of the five annual salaries? Briefly explain your answer.

According to the American Freshman, *the number of hours that college freshmen spend studying each week is normally distributed with a mean of 7 hours and a standard deviation of 5.3 hours. In Exercises 16–17, use the 68–95–99.7 Rule to find the percentage of college freshmen who study*

16. between 7 and 12.3 hours each week.
17. more than 17.6 hours each week.
18. IQ scores are normally distributed in the population. Who has a higher IQ: a student with a 120 IQ on a scale where 100 is the mean and 10 is the standard deviation, or a professor with a 128 IQ on a scale where 100 is the mean and 15 is the standard deviation? Briefly explain your answer.
19. Use the z-scores and the corresponding percentiles shown at the top of the next column to solve this exercise. Test scores are normally distributed with a mean of 74 and a standard deviation of 10. What percentage of the scores are above 88?

z-Score	Percentile
1.1	86.43
1.2	88.49
1.3	90.32
1.4	91.92
1.5	93.32

20. Use the percentiles in the table shown below to find the percentage of scores between 630 and 690.

Score	Percentile
780	99
750	87
720	72
690	49
660	26
630	8
600	1

21. Using a random sample of 100 students from a campus of approximately 12,000 students, 60% of the students in the sample said they were very satisfied with their professors.
    a. Find the margin of error in this percent.
    b. Write a statement about the percentage of the entire population of students from this campus who are very satisfied with their professors.
22. Make a scatter plot for the given data. Use the scatter plot to describe whether or not the variables appear to be related.

x	1	4	3	5	2
y	5	2	2	1	4

The scatter plot shows the number of minutes each of 16 people exercise per μweek and the number of headaches per month each person experiences. Use the scatter plot to determine whether each of the statements in Exercises 23–25 is true or false.

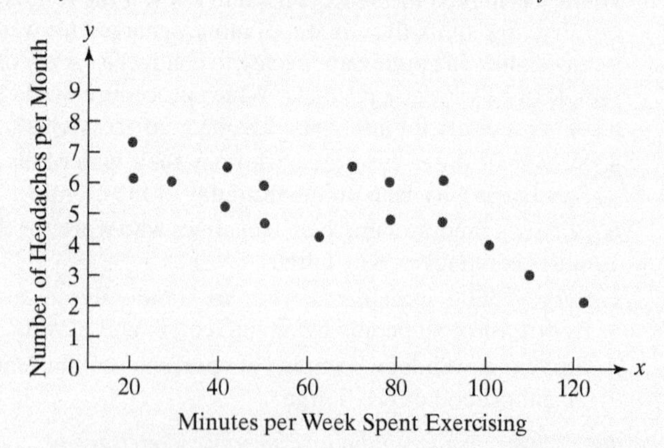

23. An increase in the number of minutes devoted to exercise causes a decrease in headaches.
24. There is a perfect negative correlation between time spent exercising and number of headaches.
25. The person who exercised most per week had the least number of headaches per month.
26. Is the relationship between the price of gas and the number of people visiting our national parks a positive correlation, a negative correlation, or is there no correlation? Explain your answer.

7

Personal Finance

"I realize, of course, that it's no shame to be poor, but it's no great honor either. So what would have been so terrible if I had a small fortune?"

—Tevye, a poor dairyman, in the musical *Fiddler on the Roof*

WE ALL WANT A WONDERFUL LIFE WITH FULFILLING WORK, GOOD HEALTH, AND loving relationships. And let's be honest: Financial security, or even a small fortune, wouldn't hurt! Achieving this goal depends on understanding basic ideas about savings, loans, and investments. A solid understanding of the topics in this chapter can pay, literally, by making your financial goals a reality.

Here's where you'll find these applications:

A number of examples illustrate how to attain fortunes ranging from over a half-million dollars to $4 million through regular savings. See Example 3 in Section 7.5 and Exercises 33–36 in Exercise Set 7.5.

7.1

WHAT AM I SUPPOSED TO LEARN?

After you have read this section, you should be able to:

1. Express a fraction as a percent.
2. Express a decimal as a percent.
3. Express a percent as a decimal.
4. Solve applied problems involving sales tax and discounts.
5. Determine percent increase or decrease.
6. Investigate some of the ways percent can be abused.

Percent, Sales Tax, and Discounts

"And if elected, it is my solemn pledge to cut your taxes by 10% for each of my first three years in office, for a total cut of 30%."

PERSONAL FINANCE INCLUDES every area of your life that involves money. It's about what you do with your money and how financial management will affect your future. Because an understanding of *percent* plays an important role in personal finance, we open the chapter with a discussion on the meaning, uses, and abuses of percent.

Basics of Percent

Kinds of Textbooks College Students Prefer: Preferences per 100 Students

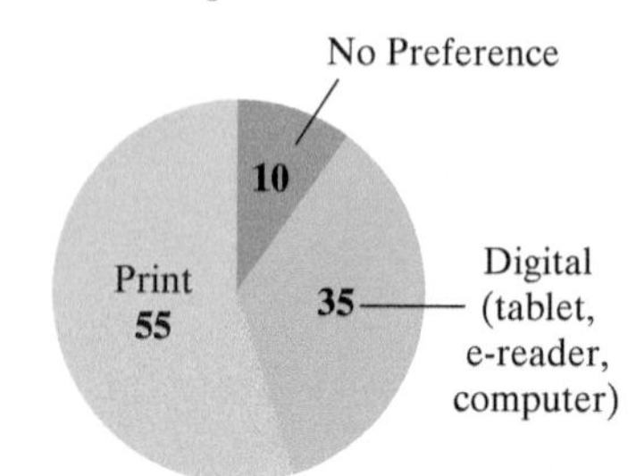

FIGURE 7.1
Source: Harris Interactive for Pearson Foundation

Percents are the result of expressing numbers as part of 100. The word *percent* means *per hundred.* For example, the circle graph in **Figure 7.1** shows that 55 out of every 100 college students prefer print textbooks. Thus, $\frac{55}{100} = 55\%$, indicating that 55% of college students prefer print textbooks. The percent sign, %, is used to indicate the number of parts out of 100 parts.

A fraction can be expressed as a percent using the following procedure:

1 Express a fraction as a percent.

EXPRESSING A FRACTION AS A PERCENT

1. Divide the numerator by the denominator.
2. Multiply the quotient by 100. This is done by moving the decimal point in the quotient two places to the right.
3. Add a percent sign.

EXAMPLE 1 *Expressing a Fraction as a Percent*

Express $\frac{5}{8}$ as a percent.

SOLUTION

Step 1 Divide the numerator by the denominator.

$$5 \div 8 = 0.625$$

Step 2 Multiply the quotient by 100.

$$0.625 \times 100 = 62.5$$

Step 3 Attach a percent sign.

$$62.5\%$$

Thus, $\frac{5}{8} = 62.5\%$.

CHECK POINT 1 Express $\frac{1}{8}$ as a percent.

2 Express a decimal as a percent.

Our work in Example 1 shows that $0.625 = 62.5\%$. This illustrates the procedure for expressing a decimal number as a percent.

EXPRESSING A DECIMAL NUMBER AS A PERCENT

1. Move the decimal point two places to the right.
2. Attach a percent sign.

GREAT QUESTION!

What's the difference between the word *percentage* and the word *percent*?

Dictionaries indicate that the word *percentage* has the same meaning as the word *percent*. Use the word that sounds better in the circumstance.

EXAMPLE 2 Expressing a Decimal as a Percent

Express 0.47 as a percent.

SOLUTION

Move decimal point two places right.

$$0.47\ \%$$ Attach a percent sign.

Thus, $0.47 = 47\%$.

CHECK POINT 2 Express 0.023 as a percent.

3 Express a percent as a decimal.

We reverse the procedure of Example 2 to express a percent as a decimal number.

EXPRESSING A PERCENT AS A DECIMAL NUMBER

1. Move the decimal point two places to the left.
2. Remove the percent sign.

EXAMPLE 3 Expressing Percents as Decimals

Express each percent as a decimal:

a. 19% **b.** 180%.

SOLUTION

Use the two steps in the box.

a.

$$19\% = 19.\% = 0.19\%$$

The percent sign is removed.

The decimal point starts at the far right.

The decimal point is moved two places to the left.

Thus, $19\% = 0.19$.

b. $180\% = 1.80\% = 1.80$ or 1.8

CHECK POINT 3 Express each percent as a decimal:

a. 67% **b.** 250%.

If a fraction is part of a percent, as in $\frac{1}{4}\%$, begin by expressing the fraction as a decimal, retaining the percent sign. Then, express the percent as a decimal number. For example,

$$\frac{1}{4}\% = 0.25\% = 00.25\% = 0.0025.$$

GREAT QUESTION!

Can I expect to have lots of zeros when expressing a small percent as a decimal?

Yes. Be careful with the zeros. For example,

$$\frac{1}{100}\% = 0.01\% = 00.01\% = 0.0001.$$

4 Solve applied problems involving sales tax and discounts.

Percent, Sales Tax, and Discounts

Many applications involving percent are based on the following formula:

$$A \text{ is } P \text{ percent of } B.$$

$$A = P \cdot B.$$

Note that the word *of* implies multiplication.

We can use this formula to determine the **sales tax** collected by states, counties, and cities on sales of items to customers. The sales tax is a percent of the cost of an item.

$$\text{Sales tax amount} = \text{tax rate} \times \text{item's cost}$$

EXAMPLE 4 *Percent and Sales Tax*

Suppose that the local sales tax rate is 7.5% and you purchase a bicycle for $894.

a. How much tax is paid?

b. What is the bicycle's total cost?

SOLUTION

a. $\text{Sales tax amount} = \text{tax rate} \times \text{item's cost}$

$$= 7.5\% \times \$894 = 0.075 \times \$894 = \$67.05$$

7.5% of the item's cost, or 7.5% of $894

The tax paid is $67.05.

b. The bicycle's total cost is the purchase price, $894, plus the sales tax, $67.05.

$$\text{Total cost} = \$894.00 + \$67.05 = \$961.05$$

The bicycle's total cost is $961.05.

CHECK POINT 4 Suppose that the local sales tax rate is 6% and you purchase a computer for $1260.

a. How much tax is paid?

b. What is the computer's total cost?

None of us is thrilled about sales tax, but we do like buying things that are *on sale*. Businesses reduce prices, or **discount**, to attract customers and to reduce inventory. The discount rate is a percent of the original price.

$$\text{Discount amount} = \text{discount rate} \times \text{original price}$$

EXAMPLE 5 *Percent and Sales Price*

A computer with an original price of $1460 is on sale at 15% off.

a. What is the discount amount?

b. What is the computer's sale price?

TECHNOLOGY

A calculator is useful, and sometimes essential, in this chapter. The keystroke sequence that gives the sale price in Example 5 is

1460 [−] .15 [×] 1460.

Press [=] or [ENTER] to display the answer, 1241.

SOLUTION

a. Discount amount = discount rate × original price

$$= 15\% \times \$1460 = 0.15 \times \$1460 = \$219$$

15% of the original price, or 15% of $1460

The discount amount is $219.

b. The computer's sale price is the original price, $1460, minus the discount amount, $219.

$$\text{Sale price} = \$1460 - \$219 = \$1241$$

The computer's sale price is $1241.

CHECK POINT 5 A CD player with an original price of $380 is on sale at 35% off.

a. What is the discount amount?

b. What is the CD player's sale price?

GREAT QUESTION!

Do I have to determine the discount amount before finding the sale price?

No. For example, in Example 5 the computer is on sale at 15% off. This means that the sale price must be 100% − 15%, or 85%, of the original price.

$$\text{Sale price} = 85\% \times \$1460 = 0.85 \times \$1460 = \$1241$$

5 Determine percent increase or decrease.

Percent and Change

Percents are used for comparing changes, such as increases or decreases in sales, population, prices, and production. If a quantity changes, its **percent increase** or its **percent decrease** can be found as follows:

FINDING PERCENT INCREASE OR PERCENT DECREASE

1. Find the fraction for the percent increase or the percent decrease:

$$\frac{\text{amount of increase}}{\text{original amount}} \quad \text{or} \quad \frac{\text{amount of decrease}}{\text{original amount}}.$$

2. Find the percent increase or the percent decrease by expressing the fraction in step 1 as a percent.

EXAMPLE 6 *Finding Percent Increase and Decrease*

In 2000, world population was approximately 6 billion. **Figure 7.2** shows world population projections through the year 2150. The data are from the United Nations Family Planning Program and are based on optimistic or pessimistic expectations for successful control of human population growth.

a. Find the percent increase in world population from 2000 to 2150 using the high projection data.

b. Find the percent decrease in world population from 2000 to 2150 using the low projection data.

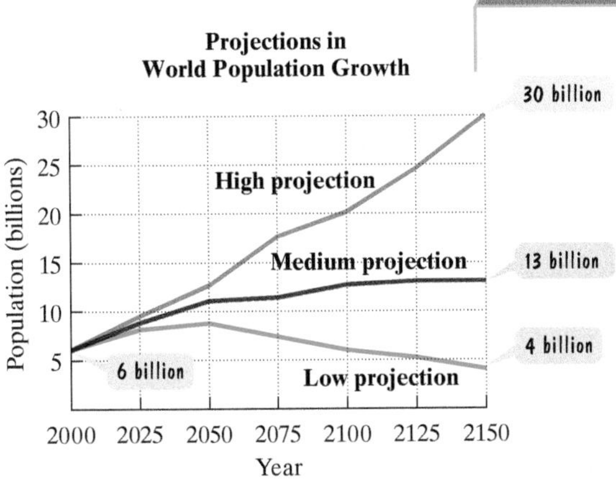

FIGURE 7.2
Source: United Nations

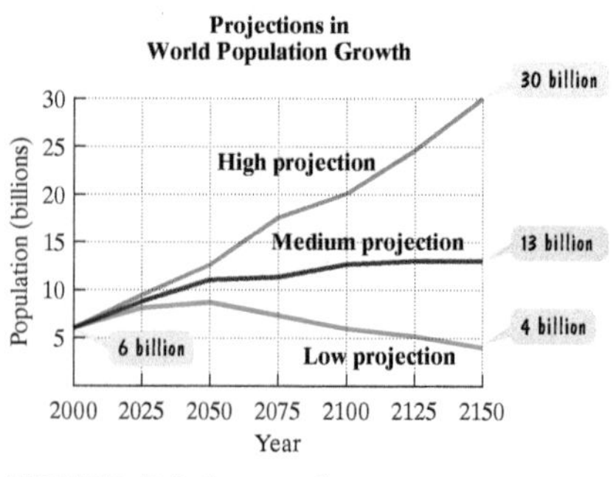

FIGURE 7.2 (repeated)

SOLUTION

a. Use the data shown on the blue, high-projection, graph.

$$\text{Percent increase} = \frac{\text{amount of increase}}{\text{original amount}}$$

$$= \frac{30 - 6}{6} = \frac{24}{6} = 4 = 400\%$$

The projected percent increase in world population is 400%.

b. Use the data shown on the green, low-projection, graph.

$$\text{Percent decrease} = \frac{\text{amount of decrease}}{\text{original amount}}$$

$$= \frac{6 - 4}{6} = \frac{2}{6} = \frac{1}{3} = 0.33\frac{1}{3} = 33\frac{1}{3}\%$$

The projected percent decrease in world population is $33\frac{1}{3}\%$.

In Example 6, we expressed the percent decrease as $33\frac{1}{3}\%$ because of the familiar conversion $\frac{1}{3} = 0.33\frac{1}{3}$. However, in many situations, rounding is needed. We suggest that you round to the nearest tenth of a percent. Carry the division in the fraction for percent increase or decrease to four places after the decimal point. Then round the decimal to three places, or to the nearest thousandth. Expressing this rounded decimal as a percent gives percent increase or decrease to the nearest tenth of a percent.

GREAT QUESTION!

I know that increasing 2 to 8 is a 300% increase. Does that mean decreasing 8 to 2 is a 300% decrease?

No. Notice the difference between the following examples:

- 2 is increased to 8.

$$\text{Percent increase} = \frac{\text{amount of increase}}{\text{original amount}} = \frac{6}{2} = 3 = 300\%$$

- 8 is decreased to 2.

$$\text{Percent decrease} = \frac{\text{amount of decrease}}{\text{original amount}} = \frac{6}{8} = \frac{3}{4} = 0.75 = 75\%$$

Although an increase from 2 to 8 is a 300% increase, a decrease from 8 to 2 is *not* a 300% decrease. **A percent decrease involving nonnegative quantities can never exceed 100%.** When a quantity is decreased by 100%, it is reduced to zero.

CHECK POINT 6

a. If 6 is increased to 10, find the percent increase.

b. If 10 is decreased to 6, find the percent decrease.

EXAMPLE 7 *Finding Percent Decrease*

A jacket regularly sells for \$135.00. The sale price is \$60.75. Find the percent decrease of the sale price from the regular price.

SOLUTION

$$\text{Percent decrease} = \frac{\text{amount of decrease}}{\text{original amount}}$$

$$= \frac{135.00 - 60.75}{135} = \frac{74.25}{135} = 0.55 = 55\%$$

The percent decrease of the sale price from the regular price is 55%. This means that the sale price of the jacket is 55% lower than the regular price.

CHECK POINT 7 A television regularly sells for $940. The sale price is $611. Find the percent decrease of the sale price from the regular price.

6 Investigate some of the ways percent can be abused.

Abuses of Percent

In our next examples, we look at a few of the many ways that percent can be used incorrectly. Confusion often arises when percent increase (or decrease) refers to a changing quantity that is itself a percent.

EXAMPLE 8 *Percents of Percents*

John Tesh, while he was still coanchoring *Entertainment Tonight*, reported that the PBS series *The Civil War* had an audience of 13% versus the usual 4% PBS audience, "an increase of more than 300%." Did Tesh report the percent increase correctly?

SOLUTION

We begin by finding the percent increase.

$$\text{Percent increase} = \frac{\text{amount of increase}}{\text{original amount}}$$

$$= \frac{13\% - 4\%}{4\%} = \frac{9\%}{4\%} = \frac{9}{4} = 2.25 = 225\%$$

The percent increase for PBS was 225%. This is not more than 300%, so Tesh did not report the percent increase correctly.

CHECK POINT 8 An episode of a television series had an audience of 12% versus its usual 10%. What was the percent increase for this episode?

EXAMPLE 9 *Promises of a Politician*

A politician states, "If you elect me to office, I promise to cut your taxes for each of my first three years in office by 10% each year, for a total reduction of 30%." Evaluate the accuracy of the politician's statement.

SOLUTION

To make things simple, let's assume that a taxpayer paid $100 in taxes in the year previous to the politician's election. A 10% reduction during year 1 is 10% of $100.

$$10\% \text{ of previous year tax} = 10\% \text{ of } \$100 = 0.10 \times \$100 = \$10$$

With a 10% reduction the first year, the taxpayer will pay only $100 − $10, or $90, in taxes during the politician's first year in office.

The following table shows how we calculate the new, reduced tax for each of the first three years in office:

Year	Tax Paid the Year Before	10% Reduction	Taxes Paid This Year
1	\$100	$0.10 \times \$100 = \$10$	$\$100 - \$10 = \$90$
2	\$90	$0.10 \times \$90 = \$9$	$\$90 - \$9 = \$81$
3	\$81	$0.10 \times \$81 = \$8.10$	$\$81 - \$8.10 = \$72.90$

Now, we determine the percent decrease in taxes over the three years.

$$\text{Percent decrease} = \frac{\text{amount of decrease}}{\text{original amount}}$$

$$= \frac{\$100 - \$72.90}{\$100} = \frac{\$27.10}{\$100} = \frac{27.1}{100} = 0.271 = 27.1\%$$

The taxes decline by 27.1%, not by 30%. The politician is ill-informed in saying that three consecutive 10% cuts add up to a total tax cut of 30%. In our calculation, which serves as a counterexample to the promise, the total tax cut is only 27.1%.

CHECK POINT 9 Suppose you paid \$1200 in taxes. During year 1, taxes decrease by 20%. During year 2, taxes increase by 20%.

a. What do you pay in taxes for year 2?

b. How do your taxes for year 2 compare with what you originally paid, namely \$1200? If the taxes are not the same, find the percent increase or decrease.

Blitzer Bonus

Testing Your Financial Literacy

Scores have been falling on tests that measure financial literacy. Here are four items from a test given to high school seniors. Would you ace this one?

1. Which of the following is true about sales taxes?
A. The national sales-tax percentage rate is 6%.
B. The Federal Government will deduct it from your paycheck.
C. You don't have to pay the tax if your income is very low.
D. It makes things more expensive for you to buy.

58% of high school seniors answered incorrectly.

2. If you have caused an accident, which type of automobile insurance would cover damage to your own car?
A. Comprehensive
B. Liability
C. Term
D. Collision

63% of high school seniors answered incorrectly.

3. Which of the following types of investment would best protect the purchasing power of a family's savings in the event of a sudden increase in inflation?
A. A 10-year bond issued by a corporation
B. A certificate of deposit at a bank
C. A 25-year corporate bond
D. A house financed with a fixed-rate mortgage

64% of high school seniors answered incorrectly.

4. Sara and Joshua just had a baby. They received money as baby gifts and want to put it away for the baby's education. Which of the following tends to have the highest growth over periods of time as long as 18 years?
A. A checking account
B. Stocks
C. A U.S. government savings bond
D. A savings account

83% of high school seniors answered incorrectly.

Source: The Jump\$tart Coalition's 2008 Personal Financial Survey

Answers: 1. D; 2. D; 3. D; 4. B

Concept and Vocabulary Check

Fill in each blank so that the resulting statement is true.

1. Percents are the result of expressing numbers as part of ________.
2. To express $\frac{7}{8}$ as a percent, divide ________ by ________, multiply the quotient by ________, and attach ________.
3. To express 0.1 as a percent, move the decimal point ________ places to the ________ and attach ________.
4. To express 7.5% as a decimal, move the decimal point ________ places to the ________ and remove ________.
5. To find the sales tax amount, multiply the ________ and the ________.
6. To find the discount amount, multiply the ________ and the ________.
7. The numerator of the fraction for percent increase is ________ and the denominator of the fraction for percent increase is ________.
8. The numerator of the fraction for percent decrease is ________ and the denominator of the fraction for percent decrease is ________.

Exercises 9–10 are based on items from a financial literacy survey from the Center for Economic and Entrepreneurial Literacy. Determine whether each statement is true or false. If the statement is false, make the necessary change(s) to produce a true statement.

9. Santa had to lay off 25% of his eight reindeer because of the bad economy, so only seven reindeer remained. (65% answered this question incorrectly. Santa might consider leaving *Thinking Mathematically* in stockings across the country.) ________
10. You spent 1% of your $50,000-per-year salary on gifts, so you spent $5000 on gifts for the year. ________

Exercise Set 7.1

Practice Exercises

In Exercises 1–10, express each fraction as a percent.

1. $\frac{2}{5}$
2. $\frac{3}{5}$
3. $\frac{1}{4}$
4. $\frac{3}{4}$
5. $\frac{3}{8}$
6. $\frac{7}{8}$
7. $\frac{1}{40}$
8. $\frac{3}{40}$
9. $\frac{9}{80}$
10. $\frac{13}{80}$

In Exercises 11–20, express each decimal as a percent.

11. 0.59
12. 0.96
13. 0.3844
14. 0.003
15. 2.87
16. 9.83
17. 14.87
18. 19.63
19. 100
20. 95

In Exercises 21–34, express each percent as a decimal.

21. 72%
22. 38%
23. 43.6%
24. 6.25%
25. 130%
26. 260%
27. 2%
28. 6%
29. $\frac{1}{2}$%
30. $\frac{3}{4}$%
31. $\frac{5}{8}$%
32. $\frac{1}{8}$%
33. $62\frac{1}{2}$%
34. $87\frac{1}{2}$%

Use the percent formula, $A = PB$: A is P percent of B, to solve Exercises 35–38.

35. What is 3% of 200?
36. What is 8% of 300?
37. What is 18% of 40?
38. What is 16% of 90?

Practice Plus

Three basic types of percent problems can be solved using the percent formula $A = PB$.

Question	Given	Percent Formula
What is *P* percent of *B*?	*P* and *B*	Solve for *A*.
A is *P* percent of what?	*A* and *P*	Solve for *B*.
A is what percent of *B*?	*A* and *B*	Solve for *P*.

Exercises 35–38 involved using the formula to answer the first question. In Exercises 39–46, use the percent formula to answer the second or third question.

39. 3 is 60% of what?
40. 8 is 40% of what?
41. 24% of what number is 40.8?
42. 32% of what number is 51.2?
43. 3 is what percent of 15?
44. 18 is what percent of 90?
45. What percent of 2.5 is 0.3?
46. What percent of 7.5 is 0.6?

Application Exercises

47. Suppose that the local sales tax rate is 6% and you purchase a car for $32,800.
    a. How much tax is paid?
    b. What is the car's total cost?
48. Suppose that the local sales tax rate is 7% and you purchase a graphing calculator for $96.
    a. How much tax is paid?
    b. What is the calculator's total cost?
49. An exercise machine with an original price of $860 is on sale at 12% off.
    a. What is the discount amount?
    b. What is the exercise machine's sale price?
50. A dictionary that normally sells for $16.50 is on sale at 40% off.
    a. What is the discount amount?
    b. What is the dictionary's sale price?

The circle graph shows a breakdown of spending for the average U.S. household using 365 days worked as a basis of comparison. Use this information to solve Exercises 51–52. Round answers to the nearest tenth of a percent.

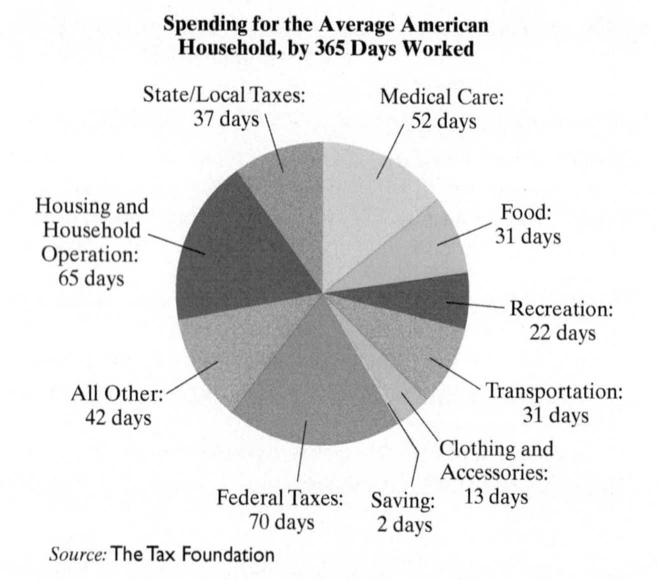

Source: The Tax Foundation

51. What percentage of work time does the average U.S. household spend paying for federal taxes?

52. What percentage of work time does the average U.S. household spend paying for state and local taxes?

Although you want to choose a career that fits your interests and abilities, it is good to have an idea of what jobs pay when looking at career options. The bar graph shows the average yearly earnings of full-time employed college graduates with only a bachelor's degree based on their college major. Use this information to solve Exercises 53–54. Round all answers to the nearest tenth of a percent.

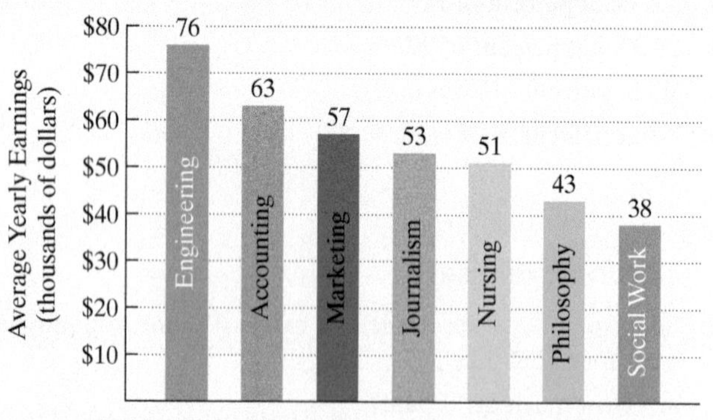

Source: Arthur J. Keown, *Personal Finance*, Fourth Edition, Pearson, 2007.

53. Find the percent increase in the average yearly earnings from students majoring in social work to students majoring in engineering.

54. Find the percent increase for the average yearly earnings from students majoring in philosophy to students majoring in accounting.

55. A sofa regularly sells for $840. The sale price is $714. Find the percent decrease of the sale price from the regular price.

56. A FAX machine regularly sells for $380. The sale price is $266. Find the percent decrease of the sale price from the regular price.

57. Suppose that you have $10,000 in a rather risky investment recommended by your financial advisor. During the first year, your investment decreases by 30% of its original value. During the second year, your investment increases by 40% of its first-year value. Your advisor tells you that there must have been a 10% overall increase of your original $10,000 investment. Is your financial advisor using percentages properly? If not, what is your actual percent gain or loss of your original $10,000 investment?

58. The price of a color printer is reduced by 30% of its original price. When it still does not sell, its price is reduced by 20% of the reduced price. The salesperson informs you that there has been a total reduction of 50%. Is the salesperson using percentages properly? If not, what is the actual percent reduction from the original price?

Writing in Mathematics

59. What is a percent?

60. Describe how to express a decimal number as a percent and give an example.

61. Describe how to express a percent as a decimal number and give an example.

62. Explain how to use the sales tax rate to determine an item's total cost.

63. Describe how to find percent increase and give an example.

64. Describe how to find percent decrease and give an example.

Critical Thinking Exercises

Make Sense? *In Exercises 65–68, determine whether each statement makes sense or does not make sense, and explain your reasoning.*

65. I have $100 and my restaurant bill comes to $80, which is not enough to leave a 20% tip.

66. I found the percent decrease in a jacket's price to be 120%.

67. My weight increased by 1% in January and 1% in February, so my increase in weight over the two months is 2%.

68. My rent increased from 20% to 30% of my income, so the percent increase is 10%.

69. What is the total cost of a $720 iPad that is on sale at 15% off if the local sales tax rate is 6%?

70. A condominium is taxed based on its $78,500 value. The tax rate is $3.40 for every $100 of value. If the tax is paid before March 1, 3% of the normal tax is given as a discount. How much tax is paid if the condominium owner takes advantage of the discount?

71. In January, each of 60 people purchased a $500 washing machine. In February, 10% fewer customers purchased the same washing machine that had increased in price by 20%. What was the change in sales from January to February?

72. When you buy something, it actually costs more than you may think—at least in terms of how much money you must earn to buy it. For example, if you pay 28% of your income in taxes, how much money would you have to earn to buy a used car for $7200?

WHAT AM I SUPPOSED TO LEARN?

After you have read this section, you should be able to:

1. Determine gross income, adjustable gross income, and taxable income.
2. Calculate federal income tax.
3. Calculate FICA taxes.
4. Solve problems involving working students and taxes.

Income Tax

"THE TROUBLE WITH TRILLIONS" EPISODE of the *Simpsons* finds Homer frantically putting together his tax return two hours before the April 15th mailing deadline. In a frenzy, he shouts to his wife, "Marge, how many kids do we have, no time to count, I'll just estimate nine. If anyone asks, you need 24-hour nursing care, Lisa is a clergyman, Maggie is seven people, and Bart was wounded in Vietnam."

"Cool!" replies Bart.

It isn't only cartoon characters who are driven into states of frantic agitation over taxes. The average American pays over $10,000 per year in income tax. Yes, it's important to pay Uncle Sam what you owe, but not a penny more. People who do not understand the federal tax system often pay more than they have to. In this section, you will learn how income taxes are determined and calculated, reinforcing the role of tax planning in personal finance.

Paying Income Tax

Income tax is a percentage of your income collected by the government to fund its services and programs. The federal government collects income tax, and most, but not all, state governments do, too. (Alaska, Florida, Nevada, South Dakota, Texas, Washington, and Wyoming have no state income tax.) Tax revenue pays for our national defense, fire and police protection, road construction, schools, libraries, and parks. Without taxes, the government would not be able to conduct medical research, provide medical care for the elderly, or send astronauts into space.

Income tax is automatically withheld from your paycheck by your employer. The precise amount withheld for federal income tax depends on how you fill out your W-4 form, which you complete when you start a new job.

Although the United States Congress determines federal tax laws, the Internal Revenue Service (IRS) is the government body that enforces the laws and collects taxes. The IRS is a branch of the Treasury Department.

1 Determine gross income, adjustable gross income, and taxable income.

Determining Taxable Income

Federal income taxes are a percentage of your *taxable income*, which is based on your earnings in the calendar year—January to December. When the year is over, you have until April 15th to file your tax return.

Calculating your federal income tax begins with **gross income**, or total income for the year. This includes income from wages, tips, interest or dividends from investments, unemployment compensation, profits from a business, rental income, and even game-show winnings. It does not matter whether these winnings are in cash or in the form of items such as cars or vacations.

The next step in calculating your federal income tax is to determine your **adjusted gross income**. Adjusted gross income is figured by taking gross income and subtracting certain allowable amounts, called **adjustments**. These untaxed portions of gross income include contributions to certain retirement accounts and tax-deferred savings plans, interest paid on student loans, and alimony payments. In a traditional tax-deferred retirement plan, you get to deduct the full amount of your contribution from your gross income. You pay taxes on the money later, when you withdraw it at retirement.

Adjusted gross income = Gross income − Adjustments

IRS rules detail exactly what can be subtracted from gross income to determine your adjusted gross income.

Blitzer Bonus

Willie Nelson's Adjustments

In 1990, the IRS sent singer Willie Nelson a bill for $32 million. Egad! But as Willie said, "Thirty-two million ain't much if you say it fast." How did this happen? On bad advice, Willie got involved in a number of investments that he declared as adjustments. This reduced his adjusted gross income to a negligible amount that made paying taxes unnecessary. The IRS ruled these "adjustments" as blatant tax-avoidance schemes. Eventually, Willie and the IRS settled on a $9 million payment.

Source: Arthur J. Keown, *Personal Finance*, Fourth Edition, Pearson, 2007.

You are entitled to certain *exemptions* and *deductions*, subtracted from your adjusted gross income, before calculating your taxes. An **exemption** is a fixed amount on your return for each person supported by your income. You are entitled to this fixed amount ($3800 in 2012) for yourself and the same amount for each dependent.

A **standard deduction** is a lump-sum amount that you can subtract from your adjusted gross income. The IRS sets this amount. Most young people take the standard deduction because their financial situations are relatively simple and they are not eligible for numerous deductions associated with owning a home or making charitable contributions. **Itemized deductions** are deductions you list separately if you have incurred a large number of deductible expenses. Itemized deductions include interest on home mortgages, state income taxes, property taxes, charitable contributions, and medical expenses exceeding 7.5% of adjusted gross income. Taxpayers should choose the greater of a standard deduction or an itemized deduction.

Taxable income is figured by subtracting exemptions and deductions from adjusted gross income.

Taxable income = Adjusted gross income − (Exemptions + Deductions)

EXAMPLE 1 *Gross Income, Adjusted Gross Income, and Taxable Income*

A single man earned wages of $46,500, received $1850 in interest from a savings account, received $15,000 in winnings on a television game show, and contributed $2300 to a tax-deferred savings plan. He is entitled to a personal exemption of $3800 and a standard deduction of $5950. The interest on his home mortgage was $6500, he paid $2100 in property taxes and $1855 in state taxes, and he contributed $3000 to charity.

a. Determine the man's gross income.

b. Determine the man's adjusted gross income.

c. Determine the man's taxable income.

SOLUTION

a. Gross income refers to this person's total income, which includes wages, interest from a savings account, and game-show winnings.

$$\text{Gross income} = \underbrace{\$46{,}500}_{\text{Wages}} + \underbrace{\$1850}_{\text{Earned interest}} + \underbrace{\$15{,}000}_{\text{Game-show winnings}} = \$63{,}350$$

The gross income is \$63,350.

b. Adjusted gross income is gross income minus adjustments. The adjustment in this case is the contribution of \$2300 to a tax-deferred savings plan. The full amount of this contribution is deducted from this year's gross income, although taxes will be paid on the money later when it is withdrawn, probably at retirement.

$$\text{Adjusted gross income} = \text{Gross income} - \text{Adjustments} = \$63{,}350 - \underbrace{\$2300}_{\text{Contribution to a tax-deferred savings plan}} = \$61{,}050$$

The adjusted gross income is \$61,050.

c. We need to subtract exemptions and deductions from the adjusted gross income to determine the man's taxable income. This taxpayer is entitled to a personal exemption of \$3800 and a standard deduction of \$5950. However, a deduction greater than \$5950 is obtained by itemizing deductions.

$$\text{Itemized deductions} = \underbrace{\$6500}_{\text{Interest on home mortgage}} + \underbrace{\$2100}_{\text{Property taxes}} + \underbrace{\$1855}_{\text{State taxes}} + \underbrace{\$3000}_{\text{Charity}} = \$13{,}455$$

We choose the itemized deductions of \$13,455 because they are greater than the standard deduction of \$5950.

$$\begin{aligned}\text{Taxable income} &= \text{Adjusted gross income} - (\text{Exemptions} + \text{Deductions})\\ &= \$61{,}050 - (\$3800 + \$13{,}455)\\ &= \$61{,}050 - \$17{,}255\\ &= \$43{,}795\end{aligned}$$

The taxable income is \$43,795.

SUMMARY OF KINDS OF INCOME ASSOCIATED WITH FEDERAL TAXES

Gross income is total income for the year.

Adjusted gross income = Gross income − Adjustments

Taxable income = Adjusted gross income − (Exemptions + Deductions)

CHECK POINT 1 A single woman earned wages of \$87,200, received \$2680 in interest from a savings account, and contributed \$3200 to a tax-deferred savings plan. She is entitled to a personal exemption of \$3800 and a standard deduction of \$5950. The interest on her home mortgage was \$11,700, she paid \$4300 in property taxes and \$5220 in state taxes, and she contributed \$15,000 to charity.

a. Determine the woman's gross income.

b. Determine the woman's adjusted gross income.

c. Determine the woman's taxable income.

2 Calculate federal income tax.

Calculating Federal Income Tax

A tax table is used to determine how much you owe based on your taxable income. However, you do not have to pay this much tax if you are entitled to any *tax credits.* **Tax credits** are sums of money that reduce the income tax owed by the full dollar-for-dollar amount of the credits.

Blitzer Bonus

Taking a Bite Out of Taxes

A tax credit is not the same thing as a tax deduction. A tax deduction reduces taxable income, saving only a percentage of the deduction in taxes. A tax credit reduces the income tax owed on the full dollar amount of the credit. There are credits available for everything from donating a kidney to buying an energy efficient dishwasher. The American Opportunity Credit, included in the economic stimulus package of 2009, provides a tax credit of up to $2500 per student. The credit can be used to lower the costs of the first four years of college. You can claim the credit for up to 100% of the first $2000 in qualified college costs and 25% of the next $2000. Significantly, 40% of this credit is refundable. This means that even if you do not have any taxable income, you could receive a check from the government for up to $1000.

Credits are awarded for a variety of activities that the government wants to encourage. Because a tax credit represents a dollar-for-dollar reduction in your tax bill, it pays to know your tax credits. You can learn more about tax credits at www.irs.gov.

Most people pay part or all of their tax bill during the year. If you are employed, your employer deducts federal taxes through *withholdings* based on a percentage of your gross pay. If you are self-employed, you pay your tax bill through *quarterly estimated taxes.*

When you file your tax return, all you are doing is settling up with the IRS over the amount of taxes you paid during the year versus the federal income tax that you owe. Many people will have paid more during the year than they owe, in which case they receive a *tax refund.* Others will not have paid enough and need to send the rest to the IRS by the deadline.

CALCULATING FEDERAL INCOME TAX

1. Determine your adjusted gross income:

Adjusted gross income = Gross income − Adjustments.

Gross income: All income for the year, including wages, tips, earnings from investments, and unemployment compensation

Adjustments: Includes payments to tax-deferred savings plans

2. Determine your taxable income:

Taxable income = Adjusted gross income − (Exemptions + Deductions).

Exemptions: A fixed amount for yourself ($3800 in 2012) and the same amount for each dependent

Deductions: Choose the greater of a standard deduction or an itemized deduction, which includes interest on home mortgages, state income taxes, property taxes, charitable contributions, and medical expenses exceeding 7.5% of adjusted gross income.

3. Determine your income tax:

$$\text{Income tax} = \text{Tax computation} - \text{Tax credits.}$$

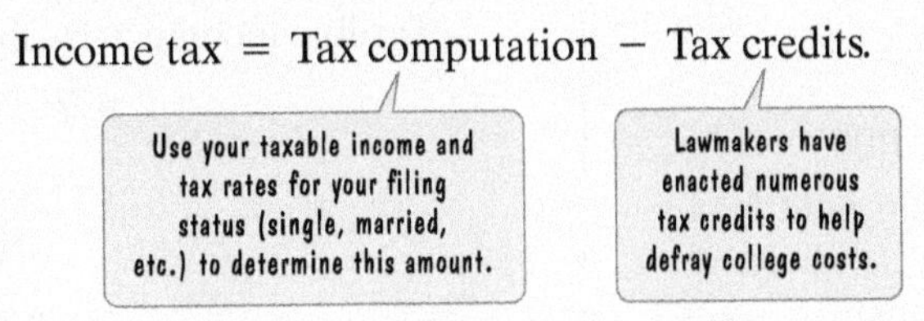

Table 7.1 shows 2012 tax rates, standard deductions, and exemptions for the four **filing status** categories described in the voice balloons. The tax rates in the left column, called **marginal tax rates**, are assigned to various income ranges, called margins. For example, suppose you are single and your taxable income is \$25,000. The singles column of the table shows that you must pay 10% tax on the first \$8700, which is

$$10\% \text{ of } \$8700 = 0.10 \times \$8700 = \$870.$$

You must also pay 15% tax on the remaining \$16,300 (\$25,000 − \$8700 = \$16,300), which is

$$15\% \text{ of } \$16,300 = 0.15 \times \$16,300 = \$2445.$$

Your total tax is \$870 + \$2445 = \$3315. In this scenario, your *marginal rate* is 15% and you are in the 15% *tax bracket.*

Table 7.1 2012 Marginal Tax Rates, Standard Deductions, and Exemptions

	Unmarried, divorced, or legally separated	Married and each partner files a separate tax return	Married and both partners file a single tax return	Unmarried and paying more than half the cost of supporting a child or parent
Tax Rate	**Single**	**Married Filing Separately**	**Married Filing Jointly**	**Head of Household**
10%	up to \$8700	up to \$8700	up to \$17,400	up to \$12,400
15%	\$8701 to \$35,350	\$8701 to \$35,350	\$17,401 to \$70,700	\$12,401 to \$47,350
25%	\$35,351 to \$85,650	\$35,351 to \$71,350	\$70,701 to \$142,700	\$47,351 to \$122,300
28%	\$85,651 to \$178,650	\$71,351 to \$108,725	\$142,701 to \$217,450	\$122,301 to \$198,050
33%	\$178,651 to \$388,350	\$108,726 to \$194,175	\$217,451 to \$388,350	\$198,051 to \$388,350
35%	more than \$388,350	more than \$194,175	more than \$388,350	more than \$388,350
Standard Deduction	\$5950	\$5950	\$11,900	\$8700
Exemptions (per person)	\$3800	\$3800	\$3800	\$3800

SINGLE WOMAN WITH NO DEPENDENTS

Gross income: \$62,000
Adjustments: \$4000 paid to a tax-deferred IRA (Individual Retirement Account)
Deductions:

- \$7500: mortgage interest
- \$2200: property taxes
- \$2400: charitable contributions
- \$1500: medical expenses not covered by insurance

Tax credit: \$500

EXAMPLE 2 *Computing Federal Income Tax*

Calculate the federal income tax owed by a single woman with no dependents whose gross income, adjustments, deductions, and credits are given in the margin. Use the 2012 marginal tax rates in **Table 7.1**.

SOLUTION

Step 1 **Determine the adjusted gross income.**

$$\begin{aligned}\text{Adjusted gross income} &= \text{Gross income} - \text{Adjustments}\\ &= \$62,000 - \$4000\\ &= \$58,000\end{aligned}$$

SINGLE WOMAN WITH NO DEPENDENTS

Gross income: $62,000

Adjustments: $4000 paid to a tax-deferred IRA (Individual Retirement Account)

Deductions:

- $7500: mortgage interest
- $2200: property taxes
- $2400: charitable contributions
- $1500: medical expenses not covered by insurance

Tax credit: $500

Step 2 Determine the taxable income.

$$\begin{aligned}\text{Taxable income} &= \text{Adjusted gross income} - (\text{Exemptions} + \text{Deductions})\\ &= \$58{,}000 - (\$3800 + \text{Deductions})\end{aligned}$$

The singles column in **Table 7.1** shows a personal exemption of $3800.

The singles column in **Table 7.1** shows a $5950 standard deduction. A greater deduction can be obtained by itemizing.

Itemized Deductions

$7500 : mortgage interest
$2200 : property taxes
$2400 : charitable contributions
~~$1500 : medical expenses~~
$12,100 : total of deductible expenditures

Can only deduct amount in excess of 7.5% of adjusted gross income: $0.075 \times \$58{,}000 = \$4350$

We substitute $12,100 for deductions in the formula for taxable income.

$$\begin{aligned}\text{Taxable income} &= \text{Adjusted gross income} - (\text{Exemptions} + \text{Deductions})\\ &= \$58{,}000 - (\$3800 + \$12{,}100)\\ &= \$58{,}000 - \$15{,}900\\ &= \$42{,}100\end{aligned}$$

Tax Rate	Single
10%	up to $8700
15%	$8701 to $35,350
25%	$35,351 to $85,650

A portion of **Table 7.1** (repeated)

Step 3 Determine the income tax.

$$\begin{aligned}\text{Income tax} &= \text{Tax computation} - \text{Tax credits}\\ &= \text{Tax computation} - \$500\end{aligned}$$

We perform the tax computation using the singles rates in **Table 7.1**, partly repeated in the margin. Our taxpayer is in the 25% tax bracket because her taxable income, $42,100, is in the $35,351 to $85,650 income range. This means that she owes 10% on the first $8700 of her taxable income, 15% on her taxable income between $8701 and $35,350, inclusive, and 25% on her taxable income above $35,350.

10% marginal rate on first $8700 of taxable income

15% marginal rate on taxable income between $8701 and $35,350

25% marginal rate on taxable income above $35,350

$$\begin{aligned}\text{Tax computation} &= 0.10 \times \$8700 + 0.15 \times (\$35{,}350 - \$8700) + 0.25 \times (\$42{,}100 - \$35{,}350)\\ &= 0.10 \times \$8700 + 0.15 \times \$26{,}650 + 0.25 \times \$6750\\ &= \$870.00 + \$3997.50 + \$1687.50\\ &= \$6555.00\end{aligned}$$

We substitute $6555.00 for the tax computation in the formula for income tax.

$$\begin{aligned}\text{Income tax} &= \text{Tax computation} - \text{Tax credits}\\ &= \$6555.00 - \$500\\ &= \$6055.00\end{aligned}$$

The federal income tax owed is $6055.00.

CHECK POINT 2 Use the 2012 marginal tax rates in **Table 7.1** on page 293 to calculate the federal tax owed by a single man with no dependents whose gross income, adjustments, deductions, and credits are given as follows:

Gross income: \$40,000
Adjustments: \$1000
Deductions: \$3000: charitable contributions
\$1500: theft loss
\$300: cost of tax preparation
Tax credit: none.

3 Calculate FICA taxes.

Social Security and Medicare (FICA)

In addition to income tax, we are required to pay the federal government **FICA** (Federal Insurance Contributions Act) taxes that are used for Social Security and Medicare benefits. **Social Security** provides payments to eligible retirees, people with health problems, eligible dependents of deceased persons, and disabled citizens. **Medicare** provides health care coverage mostly to Americans 65 and older.

The 2012 FICA tax rates are given in **Table 7.2**.

TABLE 7.2 2012 FICA Tax Rates

Employee's Rates	Matching Rates Paid by the Employer	Self-Employed Rates
• 5.65% on first \$110,000 of income • 1.45% of income in excess of \$110,000	• 7.65% on first \$110,000 paid in wages • 1.45% of wages paid in excess of \$110,000	• 13.3% on first \$110,000 of net profits • 2.9% of net profits in excess of \$110,000

Taxpayers are not permitted to subtract adjustments, exemptions, or deductions when determining FICA taxes.

EXAMPLE 3 *Computing FICA Tax*

If you are not self-employed and earn \$150,000, what are your FICA taxes?

SOLUTION

The tax rates are 5.65% on the first \$110,000 of income and 1.45% on income in excess of \$110,000.

5.65% rate on the first \$110,000 of income

1.45% rate on income in excess of \$110,000

$$\begin{aligned}\text{FICA Tax} &= 0.0565 \times \$110{,}000 + 0.0145 \times (\$150{,}000 - \$110{,}000)\\ &= 0.0565 \times \$110{,}000 + 0.0145 \times \$40{,}000\\ &= \$6215 + \$580\\ &= \$6795\end{aligned}$$

The FICA taxes are \$6795.

CHECK POINT 3 If you are not self-employed and earn \$200,000, what are your FICA taxes?

4 Solve problems involving working students and taxes.

Blitzer Bonus

Percents and Tax Rates

In 1944 and 1945, the highest marginal tax rate in the United States was a staggering 94%. The tax rate on the highest-income Americans remained at approximately 90% throughout the 1950s, decreased to 70% in the 1960s and 1970s, and to 50% in the early 1980s before reaching a post–World War II low of 28% in 1998. (*Source*: IRS) In 2012, Sweden had the world's highest tax rate among industrialized countries (56.6%), followed by Nordic neighbor Denmark (55.3%) and crisis-laden Spain (52%). (*Source*: KPMG)

Working Students and Taxes

For those of you who work part-time, getting paid is great. However, because employers withhold federal and state taxes, as well as FICA, your paychecks probably contain less spending money than you had anticipated.

A pay stub attached to your paycheck provides a lot of information about the money you earned, including both your *gross pay* and your *net pay*. **Gross pay**, also known as **base pay**, is your salary prior to any withheld taxes for the pay period the check covers. Your gross pay is what you would receive if nothing were deducted. **Net pay** is the actual amount of your check after taxes have been withheld.

EXAMPLE 4 *Taxes for a Working Student*

You would like to have extra spending money, so you decide to work part-time at the local gym. The job pays \$10 per hour and you work 20 hours per week. Your employer withholds 10% of your gross pay for federal taxes, 5.65% for FICA taxes, and 3% for state taxes.

a. What is your weekly gross pay?

b. How much is withheld per week for federal taxes?

c. How much is withheld per week for FICA taxes?

d. How much is withheld per week for state taxes?

e. What is your weekly net pay?

f. What percentage of your gross pay is withheld for taxes? Round to the nearest tenth of a percent.

SOLUTION

a. Your weekly gross pay is the number of hours worked, 20, times your hourly wage, \$10 per hour.

$$\text{Gross pay} = 20\ \cancel{\text{hours}} \times \frac{\$10}{\cancel{\text{hour}}} = 20 \times \$10 = \$200$$

Your weekly gross pay, or what you would receive if nothing were deducted, is \$200.

b. Your employer withholds 10% of your gross pay for federal taxes.

$$\text{Federal taxes} = 10\% \text{ of } \$200 = 0.10 \times \$200 = \$20$$

\$20 is withheld per week for federal taxes.

c. Your employer withholds 5.65% of your gross pay for FICA taxes.

$$\text{FICA taxes} = 5.65\% \text{ of } \$200 = 0.0565 \times \$200 = \$11.30$$

\$11.30 is withheld per week for FICA taxes.

d. Your employer withholds 3% of your gross pay for state taxes.

$$\text{State taxes} = 3\% \text{ of } \$200 = 0.03 \times \$200 = \$6$$

\$6 is withheld per week for state taxes.

e. Your weekly net pay is your gross pay minus the amounts withheld for federal, FICA, and state taxes.

Gross pay · Federal taxes · FICA taxes · State taxes

$$\begin{aligned}\text{Net pay} &= \$200 - (\$20 + \$11.30 + \$6)\\ &= \$200.00 - \$37.30\\ &= \$162.70\end{aligned}$$

Your weekly net pay is \$162.70. This is the actual amount of your paycheck.

f. Our work in part (e) shows that \$37.30 is withheld for taxes. The fractional part of your gross pay that is withheld for taxes is the amount that is withheld, \$37.30, divided by your gross pay, \$200.00. We then express this fraction as a percent.

$$\text{Percent of gross pay withheld for taxes} = \frac{\$37.30}{\$200.00} = 0.1865 = 18.65\% \approx 18.7\%$$

Taxes
Gross pay

Your employer takes \$37.30 from your weekly gross salary and sends the money to the government. This represents approximately 18.7% of your gross pay.

Figure 7.3 contains a sample pay stub for the working student in Example 4.

YOUR WORKPLACE 10 MAIN STREET ANY TOWN, STATE	YOUR NAME YOUR ADDRESS YOUR CITY, STATE, ZIP CODE SSN: 000-00-0000	Pay End Date: 0/00/12	
		Federal	State
		Single 1	Single 1

HOURS AND EARNINGS

Current			Year to Date	
Base Rate (\$10 per hour)	Hours	Earnings	Hours	Earnings
	20	\$200	400	\$4000

TAXES

Description:	Current	Year to Date
Federal	\$20.00	\$400.00
FICA	\$11.30	\$226.00
State	\$ 6.00	\$120.00
TOTAL	\$37.30	\$746.00
	Current	Year to Date
TOTAL GROSS	\$200.00	\$4000.00
TOTAL DEDUCTIONS	\$ 37.30	\$ 746.00
NET PAY	\$162.70	\$3254.00

FIGURE 7.3 A working student's sample pay stub

Pay stubs are attached to your paycheck and usually contain four sections:

- Personal information about the employee: This may include your name, your address, your social security number, and your marital status.
- Information about earnings: This includes your hourly wage, the number of hours worked in the current pay period, and the number of hours worked year-to-date, which is usually the total number of hours worked since January 1 of the current year (the first pay of the year may include the latter part of December), and the amount earned during the current pay period and the amount earned year-to-date.
- Information about tax deductions, summarizing withholdings for the current pay period and the withholdings year-to-date.
- Gross pay, total deductions, and net pay for the current period, and the year-to-date total for each.

CHECK POINT 4 You decide to work part-time at a local nursery. The job pays \$12 per hour and you work 15 hours per week. Your employer withholds 10% of your gross pay for federal taxes, 5.65% for FICA taxes, and 4% for state taxes.

a. What is your weekly gross pay?
b. How much is withheld per week for federal taxes?
c. How much is withheld per week for FICA taxes?
d. How much is withheld per week for state taxes?
e. What is your weekly net pay?
f. What percentage of your gross pay is withheld for taxes? Round to the nearest tenth of a percent.

Concept and Vocabulary Check

Fill in each blank so that the resulting statement is true.

1. Your ________ income is your total income for the year.
2. Subtracting certain allowable amounts from the income in Exercise 1 results in your __________ income. These allowable amounts, or untaxed portions of income, are called ________.
3. A fixed amount deducted on your tax return for each person supported by your income, including yourself, is called a/an ________.
4. Your taxable income is your __________ income minus the sum of your ________ and ________.
5. Sums of money that reduce federal income tax by the full dollar-for-dollar amount are called ________.
6. Taxes used for Social Security and Medicare benefits are called ________ taxes.
7. Your base pay, or ________ pay, is your salary prior to any withheld taxes.
8. The actual amount of your paycheck after taxes have been withheld is called your ________ pay.

In Exercises 9–12, determine whether each statement is true or false. If the statement is false, make the necessary change(s) to produce a true statement.

9. Federal income tax is a percentage of your gross income. ______
10. If tax credits are equal, federal tax tables show that the greater your taxable income, the more you pay. ______
11. People in some states are not required to pay state income taxes. ______
12. FICA tax is a percentage of your gross income. ______

Exercise Set 7.2

Practice and Application Exercises

In Exercises 1–2, find the gross income, the adjusted gross income, and the taxable income.

1. A taxpayer earned wages of $52,600, received $720 in interest from a savings account, and contributed $3200 to a tax-deferred retirement plan. He was entitled to a personal exemption of $3800 and had deductions totaling $7250.
2. A taxpayer earned wages of $23,500, received $495 in interest from a savings account, and contributed $1200 to a tax-deferred retirement plan. She was entitled to a personal exemption of $3800 and had deductions totaling $5450.

In Exercises 3–4, find the gross income, the adjusted gross income, and the taxable income. Base the taxable income on the greater of a standard deduction or an itemized deduction.

3. Suppose your neighbor earned wages of $86,250, received $1240 in interest from a savings account, and contributed $2200 to a tax-deferred retirement plan. She is entitled to a personal exemption of $3800 and a standard deduction of $5950. The interest on her home mortgage was $8900, she contributed $2400 to charity, and she paid $1725 in state taxes.
4. Suppose your neighbor earned wages of $319,150, received $1790 in interest from a savings account, and contributed $4100 to a tax-deferred retirement plan. He is entitled to a personal exemption of $3800 and the same exemption for each of his two children. He is also entitled to a standard deduction of $5950. The interest on his home mortgage was $51,235, he contributed $74,000 to charity, and he paid $12,760 in state taxes.

*In Exercises 5–14, use the 2012 marginal tax rates in **Table 7.1** on page 293 to compute the tax owed by each person or couple.*

5. a single man with a taxable income of $40,000
6. a single woman with a taxable income of $42,000
7. a married woman filing separately with a taxable income of $120,000
8. a married man filing separately with a taxable income of $110,000
9. a single man with a taxable income of $15,000 and a $2500 tax credit
10. a single woman with a taxable income of $12,000 and a $3500 tax credit
11. a married couple filing jointly with a taxable income of $250,000 and a $7500 tax credit
12. a married couple filing jointly with a taxable income of $400,000 and a $4500 tax credit
13. a head of household with a taxable income of $58,000 and a $6500 tax credit
14. a head of household with a taxable income of $46,000 and a $3000 tax credit

*In Exercises 15–18, use the 2012 marginal tax rates in **Table 7.1** on page 293 to calculate the income tax owed by each person.*

15. Single male, no dependents

    Gross income: $75,000
    Adjustments: $4000
    Deductions:
    - $28,000 mortgage interest
    - $4200 property taxes
    - $3000 charitable contributions

    Tax credit: none

16. Single female, no dependents

    Gross income: $70,000
    Adjustments: $2000
    Deductions:
    - $10,000 mortgage interest
    - $2500 property taxes
    - $1200 charitable contributions

    Tax credit: none

17. Unmarried head of household with two dependent children

Gross income: $50,000
Adjustments: none
Deductions:
$4500 state taxes
$2000 theft loss
Tax credit: $2000

18. Unmarried head of household with one dependent child

Gross income: $40,000
Adjustments: $1500
Deductions:
$3600 state taxes
$800 charitable contributions
Tax credit: $2500

In Exercises 19–24, use the 2012 FICA tax rates in ***Table 7.2*** *on page 295.*

19. If you are not self-employed and earn $120,000 what are your FICA taxes?

20. If you are not self-employed and earn $140,000 what are your FICA taxes?

21. If you are self-employed and earn $150,000, what are your FICA taxes?

22. If you are self-employed and earn $160,000, what are your FICA taxes?

23. To help pay for college, you worked part-time at a local restaurant, earning $20,000 in wages and tips.

a. Calculate your FICA taxes.

b. Use **Table 7.1** on page 293 to calculate your income tax. Assume you are single with no dependents, have no adjustments or tax credit, and you take the standard deduction.

c. Including both FICA and income tax, what percentage of your gross income are your federal taxes? Round to the nearest tenth of a percent.

24. To help pay for college, you worked part-time at a local restaurant, earning $18,000 in wages and tips.

a. Calculate your FICA taxes.

b. Use **Table 7.1** on page 293 to calculate your income tax. Assume you are single with no dependents, have no adjustments or tax credit, and take the standard deduction.

c. Including both FICA and income tax, what percentage of your gross income are your federal taxes? Round to the nearest tenth of a percent.

25. You decide to work part-time at a local supermarket. The job pays $8.50 per hour and you work 20 hours per week. Your employer withholds 10% of your gross pay for federal taxes, 5.65% for FICA taxes, and 3% for state taxes.

a. What is your weekly gross pay?

b. How much is withheld per week for federal taxes?

c. How much is withheld per week for FICA taxes?

d. How much is withheld per week for state taxes?

e. What is your weekly net pay?

f. What percentage of your gross pay is withheld for taxes? Round to the nearest tenth of a percent.

26. You decide to work part-time at a local veterinary hospital. The job pays $9.50 per hour and you work 20 hours per week. Your employer withholds 10% of your gross pay for federal taxes, 5.65% for FICA taxes, and 5% for state taxes.

a. What is your weekly gross pay?

b. How much is withheld per week for federal taxes?

c. How much is withheld per week for FICA taxes?

d. How much is withheld per week for state taxes?

e. What is your weekly net pay?

f. What percentage of your gross pay is withheld for taxes? Round to the nearest tenth of a percent

Writing in Mathematics

27. What is income tax?

28. What is gross income?

29. What is adjusted gross income?

30. What are exemptions?

31. What are deductions?

32. Under what circumstances should taxpayers itemize deductions?

33. How is taxable income determined?

34. What are tax credits?

35. What is the difference between a tax credit and a tax deduction?

36. What are FICA taxes?

37. How do you determine your net pay?

Critical Thinking Exercises

Make Sense? *In Exercises 38–42, determine whether each statement makes sense or does not make sense, and explain your reasoning.*

38. The only important thing to know about my taxes is whether I receive a refund or owe money on my return.

39. Because I am a student with a part-time job, federal tax law does not allow me to itemize deductions.

40. I'm paying less federal tax on my first dollars of earnings and more federal tax on my last dollars of earnings.

41. My employer withholds the same amount of federal tax on my first dollars of earnings and my last dollars of earnings.

42. Now that I'm a college student, I can choose a $4000 deduction or a $2500 credit to offset tuition and fees. I'll pay less federal taxes by selecting the $4000 deduction.

43. Suppose you are in the 10% tax bracket. As a college student, you can choose a $4000 deduction or a $2500 credit to offset tuition and fees. Which option will reduce your tax bill by the greater amount? What is the difference in your savings between the two options?

44. A common complaint about income tax is "I can't afford to work more because it will put me in a higher tax bracket." Is it possible that being in a higher bracket means you actually lose money? Explain your answer.

45. Because of the mortgage interest tax deduction, is it possible to save money buying a house rather than renting, even though rent payments are lower than mortgage payments? Explain your answer.

Group Exercises

The following topics are appropriate for either individual or group research projects. Use the Internet to investigate each topic.

46. Proposals to Simplify Federal Tax Laws and Filing Procedures

47. The Most Commonly Recommended Tax Saving Strategies

48. The Most Commonly Audited Tax Return Sections

49. Federal Tax Procedures Questioned over Issues of Fairness (Examples include the marriage penalty, the alternative minimum tax (AMT), and capital gains rates.)

WHAT AM I SUPPOSED TO LEARN?

After you have read this section, you should be able to:

1. Calculate simple interest.
2. Use the future value formula.

Simple Interest

IN 1626, PETER MINUIT CONVINCED the Wappinger Indians to sell him Manhattan Island for \$24. If the Native Americans had put the \$24 into a bank account at a 5% interest rate compounded monthly, by the year 2010 there would have been well over \$5 billion in the account!

Although you may not yet understand terms such as *interest rate* and *compounded monthly*, one thing seems clear: Money in certain savings accounts grows in remarkable ways. You, too, can take advantage of such accounts with astonishing results. In the next two sections, we will show you how.

1 Calculate simple interest.

Simple Interest

Interest is the amount of money that we get paid for lending or investing money, or that we pay for borrowing money. When we deposit money in a savings institution, the institution pays us interest for its use. When we borrow money, interest is the price we pay for the privilege of using the money until we repay it.

The amount of money that we deposit or borrow is called the **principal**. For example, if you deposit \$2000 in a savings account, then \$2000 is the principal. The amount of interest depends on the principal, the interest **rate**, which is given as a percent and varies from bank to bank, and the length of time for which the money is deposited. In this section, the rate is assumed to be annual (per year).

Simple interest involves interest calculated only on the principal. The following formula is used to find simple interest:

CALCULATING SIMPLE INTEREST

$$\text{Interest} = \text{principal} \times \text{rate} \times \text{time}$$
$$I = Prt$$

The rate, r, is expressed as a decimal when calculating simple interest.

Throughout this section and the chapter, keep in mind that all given rates are assumed to be *per year*, unless otherwise stated.

EXAMPLE 1 *Calculating Simple Interest for a Year*

You deposit \$2000 in a savings account at Hometown Bank, which has a rate of 6%. Find the interest at the end of the first year.

SOLUTION

To find the interest at the end of the first year, we use the simple interest formula.

$$I = Prt = (2000)(0.06)(1) = 120$$

Principal, or amount deposited, is \$2000. Rate is 6% = 0.06. Time is 1 year.

At the end of the first year, the interest is \$120. You can withdraw the \$120 interest and you still have \$2000 in the savings account.

CHECK POINT 1 You deposit \$3000 in a savings account at Yourtown Bank, which has a rate of 5%. Find the interest at the end of the first year.

EXAMPLE 2 *Calculating Simple Interest for More Than a Year*

A student took out a simple interest loan for \$1800 for two years at a rate of 8% to purchase a used car. What is the interest on the loan?

SOLUTION

To find the interest on the loan, we use the simple interest formula.

$$I = Prt = (1800)(0.08)(2) = 288$$

Principal, or amount borrowed, is \$1800. Rate is 8% = 0.08. Time is 2 years.

The interest on the loan is \$288.

CHECK POINT 2 A student took out a simple interest loan for \$2400 for two years at a rate of 7%. What is the interest on the loan?

Simple interest is used for many short-term loans, including automobile and consumer loans. Imagine that a short-term loan is taken for 125 days. The time of the loan is $\frac{125}{365}$ because there are 365 days in a year. However, before the modern use of calculators and computers, the **Banker's rule** allowed financial institutions to use 360 in the denominator of such a fraction because this simplified the interest calculation. Using the Banker's rule, the time, t, for a 125-day short-term loan is

$$\frac{125 \text{ days}}{360 \text{ days}} = \frac{125}{360}.$$

Compare the values for time, t, for a 125-day short-term loan using denominators of 360 and 365.

$$\frac{125}{360} \approx 0.347 \qquad \frac{125}{365} \approx 0.342$$

The denominator of 360 benefits the bank by resulting in a greater period of time for the loan, and consequently more interest.

With the widespread use of calculators and computers, government agencies and the Federal Reserve Bank calculate simple interest using 365 days in a year, as do many credit unions and banks. However, there are still some financial institutions that use the Banker's rule with 360 days in a year because it produces a greater amount of interest.

2 Use the future value formula.

Future Value: Principal Plus Interest

When a loan is repaid, the interest is added to the original principal to find the total amount due. In Example 2, at the end of two years, the student will have to repay

$$\text{principal} + \text{interest} = \$1800 + \$288 = \$2088.$$

In general, if a principal P is borrowed at a simple interest rate r, then after t years the amount due, A, can be determined as follows:

$$A = P + I = P + Prt = P(1 + rt).$$

The amount due, A, is called the **future value** of the loan. The principal borrowed now, P, is also known as the loan's **present value**.

CALCULATING FUTURE VALUE FOR SIMPLE INTEREST

The future value, A, of P dollars at simple interest rate r (as a decimal) for t years is given by

$$A = P(1 + rt).$$

EXAMPLE 3 *Calculating Future Value*

A loan of $1060 has been made at 6.5% for three months. Find the loan's future value.

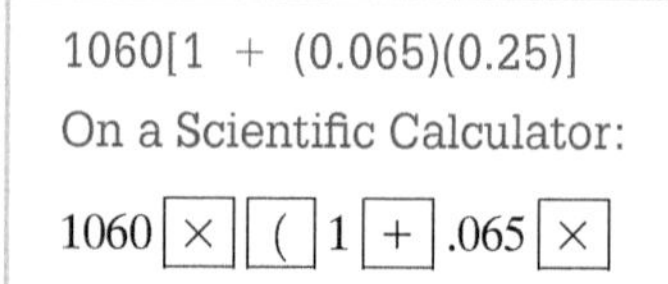
TECHNOLOGY

1060[1 + (0.065)(0.25)]

On a Scientific Calculator:

1060 [×] [(] 1 [+] .065 [×]

.25 [)] [=]

SOLUTION

The amount borrowed, or principal, P, is $1060. The rate, r, is 6.5%, or 0.065. The time, t, is given as three months. We need to express the time in years because the rate is understood to be 6.5% per year. Because three months is $\frac{3}{12}$ of a year, $t = \frac{3}{12} = \frac{1}{4} = 0.25$.

The loan's future value, or the total amount due after three months, is

$$A = P(1 + rt) = 1060[1 + (0.065)(0.25)] \approx \$1077.23.$$

Rounded to the nearest cent, the loan's future value is $1077.23.

CHECK POINT 3 A loan of $2040 has been made at 7.5% for four months. Find the loan's future value.

EXAMPLE 4 *Earning Money by Putting Your Wallet Away Today*

Suppose you spend $4 each day, five days per week, on gourmet coffee.

a. How much do you spend on this item in a year?

b. If you invested your yearly spending on gourmet coffee in a savings account with a rate of 5%, how much would you have after one year?

SOLUTION

a. Because you are spending $4 each day, five days per week, you are spending

$$\frac{\$4}{\text{day}} \times \frac{5 \text{ days}}{\text{week}} = \frac{\$4 \times 5}{\text{week}} = \frac{\$20}{\text{week}},$$

or $20 each week on gourmet coffee. Assuming that this continues throughout the 52 weeks in the year, you are spending

$$\frac{\$20}{\text{week}} \times \frac{52 \text{ weeks}}{\text{year}} = \frac{\$20 \times 52}{\text{year}} = \frac{\$1040}{\text{year}},$$

or $1040 each year on gourmet coffee.

b. Now suppose you invest $1040 in a savings account with a rate of 5%. To find your savings after one year, we use the future value formula for simple interest.

$$A = P(1 + rt) = 1040[1 + (0.05)(1)] = 1040(1.05) = 1092$$

Giving up the day-to-day expense of gourmet coffee can result in potential savings of $1092.

CHECK POINT 4 In addition to jeopardizing your health, cigarette smoking is a costly addiction. Consider, for example, a person with a pack-a-day cigarette habit who spends $5 per day, seven days each week, on cigarettes.

a. How much is spent on this item in a year?

b. If this person invested the yearly spending on cigarettes in a savings account with a rate of 4%, how much would be saved after one year?

The formula for future value, $A = P(1 + rt)$, has four variables. If we are given values for any three of these variables, we can solve for the fourth.

EXAMPLE 5 *Determining a Simple Interest Rate*

You borrow $2500 from a friend and promise to pay back $2655 in six months. What simple interest rate will you pay?

SOLUTION

We use the formula for future value, $A = P(1 + rt)$. You borrow $2500: $P = 2500$. You will pay back $2655, so this is the future value: $A = 2655$. You will do this in six months, which must be expressed in years: $t = \frac{6}{12} = \frac{1}{2} = 0.5$. To determine the simple interest rate you will pay, we solve the future value formula for r.

$$A = P(1 + rt) \quad \text{This is the formula for future value.}$$
$$2655 = 2500[1 + r(0.5)] \quad \text{Substitute the given values.}$$
$$2655 = 2500 + 1250r \quad \text{Use the distributive property.}$$
$$155 = 1250r \quad \text{Subtract 2500 from both sides.}$$
$$\frac{155}{1250} = \frac{1250r}{1250} \quad \text{Divide both sides by 1250.}$$
$$r = 0.124 = 12.4\% \quad \text{Express } \frac{155}{1250} \text{ as a percent.}$$

You will pay a simple interest rate of 12.4%.

CHECK POINT 5 You borrow $5000 from a friend and promise to pay back $6800 in two years. What simple interest rate will you pay?

EXAMPLE 6 *Determining a Present Value*

You plan to save $2000 for a trip to Europe in two years. You decide to purchase a certificate of deposit (CD) from your bank that pays a simple interest rate of 4%. How much must you put in this CD now in order to have the $2000 in two years?

SOLUTION

We use the formula for future value, $A = P(1 + rt)$. We are interested in finding the principal, P, or the present value.

$$A = P(1 + rt) \quad \text{This is the formula for future value.}$$
$$2000 = P[1 + (0.04)(2)] \quad A\text{(future value)} = \$2000,\ r\text{(interest rate)} = 0.04, \text{ and } t = 2 \text{ (you want \$2000 in two years).}$$
$$2000 = 1.08P \quad \text{Simplify: } 1 + (0.04)(2) = 1.08.$$
$$\frac{2000}{1.08} = \frac{1.08P}{1.08} \quad \text{Divide both sides by 1.08.}$$
$$P \approx 1851.852 \quad \text{Simplify.}$$

To make sure you will have enough money for the vacation, let's round this principal *up* to $1851.86. Thus, you should put $1851.86 in the CD now to have $2000 in two years.

GREAT QUESTION!

How should I round when finding present value?

When computing present value, round the principal, or present value, *up*. To round up to the nearest cent, add 1 to the hundredths digit, regardless of the digit to the right. In this way, you'll be sure to have enough money to meet future goals.

CHECK POINT 6 How much should you put in an investment paying a simple interest rate of 8% if you need \$4000 in six months?

Concept and Vocabulary Check

Fill in each blank so that the resulting statement is true.

1. The formula for calculating simple interest, I, is ________, where P is the ________, r is the ________, and t is the ________.
2. The future value, A, of P dollars at simple interest rate r for t years is given by the formula ____________.
3. The Banker's rule allows using ________ days in a year.

In Exercises 4–6, determine whether each statement is true or false. If the statement is false, make the necessary change(s) to produce a true statement.

4. Interest is the amount of money we get paid for borrowing money or that we pay for investing money. ______
5. In simple interest, only the original money invested or borrowed generates interest over time. ______
6. If \$4000 is borrowed at 7.6% for three months, the loan's future value is \$76. ______

Exercise Set 7.3

Practice Exercises

In Exercises 1–8, the principal P is borrowed at simple interest rate r for a period of time t. Find the simple interest owed for the use of the money. Assume 360 days in a year.

1. $P = \$4000, r = 6\%, t = 1$ year
2. $P = \$7000, r = 5\%, t = 1$ year
3. $P = \$180, r = 3\%, t = 2$ years
4. $P = \$260, r = 4\%, t = 3$ years
5. $P = \$5000, r = 8.5\%, t = 9$ months
6. $P = \$18{,}000, r = 7.5\%, t = 18$ months
7. $P = \$15{,}500, r = 11\%, t = 90$ days
8. $P = \$12{,}600, r = 9\%, t = 60$ days

In Exercises 9–14, the principal P is borrowed at simple interest rate r for a period of time t. Find the loan's future value, A, or the total amount due at time t.

9. $P = \$3000, r = 7\%, t = 2$ years
10. $P = \$2000, r = 6\%, t = 3$ years
11. $P = \$26{,}000, r = 9.5\%, t = 5$ years
12. $P = \$24{,}000, r = 8.5\%, t = 6$ years
13. $P = \$9000, r = 6.5\%, t = 8$ months
14. $P = \$6000, r = 4.5\%, t = 9$ months

In Exercises 15–20, the principal P is borrowed and the loan's future value, A, at time t is given. Determine the loan's simple interest rate, r, to the nearest tenth of a percent.

15. $P = \$2000, A = \$2150, t = 1$ year
16. $P = \$3000, A = \$3180, t = 1$ year
17. $P = \$5000, A = \$5900, t = 2$ years
18. $P = \$10{,}000, A = \$14{,}060, t = 2$ years
19. $P = \$2300, A = \$2840, t = 9$ months
20. $P = \$1700, A = \$1820, t = 6$ months

In Exercises 21–26, determine the present value, P, you must invest to have the future value, A, at simple interest rate r after time t. Round answers up to the nearest cent.

21. $A = \$6000, r = 8\%, t = 2$ years
22. $A = \$8500, r = 7\%, t = 3$ years
23. $A = \$14{,}000, r = 9.5\%, t = 6$ years
24. $A = \$16{,}000, r = 11.5\%, t = 5$ years
25. $A = \$5000, r = 14.5\%, t = 9$ months
26. $A = \$2000, r = 12.6\%, t = 8$ months

Practice Plus

27. Solve for r: $A = P(1 + rt)$.
28. Solve for t: $A = P(1 + rt)$.
29. Solve for P: $A = P(1 + rt)$.
30. Solve for P: $A = P(1 + \frac{r}{n})^{nt}$. (We will be using this formula in the next section.)

Application Exercises

31. In order to start a small business, a student takes out a simple interest loan for \$4000 for nine months at a rate of 8.25%.
    a. How much interest must the student pay?
    b. Find the future value of the loan.
32. In order to pay for baseball uniforms, a school takes out a simple interest loan for \$20,000 for seven months at a rate of 12%.
    a. How much interest must the school pay?
    b. Find the future value of the loan.
33. You borrow \$1400 from a friend and promise to pay back \$2000 in two years. What simple interest rate, to the nearest tenth of a percent, will you pay?

34. Treasury bills (T-bills) can be purchased from the U.S. Treasury Department. You buy a T-bill for \$981.60 that pays \$1000 in 13 weeks. What simple interest rate, to the nearest tenth of a percent, does this T-bill earn?

35. To borrow money, you pawn your guitar. Based on the value of the guitar, the pawnbroker loans you \$960. One month later, you get the guitar back by paying the pawnbroker \$1472. What annual interest rate did you pay?

36. To borrow money, you pawn your mountain bike. Based on the value of the bike, the pawnbroker loans you \$552. One month later, you get the bike back by paying the pawnbroker \$851. What annual interest rate did you pay?

37. A bank offers a CD that pays a simple interest rate of 6.5%. How much must you put in this CD now in order to have \$3000 for a home-entertainment center in two years?

38. A bank offers a CD that pays a simple interest rate of 5.5%. How much must you put in this CD now in order to have \$8000 for a kitchen remodeling project in two years?

Writing in Mathematics

39. Explain how to calculate simple interest.

40. What is the future value of a loan and how is it determined?

Critical Thinking Exercises

Make Sense? *In Exercises 41–43, determine whether each statement makes sense or does not make sense, and explain your reasoning.*

41. After depositing \$1500 in an account at a rate of 4%, my balance at the end of the first year was \$(1500)(0.04).

42. I saved money on my short-term loan for 90 days by finding a financial institution that used the Banker's rule rather than one that calculated interest using 365 days in a year.

43. I planned to save \$5000 in four years, computed the present value to be \$3846.153, so I rounded the principal to \$3846.15.

44. Use the future value formula to show that the time required for an amount of money P to double in value to $2P$ is given by

$$t = \frac{1}{r}.$$

45. You deposit \$5000 in an account that earns 5.5% simple interest.

a. Express the future value in the account as a linear function of time, t.

b. Determine the slope of the function in part (a) and describe what this means. Use the phrase "rate of change" in your description.

Compound Interest

WHAT AM I SUPPOSED TO LEARN?

After you have read this section, you should be able to:

1. Use compound interest formulas.
2. Calculate present value.
3. Understand and compute effective annual yield.

SO, HOW DID THE PRESENT value of Manhattan in 1626—that is, the \$24 paid to the Native Americans—attain a future value of over \$5 billion in 2010, 384 years later, at a mere 5% interest rate? After all, the future value on \$24 for 384 years at 5% simple interest is

$$A = P(1 + rt)$$
$$= 24[1 + (0.05)(384)] = 484.8,$$

or a paltry \$484.80, compared to over \$5 billion. To understand this dramatic difference in future value, we turn to the concept of *compound interest.*

1 Use compound interest formulas.

Compound Interest

Compound interest is interest computed on the original principal as well as on any accumulated interest. Many savings accounts pay compound interest. For example, suppose you deposit \$1000 in a savings account at a rate of 5%. **Table 7.3** on the next page shows how the investment grows if the interest earned is automatically added on to the principal.

TABLE 7.3 Calculating the Amount in an Account Subject to Compound Interest

Use $A = P(1 + rt)$ with $r = 0.05$ and $t = 1$, or $A = P(1 + 0.05)$.

Year	Starting Balance	Amount in the Account at Year's End
1	\$1000	$A = \$1000(1 + 0.05) = \$1050$
2	\$1050 or $\$1000(1 + 0.05)$	$A = \$1050(1 + 0.05) = \$1102.50$ or $A = \$1000(1 + 0.05)(1 + 0.05) = \$1000(1 + 0.05)^2$
3	\$1102.50 or $\$1000(1 + 0.05)^2$	$A = \$1102.50(1 + 0.05) \approx \$1157.63$ or $A = \$1000(1 + 0.05)^2(1 + 0.05) = \$1000(1 + 0.05)^3$

Using inductive reasoning, the amount, A, in the account after t years is the original principal, \$1000, times $(1 + 0.05)^t$: $A = 1000(1 + 0.05)^t$.

If the original principal is P and the interest rate is r, we can use this same approach to determine the amount, A, in an account subject to compound interest.

CALCULATING THE AMOUNT IN AN ACCOUNT FOR COMPOUND INTEREST PAID ONCE A YEAR

If you deposit P dollars at rate r, in decimal form, subject to compound interest, then the amount, A, of money in the account after t years is given by

$$A = P(1 + r)^t.$$

The amount A is called the account's **future value** and the principal P is called its **present value**.

EXAMPLE 1 *Using the Compound Interest Formula*

You deposit \$2000 in a savings account at Hometown Bank, which has a rate of 6%.

a. Find the amount, A, of money in the account after three years subject to interest compounded once a year.

b. Find the interest.

TECHNOLOGY

Here are the calculator keystrokes to compute $2000(1.06)^3$:

Many Scientific Calculators

2000 [×] 1.06 [y^x] 3 [=]

Many Graphing Calculators

2000 [×] 1.06 [∧] 3 [ENTER]

SOLUTION

a. The amount deposited, or principal, P, is \$2000. The rate, r, is 6%, or 0.06. The time of the deposit, t, is three years. The amount in the account after three years is

$$A = P(1 + r)^t = 2000(1 + 0.06)^3 = 2000(1.06)^3 \approx 2382.03.$$

Rounded to the nearest cent, the amount in the savings account after three years is \$2382.03.

b. Because the amount in the account is \$2382.03 and the original principal is \$2000, the interest is \$2382.03 − \$2000, or \$382.03.

CHECK POINT 1 You deposit \$1000 in a savings account at a bank that has a rate of 4%.

a. Find the amount, A, of money in the account after five years subject to interest compounded once a year. Round to the nearest cent.

b. Find the interest.

Compound Interest Paid More Than Once a Year

The period of time between two interest payments is called the **compounding period.** When compound interest is paid once per year, the compounding period is one year. We say that the interest is **compounded annually.**

Most savings institutions have plans in which interest is paid more than once per year. If compound interest is paid twice per year, the compounding period is six months. We say that the interest is **compounded semiannually.** When compound interest is paid four times per year, the compounding period is three months and the interest is said to be **compounded quarterly.** Some plans allow for monthly compounding or daily compounding.

In general, when compound interest is paid n times a year, we say that there are ***n*** **compounding periods per year. Table 7.4** shows the three most frequently used plans in which interest is paid more than once a year.

TABLE 7.4 Interest Plans

Name	Number of Compounding Periods per Year	Length of Each Compounding Period
Semiannual Compounding	$n = 2$	6 months
Quarterly Compounding	$n = 4$	3 months
Monthly Compounding	$n = 12$	1 month

The following formula is used to calculate the amount in an account subject to compound interest with n compounding periods per year:

CALCULATING THE AMOUNT IN AN ACCOUNT FOR COMPOUND INTEREST PAID *n* TIMES A YEAR

If you deposit P dollars at rate r, in decimal form, subject to compound interest paid n times per year, then the amount, A, of money in the account after t years is given by

$$A = P\left(1 + \frac{r}{n}\right)^{nt}.$$

A is the account's **future value** and the principal P is its **present value.**

TECHNOLOGY

Here are the calculator keystrokes to compute

$$7500\left(1 + \frac{0.06}{12}\right)^{12 \cdot 5}.$$

Many Scientific Calculators

7500 [×] [(] 1 [+] .06 [÷] 12 [)]

[y^x] [(] 12 [×] 5 [)] [=]

Many Graphing Calculators

7500 [(] 1 [+] .06 [÷] 12 [)]

[^] [(] 12 [×] 5 [)] [ENTER]

You may find it easier to compute the value of the exponent nt (12×5 or 60) before using these keystrokes. By entering 60 instead of 12×5, you're less likely to make a careless mistake by forgetting to enclose the exponent n times t in parentheses.

EXAMPLE 2 *Using the Compound Interest Formula*

You deposit \$7500 in a savings account that has a rate of 6%. The interest is compounded monthly.

a. How much money will you have after five years?

b. Find the interest after five years.

SOLUTION

a. The amount deposited, or principal, P, is \$7500. The rate, r, is 6%, or 0.06. Because interest is compounded monthly, there are 12 compounding periods per year, so $n = 12$. The time of the deposit, t, is five years. The amount in the account after five years is

$$A = P\left(1 + \frac{r}{n}\right)^{nt} = 7500\left(1 + \frac{0.06}{12}\right)^{12 \cdot 5} = 7500(1.005)^{60} \approx 10{,}116.38.$$

Rounded to the nearest cent, you will have \$10,116.38 after five years.

b. Because the amount in the account is \$10,116.38 and the original principal is \$7500, the interest after five years is \$10,116.38 − \$7500, or \$2616.38.

GREAT QUESTION!

Can I use the formula for compound interest paid n times a year to calculate the amount in an account that pays compound interest only once a year?

Yes. If $n = 1$ (interest paid once a year), the formula

$$A = P\left(1 + \frac{r}{n}\right)^{nt}$$

becomes

$$A = P\left(1 + \frac{r}{1}\right)^{1t}, \text{ or}$$

$$A = P(1 + r)^t.$$

This shows that the amount in an account subject to annual compounding is just one application of the general formula for compound interest paid n times a year. With this general formula, you no longer need a separate formula for annual compounding.

CHECK POINT 2 You deposit $4200 in a savings account that has a rate of 4%. The interest is compounded quarterly.

a. How much money will you have after 10 years? Round to the nearest cent.

b. Find the interest after 10 years.

Continuous Compounding

Some banks use **continuous compounding**, where the compounding periods increase infinitely (compounding interest every trillionth of a second, every quadrillionth of a second, etc.). As n, the number of compounding periods in a year, increases without bound, the expression $\left(1 + \frac{1}{n}\right)^n$ approaches the irrational number e: $e \approx 2.71828$. This is illustrated in **Table 7.5**. As a result, the formula for the balance in an account with n compounding periods per year, $A = P(1 + \frac{r}{n})^{nt}$, becomes $A = Pe^{rt}$ with continuous compounding. Although continuous compounding sounds terrific, it yields only a fraction of a percent more interest over a year than daily compounding.

TABLE 7.5 As n Takes on Increasingly Large Values, the Expression $\left(1 + \frac{1}{n}\right)^n$ Approaches the Irrational Number e.

n	$\left(1 + \frac{1}{n}\right)^n$
1	2
2	2.25
5	2.48832
10	2.59374246
100	2.704813829
1000	2.716923932
10,000	2.718145927
100,000	2.718268237
1,000,000	2.718280469
1,000,000,000	2.718281827

FORMULAS FOR COMPOUND INTEREST

After t years, the balance, A, in an account with principal P and annual interest rate r (in decimal form) is given by the following formulas:

1. For n compounding periods per year: $A = P\left(1 + \frac{r}{n}\right)^{nt}$
2. For continuous compounding: $A = Pe^{rt}$.

TECHNOLOGY

You can compute e to a power using the $\boxed{e^x}$ key on your calculator. Use the key to enter e^1 and verify that e is approximately equal to 2.71828.

Scientific Calculators	Graphing Calculators
1 $\boxed{e^x}$	$\boxed{e^x}$ 1 $\boxed{\text{ENTER}}$

EXAMPLE 3 *Choosing between Investments*

You decide to invest $8000 for six years and you have a choice between two accounts. The first pays 7% per year, compounded monthly. The second pays 6.85% per year, compounded continuously. Which is the better investment?

SOLUTION

The better investment is the one with the greater balance in the account after six years. Let's begin with the account with monthly compounding. We use the compound interest formula with $P = 8000$, $r = 7\% = 0.07$, $n = 12$ (monthly compounding means 12 compounding periods per year), and $t = 6$.

$$A = P\left(1 + \frac{r}{n}\right)^{nt} = 8000\left(1 + \frac{0.07}{12}\right)^{12 \cdot 6} \approx 12{,}160.84$$

The balance in this account after six years would be $12,160.84.

TECHNOLOGY

Here are the calculator keystrokes to compute $8000e^{0.0685(6)}$:

Many Scientific Calculators

8000 [×] [(] .0685 [×] 6 [)] [e^x] [=]

Many Graphing Calculators

8000 [e^x] [(] .0685 [×] 6 [)] [ENTER]

For the second investment option, we use the formula for continuous compounding with $P = 8000$, $r = 6.85\% = 0.0685$, and $t = 6$.

$$A = Pe^{rt} = 8000e^{0.0685(6)} \approx 12{,}066.60$$

The balance in this account after six years would be $12,066.60, slightly less than the previous amount. Thus, the better investment is the 7% monthly compounding option.

CHECK POINT 3 A sum of $10,000 is invested at an annual rate of 8%. Find the balance in the account after five years subject to **a.** quarterly compounding and **b.** continuous compounding.

2 Calculate present value.

Planning for the Future with Compound Interest

Just as we did in Section 7.3, we can determine P, the principal or present value, that should be deposited now in order to have a certain amount, A, in the future. If an account earns compound interest, the amount of money that should be invested today to obtain a future value of A dollars can be determined by solving the compound interest formula for P:

CALCULATING PRESENT VALUE

If A dollars are to be accumulated in t years in an account that pays rate r compounded n times per year, then the present value, P, that needs to be invested now is given by

$$P = \frac{A}{\left(1 + \frac{r}{n}\right)^{nt}}.$$

Remember to round the principal *up* to the nearest cent when computing present value so there will be enough money to meet future goals.

EXAMPLE 4 *Calculating Present Value*

How much money should be deposited today in an account that earns 6% compounded monthly so that it will accumulate to $20,000 in five years?

TECHNOLOGY

Here are the keystrokes for Example 4:

Many Scientific Calculators

20000 [÷] [(] 1 [+] .06 [÷] 12 [)]

[y^x] [(] 12 [×] 5 [)] [=]

Many Graphing Calculators

20000 [÷] [(] 1 [+] .06 [÷] 12 [)]

[∧] [(] 12 [×] 5 [)] [ENTER]

SOLUTION

The amount we need today, or the present value, is determined by the present value formula. Because the interest is compounded monthly, $n = 12$. Furthermore, A (the future value) $= \$20{,}000$, r (the rate) $= 6\% = 0.06$, and t (time in years) $= 5$.

$$P = \frac{A}{\left(1 + \frac{r}{n}\right)^{nt}} = \frac{20{,}000}{\left(1 + \frac{0.06}{12}\right)^{12 \cdot 5}} \approx 14{,}827.4439$$

To make sure there will be enough money, we round the principal *up* to $14,827.45. Approximately $14,827.45 should be invested today in order to accumulate to $20,000 in five years.

CHECK POINT 4 How much money should be deposited today in an account that earns 7% compounded weekly so that it will accumulate to $10,000 in eight years?

Blitzer Bonus

The Time Value of Money

When you complete your education and begin earning money, it will be tempting to spend every penny earned. By doing this, you will fail to take advantage of the *time value of money*. The **time value of money** means that a dollar received today is worth more than a dollar received next year or the year after. This is because a sum of money invested today starts earning compound interest sooner than a sum of money invested some time in the future. **A significant way to increase your wealth is to spend less than you earn and invest the difference.** With time on your side, even a small amount of money can be turned into a substantial sum through the power of compounding. Make the time value of money work for you by postponing certain purchases now and investing the savings instead. Pay close attention to your spending habits as you study the time value of money.

3 Understand and compute effective annual yield.

Effective Annual Yield

As we've seen before, a common problem in financial planning is selecting the best investment from two or more investments. For example, is an investment that pays 8.25% interest compounded quarterly better than one that pays 8.3% interest compounded semiannually? Another way to answer the question is to compare the *effective rates* of the investments, also called their *effective annual yields*.

EFFECTIVE ANNUAL YIELD

The **effective annual yield**, or the **effective rate**, is the simple interest rate that produces the same amount of money in an account at the end of one year as when the account is subject to compound interest at a stated rate.

Blitzer Bonus

Doubling Your Money: The Rule of 72

Here's a shortcut for estimating the number of years it will take for your investment to double: Divide 72 by the effective annual yield without the percent sign. For example, if the effective annual yield is 6%, your money will double in approximately

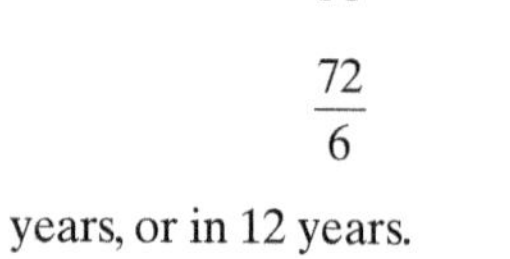

$$\frac{72}{6}$$

years, or in 12 years.

EXAMPLE 5 *Understanding Effective Annual Yield*

You deposit \$4000 in an account that pays 8% interest compounded monthly.

a. Find the future value after one year.

b. Use the future value formula for simple interest to determine the effective annual yield.

SOLUTION

a. We use the compound interest formula to find the account's future value after one year.

$$A = P\left(1 + \frac{r}{n}\right)^{nt} = 4000\left(1 + \frac{0.08}{12}\right)^{12 \cdot 1} \approx \$4332.00$$

Principal is \$4000. Stated rate is 8% = 0.08. Monthly compounding: $n = 12$ Time is one year: $t = 1$.

Rounded to the nearest cent, the future value after one year is \$4332.00.

b. The effective annual yield, or effective rate, is a simple interest rate. We use the future value formula for simple interest to determine the simple interest rate that produces a future value of \$4332 for a \$4000 deposit after one year.

Blitzer Bonus

High-Yield Savings

Online banks can afford to pay the best rates on savings accounts by avoiding the expense of managing a brick-and-mortar bank. To search for the best deals, go to BankRate.com for bank accounts and iMoneyNet.com for money-market funds.

$A = P(1 + rt)$ — This is the future value formula for simple interest.

$4332 = 4000(1 + r \cdot 1)$ — Substitute the given values.

$4332 = 4000 + 4000r$ — Use the distributive property.

$332 = 4000r$ — Subtract 4000 from both sides.

$\frac{332}{4000} = \frac{4000r}{4000}$ — Divide both sides by 4000.

$r = \frac{332}{4000} = 0.083 = 8.3\%$ — Express r as a percent.

The effective annual yield, or effective rate, is 8.3%. This means that money invested at 8.3% simple interest earns the same amount in one year as money invested at 8% interest compounded monthly.

In Example 5, the stated 8% rate is called the **nominal rate**. The 8.3% rate is the effective rate and is a simple interest rate.

CHECK POINT 5 You deposit \$6000 in an account that pays 10% interest compounded monthly.

a. Find the future value after one year.

b. Determine the effective annual yield.

Generalizing the procedure of Example 5 and Check Point 5 gives a formula for effective annual yield:

TECHNOLOGY

Here are the keystrokes for Example 6:

Many Scientific Calculators

(1 + .05 ÷ 360) y^x 360

− 1 =

Many Graphing Calculators

(1 + .05 ÷ 360) ^ 360

− 1 ENTER.

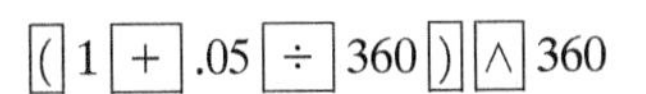

Given the nominal rate and the number of compounding periods per year, some graphing calculators display the effective annual yield. The screen shows the calculation of the effective rate in Example 6 on the TI-84 Plus.

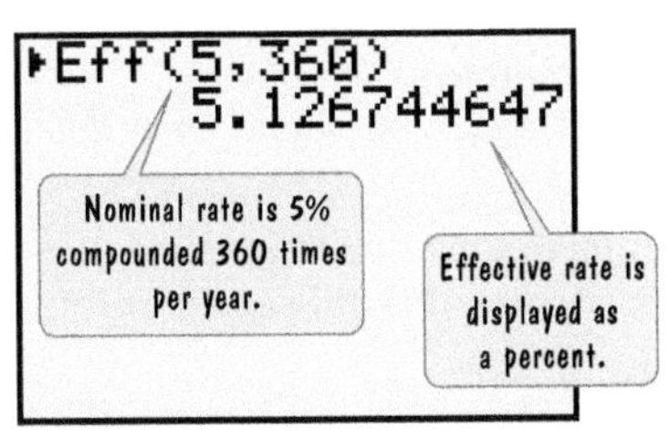

CALCULATING EFFECTIVE ANNUAL YIELD

Suppose that an investment has a nominal interest rate, r, in decimal form, and pays compound interest n times per year. The investment's effective annual yield, Y, in decimal form, is given by

$$Y = \left(1 + \frac{r}{n}\right)^n - 1.$$

The decimal form of Y given by the formula should then be converted to a percent.

EXAMPLE 6 Calculating Effective Annual Yield

A passbook savings account has a nominal rate of 5%. The interest is compounded daily. Find the account's effective annual yield. (Assume 360 days in a year.)

SOLUTION

The rate, r, is 5%, or 0.05. Because interest is compounded daily and we assume 360 days in a year, $n = 360$. The account's effective annual yield is

$$Y = \left(1 + \frac{r}{n}\right)^n - 1 = \left(1 + \frac{0.05}{360}\right)^{360} - 1 \approx 0.0513 = 5.13\%.$$

The effective annual yield is 5.13%. Thus, money invested at 5.13% simple interest earns the same amount of interest in one year as money invested at 5% interest, the nominal rate, compounded daily.

CHECK POINT 6 What is the effective annual yield of an account paying 8% compounded quarterly?

The effective annual yield is often included in the information about investments or loans. Because it's the true interest rate you're earning or paying, it's the number you should pay attention to. **If you are selecting the best investment from two or more investments, the best choice is the account with the greatest effective annual yield.** However, there are differences in the types of accounts that you need to take into consideration. Some pay interest from the day of deposit to the day of withdrawal. Other accounts start paying interest the first day of the month that follows the day of deposit. Some savings institutions stop paying interest if the balance in the account falls below a certain amount.

When *borrowing money*, the effective rate or effective annual yield is usually called the **annual percentage rate**. If all other factors are equal and you are borrowing money, select the option with the least annual percentage rate.

Concept and Vocabulary Check

Fill in each blank so that the resulting statement is true.

1. Compound interest is interest computed on the original ________ as well as on any accumulated ________.
2. The formula $A = P\left(1 + \frac{r}{n}\right)^{nt}$ gives the amount of money, A, in an account after ________ years at rate ________ subject to compound interest paid ________ times per year.
3. If interest is compounded once a year, the formula in Exercise 2 becomes ____________.
4. If compound interest is paid twice per year, the compounding period is ________ months and the interest is compounded ________.
5. If compound interest is paid four times per year, the compounding period is ________ months and the interest is compounded ________.
6. When the number of compounding periods in a year increases without bound, this is known as ________ compounding.
7. In the formula

$$P = \frac{A}{\left(1 + \frac{r}{n}\right)^{nt}},$$

the variable ________ represents the amount that needs to be invested now in order to have ________ dollars accumulated in ________ years in an account that pays rate ________ compounded ________ times per year.
8. If you are selecting the best investment from two or more investments, the best choice is the account with the greatest ____________, which is the ________ interest rate that produces the same amount of money at the end of one year as when the account is subject to compound interest at a stated rate.

In Exercises 9–12, determine whether each statement is true or false. If the statement is false, make the necessary change(s) to produce a true statement.

9. Formulas for compound interest show that a dollar invested today is worth more than a dollar invested in the future.______
10. Formulas for compound interest show that if you make the decision to postpone certain purchases and save the money instead, small amounts of money can be turned into substantial sums over a period of years.______
11. At a given annual interest rate, your money grows faster as the compounding period becomes shorter.______
12. According to the Rule of 72 (see the Blitzer Bonus on page 310), an investment with an effective annual yield of 12% can double in six years.______

Exercise Set 7.4

Here is a list of formulas needed to solve the exercises. Be sure you understand what each formula describes and the meaning of the variables in the formulas.

$$A = P\left(1 + \frac{r}{n}\right)^{nt} \qquad P = \frac{A}{\left(1 + \frac{r}{n}\right)^{nt}}$$

$$A = Pe^{rt} \qquad Y = \left(1 + \frac{r}{n}\right)^{n} - 1$$

Practice Exercises

In Exercises 1–12, the principal represents an amount of money deposited in a savings account subject to compound interest at the given rate.

a. *Find how much money there will be in the account after the given number of years. (Assume 360 days in a year.)*

b. *Find the interest earned.*

Round answers to the nearest cent.

Principal	Rate	Compounded	Time
1. $10,000	4%	annually	2 years
2. $8000	6%	annually	3 years
3. $3000	5%	semiannually	4 years
4. $4000	4%	semiannually	5 years
5. $9500	6%	quarterly	5 years
6. $2500	8%	quarterly	6 years
7. $4500	4.5%	monthly	3 years
8. $2500	6.5%	monthly	4 years
9. $1500	8.5%	daily	2.5 years
10. $1200	8.5%	daily	3.5 years
11. $20,000	4.5%	daily	20 years
12. $25,000	5.5%	daily	20 years

Solve Exercises 13–16 using appropriate compound interest formulas. Round answers to the nearest cent.

13. Find the accumulated value of an investment of $10,000 for five years at an interest rate of 5.5% if the money is **a.** compounded semiannually; **b.** compounded quarterly; **c.** compounded monthly; **d.** compounded continuously.

14. Find the accumulated value of an investment of $5000 for 10 years at an interest rate of 6.5% if the money is **a.** compounded semiannually; **b.** compounded quarterly; **c.** compounded monthly; **d.** compounded continuously.

15. Suppose that you have $12,000 to invest. Which investment yields the greater return over three years: 7% compounded monthly or 6.85% compounded continuously?

16. Suppose that you have $6000 to invest. Which investment yields the greater return over four years: 8.25% compounded quarterly or 8.3% compounded semiannually?

In Exercises 17–20, round answers up to the nearest cent.

17. How much money should be deposited today in an account that earns 6% compounded semiannually so that it will accumulate to $10,000 in three years?

18. How much money should be deposited today in an account that earns 7% compounded semiannually so that it will accumulate to $12,000 in four years?

19. How much money should be deposited today in an account that earns 9.5% compounded monthly so that it will accumulate to $10,000 in three years?

20. How much money should be deposited today in an account that earns 10.5% compounded monthly so that it will accumulate to $22,000 in four years?

21. You deposit $10,000 in an account that pays 4.5% interest compounded quarterly.

a. Find the future value after one year.

b. Use the future value formula for simple interest to determine the effective annual yield.

22. You deposit $12,000 in an account that pays 6.5% interest compounded quarterly.

a. Find the future value after one year.

b. Use the future value formula for simple interest to determine the effective annual yield.

In Exercises 23–28, a passbook savings account has a rate of 6%. Find the effective annual yield, rounded to the nearest tenth of a percent, if the interest is compounded

23. semiannually.

24. quarterly.

25. monthly.

26. daily. (Assume 360 days in a year.)

27. 1000 times per year.

28. 100,000 times per year.

In Exercises 29–32, determine the effective annual yield for each investment. Then select the better investment. Assume 360 days in a year. If rounding is required, round to the nearest tenth of a percent.

29. 8% compounded monthly; 8.25% compounded annually

30. 5% compounded monthly; 5.25% compounded quarterly

31. 5.5% compounded semiannually; 5.4% compounded daily

32. 7% compounded annually; 6.85% compounded daily

Practice Plus

In Exercises 33–36, how much more would you earn in the first investment than in the second investment? Round answers to the nearest dollar.

33.
- $25,000 invested for 40 years at 12% compounded annually
- $25,000 invested for 40 years at 6% compounded annually

34.
- $30,000 invested for 40 years at 10% compounded annually
- $30,000 invested for 40 years at 5% compounded annually

35.
- $50,000 invested for 30 years at 10% compounded annually
- $50,000 invested for 30 years at 5% compounded monthly

36.
- $20,000 invested for 30 years at 12% compounded annually
- $20,000 invested for 30 years at 6% compounded monthly

Application Exercises

Assume that the accounts described in the exercises have no other deposits or withdrawals except for what is stated. Round all answers to the nearest dollar, rounding up to the nearest dollar in present-value problems. Assume 360 days in a year.

37. At the time of a child's birth, $12,000 was deposited in an account paying 6% interest compounded semiannually. What will be the value of the account at the child's twenty-first birthday?

38. At the time of a child's birth, \$10,000 was deposited in an account paying 5% interest compounded semiannually. What will be the value of the account at the child's twenty-first birthday?

39. You deposit \$2600 in an account that pays 4% interest compounded once a year. Your friend deposits \$2200 in an account that pays 5% interest compounded monthly.

a. Who will have more money in their account after one year? How much more?

b. Who will have more money in their account after five years? How much more?

c. Who will have more money in their account after 20 years? How much more?

40. You deposit \$3000 in an account that pays 3.5% interest compounded once a year. Your friend deposits \$2500 in an account that pays 4.8% interest compounded monthly.

a. Who will have more money in their account after one year? How much more?

b. Who will have more money in their account after five years? How much more?

c. Who will have more money in their account after 20 years? How much more?

41. You deposit \$3000 in an account that pays 7% interest compounded semiannually. After 10 years, the interest rate is increased to 7.25% compounded quarterly. What will be the value of the account after 16 years?

42. You deposit \$6000 in an account that pays 5.25% interest compounded semiannually. After 10 years, the interest rate is increased to 5.4% compounded quarterly. What will be the value of the account after 18 years?

43. In 1626, Peter Minuit convinced the Wappinger Indians to sell him Manhattan Island for \$24. If the Native Americans had put the \$24 into a bank account paying compound interest at a 5% rate, how much would the investment have been worth in the year 2010 ($t = 384$ years) if interest were compounded **a.** monthly? **b.** 360 times per year?

44. In 1777, Jacob DeHaven loaned George Washington's army \$450,000 in gold and supplies. Due to a disagreement over the method of repayment (gold versus Continental money), DeHaven was never repaid, dying penniless. In 1989, his descendants sued the U.S. government over the 212-year-old debt. If the DeHavens used an interest rate of 6% and daily compounding (the rate offered by the Continental Congress in 1777), how much money did the DeHaven family demand in their suit? (*Hint:* Use the compound interest formula with $n = 360$ and $t = 212$ years.)

45. Will you earn more interest in one year by depositing \$2000 in a simple interest account that pays 6% or in an account that pays 5.9% interest compounded daily? How much more interest will you earn?

46. Will you earn more interest in one year by depositing \$1000 in a simple interest account that pays 7% or in an account that pays 6.9% interest compounded daily? How much more interest will you earn?

47. Two accounts each begin with a deposit of \$5000. Both accounts have rates of 5.5%, but one account compounds interest once a year while the other account compounds interest continuously. Make a table that shows the amount in each account and the interest earned after 1 year, 5 years, 10 years, and 20 years.

48. Two accounts each begin with a deposit of \$10,000. Both accounts have rates of 6.5%, but one account compounds interest once a year while the other account compounds interest continuously. Make a table that shows the amount in each account and the interest earned after 1 year, 5 years, 10 years, and 20 years.

49. Parents wish to have \$80,000 available for a child's education. If the child is now 5 years old, how much money must be set aside at 6% compounded semiannually to meet their financial goal when the child is 18?

50. A 30-year-old worker plans to retire at age 65. He believes that \$500,000 is needed to retire comfortably. How much should be deposited now at 7% compounded monthly to meet the \$500,000 retirement goal?

51. You would like to have \$75,000 available in 15 years. There are two options. Account A has a rate of 4.5% compounded once a year. Account B has a rate of 4% compounded daily. How much would you have to deposit in each account to reach your goal?

52. You would like to have \$150,000 available in 20 years. There are two options. Account A has a rate of 5.5% compounded once a year. Account B has a rate of 5% compounded daily. How much would you have to deposit in each account to reach your goal?

53. You invest \$1600 in an account paying 5.4% interest compounded daily. What is the account's effective annual yield? Round to the nearest hundredth of a percent.

54. You invest \$3700 in an account paying 3.75% interest compounded daily. What is the account's effective annual yield? Round to the nearest hundredth of a percent.

55. An account has a nominal rate of 4.2%. Find the effective annual yield, rounded to the nearest tenth of a percent, with quarterly compounding, monthly compounding, and daily compounding. How does changing the compounding period affect the effective annual yield?

56. An account has a nominal rate of 4.6%. Find the effective annual yield, rounded to the nearest tenth of a percent, with quarterly compounding, monthly compounding, and daily compounding. How does changing the compounding period affect the effective annual yield?

57. A bank offers a money market account paying 4.5% interest compounded semiannually. A competing bank offers a money market account paying 4.4% interest compounded daily. Which account is the better investment?

58. A bank offers a money market account paying 4.9% interest compounded semiannually. A competing bank offers a money market account paying 4.8% interest compounded daily. Which account is the better investment?

Writing in Mathematics

59. Describe the difference between simple and compound interest.

60. Give two examples that illustrate the difference between a compound interest problem involving future value and a compound interest problem involving present value.

61. What is effective annual yield?

62. Explain how to select the best investment from two or more investments.

Critical Thinking Exercises

Make Sense? *In Exercises 63–66, determine whether each statement makes sense or does not make sense, and explain your reasoning.*

63. My bank provides simple interest at 3.25% per year, but I can't determine if this is a better deal than a competing bank offering 3.25% compound interest without knowing the compounding period.

64. When choosing between two accounts, the one with the greater annual interest rate is always the better deal.

65. A bank can't increase compounding periods indefinitely without owing its customers an infinite amount of money.

66. My bank advertises a compound interest rate of 2.4%, although, without making deposits or withdrawals, the balance in my account increased by 2.43% in one year.

67. A depositor opens a new savings account with $6000 at 5% compounded semiannually. At the beginning of year 3, an additional $4000 is deposited. At the end of six years, what is the balance in the account?

68. A depositor opens a money market account with $5000 at 8% compounded monthly. After two years, $1500 is withdrawn from the account to buy a new computer. A year later, $2000 is put in the account. What will be the ending balance if the money is kept in the account for another three years?

69. Use the future value formulas for simple and compound interest in one year to derive the formula for effective annual yield.

Group Exercise

70. This activity is a group research project intended for four or five people. Present your research in a seminar on the history of interest and banking. The seminar should last about 30 minutes. Address the following questions:

When was interest first charged on loans? How was lending money for a fee opposed historically? What is usury? What connection did banking and interest rates play in the historic European rivalries between Christians and Jews? When and where were some of the highest interest rates charged? What were the rates? Where does the word *interest* come from? What is the origin of the word *shylock*? What is the difference between usury and interest in modern times? What is the history of a national bank in the United States?

Annuities, Methods of Saving, and Investments

WHAT AM I SUPPOSED TO LEARN?

After you have read this section, you should be able to:

1. Determine the value of an annuity.
2. Determine regular annuity payments needed to achieve a financial goal.
3. Understand stocks and bonds as investments.
4. Read stock tables.
5. Understand accounts designed for retirement savings.

ACCORDING TO THE *FORBES Billionaires List*, in 2012 the two richest Americans were Bill Gates (net worth: $61 billion) and Warren Buffett (net worth: $44 billion). In May 1965, Buffett's new company, Berkshire Hathaway, was selling one share of stock for $18. By the end of 2008, the price of a share had increased to $96,600. If you had purchased one share in May 1965, your **return**, or percent increase, would be

Warren Buffett and Bill Gates

$$\frac{\text{amount of increase}}{\text{original amount}} = \frac{\$96{,}600 - \$18}{\$18} \approx 5365.67 = 536{,}567\%.$$

What does a return of nearly 540,000% mean? If you had invested $250 in Warren Buffett's company in May 1965, your shares would have been worth over $1.3 million by December 2008.

Of course, investments that potentially offer outrageous returns come with great risk of losing part or all of the principal. The bottom line: Is there a safe way to save regularly and have an investment worth one million dollars or more? In this section, we consider such savings plans, some of which come with special tax treatment, as well as riskier investments in stocks and bonds.

Determine the value of an annuity.

Annuities

The compound interest formula

$$A = P(1 + r)^t$$

gives the future value, A, after t years, when a fixed amount of money, P, the principal, is deposited in an account that pays an annual interest rate r (in decimal form) compounded once a year. However, money is often invested in small amounts at periodic intervals. For example, to save for retirement, you might decide to place $1000 into an Individual Retirement Account (IRA) at the end of each year until you retire. An **annuity** is a sequence of equal payments made at equal time periods. An IRA is an example of an annuity.

The **value of an annuity** is the sum of all deposits plus all interest paid. Our first example illustrates how to find this value.

EXAMPLE 1 *Determining the Value of an Annuity*

You deposit $1000 into a savings plan at the end of each year for three years. The interest rate is 8% per year compounded annually.

a. Find the value of the annuity after three years.

b. Find the interest.

SOLUTION

a. The value of the annuity after three years is the sum of all deposits made plus all interest paid over three years.

This is the $1000 deposit at year's end.

Value at end of year 1 = $1000

This is the first-year deposit with interest earned for a year.

This is the $1000 deposit at year's end.

Value at end of year 2 = $1000(1 + 0.08) + $1000

= $1080 + $1000 = $2080

Use $A = P(1 + r)^t$ with $r = 0.08$ and $t = 1$, or $A = P(1 + 0.08)$.

This is the second-year balance, $2080, with interest earned for a year.

This is the $1000 deposit at year's end.

Value at end of year 3 = $2080(1 + 0.08) + $1000

= $2246.40 + $1000 = $3246.40

The value of the annuity at the end of three years is $3246.40.

b. You made three payments of $1000 each, depositing a total of $3 \times \$1000$, or $3000. Because the value of the annuity is $3246.40, the interest is $3246.40 − $3000, or $246.40.

CHECK POINT 1 You deposit $2000 into a savings plan at the end of each year for three years. The interest rate is 10% per year compounded annually.

a. Find the value of the annuity after three years.

b. Find the interest.

Suppose that you deposit P dollars into an account at the end of each year. The account pays an annual interest rate, r, compounded annually. At the end of the first year, the account contains P dollars. At the end of the second year, P dollars is deposited again. At the time of this deposit, the first deposit has received interest earned during the second year. Thus, the value of the annuity after two years is

$$P + P(1 + r).$$

Deposit of P dollars at end of second year

First-year deposit of P dollars with interest earned for a year

The value of the annuity after three years is

$$P + P(1 + r) + P(1 + r)^2.$$

Deposit of P dollars at end of third year

Second-year deposit of P dollars with interest earned for a year

First-year deposit of P dollars with interest earned over two years

The value of the annuity after t years is

$$P + P(1 + r) + P(1 + r)^2 + P(1 + r)^3 + \cdots + P(1 + r)^{t-1}.$$

Deposit of P dollars at end of year t

First-year deposit of P dollars with interest earned over $t - 1$ years

Each term in this sum is obtained by multiplying the preceding term by $(1 + r)$. Thus, the terms form a geometric sequence. Using a formula for the sum of the terms of a geometric sequence, we can obtain the following formula that gives the value of this annuity:

VALUE OF AN ANNUITY: INTEREST COMPOUNDED ONCE A YEAR

If P is the deposit made at the end of each year for an annuity that pays an annual interest rate r (in decimal form) compounded once a year, the value, A, of the annuity after t years is

$$A = \frac{P[(1 + r)^t - 1]}{r}.$$

EXAMPLE 2 Determining the Value of an Annuity

Although you are a long way from retirement, the time to begin retirement savings is when you begin earning a paycheck and can take advantage of the time value of your money.

Suppose that when you are 35, you decide to save for retirement by depositing \$1000 into an IRA at the end of each year for 30 years. If you can count on an interest rate of 10% per year compounded annually,

a. How much will you have from the IRA after 30 years?

b. Find the interest.

Round answers to the nearest dollar.

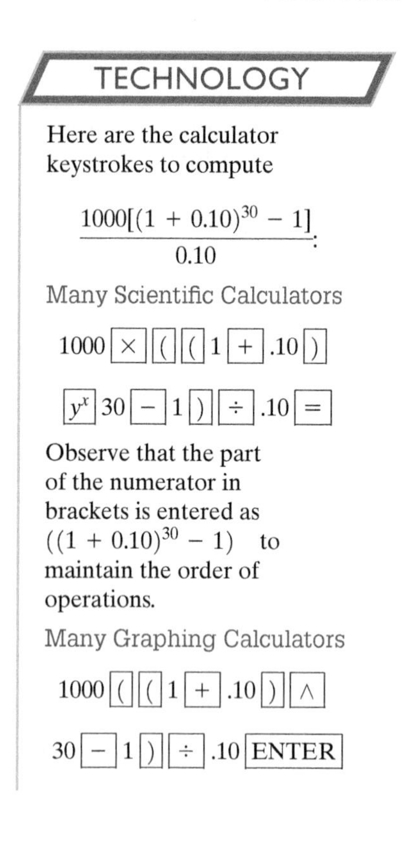

TECHNOLOGY

Here are the calculator keystrokes to compute

$$\frac{1000[(1+0.10)^{30}-1]}{0.10}:$$

Many Scientific Calculators

1000 [×] [(] [(] 1 [+] .10 [)] [y^x] 30 [−] 1 [)] [÷] .10 [=]

Observe that the part of the numerator in brackets is entered as $((1+0.10)^{30}-1)$ to maintain the order of operations.

Many Graphing Calculators

1000 [(] [(] 1 [+] .10 [)] [∧] 30 [−] 1 [)] [÷] .10 [ENTER]

SOLUTION

a. The amount that you will have from the IRA is its value after 30 years.

$$A = \frac{P[(1+r)^t - 1]}{r}$$ Use the formula for the value of an annuity.

$$A = \frac{1000[(1+0.10)^{30} - 1]}{0.10}$$ The annuity involves year-end deposits of \$1000: $P = 1000$. The interest rate is 10%: $r = 0.10$. The number of years is 30: $t = 30$. The Technology box shows how this computation can be done in a single step using parentheses keys.

$$= \frac{1000[(1.10)^{30} - 1]}{0.10}$$ Add inside parentheses: $1 + 0.10 = 1.10$.

$$\approx \frac{1000(17.4494 - 1)}{0.10}$$ Use a calculator to find $(1.10)^{30}$: 1.1 [y^x] 30 [=].

$$= \frac{1000(16.4494)}{0.10}$$ Simplify inside parentheses: $17.4494 - 1 = 16.4494$.

$$= 164{,}494$$ Use a calculator: 1000 [×] 16.4494 [÷] .10 [=].

After 30 years, you will have approximately \$164,494 from the IRA.

b. You made 30 payments of \$1000 each, depositing a total of $30 \times \$1000$, or \$30,000. Because the value of the annuity is approximately \$164,494, the interest is approximately

$$\$164{,}494 - \$30{,}000, \text{ or } \$134{,}494.$$

The interest is nearly $4\frac{1}{2}$ times the amount of your payments, illustrating the power of compounding.

GREAT QUESTION!

Can I use the formula for the value of an annuity with interest compounded *n* times per year to calculate the value of an annuity if interest is compounded only once a year?

Yes. If $n = 1$ (interest compounded once a year), the formula in the box at the right below becomes

$$A = \frac{P\left[\left(1+\frac{r}{1}\right)^{1t} - 1\right]}{\left(\frac{r}{1}\right)}, \text{ or}$$

$$A = \frac{P[(1+r)^t - 1]}{r}.$$

This was the boxed formula on page 317, showing that the value of an annuity with interest compounded once a year is just one application of the general formula in the box on the right. With this general formula, you no longer need a separate formula for annual compounding.

CHECK POINT 2 Suppose that when you are 25, you deposit \$3000 into an IRA at the end of each year for 40 years. If you can count on an interest rate of 8% per year compounded annually,

a. How much will you have from the IRA after 40 years?

b. Find the interest.

Round answers to the nearest dollar.

We can adjust the formula for the value of an annuity if equal payments are made at the end of each of *n* yearly compounding periods.

VALUE OF AN ANNUITY: INTEREST COMPOUNDED *n* TIMES PER YEAR

If *P* is the deposit made at the end of each compounding period for an annuity that pays an annual interest rate *r* (in decimal form) compounded *n* times per year, the value, *A*, of the annuity after *t* years is

$$A = \frac{P\left[\left(1+\frac{r}{n}\right)^{nt} - 1\right]}{\left(\frac{r}{n}\right)}.$$

EXAMPLE 3 *Determining the Value of an Annuity*

At age 25, to save for retirement, you decide to deposit \$200 at the end of each month into an IRA that pays 7.5% compounded monthly.

a. How much will you have from the IRA when you retire at age 65?

b. Find the interest.

Round answers to the nearest dollar.

SOLUTION

a. Because you are 25, the amount that you will have from the IRA when you retire at 65 is its value after 40 years.

$$A = \frac{P\left[\left(1+\frac{r}{n}\right)^{nt}-1\right]}{\left(\frac{r}{n}\right)}$$

Use the formula for the value of an annuity.

$$A = \frac{200\left[\left(1+\frac{0.075}{12}\right)^{12\cdot 40}-1\right]}{\left(\frac{0.075}{12}\right)}$$

The annuity involves month-end deposits of \$200: $P = 200$. The interest rate is 7.5%: $r = 0.075$. The interest is compounded monthly: $n = 12$. The number of years is 40: $t = 40$.

$$= \frac{200[(1+0.00625)^{480}-1]}{0.00625}$$

Using parentheses keys, these calculations can be performed in a single step on a calculator. Answers may slightly vary if you do the calculations in stages and round along the way.

$$= \frac{200[(1.00625)^{480}-1]}{0.00625}$$

Add inside parentheses: $1 + 0.00625 = 1.00625$.

$$\approx \frac{200(19.8989-1)}{0.00625}$$

Use a calculator to find $(1.00625)^{480}$: 1.00625 y^x 480 =.

$$\approx 604{,}765$$

After 40 years, you will have approximately \$604,765 when retiring at age 65.

b. Interest = Value of the IRA − Total deposits

$\approx \$604{,}765 - \$200 \cdot 12 \cdot 40$

\$200 per month × 12 months per year × 40 years

$= \$604{,}765 - \$96{,}000 = \$508{,}765$

The interest is approximately \$508,765, more than five times the amount of your contributions to the IRA.

Annuities can be categorized by when payments are made. The formula used to solve Example 3 describes **ordinary annuities**, where payments are made at the end of each period. The formula assumes the same number of yearly payments and yearly compounding periods. An annuity plan in which payments are made at the beginning of each period is called an **annuity due**. The formula for the value of this type of annuity is slightly different than the one used in Example 3.

CHECK POINT 3 At age 30, to save for retirement, you decide to deposit \$100 at the end of each month into an IRA that pays 9.5% compounded monthly.

a. How much will you have from the IRA when you retire at age 65?

b. Find the interest.

Round answers to the nearest dollar.

2 Determine regular annuity payments needed to achieve a financial goal.

Planning for the Future with an Annuity

By solving the annuity formula for P, we can determine the amount of money that should be deposited at the end of each compounding period so that an annuity has a future value of A dollars. The following formula gives the regular payments, P, needed to reach a financial goal, A:

REGULAR PAYMENTS NEEDED TO ACHIEVE A FINANCIAL GOAL

The deposit, P, that must be made at the end of each compounding period into an annuity that pays an annual interest rate r (in decimal form) compounded n times per year in order to achieve a value of A dollars after t years is

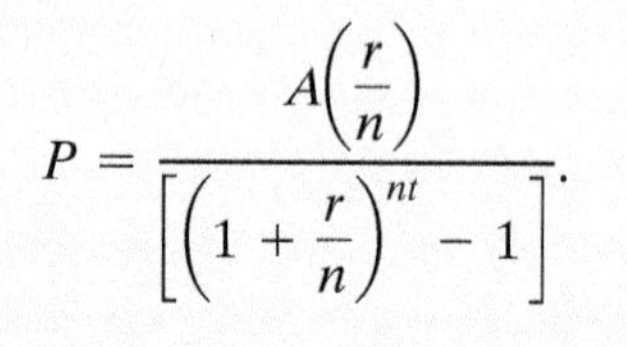

$$P = \frac{A\left(\frac{r}{n}\right)}{\left[\left(1+\frac{r}{n}\right)^{nt} - 1\right]}.$$

When computing regular payments needed to achieve a financial goal, round the deposit made at the end of each compounding period *up*. In this way, you won't fall slightly short of being able to meet future goals. In this section, we will round annuity payments up to the nearest dollar.

EXAMPLE 4 *Using Long-Term Planning to Achieve a Financial Goal*

Suppose that once you complete your college education and begin working, you would like to save \$20,000 over five years to use as a down payment for a home. You anticipate making regular, end-of-month deposits in an annuity that pays 6% compounded monthly.

a. How much should you deposit each month? Round up to the nearest dollar.

b. How much of the \$20,000 down payment comes from deposits and how much comes from interest?

SOLUTION

a. $$P = \frac{A\left(\frac{r}{n}\right)}{\left[\left(1+\frac{r}{n}\right)^{nt} - 1\right]}$$

Use the formula for regular payments, P, needed to achieve a financial goal, A.

$$P = \frac{20{,}000\left(\frac{0.06}{12}\right)}{\left[\left(1+\frac{0.06}{12}\right)^{12\cdot 5} - 1\right]}$$

Your goal is to accumulate \$20,000 ($A = 20{,}000$) over five years ($t = 5$). The interest rate is 6% ($r = 0.06$) compounded monthly ($n = 12$).

$$\approx 287$$

Use a calculator and round up to the nearest dollar to be certain you do not fall short of your goal.

You should deposit \$287 each month to be certain of having \$20,000 for a down payment on a home.

b. Total deposits $= \$287 \cdot 12 \cdot 5 = \$17{,}220$

$287 per month × 12 months per year × 5 years

Interest $= \$20{,}000 - \$17{,}220 = \$2780$

We see that $17,220 of the $20,000 comes from your deposits and the remainder, $2780, comes from interest.

CHECK POINT 4 Parents of a baby girl are in a financial position to begin saving for her college education. They plan to have $100,000 in a college fund in 18 years by making regular, end-of-month deposits in an annuity that pays 9% compounded monthly.

a. How much should they deposit each month? Round up to the nearest dollar.

b. How much of the $100,000 college fund comes from deposits and how much comes from interest?

GREAT QUESTION!

Which will earn me more money: a lump-sum deposit or an annuity?

In Example 4 of Section 7.4, we saw that a lump-sum deposit of approximately $14,828 at 6% compounded monthly would accumulate to $20,000 in five years. In Example 4 on the right, we see that total deposits of $17,220 are required to reach the same goal. With the same interest rate, compounding period, and time period, a lump-sum deposit will generate more interest than an annuity. If you don't have a large sum of money to open an account, an annuity is a realistic, although more expensive, option to a lump-sum deposit for achieving the same financial goal.

3 Understand stocks and bonds as investments.

Investments: Risk and Return

When you deposit money into a bank account, you are making a **cash investment.** Because bank accounts up to $250,000 are insured by the federal government, there is no risk of losing the principal you've invested. The account's interest rate guarantees a certain percent increase in your investment, called its **return.**

All investments involve a trade-off between risk and return. The different types of bank accounts carry little or no risk, so investors must be willing to accept low returns. There are other kinds of investments that are riskier, meaning that it is possible to lose all or part of your principal. These investments, including *stocks* and *bonds*, give a reasonable expectation of higher returns to attract investors.

Stocks

Investors purchase **stock**, shares of ownership in a company. The shares indicate the percent of ownership. For example, if a company has issued a total of one million shares and an investor owns 20,000 of these shares, that investor owns

$$\frac{20{,}000 \text{ shares}}{1{,}000{,}000 \text{ shares}} = 0.02$$

or 2% of the company. Any investor who owns some percentage of the company is called a **shareholder.**

Buying or selling stock is referred to as **trading.** Shares of stock need both a seller and a buyer to be traded. Stocks are traded on a **stock exchange.** The price of a share of stock is determined by the law of supply and demand. If a company is prospering, investors will be willing to pay a good price for its stock, and so the stock price goes up. If the company does not do well, investors may decide to sell, and the stock price goes down. Stock prices indicate the performance of the companies they represent, as well as the state of the national and global economies.

There are two ways to make money by investing in stock:

- You sell the shares for more money than what you paid for them, in which case you have a **capital gain** on the sale of stock. (There can also be a capital loss by selling for less than what you paid, or if the company goes bankrupt.)
- While you own the stock, the company distributes all or part of its profits to shareholders as **dividends.** Each share is paid the same dividend, so the amount you receive depends on the number of shares owned. (Some companies reinvest all profits and do not distribute dividends.)

When more and more average Americans began investing and making money in stocks in the 1990s, the federal government cut the capital-gains tax rate. Long-term capital gains (profits on items held for more than a year before being sold) and dividends are taxed at lower rates than wages and interest earnings.

Bonds

People who buy stock become part owners in a company. In order to raise money and not dilute the ownership of current stockholders, companies sell **bonds**. People who buy a bond are **lending money** to the company from which they buy the bond. Bonds are a commitment from a company to pay the price an investor pays for the bond at the time it was purchased, called the **face value**, along with interest payments at a given rate.

There are many reasons for issuing bonds. A company might need to raise money for research on a drug that has the potential for curing AIDS, so it issues bonds. The U.S. Treasury Department issues 30-year bonds at a fixed 7% annual rate to borrow money to cover federal deficits. Local governments often issue bonds to borrow money to build schools, parks, and libraries.

Bonds are traded like stock, and their price is a function of supply and demand. If a company goes bankrupt, bondholders are the first to claim the company's assets. They make their claims before the stockholders, even though (unlike stockholders) they do not own a share of the company. Generally speaking, investing in bonds is less risky than investing in stocks, although the return is lower.

Mutual Funds

It is not an easy job to determine which stocks and bonds to buy or sell, or when to do so. Even IRAs can be funded by mixing stocks and bonds. Many small investors have decided that they do not have the time to stay informed about the progress of corporations, even with the help of online industry research. Instead, they invest in a **mutual fund**. A mutual fund is a group of stocks and/or bonds managed by a professional investor. When you purchase shares in a mutual fund, you give your money to the **fund manager**. Your money is combined with the money of other investors in the mutual fund. The fund manager invests this pool of money, buying and selling shares of stocks and bonds to obtain the maximum possible returns.

Investors in mutual funds own a small portion of many different companies, which may protect them against the poor performance of a single company. When comparing mutual funds, consider both the fees charged for investing and how well the fund manager is doing with the fund's money. Newspapers publish ratings from 1 (worst) to 5 (best) of mutual fund performance based on whether the manager is doing a good job with its investors' money. Two numbers are given. The first number compares the performance of the mutual fund to a large group of similar funds. The second number compares the performance to funds that are nearly identical. The best rating a fund manager can receive is 5/5; the worst is 1/1.

A listing of all the investments that a person holds is called a **financial portfolio**. Most financial advisors recommend a portfolio with a mixture of low-risk and high-risk investments, called a **diversified portfolio**.

4 Read stock tables.

Reading Stock Tables

Daily newspapers and online services give current stock prices and other information about stocks. We will use FedEx (Federal Express) stock to learn how to read these daily stock tables. Look at the following newspaper listing of FedEx stock.

52-Week High	52-Week Low	Stock	SYM	Div	Yld %	PE	Vol 100s	Hi	Lo	Close	Net Chg
99.46	34.02	FedEx	FDX	.44	1.0	19	37701	45	43.47	44.08	−1.60

The headings indicate the meanings of the numbers across the row.

52-Week High
99.46

The heading **52-Week High** refers to the *highest price* at which FedEx stock traded during the past 52 weeks. The highest price was $99.46 per share. This means that during the past 52 weeks at least one investor was willing to pay $99.46 for a share of FedEx stock. Notice that 99.46 represents a quantity in dollars, although the stock table does not show the dollar sign.

52-Week Low
34.02

The heading **52-Week Low** refers to the *lowest price* at which FedEx stock traded during the past 52 weeks. This price is $34.02.

Stock	SYM
FedEx	FDX

The heading **Stock** is the *company name*, FedEx. The heading **SYM** is the *symbol* the company uses for trading. FedEx uses the symbol FDX.

Div
.44

The heading **Div** refers to *dividends* paid per share to stockholders during the past year. FedEx paid a dividend of $0.44 per share. Once again, the dollar symbol does not appear in the table. Thus, if you owned 100 shares, you received a dividend of $0.44 × 100, or $44.00.

Yld %
1.0

The heading **Yld %** stands for *percent yield*. In this case, the percent yield is 1.0%. (The stock table does not show the percent sign.) This means that the dividends alone gave investors an annual return of 1.0%. This is much lower than the average inflation rate. However, this percent does not take into account the fact that FedEx stock prices might rise. If an investor sells shares for more than the purchase price, the gain will probably make FedEx stock a much better investment than a bank account.

In order to understand the meaning of the heading PE, we need to understand some of the other numbers in the table. We will return to this column.

Vol 100s
37701

The heading **Vol 100s** stands for *sales volume in hundreds*. This is the number of shares traded yesterday, in hundreds. The number in the table is 37,701. This means that yesterday, a total of 37,701 × 100, or 3,770,100 shares of FedEx were traded.

Hi
45

The heading **Hi** stands for the *highest price* at which FedEx stock traded *yesterday*. This number is 45. Yesterday, FedEx's highest trading price was $45 a share.

Lo
43.47

The heading **Lo** stands for the *lowest price* at which FedEx stock traded *yesterday*. This number is 43.47. Yesterday, FedEx's lowest trading price was $43.47 a share.

Close
44.08

The heading **Close** stands for the *price* at which shares last traded *when the stock exchange closed yesterday*. This number is 44.08. Thus, the price at which shares of FedEx traded when the stock exchange closed yesterday was $44.08 per share. This is called yesterday's **closing price**.

Net Chg
−1.60

The heading **Net Chg** stands for *net change*. This is the change in price from the market close two days ago to yesterday's market close. This number is −1.60. Thus, the price of a share of FedEx stock went down by $1.60. For some stock listings, the notation. . . appears under Net Chg. This means that there was *no change in price* for a share of stock from the market close two days ago to yesterday's market close.

PE
19

Now, we are ready to return to the heading **PE**, standing for the *price-to-earnings ratio.*

$$\text{PE ratio} = \frac{\text{Yesterday's closing price per share}}{\text{Annual earnings per share}}$$

This can also be expressed as

$$\text{Annual earnings per share} = \frac{\text{Yesterday's closing price per share}}{\text{PE ratio}}.$$

The PE ratio for FedEx is given to be 19. Yesterday's closing price per share was 44.08. We can substitute these numbers into the formula to find annual earnings per share:

Close	PE
44.08	19

$$\text{Annual earnings per share} = \frac{44.08}{19} = 2.32.$$

The annual earnings per share for FedEx were $2.32. The PE ratio, 19, tells us that yesterday's closing price per share, $44.08, is 19 times greater than the earnings per share, $2.32.

EXAMPLE 5 *Reading Stock Tables*

52-Week High	52-Week Low	Stock	SYM	Div	Yld %	PE	Vol 100s	Hi	Lo	Close	Net Chg
42.38	22.50	Disney	DIS	.21	.6	43	115900	32.50	31.25	32.50	...

Use the stock table for Disney to answer the following questions.

a. What were the high and low prices for the past 52 weeks?

b. If you owned 3000 shares of Disney stock last year, what dividend did you receive?

c. What is the annual return for dividends alone? How does this compare to a bank account offering a 3.5% interest rate?

d. How many shares of Disney were traded yesterday?

e. What were the high and low prices for Disney shares yesterday?

f. What was the price at which Disney shares last traded when the stock exchange closed yesterday?

g. What does the value or symbol in the net change column mean?

h. Compute Disney's annual earnings per share using

$$\text{Annual earnings per share} = \frac{\text{Yesterday's closing price per share}}{\text{PE ratio}}.$$

SOLUTION

a. We find the high price for the past 52 weeks by looking under the heading **High**. The price is listed in dollars, given as 42.38. Thus, the high price for a share of stock for the past 52 weeks was $42.38. We find the low price for the past 52 weeks by looking under the heading **Low**. This price is also listed in dollars, given as 22.50. Thus, the low price for a share of Disney stock for the past 52 weeks was $22.50.

b. We find the dividend paid for a share of Disney stock last year by looking under the heading **Div**. The price is listed in dollars, given as .21. Thus, Disney paid a dividend of $0.21 per share to stockholders last year. If you owned 3000 shares, you received a dividend of $0.21 × 3000, or $630.

c. We find the annual return for dividends alone by looking under the heading **Yld %**, standing for percent yield. The number in the table, .6, is a percent. This means that the dividends alone gave Disney investors an annual return of 0.6%. This is much lower than a bank account paying a 3.5% interest rate. However, if Disney shares increase in value, the gain might make Disney stock a better investment than the bank account.

d. We find the number of shares of Disney traded yesterday by looking under the heading **Vol 100s**, standing for sales volume in hundreds. The number in the table is 115,900. This means that yesterday, a total of 115,900 × 100, or 11,590,000 shares, were traded.

e. We find the high and low prices for Disney shares yesterday by looking under the headings **Hi** and **Lo**. Both prices are listed in dollars, given as 32.50 and 31.25. Thus, the high and low prices for Disney shares yesterday were $32.50 and $31.25, respectively.

f. We find the price at which Disney shares last traded when the stock exchange closed yesterday by looking under the heading **Close**. The price is listed in dollars, given as 32.50. Thus, when the stock exchange closed yesterday, the price of a share of Disney stock was $32.50.

g. The . . . under **Net Chg** means that there was no change in price in Disney stock from the market close two days ago to yesterday's market close. In part (f), we found that the price of a share of Disney stock at yesterday's close was \$32.50, so the price at the market close two days ago was also \$32.50.

h. We are now ready to use

$$\text{Annual earnings per share} = \frac{\text{Yesterday's closing price per share}}{\text{PE ratio}}$$

to compute Disney's annual earnings per share. We found that yesterday's closing price per share was \$32.50. We find the PE ratio under the heading **PE**. The given number is 43. Thus,

$$\text{Annual earnings per share} = \frac{\$32.50}{43} \approx \$0.76.$$

The annual earnings per share for Disney were \$0.76. The PE ratio, 43, tells us that yesterday's closing price per share, \$32.50, is 43 times greater than the earnings per share, approximately \$0.76.

CHECK POINT 5 Use the stock table for Coca-Cola to solve parts (a) through (h) in Example 5 for Coca-Cola.

52-Week High	52-Week Low	Stock	SYM	Div	Yld %	PE	Vol 100s	Hi	Lo	Close	Net Chg
63.38	42.37	Coca-Cola	CocaCl	.72	1.5	37	72032	49.94	48.33	49.50	+0.03

Blitzer Bonus

The Bottom Line on Investments

Here are some investment suggestions from financial advisors:

- Do not invest money in the stock market that you will need within 10 years. Government bonds, CDs, and money-market accounts are more appropriate options for short-term goals.
- If you are a years old, approximately $(100 - a)\%$ of your investments should be in stocks. For example, at age 25, approximately $(100 - 25)\%$, or 75%, of your portfolio should be invested in stocks.
- Diversify your investments. Invest in a variety of different companies, as well as cushioning stock investments with cash investments and bonds. Diversification enables investors to take advantage of the stock market's superior returns while reducing risk to manageable levels.

Sources: Ralph Frasca, *Personal Finance*, Eighth Edition, Pearson, 2009; Eric Tyson, *Personal Finance for Dummies*, Sixth Edition, Wiley, 2010; Liz Pulliam Weston, *Easy Money*, Pearson, 2008.

5 Understand accounts designed for retirement savings.

Retirement Savings: Stashing Cash and Making Taxes Less Taxing

As you prepare for your future career, retirement probably seems very far away. However, we have seen that you can accumulate wealth much more easily if you have time to make your money work. As soon as you have a job and a paycheck, you should start putting some money away for retirement. Opening a retirement savings account early in your career is a smart way to gain more control over how you will spend a large part of your life.

You can use regular savings and investment accounts to save for retirement. There are also a variety of accounts designed specifically for retirement savings.

- A **traditional individual retirement account (IRA)** is a savings plan that allows you to set aside money for retirement, up to $5500 per year for people under 50 and $6500 per year for people 50 or older. You do not pay taxes on the money you deposit into the IRA. You can start withdrawing from your IRA when you are $59\frac{1}{2}$ years old. The withdrawals are taxed.
- A **Roth IRA** is a type of IRA with slightly different tax benefits. You pay taxes on the money you deposit into the IRA, but then you can withdraw your earnings tax-free when you are $59\frac{1}{2}$ years old. Although your contributions are not tax deductible, your earnings are never taxed, even after withdrawal.
- **Employer-sponsored retirement plans**, including 401(k) and 403(b) plans, are set up by the employer, who often makes some contribution to the plan on your behalf. These plans are not offered by all employers and are used to attract high-quality employees.

All accounts designed specifically for retirement savings have penalties for withdrawals before age $59\frac{1}{2}$.

EXAMPLE 6 *Dollars and Sense of Retirement Plans*

a. Suppose that between the ages of 25 and 35, you contribute $4000 per year to a 401(k) and your employer matches this contribution dollar for dollar on your behalf. The interest rate is 8.5% compounded annually. What is the value of the 401(k) at the end of the 10 years?

b. After 10 years of working for this firm, you move on to a new job. However, you keep your accumulated retirement funds in the 401(k). How much money will you have in the plan when you reach age 65?

c. What is the difference between the amount of money you will have accumulated in the 401(k) at age 65 and the amount you contributed to the plan?

SOLUTION

a. We begin by finding the value of your 401(k) after 10 years.

$$A = \frac{P[(1+r)^t - 1]}{r}$$

Use the formula for the value of an annuity with interest compounded once a year.

$$A = \frac{8000[(1+0.085)^{10} - 1]}{0.085}$$

You contribute $4000 and your employer matches this each year: $P = 4000 + 4000 = 8000$. The interest rate is 8.5%: $r = 0.085$. The time from age 25 to 35 is 10 years: $t = 10$.

$$\approx 118{,}681$$

Use a calculator.

The value of the 401(k) at the end of the 10 years is approximately $118,681.

b. Now we find the value of your investment at age 65.

$$A = P(1+r)^t$$

Use the formula from Section 7.4 for future value with interest compounded once a year.

$$A = 118{,}681(1+0.085)^{30}$$

The value of the 401(k) is $118,681: $P = 118{,}681$. The interest rate is 8.5%: $r = 0.085$. The time from age 35 to age 65 is 30 years: $t = 30$.

$$\approx 1{,}371{,}745$$

Use a calculator.

You will have approximately $1,371,745 in the 401(k) when you reach age 65.

c. You contributed \$4000 per year to the 401(k) for 10 years, for a total of \$4000 × 10, or \$40,000. The difference between the amount you will have accumulated in the plan at age 65, \$1,371,745, and the amount you contributed, \$40,000, is

$$\$1{,}371{,}745 - \$40{,}000, \quad \text{or} \quad \$1{,}331{,}745.$$

Even when taxes are taken into consideration, we suspect you'll be quite pleased with your earnings from 10 years of savings.

CHECK POINT 6

a. Suppose that between the ages of 25 and 40, you contribute \$2000 per year to a 401(k) and your employer contributes \$1000 per year on your behalf. The interest rate is 8% compounded annually. What is the value of the 401(k), rounded to the nearest dollar, after 15 years?

b. After 15 years of working for this firm, you move on to a new job. However, you keep your accumulated retirement funds in the 401(k). How much money, to the nearest dollar, will you have in the plan when you reach age 65?

c. What is the difference between the amount of money you will have accumulated in the 401(k) and the amount you contributed to the plan?

Concept and Vocabulary Check

Fill in each blank so that the resulting statement is true.

1. A sequence of equal payments made at equal time periods is called a/an ________.
2. In the formula

$$A = \frac{P\left[\left(1 + \frac{r}{n}\right)^{nt} - 1\right]}{\left(\frac{r}{n}\right)},$$

________ is the deposit made at the end of each compounding period, ________ is the annual interest rate compounded ________ times per year, and A is the ________ after ________ years.

3. Shares of ownership in a company are called ________. If you sell shares for more money than what you paid for them, you have a/an ________ gain on the sale. Some companies distribute all or part of their profits to shareholders as ________.
4. People who buy ________ are lending money to the company from which they buy them.
5. A listing of all the investments that a person holds is called a financial ________. To minimize risk, it should be ________, containing a mixture of low-risk and high-risk investments.
6. A group of investments managed by a professional investor is called a/an ________.
7. With a/an ________ IRA, you pay taxes on the money you deposit, but you can withdraw your earnings tax-free beginning when you are ____ years old.

In Exercises 8–11, determine whether each statement is true or false. If the statement is false, make the necessary change(s) to produce a true statement.

8. With the same interest rate, compounding period, and time period, a lump-sum deposit will generate more interest than an annuity. ______
9. People who buy bonds are purchasing shares of ownership in a company. ______
10. Stocks are generally considered higher-risk investments than bonds. ______
11. A traditional IRA requires paying taxes when withdrawing money from the account at age $59\frac{1}{2}$ or older. ______

Exercise Set 7.5

Practice Exercises

Here are the formulas needed to solve the exercises. Be sure you understand what each formula describes and the meaning of the variables in the formulas.

$$A = \frac{P[(1 + r)^t - 1]}{r} \qquad A = \frac{P\left[\left(1 + \frac{r}{n}\right)^{nt} - 1\right]}{\left(\frac{r}{n}\right)} \qquad P = \frac{A\left(\frac{r}{n}\right)}{\left[\left(1 + \frac{r}{n}\right)^{nt} - 1\right]}$$

In Exercises 1–10,

a. *Find the value of each annuity. Round to the nearest dollar.*
b. *Find the interest.*

	Periodic Deposit	Rate	Time
1.	$2000 at the end of each year	5% compounded annually	20 years
2.	$3000 at the end of each year	4% compounded annually	20 years
3.	$4000 at the end of each year	6.5% compounded annually	40 years
4.	$4000 at the end of each year	5.5% compounded annually	40 years
5.	$50 at the end of each month	6% compounded monthly	30 years

	Periodic Deposit	Rate	Time
6.	$60 at the end of each month	5% compounded monthly	30 years
7.	$100 at the end of every six months	4.5% compounded semiannually	25 years
8.	$150 at the end of every six months	6.5% compounded semiannually	25 years
9.	$1000 at the end of every three months	6.25% compounded quarterly	6 years
10.	$1200 at the end of every three months	3.25% compounded quarterly	6 years

In Exercises 11–18,

a. *Determine the periodic deposit. Round up to the nearest dollar.*
b. *How much of the financial goal comes from deposits and how much comes from interest?*

	Periodic Deposit	Rate	Time	Financial Goal
11.	$? at the end of each year	6% compounded annually	18 years	$140,000
12.	$? at the end of each year	5% compounded annually	18 years	$150,000
13.	$? at the end of each month	4.5% compounded monthly	10 years	$200,000
14.	$? at the end of each month	7.5% compounded monthly	10 years	$250,000
15.	$? at the end of each month	7.25% compounded monthly	40 years	$1,000,000
16.	$? at the end of each month	8.25% compounded monthly	40 years	$1,500,000
17.	$? at the end of every three months	3.5% compounded quarterly	5 years	$20,000
18.	$? at the end of every three months	4.5% compounded quarterly	5 years	$25,000

Exercises 19 and 20 refer to the stock tables for Goodyear (the tire company) and Dow Chemical given below. In each exercise, use the stock table to answer the following questions. Where necessary, round dollar amounts to the nearest cent.

a. *What were the high and low prices for a share for the past 52 weeks?*
b. *If you owned 700 shares of this stock last year, what dividend did you receive?*
c. *What is the annual return for the dividends alone? How does this compare to a bank offering a 3% interest rate?*
d. *How many shares of this company's stock were traded yesterday?*
e. *What were the high and low prices for a share yesterday?*
f. *What was the price at which a share last traded when the stock exchange closed yesterday?*
g. *What was the change in price for a share of stock from the market close two days ago to yesterday's market close?*
h. *Compute the company's annual earnings per share using*

$$\text{Annual earnings per share} = \frac{\text{Yesterday's closing price per share}}{\text{PE ratio}}.$$

19.

52-Week High	52-Week Low	Stock	SYM	Div	Yld %	PE	Vol 100s	Hi	Lo	Close	Net Chg
73.25	45.44	Goodyear	GT	1.20	2.2	17	5915	56.38	54.38	55.50	+1.25

20.

52-Week High	52-Week Low	Stock	SYM	Div	Yld %	PE	Vol 100s	Hi	Lo	Close	Net Chg
56.75	37.95	Dow Chemical	DOW	1.34	3.0	12	23997	44.75	44.35	44.69	+0.16

Practice Plus

Here are additional formulas that you will use to solve some of the remaining exercises. Be sure you understand what each formula describes and the meaning of the variables in the formulas.

$$A = P(1 + r)^t \qquad A = P\left(1 + \frac{r}{n}\right)^{nt}$$

In Exercises 21–22, round all answers to the nearest dollar.

21. Here are two ways of investing $30,000 for 20 years.

-

Lump-Sum Deposit	Rate	Time
$30,000	5% compounded annually	20 years

-

Periodic Deposit	Rate	Time
$1500 at the end of each year	5% compounded annually	20 years

a. After 20 years, how much more will you have from the lump-sum investment than from the annuity?

b. After 20 years, how much more interest will have been earned from the lump-sum investment than from the annuity?

22. Here are two ways of investing $40,000 for 25 years.

-

Lump-Sum Deposit	Rate	Time
$40,000	6.5% compounded annually	25 years

-

Periodic Deposit	Rate	Time
$1600 at the end of each year	6.5% compounded annually	25 years

a. After 25 years, how much more will you have from the lump-sum investment than from the annuity?

b. After 25 years, how much more interest will have been earned from the lump-sum investment than from the annuity?

23. Solve for P:

$$A = \frac{P[(1 + r)^t - 1]}{r}.$$

What does the resulting formula describe?

24. Solve for P:

$$A = \frac{P\left[\left(1 + \frac{r}{n}\right)^{nt} - 1\right]}{\left(\frac{r}{n}\right)}.$$

What does the resulting formula describe?

Application Exercises

In Exercises 25–30, round to the nearest dollar.

25. Suppose that you earned a bachelor's degree and now you're teaching high school. The school district offers teachers the opportunity to take a year off to earn a master's degree. To achieve this goal, you deposit $2000 at the end of each year in an annuity that pays 7.5% compounded annually.

a. How much will you have saved at the end of 5 years?

b. Find the interest.

26. Suppose that you earned a bachelor's degree and now you're teaching high school. The school district offers teachers the opportunity to take a year off to earn a master's degree. To achieve this goal, you deposit $2500 at the end of each year in an annuity that pays 6.25% compounded annually.

a. How much will you have saved at the end of 5 years?

b. Find the interest.

27. Suppose that at age 25, you decide to save for retirement by depositing $50 at the end of each month in an IRA that pays 5.5% compounded monthly.

a. How much will you have from the IRA when you retire at age 65?

b. Find the interest.

28. Suppose that at age 25, you decide to save for retirement by depositing $75 at the end of each month in an IRA that pays 6.5% compounded monthly.

a. How much will you have from the IRA when you retire at age 65?

b. Find the interest.

29. To offer scholarships to children of employees, a company invests $10,000 at the end of every three months in an annuity that pays 10.5% compounded quarterly.

a. How much will the company have in scholarship funds at the end of 10 years?

b. Find the interest.

30. To offer scholarships to children of employees, a company invests $15,000 at the end of every three months in an annuity that pays 9% compounded quarterly.

a. How much will the company have in scholarship funds at the end of 10 years?

b. Find the interest.

In Exercises 31–34, round up to the nearest dollar.

31. You would like to have $3500 in four years for a special vacation following college graduation by making deposits at the end of every six months in an annuity that pays 5% compounded semiannually.

a. How much should you deposit at the end of every six months?

b. How much of the $3500 comes from deposits and how much comes from interest?

32. You would like to have $4000 in four years for a special vacation following college graduation by making deposits at the end of every six months in an annuity that pays 7% compounded semiannually.

a. How much should you deposit at the end of every six months?

b. How much of the $4000 comes from deposits and how much comes from interest?

33. How much should you deposit at the end of each month into an IRA that pays 6.5% compounded monthly to have $2 million when you retire in 45 years? How much of the $2 million comes from interest?

34. How much should you deposit at the end of each month into an IRA that pays 8.5% compounded monthly to have $4 million when you retire in 45 years? How much of the $4 million comes from interest?

35. a. Suppose that between the ages of 22 and 40, you contribute $3000 per year to a 401(k) and your employer contributes $1500 per year on your behalf. The interest rate is 8.3% compounded annually. What is the value of the 401(k), rounded to the nearest dollar, after 18 years?

b. Suppose that after 18 years of working for this firm, you move on to a new job. However, you keep your accumulated retirement funds in the 401(k). How much money, to the nearest dollar, will you have in the plan when you reach age 65?

c. What is the difference between the amount of money you will have accumulated in the 401(k) and the amount you contributed to the plan?

36. a. Suppose that between the ages of 25 and 37, you contribute $3500 per year to a 401(k) and your employer matches this contribution dollar for dollar on your behalf. The interest rate is 8.25% compounded annually. What is the value of the 401(k), rounded to the nearest dollar, after 12 years?

b. Suppose that after 12 years of working for this firm, you move on to a new job. However, you keep your accumulated retirement funds in the 401(k). How much money, to the nearest dollar, will you have in the plan when you reach age 65?

c. What is the difference between the amount of money you will have accumulated in the 401(k) and the amount you contributed to the plan?

Writing in Mathematics

37. What is an annuity?

38. What is meant by the value of an annuity?

39. What is stock?

40. Describe how to find the percent ownership that a shareholder has in a company.

41. Describe the two ways that investors make money with stock.

42. What is a bond? Describe the difference between a stock and a bond.

43. If an investor sees that the return from dividends for a stock is lower than the return for a no-risk bank account, should the stock be sold and the money placed in the bank account? Explain your answer.

44. What is a mutual fund?

45. What is the difference between a traditional IRA and a Roth IRA?

46. Write a problem involving the formula for regular payments needed to achieve a financial goal. The problem should be similar to Example 4 on page 320. However, the problem should be unique to your situation. Include something for which you would like to save, how much you need to save, and how long you have to achieve your goal. Then solve the problem.

Critical Thinking Exercises

Make Sense? *In Exercises 47–53, determine whether each statement makes sense or does not make sense, and explain your reasoning.*

47. By putting $10 at the end of each month into an annuity that pays 3.5% compounded monthly, I'll be able to retire comfortably in just 30 years.

48. When I invest my money, I am making a trade-off between risk and return.

49. I have little tolerance for risk, so I must be willing to accept lower returns on my investments.

50. Diversification is like saying "don't put all your eggs in one basket."

51. Now that I've purchased bonds, I'm a shareholder in the company.

52. I've been promised a 20% return on an investment without any risk.

53. I appreciate my Roth IRA because I do not pay taxes on my deposits.

In Exercises 54–55,

a. *Determine the deposit at the end of each month. Round up to the nearest dollar.*

b. *Assume that the annuity in part (a) is a tax-deferred IRA belonging to a man whose gross income is $50,000. Use* ***Table 7.1*** *on page 293 to calculate his taxes first with and then without the IRA. Assume the man is single with no dependents, has no tax credits, and takes the standard deduction.*

c. *What percent of his gross income are the man's federal taxes with and without the IRA? Round to the nearest tenth of a percent.*

54.

Periodic Deposit	Rate	Time	Financial Goal
$? at the end of each month	8% compounded monthly	40 years	$1,000,000

55.

Periodic Deposit	Rate	Time	Financial Goal
$? at the end of each month	7% compounded monthly	40 years	$650,000

56. How much should you deposit at the end of each month in an IRA that pays 8% compounded monthly to earn $60,000 per year from interest alone, while leaving the principal untouched, when you retire in 30 years?

Group Exercises

57. Each group should have a newspaper with current stock quotations. Choose nine stocks that group members think would make good investments. Imagine that you invest $10,000 in each of these nine investments. Check the value of your stock each day over the next five weeks and then sell the nine stocks after five weeks. What is the group's profit or loss over the five-week period? Compare this figure with the profit or loss of other groups in your class for this activity.

58. This activity is a group research project intended for four or five people. Use the research to present a seminar on investments. The seminar is intended to last about 30 minutes and should result in an interesting and informative presentation to the entire class. The seminar should include investment considerations, how to read the bond section of the newspaper, how to read the mutual fund section, and higher-risk investments.

59. Group members have inherited $1 million. However, the group cannot spend any of the money for 10 years. As a group, determine how to invest this money in order to maximize the money you will make over 10 years. The money can be invested in as many ways as the group decides. Explain each investment decision. What are the risks involved in each investment plan?

7.6

WHAT AM I SUPPOSED TO LEARN?

After you have read this section, you should be able to:

1. Compute the monthly payment and interest costs for a car loan.
2. Understand the types of leasing contracts.
3. Understand the pros and cons of leasing versus buying a car.
4. Understand the different kinds of car insurance.
5. Compare monthly payments on new and used cars.
6. Solve problems related to owning and operating a car.

Cars

TO THE GUYS AT RYDELL HIGH IN THE musical *Grease!*, Kenickie's new car looks like a hunk of junk, but to him it's Greased Lightnin', a hot-rodding work of art on wheels. As with many teens, Kenickie's first car is a rite of passage—a symbol of emerging adulthood.

Our love affair with cars began in the early 1900s when Henry Ford cranked out the first Model T. Since then, we've admired cars to the point of identifying with the vehicles we drive. Cars can serve as status symbols, providing unique insights into a driver's personality.

In this section, we view cars from another vantage point—money. The money pit of owning a car ranges from financing the purchase to escalating costs of everything from fuel to tires to insurance. We open the section with the main reason people spend more money on a car than they can afford: financing.

The Mathematics of Financing a Car

A loan that you pay off with weekly or monthly payments, or payments in some other time period, is called an **installment loan**. The advantage of an installment loan is that the consumer gets to use a product immediately. The disadvantage is that the interest can add a substantial amount to the cost of a purchase.

Let's begin with car loans in which you make regular monthly payments, called **fixed installment loans**. Suppose that you borrow P dollars at interest rate r over t years.

The lender expects A dollars at the end of t years.

$$A = P\left(1 + \frac{r}{n}\right)^{nt}$$

You save the A dollars in an annuity by paying PMT dollars n times per year.

$$A = \frac{PMT\left[\left(1 + \frac{r}{n}\right)^{nt} - 1\right]}{\left(\frac{r}{n}\right)}$$

To find your regular payment amount, PMT, we set the amount the lender expects to receive equal to the amount you will save in the annuity:

$$P\left(1 + \frac{r}{n}\right)^{nt} = \frac{PMT\left[\left(1 + \frac{r}{n}\right)^{nt} - 1\right]}{\left(\frac{r}{n}\right)}.$$

Solving this equation for PMT, we obtain a formula for the loan payment for any installment loan, including payments on car loans.

Compute the monthly payment and interest costs for a car loan.

LOAN PAYMENT FORMULA FOR FIXED INSTALLMENT LOANS

The regular payment amount, PMT, required to repay a loan of P dollars paid n times per year over t years at an annual rate r is given by

$$PMT = \frac{P\left(\frac{r}{n}\right)}{\left[1 - \left(1 + \frac{r}{n}\right)^{-nt}\right]}.$$

EXAMPLE 1 *Comparing Car Loans*

Suppose that you decide to borrow \$20,000 for a new car. You can select one of the following loans, each requiring regular monthly payments:

Installment Loan A: three-year loan at 7%
Installment Loan B: five-year loan at 9%.

a. Find the monthly payments and the total interest for Loan A.
b. Find the monthly payments and the total interest for Loan B.
c. Compare the monthly payments and total interest for the two loans.

SOLUTION

For each loan, we use the loan payment formula to compute the monthly payments.

a. We first determine monthly payments and total interest for Loan A.

$$PMT = \frac{P\left(\frac{r}{n}\right)}{\left[1 - \left(1 + \frac{r}{n}\right)^{-nt}\right]} = \frac{20{,}000\left(\frac{0.07}{12}\right)}{\left[1 - \left(1 + \frac{0.07}{12}\right)^{-12(3)}\right]} \approx 618$$

P, the loan amount, is \$20,000. *Rate, r, is 7%.* *12 payments per year* *The loan is for 3 years.*

The monthly payments are approximately \$618.

Now we calculate the interest over three years, or 36 months.

Total interest over 3 years = *Total of all monthly payments* *minus* *amount of the loan.*

$$= \$618 \times 36 - \$20{,}000$$
$$= \$2248$$

The total interest paid over three years is approximately \$2248.

b. Next, we determine monthly payments and total interest for Loan B.

$$PMT = \frac{P\left(\frac{r}{n}\right)}{\left[1 - \left(1 + \frac{r}{n}\right)^{-nt}\right]} = \frac{20{,}000\left(\frac{0.09}{12}\right)}{\left[1 - \left(1 + \frac{0.09}{12}\right)^{-12(5)}\right]} \approx 415$$

P, the loan amount, is \$20,000. *Rate, r, is 9%.* *12 payments per year* *The loan is for 5 years.*

The monthly payments are approximately \$415.

TECHNOLOGY

Here are the calculator keystrokes to compute

$$\frac{20{,}000\left(\frac{0.07}{12}\right)}{\left[1 - \left(1 + \frac{0.07}{12}\right)^{-12(3)}\right]}.$$

Begin by simplifying the exponent, $-12(3)$, to -36 to avoid possible errors with parentheses:

$$\frac{20{,}000\left(\frac{0.07}{12}\right)}{\left[1 - \left(1 + \frac{0.07}{12}\right)^{-36}\right]}.$$

Scientific and graphing calculator keystrokes require placing parentheses around the expressions in both the numerator and the denominator.

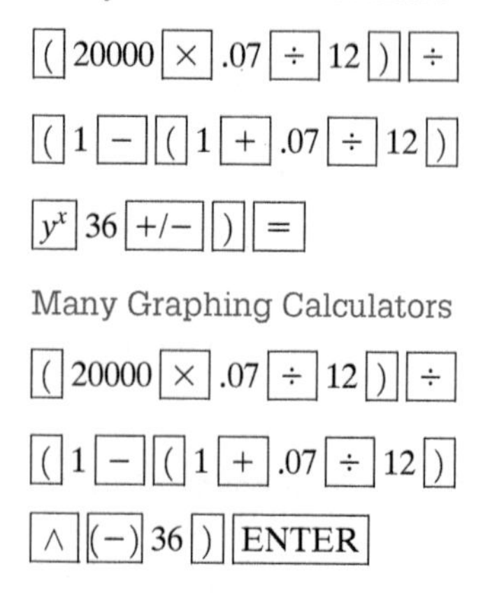

Answers may vary if you do calculations in stages and round along the way.

Now we calculate the interest over five years, or 60 months.

$$\text{Total interest over 5 years} = \text{Total of all monthly payments} \text{ minus } \text{amount of the loan.}$$

$$= \$415 \times 60 - \$20{,}000$$

$$= \$4900$$

The total interest paid over five years is approximately $4900.

c. **Table 7.6** compares the monthly payments and total interest for the two loans.

Table 7.6 Comparing Car Loans

$20,000 loan	Monthly Payment	Total Interest
3-year loan at 7%	$618	$2248
5-year loan at 9%	$415	$4900

Monthly payments are less with the longer-term loan.

Interest is more with the longer-term loan.

CHECK POINT 1 Suppose that you decide to borrow $15,000 for a new car. You can select one of the following loans, each requiring regular monthly payments:

Installment Loan A: four-year loan at 8%
Installment Loan B: six-year loan at 10%.

a. Find the monthly payments and the total interest for Loan A.

b. Find the monthly payments and the total interest for Loan B.

c. Compare the monthly payments and total interest for the two loans.

Blitzer Bonus

Financing Your Car

- Check out financing options. It's a good idea to get preapproved for a car loan through a bank or credit union before going to the dealer. You can then compare the loan offered by the dealer to your preapproved loan. Furthermore, with more money in hand, you'll have more negotiating power.
- Dealer financing often costs 1% or 2% more than a bank or credit union. Shop around for interest rates. Credit unions traditionally offer the best rates on car loans, more than 1.5% less on average than a bank loan.
- Put down as much money as you can. Interest rates generally decrease as the money you put down toward the car increases. Furthermore, you'll be borrowing less money, thereby paying less interest.
- A general rule is that you should spend no more than 20% of your net monthly income on a car payment.

2 Understand the types of leasing contracts.

The Leasing Alternative

Leasing is the practice of paying a specified amount of money over a specified time for the use of a product. Leasing is essentially a long-term rental agreement.

Leasing a car instead of buying one has become increasingly popular over the past several years. There are two types of leasing contracts:

- **A closed-end lease:** Each month, you make a fixed payment based on estimated usage. When the lease ends, you return the car and pay for mileage in excess of your estimate.

- **An open-end lease:** Each month you make a fixed payment based on the car's *residual value*. **Residual value** is the estimated resale value of the car at the end of the lease and is determined by the dealer. When the lease ends, you return the car and make a payment based on its appraised value at that time compared to its residual value. If the appraised value is less than the residual value stated in the lease, you pay all or a portion of the difference. If the appraised value is greater than or equal to the residual value, you owe nothing and you may receive a refund.

3 Understand the pros and cons of leasing versus buying a car.

Leasing a car offers both advantages and disadvantages over buying one.

Advantages of Leasing

- Leases require only a small down payment, or no down payment at all.
- Lease payments for a new car are lower than loan payments for the same car. Most people can lease a more expensive car than they would be able to buy.
- When the lease ends, you return the car to the dealer and do not have to be concerned about selling the car.

Disadvantages of Leasing

- When the lease ends, you do not own the car.
- Most lease agreements have mileage limits: 12,000 to 15,000 miles per year is common. If you exceed the number of miles allowed, there can be considerable charges.
- When mileage penalties and other costs at the end of the leasing period are taken into consideration, the total cost of leasing is almost always more expensive than financing a car.
- While leasing the car, you are responsible for keeping it in perfect condition. You are liable for any damage to the car.
- Leasing does not cover maintenance.
- There are penalties for ending the lease early.

Car leases tend to be extremely complicated. It can appear that there are as many lease deals as there are kinds of cars. A helpful pamphlet entitled "Keys to Vehicle Leasing" is published by the Federal Reserve Board. Copies are available on the Internet. Additional information can be found at websites such as home.autos.msn.com or intellichoice.com.

4 Understand the different kinds of car insurance.

The Importance of Auto Insurance

Who needs auto insurance? The simple answer is that if you own or lease a car, you do.

When you purchase **insurance**, you buy protection against loss associated with unexpected events. Different types of coverage are associated with auto insurance, but the one required by nearly every state is *liability*. There are two components of **liability coverage**:

- **Bodily injury liability** covers the costs of lawsuits if someone is injured or killed in an accident in which you are at fault.
- **Property damage liability** covers damage to other cars and property from negligent operation of your vehicle.

If you have a car loan or lease a car, you will also need *collision* and *comprehensive* coverage:

- **Collision coverage** pays for damage or loss of your car if you're in an accident.
- **Comprehensive coverage** protects your car from perils such as fire, theft, falling objects, acts of nature, and collision with an animal.

There is a big difference in auto insurance rates, so be sure to shop around. Insurance can be very expensive for younger drivers with limited driving experience. A poor driving record dramatically increases your insurance rates. Other factors that impact your insurance premium include where you live, the number of miles you drive each year, and the value of your car.

5 Compare monthly payments on new and used cars.

New or Used?

Who insists you need a new car? A new car loses an average of 12% of its value the moment it is driven off the dealer's lot. It's already a used car and you haven't even arrived home.

Used cars are a good option for many people. Your best buy is typically a two- to three-year-old car because the annual depreciation in price is greatest over the first few years. Furthermore, many sources of financing for used cars will loan money only on newer models that are less than five years old. Reputable car dealerships offer a good selection of used cars, with extended warranties and other perks.

The two most commonly used sources of pricing information for used cars are the *National Automobile Dealers Association Official Used Car Guide* (www.nada.com) and the *Kelley Blue Book Used Car Guide* (www.kbb.com). They contain the average retail price for many different makes of used cars.

EXAMPLE 2 *Saving Money with a Used Car*

Suppose that you are thinking about buying a car and have narrowed down your choices to two options:

- The new-car option: The new car costs \$25,000 and can be financed with a four-year loan at 7.9%.
- The used-car option: A three-year-old model of the same car costs \$14,000 and can be financed with a four-year loan at 8.45%.

What is the difference in monthly payments between financing the new car and financing the used car?

SOLUTION

We first determine the monthly payments for the new car that costs \$25,000, financed with a four-year loan at 7.9%.

P, the loan amount, is \$25,000. Rate, *r*, is 7.9%. 12 payments per year. The loan is for 4 years.

$$PMT = \frac{P\left(\frac{r}{n}\right)}{\left[1-\left(1+\frac{r}{n}\right)^{-nt}\right]} = \frac{25{,}000\left(\frac{0.079}{12}\right)}{\left[1-\left(1+\frac{0.079}{12}\right)^{-12(4)}\right]} \approx 609$$

The monthly payments for the new car are approximately \$609. Now we determine the monthly payments for the used car that costs \$14,000, financed with a four-year loan at 8.45%.

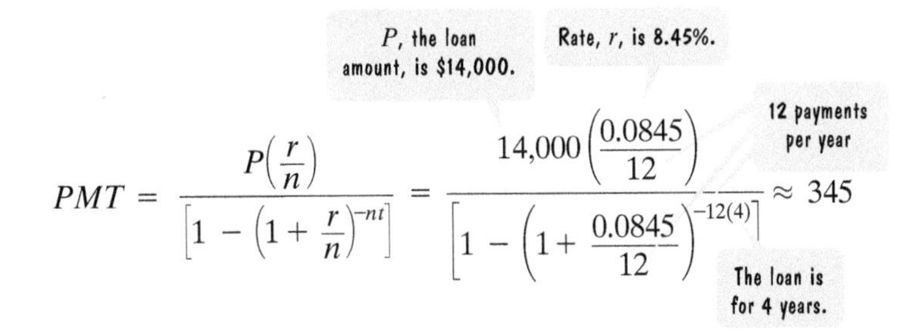

$$PMT = \frac{P\left(\frac{r}{n}\right)}{\left[1-\left(1+\frac{r}{n}\right)^{-nt}\right]} = \frac{14{,}000\left(\frac{0.0845}{12}\right)}{\left[1-\left(1+\frac{0.0845}{12}\right)^{-12(4)}\right]} \approx 345$$

The monthly payments for the used car are approximately \$345. The difference in monthly payments between the new-car loan, \$609, and the used-car loan, \$345, is

\$609 − \$345, or \$264.

You save \$264 each month over a period of four years with the used-car option.

CHECK POINT 2 Suppose that you are thinking about buying a car and have narrowed down your choices to two options:

The new-car option: The new car costs \$19,000 and can be financed with a three-year loan at 6.18%.

The used-car option: A two-year-old model of the same car costs \$11,500 and can be financed with a three-year loan at 7.5%.

What is the difference in monthly payments between financing the new car and financing the used car?

6 Solve problems related to owning and operating a car.

The Money Pit of Car Ownership

Buying a car is a huge expense. To make matters worse, the car continues costing money after you purchase it. These costs include operating expenses such as fuel, maintenance, tires, tolls, parking, and cleaning. The costs also include ownership expenses such as insurance, license fees, registration fees, taxes, and interest on loans.

The significant expense of owning and operating a car is shown in **Table 7.7**. According to the American Automobile Association (AAA), the average yearly cost of owning and operating a car is just under \$9000.

TABLE 7.7 Annual Costs of Owning and Operating a Car in 2012*

Type of Car	Small Sedan	Medium Sedan	Minivan	Large Sedan	SUV 4WD
Cost per mile	44.9¢	58.5¢	63.4¢	75.5¢	75.7¢
Cost per year	\$6735	\$8780	\$9504	\$11,324	\$11,360

* Based on driving 15,000 miles per year.
Source: AAA

A large portion of a car's operating expenses involves the cost of gasoline. As the luster of big gas-guzzlers becomes less appealing, many people are turning to fuel-efficient hybrid cars that use a combination of gasoline and rechargeable batteries as power sources.

Our next example compares fuel expenses for a gas-guzzler and a hybrid. You can estimate the annual fuel expense for a vehicle if you know approximately how many miles the vehicle will be driven each year, how many miles the vehicle can be driven per gallon of gasoline, and how much a gallon of gasoline will cost.

THE COST OF GASOLINE

$$\text{Annual fuel expense} = \frac{\text{annual miles driven}}{\text{miles per gallon}} \times \text{price per gallon}$$

EXAMPLE 3 *Comparing Fuel Expenses*

Suppose that you drive 24,000 miles per year and gas averages \$4 per gallon.

a. What will you save in annual fuel expenses by owning a hybrid car averaging 50 miles per gallon rather than an SUV (sport utility vehicle) averaging 12 miles per gallon?

b. If you deposit your monthly fuel savings at the end of each month into an annuity that pays 7.3% compounded monthly, how much will you have saved at the end of six years?

SOLUTION

a. We use the formula for annual fuel expense.

$$\text{Annual fuel expense} = \frac{\text{annual miles driven}}{\text{miles per gallon}} \times \text{price per gallon}$$

$$\text{Annual fuel expense for the hybrid} = \frac{24{,}000}{50} \times \$4 = 480 \times \$4 = \$1920$$

The hybrid averages 50 miles per gallon.

$$\text{Annual fuel expense for the SUV} = \frac{24{,}000}{12} \times \$4 = 2000 \times \$4 = \$8000$$

The SUV averages 12 miles per gallon.

Your annual fuel expense is \$1920 for the hybrid and \$8000 for the SUV. By owning the hybrid rather than the SUV, you save

$$\$8000 - \$1920, \text{ or } \$6080$$

in annual fuel expenses.

b. Because you save \$6080 per year, you save

$$\frac{\$6080}{12} \approx \$507,$$

or approximately \$507 per month. Now you deposit \$507 at the end of each month into an annuity that pays 7.3% compounded monthly. We use the formula for the value of an annuity to determine your savings at the end of six years.

$$A = \frac{P\left[\left(1 + \frac{r}{n}\right)^{nt} - 1\right]}{\left(\frac{r}{n}\right)}$$

Use the formula for the value of an annuity.

$$A = \frac{507\left[\left(1 + \frac{0.073}{12}\right)^{12 \cdot 6} - 1\right]}{\left(\frac{0.073}{12}\right)}$$

The annuity involves month-end deposits of \$507: $P = 507$. The interest rate is 7.3%: $r = 0.073$. The interest is compounded monthly: $n = 12$. The number of years is 6: $t = 6$.

$$\approx 45{,}634$$

Use a calculator.

You will have saved approximately \$45,634 at the end of six years. This illustrates how driving a car that consumes less gas can yield significant savings for your future.

CHECK POINT 3 Suppose that you drive 36,000 miles per year and gas averages \$3.50 per gallon.

a. What will you save in annual fuel expenses by owning a hybrid car averaging 40 miles per gallon rather than an SUV averaging 15 miles per gallon?

b. If you deposit your monthly fuel savings at the end of each month into an annuity that pays 7.25% compounded monthly, how much will you have saved at the end of seven years? Round all computations to the nearest dollar.

Concept and Vocabulary Check

Fill in each blank so that the resulting statement is true.

1. In the formula

$$PMT = \frac{P\left(\frac{r}{n}\right)}{\left[1 - \left(1 + \frac{r}{n}\right)^{-nt}\right]},$$

_______ is the regular payment amount required to repay a loan of _______ dollars paid _______ times per year over _______ years at an annual interest rate _______.

2. The two types of contracts involved with leasing a car are called a/an _______ lease and a/an _______ lease.
3. The estimated resale value of a car at the end of its lease is called the car's _______.
4. There are two components of liability insurance. The component that covers costs if someone is injured or killed in an accident in which you are at fault is called _______ liability. The component that covers damage to other cars if you are at fault is called _______ liability.
5. The type of car insurance that pays for damage or loss of your car if you're in an accident is called _______ coverage.
6. The type of insurance that pays for damage to your car due to fire, theft, or falling objects is called _______ coverage.

In Exercises 7–12, determine whether each statement is true or false. If the statement is false, make the necessary changes(s) to produce a true statement.

7. The interest on a car loan can be determined by taking the difference between the total of all monthly payments and the amount of the loan. _______
8. When an open-end lease terminates and the car's appraised value is less than the residual value stated in the lease, you owe nothing. _______
9. One advantage to leasing a car is that you are not responsible for any damage to the car. _______
10. One disadvantage to leasing a car is that most lease agreements have mileage limits. _______
11. Collision coverage pays for damage to another car if you cause an accident. _______
12. Due to operating and ownership expenses, a car continues costing money after you buy it. _______

Exercise Set 7.6

Practice and Application Exercises

In Exercises 1–10, use

$$PMT = \frac{P\left(\frac{r}{n}\right)}{\left[1 - \left(1 + \frac{r}{n}\right)^{-nt}\right]}.$$

Round answers to the nearest dollar.

1. Suppose that you borrow \$10,000 for four years at 8% toward the purchase of a car. Find the monthly payments and the total interest for the loan.
2. Suppose that you borrow \$30,000 for four years at 8% for the purchase of a car. Find the monthly payments and the total interest for the loan.
3. Suppose that you decide to borrow \$15,000 for a new car. You can select one of the following loans, each requiring regular monthly payments:

   Installment Loan A: three-year loan at 5.1%
   Installment Loan B: five-year loan at 6.4%.

   a. Find the monthly payments and the total interest for Loan A.
   b. Find the monthly payments and the total interest for Loan B.
   c. Compare the monthly payments and the total interest for the two loans.
4. Suppose that you decide to borrow \$40,000 for a new car. You can select one of the following loans, each requiring regular monthly payments:

   Installment Loan A: three-year loan at 6.1%
   Installment Loan B: five-year loan at 7.2%.

   a. Find the monthly payments and the total interest for Loan A.
   b. Find the monthly payments and the total interest for Loan B.
   c. Compare the monthly payments and the total interest for the two loans.
5. Suppose that you are thinking about buying a car and have narrowed down your choices to two options:

   The new-car option: The new car costs \$28,000 and can be financed with a four-year loan at 6.12%.

   The used-car option: A three-year old model of the same car costs \$16,000 and can be financed with a four-year loan at 6.86%.

   What is the difference in monthly payments between financing the new car and financing the used car?
6. Suppose that you are thinking about buying a car and have narrowed down your choices to two options:

   The new-car option: The new car costs \$68,000 and can be financed with a four-year loan at 7.14%.

   The used-car option: A three-year old model of the same car costs \$28,000 and can be financed with a four-year loan at 7.92%.

   What is the difference in monthly payments between financing the new car and financing the used car?

7. Suppose that you decide to buy a car for $29,635, including taxes and license fees. You saved $9000 for a down payment and can get a five-year car loan at 6.62%. Find the monthly payment and the total interest for the loan.

8. Suppose that you decide to buy a car for $37,925, including taxes and license fees. You saved $12,000 for a down payment and can get a five-year loan at 6.58%. Find the monthly payment and the total interest for the loan.

9. Suppose that you are buying a car for $60,000, including taxes and license fees. You saved $10,000 for a down payment. The dealer is offering you two incentives:

Incentive A is $5000 off the price of the car, followed by a five-year loan at 7.34%.

Incentive B does not have a cash rebate, but provides free financing (no interest) over five years.

What is the difference in monthly payments between the two offers? Which incentive is the better deal?

10. Suppose that you are buying a car for $56,000, including taxes and license fees. You saved $8000 for a down payment. The dealer is offering you two incentives:

Incentive A is $10,000 off the price of the car, followed by a four-year loan at 12.5%.

Incentive B does not have a cash rebate, but provides free financing (no interest) over four years.

What is the difference in monthly payments between the two offers? Which incentive is the better deal?

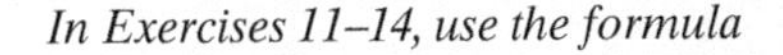

In Exercises 11–14, use the formula

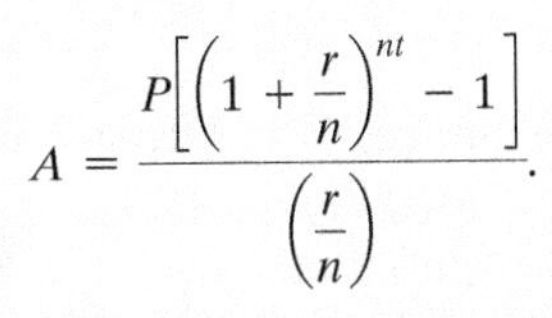

$$A = \frac{P\left[\left(1 + \frac{r}{n}\right)^{nt} - 1\right]}{\left(\frac{r}{n}\right)}.$$

Round all computations to the nearest dollar.

11. Suppose that you drive 40,000 miles per year and gas averages $4 per gallon.

a. What will you save in annual fuel expenses by owning a hybrid car averaging 40 miles per gallon rather than an SUV averaging 16 miles per gallon?

b. If you deposit your monthly fuel savings at the end of each month into an annuity that pays 5.2% compounded monthly, how much will you have saved at the end of six years?

12. Suppose that you drive 15,000 miles per year and gas averages $3.50 per gallon.

a. What will you save in annual fuel expenses by owning a hybrid car averaging 60 miles per gallon rather than an SUV averaging 15 miles per gallon?

b. If you deposit your monthly fuel savings at the end of each month into an annuity that pays 5.7% compounded monthly, how much will you have saved at the end of six years?

The table shows the expense of operating and owning four selected cars, by average costs per mile. Use the appropriate information in the table to solve Exercises 13–16.

AVERAGE ANNUAL COSTS OF OWNING AND OPERATING A CAR

	Average Costs per Mile		
Make and Model	**Operating**	**Ownership**	**Total**
Cadillac STS	$0.26	$0.72	$0.98
Mercury Grand Marquis GS	$0.23	$0.42	$0.65
Honda Accord LX	$0.21	$0.34	$0.55
Toyota Corolla CE	$0.15	$0.25	$0.40

Source: Runzheimer International

13. a. If you drive 20,000 miles per year, what is the total annual expense for a Cadillac STS?

b. If the total annual expense for a Cadillac STS is deposited at the end of each year into an IRA paying 8.5% compounded yearly, how much will be saved at the end of six years?

14. a. If you drive 14,000 miles per year, what is the total annual expense for a Toyota Corolla CE?

b. If the total annual expense for a Toyota Corolla CE is deposited at the end of each year into an IRA paying 8.2% compounded yearly, how much will be saved at the end of six years?

15. If you drive 30,000 miles per year, by how much does the total annual expense for a Cadillac STS exceed that of a Toyota Corolla CE over six years?

16. If you drive 25,000 miles per year, by how much does the total annual expense for a Mercury Grand Marquis GS exceed that of a Honda Accord LX over six years?

Writing in Mathematics

17. If a three-year car loan has the same interest rate as a six-year car loan, how do the monthly payments and the total interest compare for the two loans?

18. What is the difference between a closed-end car lease and an open-end car lease?

19. Describe two advantages of leasing a car over buying one.

20. Describe two disadvantages of leasing a car over buying one.

21. What are the two components of liability coverage and what is covered by each component?

22. What does collision coverage pay for?

23. What does comprehensive coverage pay for?

24. How can you estimate a car's annual fuel expense?

Critical Thinking Exercises

Make Sense? *In Exercises 25–30, determine whether each statement makes sense or does not make sense, and explain your reasoning.*

25. If I purchase a car using money that I've saved, I can eliminate paying interest on a car loan, but then I have to give up the interest income I could have earned on my savings.

26. The problem with my car lease is that when it ends, I have to be concerned about selling the car.
27. Although lease payments for a new car are lower than loan payments for the same car, once I take mileage penalties and other costs into consideration, the total cost of leasing is more expensive than financing the car.
28. I've paid off my car loan, so I am not required to have liability coverage.
29. Buying a used car or a fuel-efficient car can yield significant savings for my future.
30. Because it is extremely expensive to own and operate a car, I plan to look closely at whether or not a car is essential and consider other modes of transportation.
31. Use the discussion at the bottom of page 331 to prove the loan payment formula shown in the box at the top of page 332. Work with the equation in which the amount the lender expects to receive is equal to the amount saved in the annuity. Multiply both sides of this equation by $\frac{r}{n}$ and then solve for PMT by dividing both sides by the appropriate expression. Finally, divide the numerator and the denominator of the resulting formula for PMT by $(1 + \frac{r}{n})^{nt}$ to obtain the form of the loan payment formula shown in the box.
32. The unpaid balance of an installment loan is equal to the present value of the remaining payments. The unpaid balance, P, is given by

$$P = PMT\frac{\left[1 - \left(1 + \frac{r}{n}\right)^{-nt}\right]}{\left(\frac{r}{n}\right)},$$

where PMT is the regular payment amount, r is the annual interest rate, n is the number of payments per year, and t is the number of years remaining in the loan.

a. Use the loan payment formula to derive the unpaid balance formula.

b. The price of a car is \$24,000. You have saved 20% of the price as a down payment. After the down payment, the balance is financed with a 5-year loan at 9%. Determine the unpaid balance after three years. Round all calculations to the nearest dollar.

Group Exercises

33. Group members should go to the Internet and select a car that they might like to buy. Price the car and its options. Then find two loans with the best rates, but with different terms. For each loan, calculate the monthly payments and total interest.

34. **Student Loans**

Group members should present a report on federal loans to finance college costs, including Stafford loans, Perkins loans, and PLUS loans. Also include a discussion of grants that do not have to be repaid, such as Pell Grants and National Merit Scholarships. Refer to *Funding Education Beyond High School*, published by the Department of Education and available at studentaid.ed.gov. Use the loan repayment formula that we applied to car loans to determine regular payments and interest on some of the loan options presented in your report.

7.7 The Cost of Home Ownership

WHAT AM I SUPPOSED TO LEARN?

After you have read this section, you should be able to:

1 Compute the monthly payment and interest costs for a mortgage.

2 Prepare a partial loan amortization schedule.

3 Solve problems involving what you can afford to spend for a mortgage.

4 Understand the pros and cons of renting versus buying.

THE BIGGEST SINGLE PURCHASE THAT MOST PEOPLE make in their lives is the purchase of a home. If you choose home ownership at some point in the future, it is likely that you will finance the purchase with an installment loan. Knowing the unique issues surrounding the purchase of a home, and whether or not this aspect of the American dream is right for you, can play a significant role in your financial future.

Mortgages

A **mortgage** is a long-term installment loan (perhaps up to 30, 40, or even 50 years) for the purpose of buying a home, and for which the property is pledged as security for payment. If payments are not made on the loan, the lender may take possession of the property. The **down payment** is the portion of the sale price of the home that the buyer initially pays to the seller. The minimum required down payment is computed as a percentage of the sale price. For example, suppose you decide to buy a \$220,000 home. The lender requires you to pay the seller 10% of the sale price. You must pay 10% of \$220,000, which is $0.10 \times 220{,}000$ or \$22,000, to the seller. Thus, \$22,000 is the down payment. The **amount of the mortgage** is the difference between the sale price and the down payment. For your \$220,000 home, the amount of the mortgage is \$220,000 − \$22,000, or \$198,000.

Monthly payments for a mortgage depend on the amount of the mortgage (the principal), the interest rate, and the duration of the mortgage. Mortgages can have a fixed interest rate or a variable interest rate. **Fixed-rate mortgages** have the same monthly principal and interest payment during the entire time of the loan. A loan like this that has a schedule for paying a fixed amount each period is called a **fixed installment loan**. **Variable-rate mortgages**, also known as **adjustable-rate mortgages** (ARMs), have payment amounts that change from time to time depending on changes in the interest rate. ARMs are less predictable than fixed-rate mortgages. They start out at lower rates than fixed-rate mortgages. Caps limit how high rates can go over the term of the loan.

Compute the monthly payment and interest costs for a mortgage.

Computations Involved with Buying a Home

Although monthly payments for a mortgage depend on the amount of the mortgage, the duration of the loan, and the interest rate, the interest is not the only cost of a mortgage. Most lending institutions require the buyer to pay one or more **points** at the time of closing—that is, the time at which the mortgage begins. A point is a one-time charge that equals 1% of the loan amount. For example, two points means that the buyer must pay 2% of the loan amount at closing. Often, a buyer can pay fewer points in exchange for a higher interest rate or more points for a lower rate. A document, called the **Truth-in-Lending Disclosure Statement**, shows the buyer the APR, or the annual percentage rate, for the mortgage. The APR takes into account the interest rate and points.

A monthly mortgage payment is used to repay the principal plus interest. In addition, lending institutions can require monthly deposits into an **escrow account**, an account used by the lender to pay real estate taxes and insurance. These deposits increase the amount of the monthly payment.

In the previous section, we used the loan payment formula for fixed installment loans to determine payments on car loans. Because a fixed-rate mortgage is a fixed installment loan, we use the same formula to compute the monthly payment for a mortgage.

LOAN PAYMENT FORMULA FOR FIXED INSTALLMENT LOANS

The regular payment amount, PMT, required to repay a loan of P dollars paid n times per year over t years at an annual rate r is given by

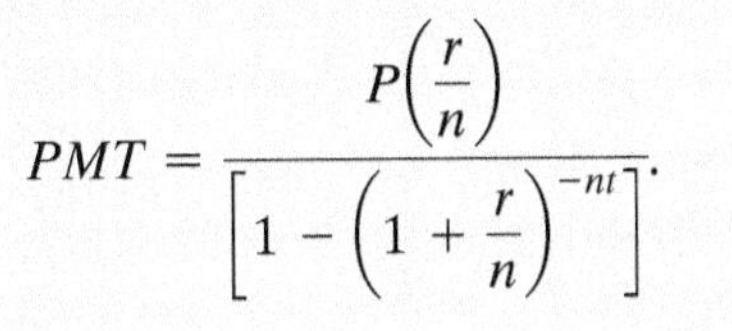

$$PMT = \frac{P\left(\frac{r}{n}\right)}{\left[1 - \left(1 + \frac{r}{n}\right)^{-nt}\right]}.$$

EXAMPLE 1 *Computing the Monthly Payment and Interest Costs for a Mortgage*

The price of a home is \$195,000. The bank requires a 10% down payment and two points at the time of closing. The cost of the home is financed with a 30-year fixed-rate mortgage at 7.5%.

a. Find the required down payment.

b. Find the amount of the mortgage.

c. How much must be paid for the two points at closing?

d. Find the monthly payment (excluding escrowed taxes and insurance).

e. Find the total interest paid over 30 years.

SOLUTION

a. The required down payment is 10% of \$195,000 or

$$0.10 \times \$195,000 = \$19,500.$$

b. The amount of the mortgage is the difference between the price of the home and the down payment.

Amount of the mortgage = sale price − down payment

$= \$195{,}000 - \$19{,}500$

$= \$175{,}500$

c. To find the cost of two points on a mortgage of \$175,500, find 2% of \$175,500.

$$0.02 \times \$175{,}500 = \$3510$$

The down payment (\$19,500) is paid to the seller and the cost of two points (\$3510) is paid to the lending institution.

d. We are interested in finding the monthly payment for a \$175,500 mortgage at 7.5% for 30 years. We use the loan payment formula for installment loans.

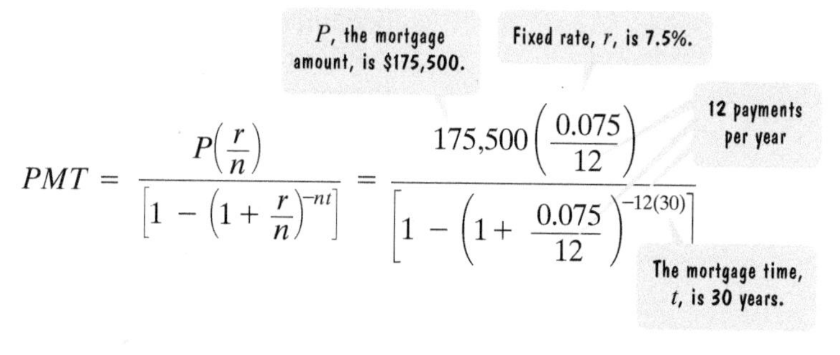

$$PMT = \frac{P\left(\frac{r}{n}\right)}{\left[1-\left(1+\frac{r}{n}\right)^{-nt}\right]} = \frac{175{,}500\left(\frac{0.075}{12}\right)}{\left[1-\left(1+\frac{0.075}{12}\right)^{-12(30)}\right]}$$

$$\approx 1227$$

The monthly mortgage payment for principal and interest is approximately \$1227. (Keep in mind that this payment does not include escrowed taxes and insurance.)

TECHNOLOGY

Here are the calculator keystrokes to compute

$$\frac{175{,}500\left(\frac{0.075}{12}\right)}{\left[1-\left(1+\frac{0.075}{12}\right)^{-12(30)}\right]}.$$

Begin by simplifying the exponent, −12(30), to −360 to avoid possible errors with parentheses:

$$\frac{175{,}500\left(\frac{0.075}{12}\right)}{\left[1-\left(1+\frac{0.075}{12}\right)^{-360}\right]}.$$

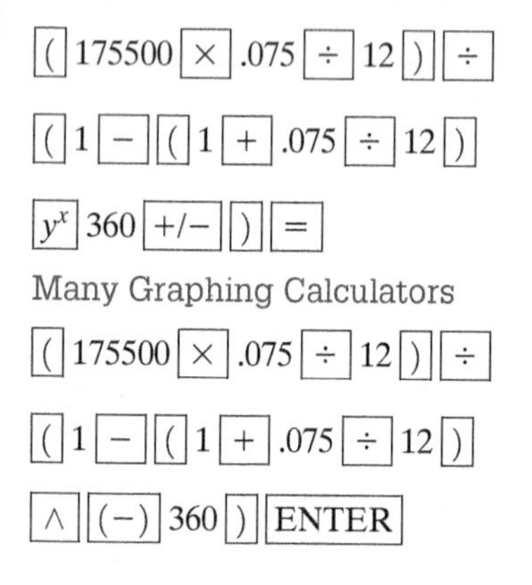

e. The total cost of interest over 30 years is equal to the difference between the total of all monthly payments and the amount of the mortgage. The total of all monthly payments is equal to the amount of the monthly payment multiplied by the number of payments. We found the amount of each monthly payment in (d): \$1227. The number of payments is equal to the number of months in a year, 12, multiplied by the number of years in the mortgage, 30: $12 \times 30 = 360$. Thus, the total of all monthly payments $= \$1227 \times 360$.
Now we can calculate the interest over 30 years.

Total interest paid = total of all monthly payments minus amount of the mortgage.

$= \$1227 \times 360 - \$175{,}500$

$= \$441{,}720 - \$175{,}500 = \$266{,}220$

The total interest paid over 30 years is approximately \$266,220.

CHECK POINT 1 In Example 1, the \$175,500 mortgage was financed with a 30-year fixed rate at 7.5%. The total interest paid over 30 years was approximately \$266,220.

a. Use the loan payment formula for installment loans to find the monthly payment if the time of the mortgage is reduced to 15 years. Round to the nearest dollar.

b. Find the total interest paid over 15 years.

c. How much interest is saved by reducing the mortgage from 30 to 15 years?

2 Prepare a partial loan amortization schedule.

Loan Amortization Schedules

When a mortgage loan is paid off through a series of regular payments, it is said to be **amortized**, which literally means "killed off." In working Check Point 1(c), were you surprised that nearly $150,000 was saved when the mortgage was amortized over 15 years rather than over 30 years? What adds to the interest cost is the long period over which the loan is financed. **Although each payment is the same, with each successive payment the interest portion decreases and the portion applied toward paying off the principal increases.** The interest is computed using the simple interest formula $I = Prt$. The principal, P, is equal to the balance of the loan, which decreases each month. The rate, r, is the annual interest rate of the mortgage loan. Because a payment is made each month, the time, t, is

$$\frac{1 \text{ month}}{12 \text{ months}} = \frac{1 \cancel{\text{month}}}{12 \cancel{\text{months}}}$$

or $\frac{1}{12}$ of a year.

A document showing how the payment each month is split between interest and principal is called a **loan amortization schedule**. Typically, for each payment, this document includes the payment number, the interest for the payment, the amount of the payment applied to the principal, and the balance of the loan after the payment is applied.

EXAMPLE 2 *Preparing a Loan Amortization Schedule*

Prepare a loan amortization schedule for the first two months of the mortgage loan shown in the table below. Round entries to the nearest cent.

LOAN AMORTIZATION SCHEDULE

Annual % Rate: 9.5% **Amount of Mortgage: $130,000** **Number of Monthly Payments: 180**		**Monthly Payment: $1357.50** **Term: Years 15, Months 0**	
Payment Number	**Interest Payment**	**Principal Payment**	**Balance of Loan**
1			
2			

SOLUTION

We begin with payment number 1.

$$\text{Interest for the month} = Prt = \$130{,}000 \times 0.095 \times \frac{1}{12} \approx \$1029.17$$

$$\text{Principal payment} = \text{Monthly payment} - \text{Interest payment}$$
$$= \$1357.50 - \$1029.17 = \$328.33$$

$$\text{Balance of loan} = \text{Principal balance} - \text{Principal payment}$$
$$= \$130{,}000 - \$328.33 = \$129{,}671.67$$

Now, starting with a loan balance of $129,671.67, we repeat these computations for the second payment.

$$\text{Interest for the month} = Prt = \$129{,}671.67 \times 0.095 \times \frac{1}{12} \approx \$1026.57$$

$$\text{Principal payment} = \text{Monthly payment} - \text{Interest payment}$$
$$= \$1357.50 - \$1026.57 = \$330.93$$

$$\text{Balance of loan} = \text{Principal balance} - \text{Principal payment}$$
$$= \$129{,}671.67 - \$330.93 = \$129{,}340.74$$

The results of these computations are included in **Table 7.8** on the next page, a partial loan amortization schedule. By using the simple interest formula month-to-month on the loan's balance, a complete loan amortization schedule for all 180 payments can be calculated.

Blitzer Bonus

The Mortgage Crisis

In 2006, the median U.S. home price jumped to $206,000, up a stunning 15% in just one year and 55% over five years. This rise in home values made real estate an attractive investment to many people, including those with poor credit records and low incomes. Credit standards for mortgages were lowered and loans were made to high-risk borrowers. By 2008, America's raucous house party was over. A brief period of easy lending, especially lax mortgage practices from 2002 through 2006, exploded into the worst financial crisis since the Great Depression. The plunge in home prices wiped out trillions of dollars in home equity, setting off fears that foreclosures and tight credit could send home prices falling to the point that millions of families and thousands of banks might be thrust into insolvency.

TABLE 7.8 Loan Amortization Schedule

Annual % Rate: 9.5%
Amount of Mortgage: $130,000 — **Monthly Payment: $1357.50**
Number of Monthly Payments: 180 — **Term: Years 15, Months 0**

Payment Number	Interest Payment	Principal Payment	Balance of Loan
1	$1029.17	$ 328.33	$129,671.67
2	$1026.57	$ 330.93	$129,340.74
3	$1023.96	$ 333.54	$129,007.22
4	$1021.32	$ 336.18	$128,671.04
30	$ 944.82	$ 412.68	$118,931.35
31	$ 941.55	$ 415.95	$118,515.52
125	$ 484.62	$ 872.88	$ 60,340.84
126	$ 477.71	$ 879.79	$ 59,461.05
179	$ 21.26	$1336.24	$ 1347.74
180	$ 9.76	$ 1347.74	

Many lenders supply a loan amortization schedule like the one in Example 2 at the time of closing. Such a schedule shows how the buyer pays slightly less in interest and more in principal for each payment over the entire life of the loan.

CHECK POINT 2 Prepare a loan amortization schedule for the first two months of the mortgage loan shown in the following table. Round entries to the nearest cent.

Annual % Rate: 7.0%
Amount of Mortgage: $200,000 — **Monthly Payment: $1550.00**
Number of Monthly Payments: 240 — **Term: Years 20, Months 0**

Payment Number	Interest Payment	Principal Payment	Balance of Loan
1			
2			

Blitzer Bonus

Bittersweet Interest

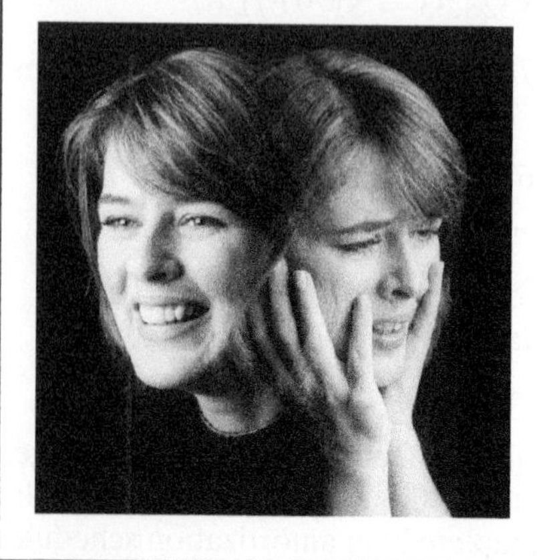

Looking at amortization tables, you could get discouraged by how much of your early mortgage payments goes toward interest and how little goes toward paying off the principal. Although you get socked with tons of interest in the early years of a loan, the one bright side to the staggering cost of a mortgage is the **mortgage interest tax deduction.** To make the cost of owning a home more affordable, the tax code permits deducting all the mortgage interest (but not the principal) that you pay per year on the loan. **Table 7.9** illustrates how this tax loophole reduces the cost of the mortgage.

TABLE 7.9 Tax Deductions for a $100,000 Mortgage at 7% for a Taxpayer in the 28% Tax Bracket

Year	Interest	Tax Savings	Net Cost of Mortgage
1	$6968	$1951	$5017
2	$6895	$1931	$4964
3	$6816	$1908	$4908
4	$6732	$1885	$4847
5	$6641	$1859	$4782

3 Solve problems involving what you can afford to spend for a mortgage.

Determining What You Can Afford

Here's the bottom line from most financial advisers:

- Spend no more than 28% of your gross monthly income for your mortgage payment.
- Spend no more than 36% of your gross monthly income for your total monthly debt, including mortgage payments, car payments, credit card bills, student loans, and medical debt.

Using these guidelines, **Table 7.10** shows the maximum monthly amount you could afford for mortgage payments and total credit obligations for a variety of income levels.

TABLE 7.10 Maximum Amount You Can Afford

Gross Annual Income	Monthly Mortgage Payment	Total Monthly Credit Obligations
$20,000	$467	$600
$30,000	$700	$900
$40,000	$933	$1200
$50,000	$1167	$1500
$60,000	$1400	$1800
$70,000	$1633	$2100
$80,000	$1867	$2400
$90,000	$2100	$2700
$100,000	$2333	$3000

Source: Fannie Mae

EXAMPLE 3 *What Can You Afford?*

Suppose that your gross annual income is $25,000.

a. What is the maximum amount you should spend each month on a mortgage payment?

b. What is the maximum amount you should spend each month for total credit obligations?

c. If your monthly mortgage payment is 80% of the maximum amount you can afford, what is the maximum amount you should spend each month for all other debt?

Round all computations to the nearest dollar.

SOLUTION

With a gross annual income of $25,000, your gross monthly income is

$$\frac{\$25{,}000}{12},$$

or approximately $2083.

a. You should spend no more than 28% of your gross monthly income, $2083, on a mortgage payment.

$$28\% \text{ of } \$2083 = 0.28 \times \$2083 \approx \$583.$$

Your monthly mortgage payment should not exceed $583.

b. You should spend no more than 36% of your gross monthly income, \$2083, for total monthly debt.

$$36\% \text{ of } \$2083 = 0.36 \times \$2083 \approx \$750.$$

Your total monthly credit obligations should not exceed \$750.

c. The problem's conditions state that your monthly mortgage payment is 80% of the maximum you can afford, which is \$583. This means that your monthly mortgage payment is 80% of \$583.

$$80\% \text{ of } \$583 = 0.8 \times \$583 \approx \$466.$$

In part (b), we saw that your total monthly debt should not exceed \$750. Because you are paying \$466 for your mortgage payment, this leaves \$750 – \$466, or \$284, for all other debt. Your monthly credit obligations, excluding mortgage payments, should not exceed \$284.

CHECK POINT 3 Suppose that your gross annual income is \$240,000.

a. What is the maximum amount you should spend each month on a mortgage payment?

b. What is the maximum amount you should spend each month for total credit obligations?

c. If your monthly mortgage payment is 90% of the maximum amount you can afford, what is the maximum amount you should spend each month for all other debt?

Round all computations to the nearest dollar.

4 Understand the pros and cons of renting versus buying.

Renting versus Buying

Nearly everyone is faced at some stage in life with the dilemma "should I rent or should I buy a home?" The rent-or-buy decision can be highly complex and is often based on lifestyle rather than finances. Aside from a changing economic climate, there are many factors to consider. Here are some advantages of both renting and buying to help smooth the way:

Benefits of Renting

- No down payment or points are required. You generally have a security deposit that is returned at the end of your lease.
- Very mobile: You can easily relocate, moving as often as you like and as your lease permits.
- Does not tie up hundreds of thousands of dollars that might be invested more safely and lucratively elsewhere. Most financial advisers agree that you should buy a home because you want to live in it, not because you want to fund your retirement.
- Does not clutter what you can afford for your total monthly debt with mortgage payments.
- May involve lower monthly expenses. You pay rent, whereas a homeowner pays the mortgage, taxes, insurance, and upkeep.
- Can provide amenities like swimming pools, tennis courts, and health clubs.
- Avoids the risk of falling housing prices.
- Does not require home repair, maintenance, and groundskeeping.
- There are no property taxes.
- Generally less costly than buying a home when staying in it for fewer than three years.

Benefits of Home Ownership

- Peace of mind and stability.
- Provides significant tax advantages, including deduction of mortgage interest and property taxes.
- There is no chance of rent increasing over time.
- Allows for freedom to remodel, landscape, and redecorate.
- You can build up **equity**, the difference between the home's value and what you owe on the mortgage, as the mortgage is paid off. The possibility of home appreciation is a potential source of cash in the form of home equity loans.
- When looking at seven-year time frames, the total cost of renting (monthly rent, renter's insurance, loss of potential interest on a security deposit) is more than twice the total cost of buying for home owners who itemize their tax deductions.

Source: Arthur J. Keown, *Personal Finance*, Fourth Edition, Pearson, 2007.

Blitzer Bonus

Reducing Rental Costs

Let's assume that one of your long-term financial goals involves home ownership. It's still likely that you'll be renting for a while once you complete your education and begin your first job. Other than living in a tent, here are some realistic suggestions for reducing costs on your first rental:

- Select a lower-cost rental. Who says you should begin your career in a large apartment with fancy amenities, private parking spots, and lakefront views? The less you spend renting, the more you can save for a down payment toward buying your own place. You will ultimately qualify for the most favorable mortgage terms by making a down payment of at least 20% of the purchase price of the property.
- Negotiate rental increases. Landlords do not want to lose good tenants who are respectful of their property and pay rent on time. Filling vacancies can be time consuming and costly.
- Rent a larger place with roommates. By sharing a rental, you will decrease rental costs and get more home for your rental dollars.

Concept and Vocabulary Check

Fill in each blank so that the resulting statement is true.

1. A long-term installment loan for the purpose of buying a home is called a/an ________. The portion of the sale price of the home that the buyer initially pays to the seller is called the ________.
2. A document showing how each monthly installment payment is split between interest and principal is called a/an ________.

In Exercises 3–6, determine whether each statement is true or false. If the statement is false, make the necessary change(s) to produce a true statement.

3. Over the life of an installment loan, the interest portion increases and the portion applied to paying off the principal decreases with each successive payment. ______
4. Financial advisors suggest spending no more than 5% of your gross monthly income for your mortgage payment. ______
5. Renters are not required to pay property taxes. ______
6. Renters can build up equity as the rent is paid each month. ______

Exercise Set 7.7

Practice and Application Exercises

In Exercises 1–10, use

$$PMT = \frac{P\left(\frac{r}{n}\right)}{\left[1 - \left(1 + \frac{r}{n}\right)^{-nt}\right]}$$

to determine the regular payment amount, rounded to the nearest dollar.

1. The price of a home is \$220,000. The bank requires a 20% down payment and three points at the time of closing. The cost of the home is financed with a 30-year fixed-rate mortgage at 7%.
   a. Find the required down payment.
   b. Find the amount of the mortgage.
   c. How much must be paid for the three points at closing?

d. Find the monthly payment (excluding escrowed taxes and insurance).

e. Find the total cost of interest over 30 years.

2. The price of a condominium is $180,000. The bank requires a 5% down payment and one point at the time of closing. The cost of the condominium is financed with a 30-year fixed-rate mortgage at 8%.

a. Find the required down payment.

b. Find the amount of the mortgage.

c. How much must be paid for the one point at closing?

d. Find the monthly payment (excluding escrowed taxes and insurance).

e. Find the total cost of interest over 30 years.

3. The price of a small cabin is $100,000. The bank requires a 5% down payment. The buyer is offered two mortgage options: 20-year fixed at 8% or 30-year fixed at 8%. Calculate the amount of interest paid for each option. How much does the buyer save in interest with the 20-year option?

4. The price of a home is $160,000. The bank requires a 15% down payment. The buyer is offered two mortgage options: 15-year fixed at 8% or 30-year fixed at 8%. Calculate the amount of interest paid for each option. How much does the buyer save in interest with the 15-year option?

5. In terms of paying less in interest, which is more economical for a $150,000 mortgage: a 30-year fixed-rate at 8% or a 20-year fixed-rate at 7.5%? How much is saved in interest?

6. In terms of paying less in interest, which is more economical for a $90,000 mortgage: a 30-year fixed-rate at 8% or a 15-year fixed-rate at 7.5%? How much is saved in interest?

In Exercises 7–8, which mortgage loan has the greater total cost (closing costs + the amount paid for points + total cost of interest)? By how much?

7. A $120,000 mortgage with two loan options:

Mortgage A: 30-year fixed at 7% with closing costs of $2000 and one point

Mortgage B: 30-year fixed at 6.5% with closing costs of $1500 and four points

8. A $250,000 mortgage with two loan options:

Mortgage A: 30-year fixed at 7.25% with closing costs of $2000 and one point

Mortgage B: 30-year fixed at 6.25% with closing costs of $350 and four points

9. The cost of a home is financed with a $120,000 30-year fixed-rate mortgage at 4.5%.

a. Find the monthly payments and the total interest for the loan.

b. Prepare a loan amortization schedule for the first three months of the mortgage. Round entries to the nearest cent.

Payment Number	Interest	Principal	Loan Balance
1			
2			
3			

10. The cost of a home is financed with a $160,000 30-year fixed-rate mortgage at 4.2%.

a. Find the monthly payments and the total interest for the loan.

b. Prepare a loan amortization schedule for the first three months of the mortgage. Round entries to the nearest cent.

Payment Number	Interest	Principal	Loan Balance
1			
2			
3			

Use this advice from most financial advisers to solve Exercises 11–12.

- *Spend no more than 28% of your gross monthly income for your mortgage payment.*
- *Spend no more than 36% of your gross monthly income for your total monthly debt.*

Round all computations to the nearest dollar.

11. Suppose that your gross annual income is $36,000.

a. What is the maximum amount you should spend each month on a mortgage payment?

b. What is the maximum amount you should spend each month for total credit obligations?

c. If your monthly mortgage payment is 70% of the maximum you can afford, what is the maximum amount you should spend each month for all other debt?

12. Suppose that your gross annual income is $62,000.

a. What is the maximum amount you should spend each month on a mortgage payment?

b. What is the maximum amount you should spend each month for total credit obligations?

c. If your monthly mortgage payment is 90% of the maximum you can afford, what is the maximum amount you should spend each month for all other debt?

Writing in Mathematics

13. What is a mortgage?

14. What is a down payment?

15. How is the amount of a mortgage determined?

16. Describe why a buyer would select a 30-year fixed-rate mortgage instead of a 15-year fixed-rate mortage if interest rates are $\frac{1}{4}$% to $\frac{1}{2}$% lower on a 15-year mortgage.

17. Describe one advantage and one disadvantage of an adjustable-rate mortage over a fixed-rate mortgage.

18. What is a loan amortization schedule?

19. Describe what happens to the portions of payments going to principal and interest over the life of an installment loan.

20. Describe how to determine what you can afford for your monthly mortgage payment.

21. Describe two advantages of renting over home ownership.

22. Describe two advantages of home ownership over renting.

Critical Thinking Exercises

Make Sense? *In Exercises 23–26, determine whether each statement makes sense or does not make sense, and explain your reasoning.*

23. I use the same formula to determine mortgage payments and payments for car loans.
24. There must be an error in the loan amortization schedule for my mortgage because the annual interest rate is only 3.5%, yet the schedule shows that I'm paying more on interest than on the principal for many of my payments.
25. My landlord required me to pay 2 points when I signed my rental lease.
26. I include rental payments among my itemized tax deductions.

27. If your gross annual income is $75,000, use appropriate computations to determine whether you could afford a $200,000 30-year fixed-rate mortgage at 5.5%.
28. The partial loan amortization schedule shows payments 50–54. Although payment 50 is correct, there are errors in one or more of the payments from 51 through 54. Find the errors and correct them.

LOAN AMORTIZATION SCHEDULE

Annual % Rate: 6.0% **Amount of Mortgage: $120,000** **Number of Monthly Payments: 180**		**Monthly Payment: $1012.63** **Term: Years 15, Months 0**	
Payment Number	**Interest Payment**	**Principal Payment**	**Balance of Loan**
50	$485.77	$526.86	$96,626.51
51	$483.13	$529.50	$96,097.01
52	$477.82	$534.81	$95,030.06
53	$480.49	$532.14	$95,564.87
54	$495.15	$537.48	$94,492.58

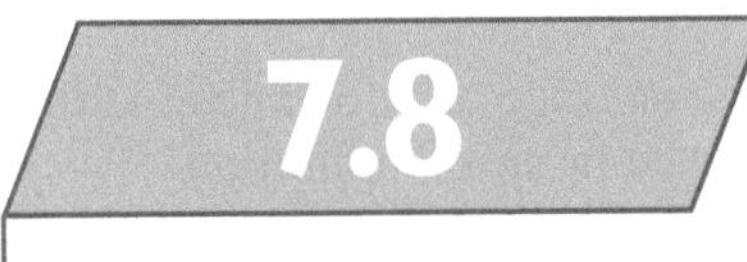

WHAT AM I SUPPOSED TO LEARN?

After you have read this section, you should be able to:

1 Find the interest, the balance due, and the minimum monthly payment for credit card loans.
2 Understand the pros and cons of using credit cards.
3 Understand the difference between credit cards and debit cards.
4 Know what is contained in a credit report.
5 Understand credit scores as measures of creditworthiness.

Credit Cards

WOULD YOU LIKE TO BUY PRODUCTS WITH A CREDIT card? Although the card will let you use a product while paying for it, the costs associated with such cards, including their high interest rates, fees, and penalties, stack the odds in favor of your getting hurt by them. In 2012, the average credit-card debt per U.S. household was $15,374. One advantage of making a purchase with a credit card is that the consumer gets to use a product immediately. In this section, we will see that a significant disadvantage is that it can add a substantial amount to the cost of a purchase. When it comes to using a credit card, consumer beware!

Open-End Installment Loans

Using a credit card is an example of an open-end installment loan, commonly called **revolving credit**. Open-end loans differ from fixed installment loans such as car loans and mortgages in that there is no schedule for paying a fixed amount each period. Credit card loans require users to make only a minimum monthly payment that depends on the unpaid balance and the interest rate. Credit cards have high interest rates compared to other kinds of loans. The interest on credit cards is computed using the simple interest formula $I = Prt$. However, r represents the *monthly* interest rate and t is time in months rather than in years. A typical interest rate is 1.57% monthly. This is equivalent to a yearly rate of $12 \times 1.57\%$, or 18.84%. With such a high annual percentage rate, credit card balances should be paid off as quickly as possible.

Most credit card customers are billed every month. A typical billing period is May 1 through May 31, but it can also run from, say, May 5 through June 4. Customers receive a statement, called an **itemized billing**, that includes the unpaid balance on the first day of the billing period, the total balance owed on the last day of the billing period, a list of purchases and cash advances made during the billing period, any finance charges or other fees incurred, the date of the last day of the billing period, the payment due date, and the minimum payment required.

Customers who make a purchase during the billing period and pay the entire amount of the purchase by the payment due date are not charged interest. By contrast, customers who make cash advances using their credit cards must pay interest from the day the money is advanced until the day it is repaid.

Find the interest, the balance due, and the minimum monthly payment for credit card loans.

Interest on Credit Cards: The Average Daily Balance Method

Methods for calculating interest, or finance charges, on credit cards may vary and the interest can differ on credit cards that show the same annual percentage rate, or APR. The method used for calculating interest on most credit cards is called the *average daily balance method.*

THE AVERAGE DAILY BALANCE METHOD

Interest is calculated using $I = Prt$, where r is the monthly rate and t is one month. The principal, P, is the *average daily balance.* The **average daily balance** is the sum of the unpaid balances for each day in the billing period divided by the number of days in the billing period.

$$\text{Average daily balance} = \frac{\text{Sum of the unpaid balances for each day in the billing period}}{\text{Number of days in the billing period}}$$

In Example 1, we illustrate how to determine the average daily balance. At the conclusion of the example, we summarize the steps used in the computation.

EXAMPLE 1 *Balance Due on a Credit Card*

The issuer of a particular VISA card calculates interest using the average daily balance method. The monthly interest rate is 1.3% of the average daily balance. The following transactions occurred during the May 1–May 31 billing period.

Transaction Description	Transaction Amount
Previous balance, $1350.00	
May 1 Billing date	
May 8 Payment	$250.00 credit
May 10 Charge: Airline Tickets	$375.00
May 20 Charge: Books	$ 57.50
May 28 Charge: Restaurant	$ 65.30
May 31 End of billing period	
Payment Due Date: June 9	

a. Find the average daily balance for the billing period. Round to the nearest cent.

b. Find the interest to be paid on June 1, the next billing date. Round to the nearest cent.

c. Find the balance due on June 1.

d. This credit card requires a $10 minimum monthly payment if the balance due at the end of the billing period is less than $360. Otherwise, the minimum monthly payment is $\frac{1}{36}$ of the balance due at the end of the billing period, rounded up to the nearest whole dollar. What is the minimum monthly payment due by June 9?

SOLUTION

a. We begin by finding the average daily balance for the billing period. First make a table that shows the beginning date of the billing period, each transaction date, and the unpaid balance for each date.

Date	Unpaid Balance	
May 1	\$1350.00	previous balance
May 8	\$1350.00 − \$250.00 = \$1100.00	\$250.00 payment
May 10	\$1100.00 + \$375.00 = \$1475.00	\$375.00 charge
May 20	\$1475.00 + \$57.50 = \$1532.50	\$57.50 charge
May 28	\$1532.50 + \$65.30 = \$1597.80	\$65.30 charge

We now extend our table by adding two columns. One column shows the number of days at each unpaid balance. The final column shows each unpaid balance multiplied by the number of days that the balance is outstanding.

Date	Unpaid Balance	Number of Days at Each Unpaid Balance	(Unpaid Balance) · (Number of Days)
May 1	\$1350.00	7	(\$1350.00)(7) = \$9450.00
May 8	\$1100.00	2	(\$1100.00)(2) = \$2200.00
May 10	\$1475.00	10	(\$1475.00)(10) = \$14,750.00
May 20	\$1532.50	8	(\$1532.50)(8) = \$12,260.00
May 28	\$1597.80	4	(\$1597.80)(4) = \$6391.20
		Total: 31	Total: \$45,051.20

There are 4 days at this unpaid balance, May 28, 29, 30, and 31, before the beginning of the next billing period, June 1.

This is the number of days in the billing period.

This is the sum of the unpaid balances for each day in the billing period.

Notice that we found the sum of the products in the final column of the table. This dollar amount, \$45,051.20, gives the sum of the unpaid balances for each day in the billing period.

Now we divide the sum of the unpaid balances for each day in the billing period, \$45,051.20, by the number of days in the billing period, 31. This gives the average daily balance.

Average daily balance

$$= \frac{\text{Sum of the unpaid balances for each day in the billing period}}{\text{Number of days in the billing period}}$$

$$= \frac{\$45{,}051.20}{31} \approx \$1453.26$$

The average daily balance is approximately \$1453.26.

b. Now we find the interest to be paid on June 1, the next billing date. The monthly interest rate is 1.3% of the average daily balance. The interest due is computed using $I = Prt$.

$$I = Prt = (\$1453.26)\,(0.013)\,(1) \approx \$18.89$$

The average daily balance serves as the principal.

Time, t, is measured in months, and $t = 1$ month.

The interest, or finance charge, for the June 1 billing will be \$18.89.

GREAT QUESTION!

How do credit card companies round when determining a minimum monthly payment?

They round *up* to the nearest dollar. For example, the quotient in part (d) is approximately 44.908, which rounds to 45. Because the minimum monthly payment is rounded up, $45 would still be the payment if the approximate quotient had been 44.098.

c. The balance due on June 1, the next billing date, is the unpaid balance on May 31 plus the interest.

$$\text{Balance due} = \$1597.80 + \$18.89 = \$1616.69$$

Unpaid balance on May 31, obtained from the second table on the previous page

Interest, or finance charge, obtained from part (b)

The balance due on June 1 is $1616.69.

d. Because the balance due, $1616.69, exceeds $360, the customer must pay a minimum of $\frac{1}{36}$ of the balance due.

$$\text{Minimum monthly payment} = \frac{\text{balance due}}{36} = \frac{\$1616.69}{36} \approx \$45$$

Rounded up to the nearest whole dollar, the minimum monthly payment due by June 9 is $45.

The following box summarizes the steps used in Example 1 to determine the average daily balance. Calculating the average daily balance can be quite tedious when there are numerous transactions during a billing period.

DETERMINING THE AVERAGE DAILY BALANCE

Step 1 Make a table that shows the beginning date of the billing period, each transaction date, and the unpaid balance for each date.
Step 2 Add a column to the table that shows the number of days at each unpaid balance.
Step 3 Add a final column to the table that shows each unpaid balance multiplied by the number of days that the balance is outstanding.
Step 4 Find the sum of the products in the final column of the table. This dollar amount is the sum of the unpaid balances for each day in the billing period.
Step 5 Compute the average daily balance.

$$\text{Average daily balance} = \frac{\text{Sum of the unpaid balances for each day in the billing period}}{\text{Number of days in the billing period}}$$

CHECK POINT 1 A credit card company calculates interest using the average daily balance method. The monthly interest rate is 1.6% of the average daily balance. The following transactions occurred during the May 1–May 31 billing period.

Transaction Description	Transaction Amount
Previous balance, $8240.00	
May 1 Billing date	
May 7 Payment	$ 350.00 credit
May 15 Charge: Computer	$ 1405.00
May 17 Charge: Restaurant	$ 45.20
May 30 Charge: Clothing	$ 180.72
May 31 End of billing period	
Payment Due Date: June 9	

Answer parts (a) through (d) in Example 1 on page 350 using this information.

2 Understand the pros and cons of using credit cards.

Credit Cards: Marvelous Tools or Snakes in Your Wallet?

Credit cards are convenient. Pay the entire balance by the due date for each monthly billing and you avoid interest charges. Carry over a balance and interest charges quickly add up. With this in mind, let's consider the positives and the negatives involved with credit card usage.

Advantages of Using Credit Cards

- Get to use a product before actually paying for it.
- No interest charges by paying the balance due at the end of each billing period.
- Responsible use is an effective way to build a good credit score. (See page 354 for a discussion of credit scores.)
- No need to carry around large amounts of cash.
- More convenient to use than checks.
- Offer consumer protections: If there is a disputed or fraudulent charge on your credit card statement, let the card issuer know and the amount is generally removed.
- Provide a source of temporary emergency funds.
- Extend shopping opportunities to purchases over the phone or the Internet.
- Simple tasks like renting a car or booking a hotel room can be difficult or impossible without a credit card.
- Monthly statements can help keep track of spending. Some card issuers provide an annual statement that aids in tax preparation.
- May provide amenities such as free miles toward air travel.
- Useful as identification when multiple pieces of identification are needed.

Credit Card Woes

- High interest rates on unpaid balances. In 2009, interest rates were as high as 30%.
- No cap on interest rates. In 2009, the U.S. Senate defeated an amendment that would have imposed a 15% cap on credit card interest rates. (The Credit Card Act, passed by Congress in 2009, does restrict when issuers can raise rates on existing unpaid balances.) Your initial credit card interest rate is unlikely to go down, but it can sure go up.
- No cap on fees. *Consumer Reports* (October 2008) cited a credit card with an enticing 9.9% annual interest rate. But the fine print revealed a $29 account-setup fee, a $95 program fee, a $48 annual fee, and a $7 monthly servicing fee. Nearly 40% of the $40 billion in profits that U.S. card issuers earned in 2008 came from fees. Furthermore, issuers can hike fees at any time, for any reason. Read the fine print of a credit card agreement before you sign up.
- Easy to overspend. Purchases with credit cards can create the illusion that you are not actually spending money.
- Can serve as a tool for financial trouble. Using a credit card to buy more than you can afford and failing to pay the bill in full each month can result in serious debt. Fees and interest charges are added to the balance, which continues to grow, even if there are no new purchases.
- The minimum-payment trap: Credit-card debt is made worse by paying only the required minimum, a mistake made by 11% of credit-card debtors. Pay the minimum and most of it goes to interest charges.

Credit card statements now include a Minimum Payment Warning: "If you make only the minimum payment each period, you will pay more in interest and it will take you longer to pay off your balance."

Debit Cards

Credit cards have been around since the 1950s. Their plastic lookalikes, debit cards, were introduced in the mid-1970s. Although debit cards look like credit cards, the big difference is that debit cards are linked to your bank account. When you use a debit card,

3 Understand the difference between credit cards and debit cards.

the money you spend is deducted electronically from your bank account. It's similar to writing an electronic check, but there's no paper involved and the check gets "cashed" instantly.

Debit cards offer the convenience of making purchases with a piece of plastic without the temptation or ability to run up credit card debt. You can't spend money you don't have because the card won't work if the money isn't in your checking or savings account.

Debit cards have drawbacks. They may not offer the protection a credit card does for disputed purchases. It's easy to rack up overdraft charges if your bank enrolls you in an "overdraft protection" program. That means your card won't be turned down if you do not have sufficient funds in your account to cover your purchase. You are spared the embarrassment of having your card rejected, but it will cost you fees of approximately $27 per overdraft.

Debit card purchases should be treated like those for which you use a check. Record all transactions and their amounts in your checkbook, including any cash received from an ATM. Always keep track of how much money is available in your account. Your balance can be checked at an ATM or online.

4 Know what is contained in a credit report.

Credit Reports and Credit Scores

As a college student, it is unlikely that you have a credit history. Once you apply for your first credit card, your personal *credit report* will begin. A **credit report** contains the following information:

- **Identifying Information:** This includes your name, social security number, current address, and previous addresses.
- **Record of Credit Accounts:** This includes details about all open or closed credit accounts, such as when each account was opened, the latest balance, and the payment history.
- **Public Record Information:** Any of your public records, such as bankruptcy information, appears in this section of the credit report.
- **Collection Agency Account Information:** Unpaid accounts are turned over to collection agencies. Information about such actions appear in this section of the credit report.
- **Inquiries:** Companies that have asked for your credit information because you applied for credit are listed here.

Organizations known as **credit bureaus** collect credit information on individual consumers and provide credit reports to potential lenders, employers, and others upon request. The three main credit bureaus are Equifax, Experian, and TransUnion. You can get your credit report from the three bureaus free at www.annualcreditreport.com.

5 Understand credit scores as measures of creditworthiness.

Credit bureaus use data from your credit report to create a *credit score*, which is used to measure your creditworthiness. **Credit scores**, or **FICO scores**, range from 300 to 850, with a higher score indicating better credit. **Table 7.11** contains ranges of credit scores and their measures of creditworthiness.

TABLE 7.11 Credit Scores and Their Significance

Scores	Creditworthiness
720–850	Very good to excellent; Best interest rates on loans
650–719	Good; Likely to get credit, but not the best interest rates on loans
630–649	Fair; May get credit, but only at higher rates
580–629	Poor; Likely to be denied credit by all but a high-interest lender
300–579	Bad; Likely to be denied credit

Your credit score will have an enormous effect on your financial life. Individuals with higher credit scores get better interest rates on loans because they are considered to have a lower risk of defaulting. A good credit score can save you thousands of dollars in interest charges over your lifetime.

Blitzer Bonus

College Students and Credit Cards

If you have no credit history but are at least 18 years old with a job, you may be able to get a card with a limited amount of credit, usually $500 to $1000. Your chances of getting a credit card increase if you apply through a bank with which you have an account.

Prior to 2010, it was not necessary for college students to have a job to get a credit card. Credit card companies viewed college students as good and responsible customers who would continue to have a lifelong need for credit. The issuers anticipated retaining these students after graduation when their accounts would become more valuable. Many resorted to aggressive marketing tactics, offering everything from T-shirts to iPods to students who signed up.

Times have changed. In May 2009, President Obama signed legislation that prohibits issuing credit cards to college students younger than 21 unless they can prove they are able to make payments or get a parent or guardian to co-sign. Because college students do not have much money, most won't be able to get a credit card without permission from their parents. The bill also requires lenders to get permission from the co-signer before increasing the card's credit limit.

Before credit card reform swiped easy plastic from college students, those who fell behind on their credit card bills often left college with blemished credit reports. This made it more difficult for them to rent an apartment, get a car loan, or even find a job. "A lot of kids got themselves in trouble," said Adam Levin, founder of Credit.com, a consumer Web site. "As much as college students are obsessed with GPAs, their credit score is the most important number they're going to have to deal with after graduation."

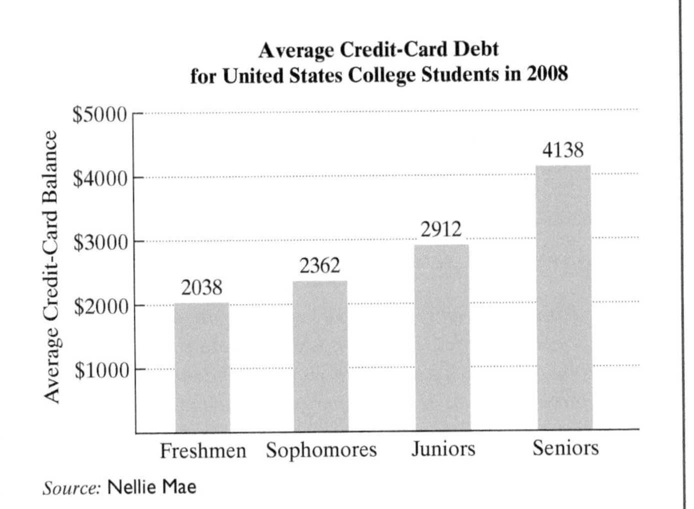

Source: Nellie Mae

GREAT QUESTION!

What's the bottom line on responsible credit card use?

A critical component of financial success involves demonstrating that you can handle the responsibility of using a credit card. Responsible credit card use means:

- You pay the entire balance by the due date for each monthly billing.
- You only use the card to make purchases that you can afford.
- You save all receipts for credit card purchases and check each itemized billing carefully for any errors.
- You use your credit card sometimes, but also use cash, checks, or your debit card.

When you decide to apply for your first credit card, you should look for a card with no annual fee and a low interest rate. You can compare rates and fees at www.creditcards.com, www.bankrate.com, and www.indexcreditcards.com.

Concept and Vocabulary Check

Fill in each blank so that the resulting statement is true.

1. Using a credit card is an example of a/an ________ installment loan for which there is no schedule for paying a fixed amount each period.
2. The average daily balance for a credit card's billing period is ________ divided by ________________.
3. When you use a/an ________ card, the money you spend is deducted electronically from your bank account.
4. Details about when all your credit accounts were opened, their latest balance, and their payment history are included in a/an ________.
5. Credit scores range from ________ to ________, with a higher score indicating ____________.

In Exercises 6–9, determine whether each statement is true or false. If the statement is false, make the necessary change(s) to produce a true statement.

6. Interest on a credit card is calculated using $I = Prt$, where r is the monthly rate, t is one month, and P is the balance due. _______

7. When using a credit card, the money spent is deducted electronically from the user's bank account. _______

8. Credit reports contain bankruptcy information. _______

9. Higher credit scores indicate better credit. _______

Exercise Set 7.8

Practice and Application Exercises

Exercises 1–2 involve credit cards that calculate interest using the average daily balance method. The monthly interest rate is 1.5% of the average daily balance. Each exercise shows transactions that occurred during the March 1–March 31 billing period. In each exercise,

a. *Find the average daily balance for the billing period. Round to the nearest cent.*

b. *Find the interest to be paid on April 1, the next billing date. Round to the nearest cent.*

c. *Find the balance due on April 1.*

d. *This credit card requires a $10 minimum monthly payment if the balance due at the end of the billing period is less than $360. Otherwise, the minimum monthly payment is $\frac{1}{36}$ of the balance due at the end of the billing period, rounded up to the nearest whole dollar. What is the minimum monthly payment due by April 9?*

1.

Transaction Description	Transaction Amount
Previous balance, $6240.00	
March 1 Billing date	
March 5 Payment	$300 credit
March 7 Charge: Restaurant	$ 40
March 12 Charge: Groceries	$ 90
March 21 Charge: Car Repairs	$230
March 31 End of billing period	
Payment Due Date: April 9	

2.

Transaction Description	Transaction Amount
Previous balance, $7150.00	
March 1 Billing date	
March 4 Payment	$ 400 credit
March 6 Charge: Furniture	$ 1200
March 15 Charge: Gas	$ 40
March 30 Charge: Groceries	$ 50
March 31 End of billing period	
Payment Due Date: April 9	

Exercises 3–4 involve credit cards that calculate interest using the average daily balance method. The monthly interest rate is 1.2% of the average daily balance. Each exercise shows transactions that occurred during the June 1–June 30 billing period. In each exercise,

a. *Find the average daily balance for the billing period. Round to the nearest cent.*

b. *Find the interest to be paid on July 1, the next billing date. Round to the nearest cent.*

c. *Find the balance due on July 1.*

d. *This credit card requires a $30 minimum monthly payment if the balance due at the end of the billing period is less than $400. Otherwise, the minimum monthly payment is $\frac{1}{25}$ of the balance due at the end of the billing period, rounded up to the nearest whole dollar. What is the minimum monthly payment due by July 9?*

3.

Transaction Description	Transaction Amount
Previous balance, $2653.48	
June 1 Billing date	
June 6 Payment	$1000.00 credit
June 8 Charge: Gas	$ 36.25
June 9 Charge: Groceries	$ 138.43
June 17 Charge: Gas Charge: Groceries	$ 42.36 $ 127.19
June 27 Charge: Clothing	$ 214.83
June 30 End of billing period	
Payment Due Date: July 9	

4.

Transaction Description	Transaction Amount
Previous balance, $4037.93	
June 1 Billing date	
June 5 Payment	$ 350.00 credit
June 10 Charge: Gas	$ 31.17
June 15 Charge: Prescriptions	$ 42.50
June 22 Charge: Gas Charge: Groceries	$ 43.86 $ 112.91
June 29 Charge: Clothing	$ 96.73
June 30 End of billing period	
Payment Due Date: July 9	

In Exercises 5–10, use

$$PMT = \frac{P\left(\frac{r}{n}\right)}{\left[1 - \left(1 + \frac{r}{n}\right)^{-nt}\right]}$$

to determine the regular payment amount, rounded to the nearest dollar.

5. Suppose your credit card has a balance of \$4200 and an annual interest rate of 18%. You decide to pay off the balance over two years. If there are no further purchases charged to the card,

a. How much must you pay each month?

b. How much total interest will you pay?

6. Suppose your credit card has a balance of \$3600 and an annual interest rate of 16.5%. You decide to pay off the balance over two years. If there are no further purchases charged to the card,

a. How much must you pay each month?

b. How much total interest will you pay?

7. To pay off the \$4200 credit card balance in Exercise 5, suppose that you can get a bank loan at 10.5% with a term of three years.

a. How much will you pay each month? How does this compare with your credit card payment in Exercise 5?

b. How much total interest will you pay? How does this compare with your total credit card interest in Exercise 5?

8. To pay off the \$3600 credit card balance in Exercise 6, suppose that you can get a bank loan at 9.5% with a term of three years.

a. How much will you pay each month? How does this compare with your credit card payment in Exercise 6?

b. How much total interest will you pay? How does this compare with your total credit card interest in Exercise 6?

9. Rework Exercise 5 assuming you decide to pay off the balance over one year rather than two. How much more must you pay each month and how much less will you pay in total interest?

10. Rework Exercise 6 assuming you decide to pay off the balance over one year rather than two. How much more must you pay each month and how much less will you pay in total interest?

Writing in Mathematics

11. Describe the difference between a fixed installment loan and an open-end installment loan.

12. For a credit card billing period, describe how the average daily balance is determined. Why is this computation somewhat tedious when done by hand?

13. Describe two advantages of using credit cards.

14. Describe two disadvantages of using credit cards.

15. What is a debit card?

16. Describe what is contained in a credit report.

17. What are credit scores?

18. Describe two aspects of responsible credit card use.

Critical Thinking Exercises

Make Sense? *In Exercises 19–25, determine whether each statement makes sense or does not make sense, and explain your reasoning.*

19. I like to keep all my money, so I pay only the minimum required payment on my credit card.

20. One advantage of using credit cards is that there are caps on interest rates and fees.

21. The balance due on my credit card from last month to this month increased even though I made no new purchases.

22. My debit card offers the convenience of making purchases with a piece of plastic without the ability to run up credit-card debt.

23. My debit score is 630, so I anticipate an offer on a car loan at a very low interest rate.

24. In order to achieve financial success, I should consistently pay my entire credit card balance by the due date.

25. As a college student, I'm frequently enticed to sign up for credit cards with offers of free T-shirts or iPods.

26. A bank bills its credit card holders on the first of each month for each itemized billing. The card provides a 20-day period in which to pay the bill before charging interest. If the card holder wants to buy an expensive gift for a September 30 wedding but can't pay for it until November 5, explain how this can be done without adding an interest charge.

Group Exercises

27. Cellphone Plans

If credit cards can cause financial woes, cellphone plans are not far behind. Group members should present a report on cellphone plans, addressing each of the following questions: What are the monthly fees for these plans and what features are included? What happens if you use the phone more than the plan allows? Are there higher rates for texting and Internet access? What additional charges are imposed by the carrier on top of the monthly fee? What are the termination fees if you default on the plan? What can happen to your credit report and your credit score in the event of early termination? Does the carrier use free T-shirts, phones, and other items to entice new subscribers into binding contracts? What suggestions can the group offer to avoid financial difficulties with these plans?

28. Risky Credit Arrangements

Group members should present a report on the characteristics and financial risks associated with payday lending, tax refund loans, and pawn shops.

Chapter Summary, Review, and Test

SUMMARY – DEFINITIONS AND CONCEPTS	EXAMPLES
7.1 Percent, Sales Tax, and Discounts	
a. Percent means per hundred. Thus, $97\% = \frac{97}{100}$.	
b. To express a fraction as a percent, divide the numerator by the denominator, move the decimal point in the quotient two places to the right, and add a percent sign.	Ex. 1, p. 280
c. To express a decimal number as a percent, move the decimal point two places to the right and add a percent sign.	Ex. 2, p. 281
d. To express a percent as a decimal number, move the decimal point two places to the left and remove the percent sign.	Ex. 3, p. 281
e. The percent formula, $A = PB$, means A is P percent of B.	
f. Sales tax amount = tax rate × item's cost	Ex. 4, p. 282
g. Discount amount = discount rate × original price	Ex. 5, p. 282
h. The fraction for percent increase (or decrease) is $\dfrac{\text{amount of increase (or decrease)}}{\text{original amount}}$. Find the percent increase (or decrease) by expressing this fraction as a percent.	Ex. 6, p. 283; Ex. 7, p. 284; Ex. 8, p. 285; Ex. 9, p. 285
7.2 Income Tax	
a. Calculating Income Tax **1.** Determine adjusted gross income: Adjusted gross income = Gross income − Adjustments. **2.** Determine taxable income: Taxable income = Adjusted gross income − (Exemptions + Deductions). **3.** Determine the income tax: Income tax = Tax computation − Tax credits. See details in the box on page 292.	Ex. 1, p. 290; Ex. 2, p. 293
b. FICA taxes are used for Social Security and Medicare benefits. FICA tax rates are given in Table 7.2 on page 295.	Ex. 3, p. 295
c. Gross pay is your salary prior to any withheld taxes for a pay period. Net pay is the actual amount of your check after taxes have been withheld.	Ex. 4, p. 296
7.3 Simple Interest	
a. Interest is the amount of money that we get paid for lending or investing money, or that we pay for borrowing money. The amount deposited or borrowed is the principal. The charge for interest, given as a percent, is the rate, assumed to be per year.	
b. Simple interest involves interest calculated only on the principal and is computed using $I = Prt$.	Ex. 1, p. 300; Ex. 2, p. 301
c. The future value, A, of P dollars at simple interest rate r for t years is $A = P(1 + rt)$.	Ex. 3, p. 302; Ex. 4, p. 302; Ex. 5, p. 303; Ex. 6, p. 303
7.4 Compound Interest	
a. Compound interest involves interest computed on the original principal as well as on any accumulated interest. The amount in an account for one compounding period per year is $A = P(1 + r)^t$. For n compounding periods per year, the amount is $A = P\left(1 + \frac{r}{n}\right)^{nt}$. For continuous compounding, the amount is $A = Pe^{rt}$, where $e \approx 2.72$.	Ex. 1, p. 306; Ex. 2, p. 307; Ex. 3, p. 308

b. Calculating Present Value
If A dollars are to be accumulated in t years in an account that pays rate r compounded n times per year, then the present value, P, that needs to be invested now is given by

$$P = \frac{A}{\left(1 + \frac{r}{n}\right)^{nt}}.$$

Ex. 4, p. 309

c. Effective Annual Yield
Effective annual yield is defined in the box on page 310. The effective annual yield, Y, for an account that pays rate r compounded n times per year is given by

$$Y = \left(1 + \frac{r}{n}\right)^{n} - 1.$$

Ex. 5, p. 310; Ex. 6, p. 311

7.5 Annuities, Methods of Saving, and Investments

a. An annuity is a sequence of equal payments made at equal time periods. The value of an annuity is the sum of all deposits plus all interest paid.

Ex. 1, p. 316

b. The value of an annuity after t years is

$$A = \frac{P\left[\left(1 + \frac{r}{n}\right)^{nt} - 1\right]}{\left(\frac{r}{n}\right)},$$

where interest is compounded n times per year. See the box on page 318.

Ex. 2, p. 317; Ex. 3, p. 319

c. The formula

$$P = \frac{A\left(\frac{r}{n}\right)}{\left[\left(1 + \frac{r}{n}\right)^{nt} - 1\right]}$$

gives the deposit, P, into an annuity at the end of each compounding period needed to achieve a value of A dollars after t years. See the box on page 320.

Ex. 4, p. 320

d. The return on an investment is the percent increase in the investment.

e. Investors purchase stock, shares of ownership in a company. The shares indicate the percent of ownership. Trading refers to buying and selling stock. Investors make money by selling a stock for more money than they paid for it. They can also make money while they own stock if a company distributes all or part of its profits as dividends. Each share of stock is paid the same dividend.

f. Investors purchase a bond, lending money to the company from which they purchase the bond. The company commits itself to pay the price an investor pays for the bond at the time it was purchased, called its face value, along with interest payments at a given rate.

A listing of all the investments a person holds is called a financial portfolio. A portfolio with a mixture of low-risk and high-risk investments is called a diversified portfolio.

A mutual fund is a group of stocks and/or bonds managed by a professional investor, called the fund manager.

g. Reading stock tables is explained on pages 322–323.

Ex. 5, p. 324

h. Accounts designed for retirement savings include traditional IRAs (requires paying taxes when withdrawing money at age $59\frac{1}{2}$ or older), Roth IRAs (requires paying taxes on deposits, but not withdrawals/earnings at age $59\frac{1}{2}$ or older), and employer-sponsored plans, such as 401(k) and 403(b) plans.

Ex. 6, p. 326

7.6 Cars

a. A fixed installment loan is paid off with a series of equal periodic payments. A car loan is an example of a fixed installment loan.
Loan Payment Formula for Fixed Installment Loans

$$PMT = \frac{P\left(\frac{r}{n}\right)}{\left[1 - \left(1 + \frac{r}{n}\right)^{-nt}\right]}$$

PMT is the regular payment amount required to repay a loan of P dollars paid n times per year over t years at an annual interest rate r.

Ex. 1, p. 332; Ex. 2, p. 335

b. Leasing is a long-term rental agreement. Leasing a car offers some advantages over buying one (small down payment; lower monthly payments; no concerns about selling the car when the lease ends). Leasing also offers some disadvantages over buying (mileage penalties and other costs at the end of the leasing period often make the total cost of leasing more expensive than buying; penalties for ending the lease early; not owning the car when the lease ends; liability for damage to the car).

Auto insurance includes liability coverage: Bodily injury liability covers the costs of lawsuits if someone is injured or killed in an accident in which you are at fault. Property damage liability covers damage to other cars and property from negligent operation of your vehicle. If you have a car loan or lease a car, you also need collision coverage (pays for damage or loss of your car if you're in an accident) and comprehensive coverage (protects your car from fire, theft, and acts of nature).
The Cost of Gasoline

$$\text{Annual fuel expense} = \frac{\text{annual miles driven}}{\text{miles per gallon}} \times \text{price per gallon}$$

Ex. 3, p. 336

7.7 The Cost of Home Ownership

a. A mortgage is a long-term loan for the purpose of buying a home, and for which the property is pledged as security for payment. The term of the mortgage is the number of years until final payoff. The down payment is the portion of the sale price of the home that the buyer initially pays. The amount of the mortgage is the difference between the sale price and the down payment.

b. Fixed-rate mortgages have the same monthly payment during the entire time of the loan. Variable-rate mortgages, or adjustable-rate mortgages, have payment amounts that change from time to time depending on changes in the interest rate.

c. A point is a one-time charge that equals 1% of the amount of a mortgage loan.

d. The loan payment formula for fixed installment loans can be used to determine the monthly payment for a mortgage.

Ex. 1, p. 341

e. Amortizing a mortgage loan is the process of making regular payments on the principal and interest until the loan is paid off. A loan amortization schedule is a document showing the following information for each mortgage payment: the payment number, the interest paid from the payment, the amount of the payment applied to the principal, and the balance of the loan after the payment. Such a schedule shows how the buyer pays slightly less in interest and more in principal for each payment over the entire life of the loan.

Ex. 2, p. 343

f. Here are the guidelines for what you can spend for a mortgage:
- Spend no more than 28% of your gross monthly income for your mortgage payment.
- Spend no more than 36% of your gross monthly income for your total monthly debt.

Ex. 3, p. 345

g. Home ownership provides significant tax advantages, including deduction of mortgage interest and property taxes. Renting does not provide tax benefits, although renters do not pay property taxes.

7.8 Credit Cards

a. A fixed installment loan is paid off with a series of equal periodic payments. An open-end installment loan is paid off with variable monthly payments. Credit card loans are open-end installment loans.

Most credit cards calculate interest using the average daily balance method. Interest is calculated using $I = Prt$, where P is the average daily balance, r is the monthly rate, and t is one month.
Average daily balance

$$= \frac{\text{Sum of the unpaid balances for each day in the billing period}}{\text{Number of days in the billing period}}$$

The steps needed to determine the average daily balance are given in the box on page 352.

Ex. 1, p. 350

b. One advantage of using a credit card is that there are no interest charges by paying the balance due at the end of each billing period. A disadvantage is the high interest rate on unpaid balances. Failing to pay the bill in full each month can result in serious debt.

c. The difference between debit cards and credit cards is that debit cards are linked to your bank account. When you use a debit card, the money you spend is deducted electronically from your account balance.

d. Credit reports include details about all open or closed credit accounts, such as when each account was opened, the latest balance, and the payment history. They also contain bankruptcy information and information about unpaid accounts that were turned over to collection agencies. Credit scores range from 300 to 850, with a higher score indicating better credit.

PERSONAL FINANCE FORMULAS

Simple Interest

$$I = Prt$$
$$A = P(1 + rt)$$

Compound Interest

$$A = P\left(1 + \frac{r}{n}\right)^{nt}$$

$$P = \frac{A}{\left(1 + \frac{r}{n}\right)^{nt}}$$

$$Y = \left(1 + \frac{r}{n}\right)^{n} - 1$$

Annuities

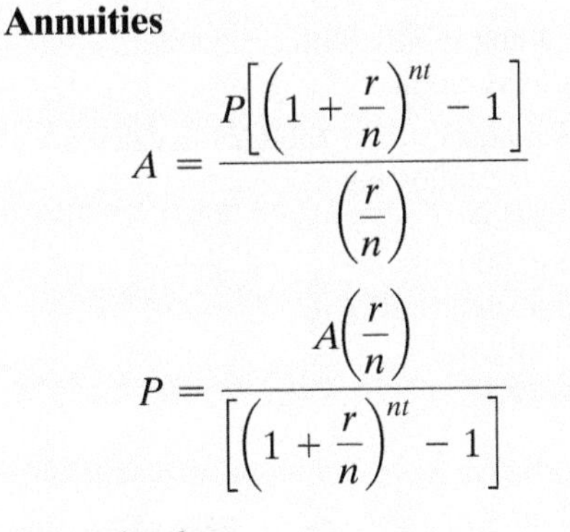

$$A = \frac{P\left[\left(1 + \frac{r}{n}\right)^{nt} - 1\right]}{\left(\frac{r}{n}\right)}$$

$$P = \frac{A\left(\frac{r}{n}\right)}{\left[\left(1 + \frac{r}{n}\right)^{nt} - 1\right]}$$

Amortization

$$PMT = \frac{P\left(\frac{r}{n}\right)}{\left[1 - \left(1 + \frac{r}{n}\right)^{-nt}\right]}$$

Be sure you understand what each formula in the box describes and the meaning of the variables in the formulas. Select the appropriate formula or formulas as you work the exercises in the Review Exercises and the Chapter 7 Test.

Review Exercises

7.1

In Exercises 1–3, express each fraction as a percent.

1. $\frac{4}{5}$ **2.** $\frac{1}{8}$ **3.** $\frac{3}{4}$

In Exercises 4–6, express each decimal as a percent.

4. 0.72 **5.** 0.0035 **6.** 4.756

In Exercises 7–12, express each percent as a decimal.

7. 65% **8.** 99.7% **9.** 150%

10. 3% **11.** 0.65% **12.** $\frac{1}{4}$%

13. What is 8% of 120?

14. Suppose that the local sales-tax rate is 6% and you purchase a backpack for $24.
a. How much tax is paid?
b. What is the backpack's total cost?

15. A television with an original price of $850 is on sale at 35% off.
a. What is the discount amount?
b. What is the television's sale price?

16. A college that had 40 students for each lecture course increased the number to 45 students. What is the percent increase in the number of students in a lecture course?

17. A dictionary regularly sells for $56.00. The sale price is $36.40. Find the percent decrease of the sale price from the regular price.

18. Consider the following statement:

> My investment portfolio fell 10% last year, but then it rose 10% this year, so at least I recouped my losses.

Is this statement true? In particular, suppose you invested $10,000 in the stock market last year. How much money would be left in your portfolio with a 10% fall and then a 10% rise? If there is a loss, what is the percent decrease, to the nearest tenth of a percent, in your portfolio?

7.2

In Exercises 19–20, find the gross income, the adjusted gross income, and the taxable income. In Exercise 20, base the taxable income on the greater of a standard deduction or an itemized deduction.

19. Your neighbor earned wages of $30,200, received $130 in interest from a savings account, and contributed $1100 to a tax-deferred retirement plan. He was entitled to a personal exemption of $3800 and had deductions totaling $5450.

20. Your neighbor earned wages of $86,400, won $350,000 on a television game show, and contributed $50,000 to a tax-deferred savings plan. She is entitled to a personal exemption of $3800 and a standard deduction of $5950. The interest on her home mortgage was $9200 and she contributed $95,000 to charity.

*In Exercises 21–22, use the 2012 marginal tax rates in **Table 7.1** on page 293 to compute the tax owed by each person or couple.*

21. A single woman with a taxable income of \$600,000

22. A married couple filing jointly with a taxable income of \$82,000 and a \$7500 tax credit

23. Use the 2012 marginal tax rates in **Table 7.1** to calculate the income tax owed by the following person:
- Single, no dependents
- Gross income: \$40,000
- \$2500 paid to a tax-deferred IRA
- \$6500 mortgage interest
- \$1800 property taxes
- No tax credits

*Use the 2012 FICA tax rates in **Table 7.2** on page 295 to solve Exercises 24–25.*

24. If you are not self-employed and earn \$86,000, what are your FICA taxes?

25. If you are self-employed and earn \$260,000, what are your FICA taxes?

26. You decide to work part-time at a local clothing store. The job pays \$8.50 per hour and you work 16 hours per week. Your employer withholds 10% of your gross pay for federal taxes, 5.65% for FICA taxes, and 4% for state taxes.
a. What is your weekly gross pay?
b. How much is withheld per week for federal taxes?
c. How much is withheld per week for FICA taxes?
d. How much is withheld per week for state taxes?
e. What is your weekly net pay?
f. What percentage of your gross pay is withheld for taxes? Round to the nearest tenth of a percent.

7.3

In Exercises 27–30, find the simple interest. (Assume 360 days in a year.)

	Principal	Rate	Time
27.	\$6000	3%	1 year
28.	\$8400	5%	6 years
29.	\$20,000	8%	9 months
30.	\$36,000	15%	60 days

31. In order to pay for tuition and books, a college student borrows \$3500 for four months at 10.5% interest.
a. How much interest must the student pay?
b. Find the future value of the loan.

In Exercises 32–34, use the formula for future value with simple interest to find the missing quantity. Round dollar amounts to the nearest cent and rates to the nearest tenth of a percent.

32. $A = ?, P = \$12{,}000, r = 8.2\%, t = 9$ months

33. $A = \$5750, P = \$5000, r = ?, t = 2$ years

34. $A = \$16{,}000, P = ?, r = 6.5\%, t = 3$ years

35. You plan to buy a \$12,000 sailboat in four years. How much should you invest now, at 7.3% simple interest, to have enough for the boat in four years? (Round up to the nearest cent.)

36. You borrow \$1500 from a friend and promise to pay back \$1800 in six months. What simple interest rate will you pay?

7.4

In Exercises 37–39, the principal represents an amount of money deposited in a savings account that provides the lender compound interest at the given rate.

a. *Find how much money, to the nearest cent, there will be in the account after the given number of years.*
b. *Find the interest earned.*

	Principal	Rate	Compounding Periods per Year	Time
37.	\$7000	3%	1	5 years
38.	\$30,000	2.5%	4	10 years
39.	\$2500	4%	12	20 years

40. Suppose that you have \$14,000 to invest. Which investment yields the greater return over 10 years: 7% compounded monthly or 6.85% compounded continuously? How much more (to the nearest dollar) is yielded by the better investment?

In Exercises 41–42, round answers up to the nearest cent.

41. How much money should parents deposit today in an account that earns 7% compounded monthly so that it will accumulate to \$100,000 in 18 years for their child's college education?

42. How much money should be deposited today in an account that earns 5% compounded quarterly so that it will accumulate to \$75,000 in 35 years for retirement?

43. You deposit \$2000 in an account that pays 6% interest compounded quarterly.
a. Find the future value, to the nearest cent, after one year.
b. Use the future value formula for simple interest to determine the effective annual yield. Round to the nearest tenth of a percent.

44. What is the effective annual yield, to the nearest hundredth of a percent, of an account paying 5.5% compounded quarterly? What does your answer mean?

45. Which investment is the better choice: 6.25% compounded monthly or 6.3% compounded annually?

7.5

In Exercises 46–48, round the value of each annuity to the nearest dollar.

46. A person who does not understand probability theory wastes \$10 per week on lottery tickets, averaging \$520 per year. Instead of buying tickets, if this person deposits the \$520 at the end of each year in an annuity paying 6% compounded annually,
a. How much would he or she have after 20 years?
b. Find the interest.

47. To save for retirement, you decide to deposit \$100 at the end of each month in an IRA that pays 5.5% compounded monthly.
a. How much will you have from the IRA after 30 years?
b. Find the interest.

48. Suppose that you would like to have $25,000 to use as a down payment for a home in five years by making regular deposits at the end of every three months in an annuity that pays 7.25% compounded quarterly.
a. Determine the amount of each deposit. Round up to the nearest dollar.
b. How much of the $25,000 comes from deposits and how much comes from interest?

For Exercises 49–56, refer to the stock table for Harley Davidson (the motorcycle company). Where necessary, round dollar amounts to the nearest cent.

52-Week High	52-Week Low	Stock	SYM	Div	Yld %	PE
64.06	26.13	Harley Dav	HOG	.16	.3	41

Vol 100s	Hi	Lo	Close	Net Chg
5458	61.25	59.25	61	+1.75

49. What were the high and low prices for a share for the past 52 weeks?

50. If you owned 900 shares of this stock last year, what dividend did you receive?

51. What is the annual return for the dividends alone?

52. How many shares of this company's stock were traded yesterday?

53. What were the high and low prices for a share yesterday?

54. What was the price at which a share last traded when the stock exchange closed yesterday?

55. What was the change in price for a share of stock from the market close two days ago to yesterday's market close?

56. Compute the company's annual earnings per share using

$$\frac{\text{Yesterday's closing price per share}}{\text{PE ratio}}.$$

57. Explain the difference between investing in a stock and investing in a bond.

58. What is the difference between tax benefits for a traditional IRA and a Roth IRA?

7.6

59. Suppose that you decide to take a $15,000 loan for a new car. You can select one of the following loans, each requiring regular monthly payments:
Loan A: three-year loan at 7.2%
Loan B: five-year loan at 8.1%.
a. Find the monthly payments and the total interest for Loan A.
b. Find the monthly payments and the total interest for Loan B.
c. Compare the monthly payments and interest for the longer-term loan to the monthly payments and interest for the shorter-term loan.

60. Describe two advantages of leasing a car.

61. Describe two disadvantages of leasing a car.

62. Two components of auto insurance are property damage liability and collision. What is the difference between these types of coverage?

63. Suppose that you drive 36,000 miles per year and gas averages $3.60 per gallon.
a. What will you save in annual fuel expenses by owning a hybrid car averaging 40 miles per gallon rather than an SUV averaging 12 miles per gallon?
b. If you deposit your monthly fuel savings at the end of each month into an annuity that pays 5.2% compounded monthly, how much will you have saved at the end of six years? Round all computations to the nearest dollar.

7.7

In Exercises 64–66, round to the nearest dollar.

64. The price of a home is $240,000. The bank requires a 20% down payment and two points at the time of closing. The cost of the home is financed with a 30-year fixed-rate mortgage at 7%.
a. Find the required down payment.
b. Find the amount of the mortgage.
c. How much must be paid for the two points at closing?
d. Find the monthly payment (excluding escrowed taxes and insurance).
e. Find the total cost of interest over 30 years.

65. In terms of paying less in interest, which is more economical for a $70,000 mortgage: a 30-year fixed-rate at 8.5% or a 20-year fixed-rate at 8%? How much is saved in interest? Discuss one advantage and one disadvantage for each mortgage option.

66. Suppose that you need a loan of $100,000 to buy a home. Here are your options:
Option A: 30-year fixed-rate at 8.5% with no closing costs and no points
Option B: 30-year fixed-rate at 7.5% with closing costs of $1300 and three points.
a. Determine your monthly payments for each option and discuss how you would decide between the two options.
b. Which mortgage loan has the greater total cost (closing costs + the amount paid for points + total cost of interest)? By how much?

67. The cost of a home is financed with a $300,000 30-year fixed rate mortgage at 6.5%.
a. Find the monthly payments, rounded to the nearest dollar, for the loan.
b. Prepare a loan amortization schedule for the first three months of the mortgage. Round entries to the nearest cent.

Payment Number	Interest	Principal	Loan Balance
1			
2			
3			

68. Use these guidelines to solve this exercise: Spend no more than 28% of your gross monthly income for your mortgage payment and no more than 36% for your total monthly debt. Round all computations to the nearest dollar. Suppose that your gross annual income is $54,000.

a. What is the maximum amount you should spend each month on a mortgage payment?

b. What is the maximum amount you should spend each month for total credit obligations?

c. If your monthly mortgage payment is 80% of the maximum amount you can afford, what is the maximum amount you should spend each month for all other debt?

69. Describe three benefits of renting over home ownership.

70. Describe three benefits of home ownership over renting.

7.8

71. A credit card issuer calculates interest using the average daily balance method. The monthly interest rate is 1.1% of the average daily balance. The following transactions occurred during the November 1–November 30 billing period.

Transaction Description		Transaction Amount
Previous balance, $4620.80		
November 1	Billing date	
November 7	Payment	$650.00 credit
November 11	Charge: Airline Tickets	$350.25
November 25	Charge: Groceries	$125.70
November 28	Charge: Gas	$ 38.25
November 30	End of billing period	
Payment Due Date: December 9		

a. Find the average daily balance for the billing period. Round to the nearest cent.

b. Find the interest to be paid on December 1, the next billing date. Round to the nearest cent.

c. Find the balance due on December 1.

d. This credit card requires a $10 minimum monthly payment if the balance due at the end of the billing period is less than $360. Otherwise, the minimum monthly payment is $\frac{1}{36}$ of the balance due at the end of the billing period, rounded up to the nearest whole dollar. What is the minimum monthly payment due by December 9?

72. In 2012, the average credit-card debt was $15,374. Suppose your card has this balance and an annual interest rate of 18%. You decide to pay off the balance over two years. If there are no further purchases charged to the card,

a. How much must you pay each month?

b. How much total interest will you pay?

Round answers to the nearest dollar.

73. Describe two advantages of using credit cards.

74. Describe two disadvantages of using credit cards.

75. How does a debit card differ from a credit card?

76. Is a credit report the same thing as a credit score? If not, what is the difference?

77. Describe two ways to demonstrate that you can handle the responsibility of using a credit card.

Chapter 7 Test

The box on page 361 summarizes the finance formulas you have worked with throughout the chapter. Where applicable, use the appropriate formula to solve an exercise in this test. Unless otherwise stated, round dollar amounts to the nearest cent and rates to the nearest tenth of a percent.

1. A CD player with an original price of $120 is on sale at 15% off.

a. What is the amount of the discount?

b. What is the sale price of the CD player?

2. You purchased shares of stock for $2000 and sold them for $3500. Find the percent increase, or your return, on this investment.

3. You earned wages of $46,500, received $790 in interest from a savings account, and contributed $1100 to a tax-deferred savings plan. You are entitled to a personal exemption of $3800 and a standard deduction of $5950. The interest on your home mortgage was $7300, you contributed $350 to charity, and you paid $1395 in state taxes.

a. Find your gross income.

b. Find your adjusted gross income.

c. Find your taxable income. Base your taxable income on the greater of the standard deduction or an itemized deduction.

4. Use the 2012 marginal tax rates in **Table 7.1** on page 293 to calculate the federal income tax owed by the following person:

- Single, no dependents
- Gross income: $36,500
- $2000 paid to a tax-deferred IRA
- $4700 mortgage interest
- $1300 property taxes
- No tax credits

5. Use FICA tax rates for people who are not self-employed, 5.65% on the first $110,000 of income and 1.45% on income in excess of $110,000, to answer this question: If a person is not self-employed and earns $150,000, what are that person's FICA taxes?

6. You decide to work part-time at a local stationery store. The job pays $10 per hour and you work 15 hours per week. Your employer withholds 10% of your gross pay for federal taxes, 5.65% for FICA taxes, and 3% for state taxes.
   a. What is your weekly gross pay?
   b. How much is withheld per week for federal taxes?
   c. How much is withheld per week for FICA taxes?
   d. How much is withheld per week for state taxes?
   e. What is your weekly net pay?
   f. What percentage of your gross pay is withheld for taxes? Round to the nearest tenth of a percent.
7. You borrow $2400 for three months at 12% simple interest. Find the amount of interest paid and the future value of the loan.
8. You borrow $2000 from a friend and promise to pay back $3000 in two years. What simple interest rate will you pay?
9. In six months, you want to have $7000 worth of remodeling done to your home. How much should you invest now, at 9% simple interest, to have enough money for the project? (Round up to the nearest cent.)
10. Find the effective annual yield, to the nearest hundredth of a percent, of an account paying 4.5% compounded quarterly. What does your answer mean?
11. You receive an inheritance of $20,000 and invest it in an account that pays 6.5% compounded monthly.
    a. How much, to the nearest dollar, will you have after 40 years?
    b. Find the interest.
12. You would like to have $3000 in four years for a special vacation by making a lump-sum investment in an account that pays 9.5% compounded semiannually. How much should you deposit now? Round up to the nearest dollar.
13. Suppose that you save money for a down payment to buy a home in five years by depositing $6000 in an account that pays 6.5% compounded monthly.
    a. How much, to the nearest dollar, will you have as a down payment after five years?
    b. Find the interest.
14. Instead of making the lump-sum deposit of $6000 described in Exercise 13, suppose that you decide to deposit $100 at the end of each month in an annuity that pays 6.5% compounded monthly.
    a. How much, to the nearest dollar, will you have as a down payment after five years?
    b. Find the interest.
    c. Why is less interest earned from this annuity than from the lump-sum deposit in Exercise 13? With less interest earned, why would one select the annuity rather than the lump-sum deposit?
15. Suppose that you want to retire in 40 years. How much should you deposit at the end of each month in an IRA that pays 6.25% compounded monthly to have $1,500,000 in 40 years? Round up to the nearest dollar. How much of the $1.5 million comes from interest?

Use the stock table for AT&T to solve Exercises 16–18.

52-Week High	52-Week Low	Stock	SYM	Div	Yld %	PE
26.50	24.25	AT&T	PNS	2.03	7.9	18

Vol 100s	Hi	Lo	Close	Net Chg
961	25.75	25.50	25.75	+0.13

16. What were the high and low prices for a share yesterday?
17. If you owned 1000 shares of this stock last year, what dividend did you receive?
18. Suppose that you bought 600 shares of AT&T, paying the price per share at which a share traded when the stock exchange closed yesterday. If the broker charges 2.5% of the price paid for all 600 shares, find the broker's commission.
19. Suppose that you drive 30,000 miles per year and gas averages $3.80 per gallon. What will you save in annual fuel expense by owning a hybrid car averaging 50 miles per gallon rather than a pickup truck averaging 15 miles per gallon?

Use this information to solve Exercises 20–25. The price of a home is $120,000. The bank requires a 10% down payment and two points at the time of closing. The cost of the home is financed with a 30-year fixed-rate mortgage at 8.5%.

20. Find the required down payment.
21. Find the amount of the mortgage.
22. How much must be paid for the two points at closing?
23. Find the monthly payment (excluding escrowed taxes and insurance). Round to the nearest dollar.
24. Find the total cost of interest over 30 years.
25. Prepare a loan amortization schedule for the first two months of the mortgage. Round entries to the nearest cent.

Payment Number	Interest	Principal	Loan Balance
1			
2			

26. Use these guidelines to solve this exercise. Spend no more than 28% of your gross monthly income for your mortgage payment and no more than 36% for your total monthly debt. Round all computations to the nearest dollar. Suppose that your gross annual income is $66,000.
    a. What is the maximum amount you should spend each month on a mortgage payment?
    b. What is the maximum amount you should spend each month for total credit obligations?
    c. If your monthly mortgage payment is 90% of the maximum amount you can afford, what is the maximum amount you should spend each month for all other debt?

27. A credit card issuer calculates interest using the average daily balance method. The monthly interest rate is 2% of the average daily balance. The following transactions occurred during the September 1–September 30 billing period.

Transaction Description		Transaction Amount
Previous balance, $3800.00		
September 1	Billing date	
September 5	Payment	$800.00 credit
September 9	Charge: Gas	$ 40.00
September 19	Charge: Clothing	$160.00
September 27	Charge: Airline Ticket	$200.00
September 30	End of billing period	
Payment Due Date: October 9		

a. Find the average daily balance for the billing period. Round to the nearest cent.
b. Find the interest to be paid on October 1, the next billing date. Round to the nearest cent.
c. Find the balance due on October 1.
d. Terms for the credit card require a $10 minimum monthly payment if the balance due is less than $360. Otherwise, the minimum monthly payment is $\frac{1}{36}$ of the balance due, rounded up to the nearest whole dollar. What is the minimum monthly payment due by October 9?

In Exercises 28–34, determine whether each statement is true or false. If the statement is false, make the necessary change(s) to produce a true statement.

28. By buying bonds, you purchase shares of ownership in a company.

29. A traditional IRA requires paying taxes when withdrawing money from the account at age $59\frac{1}{2}$ or older.

30. One advantage to leasing a car is that there are no penalties for ending the lease early.

31. If you cause an accident, collision coverage pays for damage to the other car.

32. Home ownership provides significant tax advantages, including deduction of mortgage interest.

33. Money spent using a credit card is deducted electronically from your bank account.

34. Credit scores range from 100 to 1000, with a higher score indicating better credit.

Answers to Previews

Answers to Preview 2

1. (a) 5:2 or 2:5 (b) $8\frac{2}{3}$ to 1
2. (a) $x = 10$ (b) $y = 14.3$
3. (a) 64 ounces (b) 18 ft (c) 12 machines

Answers to Preview 5

1. (a) 70 (b) 27% (c) 65 in May (d) 40% (e) $40.95
2. (a)

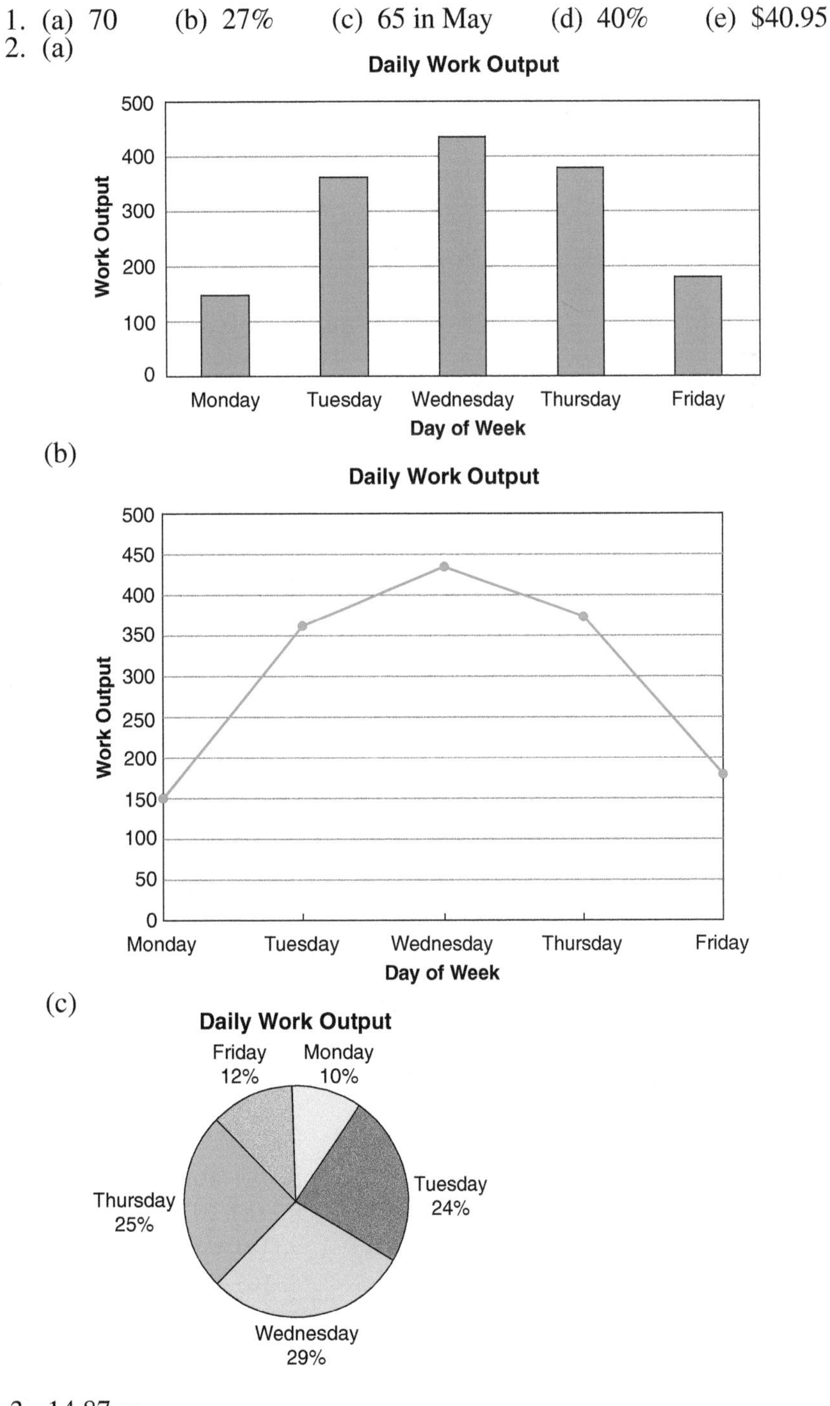

3. 14.87 m

Answers to Odd-Numbered Problems

Chapter 2

Exercises 2-1, page 60

A. (In each case only the missing answer is given.)

1. (a) 7:1 (b) 12:7 (c) 6 (d) 6 (e) 45 (f) 9 (g) 16 (h) 50 (i) 3:2 (j) 2:5
3. (a) 16:12 (b) 8 ft (c) 28 ft (d) 6.88:12 (e) 7.2:12 (f) 4 ft (g) 20 ft (h) 5 ft 1 in.

B. 1. $x = 12$ 3. $y = 100$ 5. $P = \frac{7}{6}$ 7. $A = 3.25$ 9. $T = 1.8$ 11. $x = 3$ 13. $x = 5.04$ 15. $L = 5$ ft 17. $x = 4$ cm

C. 1. 5 cu in. 3. 21 pins 5. 5.25 cu yd 7. 288.75 gal 9. 124.8 lb 11. \$856 13. 375 ft 15. 37.9 lb 17. 12.9 mL 19. 40,000 cal 21. 132 lb 23. 24 lb 25. (a) 0.5 mL (b) 0.33 mL (c) 6.67 mL 27. (a) 2 (b) $1\frac{1}{2}$ (c) $4\frac{1}{2}$ 29. 7500 bu 31. \$15,636 33. \$3856 35. 6

Exercises 2-2, page 73

A. 1. (a) $\frac{5}{8}$ in. (b) 31.2 cm (c) 8 ft (d) 3 m
3. (a) 100 (b) 9 (c) 25 (d) 1500

B. 1. 24 in. 3. 139 hp 5. 109.1 lb 7. 980 rpm 9. (a) 5310 sq ft (b) 8800 sq ft 11. 500 rpm 13. 6 hr 15. 1470 ft 17. 0.96 sq in. 19. 4 in. 21. 22.4 psi 23. \$377.54 25. 14.4 hr, rounded 27. (a) 6 in. (b) 8 to 3 29. 458 lb 31. 16

Problem Set 2, page 78

A. 1. (a) 30 in. (b) 5 to 2 (c) 25 in.

B. 1. $x = 35$ 3. $x = 20$ 5. $x = 14.3$

C. 1. 72% 3. 60% 5. 130% 7. 400% 9. $16\frac{2}{3}$%

D. 1. 0.04 3. 0.11 5. 0.0125 7. 0.002 9. 0.03875 11. 1.15

E. 1. $\frac{7}{25}$ 3. $\frac{81}{100}$ 5. $\frac{1}{200}$ 7. $\frac{7}{50}$

F. 1. 60% 3. 5.6 5. 42 7. \$28.97 9. 8000

G. 1. 29.92 in. 3. (a) \$6977.25 (b) \$598.50 (c) \$1699 5. (a) \$20.13 (b) \$18.54 (c) 73¢ (d) \$125.72 (e) \$148.39 7. 1748 ft 9. (a) 0.06% (b) 2.82% (c) ± 0.009 in. (d) 0.03% (e) ± 0.62 mm

11. \$7216.25 13. ± 135 ohms; 4365 to 4635 ohms 15. 0.9% 17. 72% 19. 9.12 hp 21. 3.6% 23. (a) 66 fps (b) 15 mph 25. $5\frac{1}{4}$ in. 27. 150 seconds or $2\frac{1}{2}$ minutes

29. 450 parts 31. $3\frac{3}{4}$ hr 33. 6 sacks
35. 960 lb 37. 1.47 amperes 39. $673.98
41. 35 employees 43. 83.96 psi 45. 158 hp
47. $368,600 49. Yes (13%) 51. 74
53. (a) 12 mL (b) 6 mL (c) 0.8 mL
55. (a) 17.65% (b) 460% 57. 34% 59. 55.1%

61. Small: $5875; Medium: $14,125; Large: $12,000; Extra Large: $8000

63. 700,000 ppm 65. 64 mL

Chapter 5 *Exercises 5-1, page 194*

A. 1. (a) 2005 (b) 2009 (c) approximately 330,000
(d) 200,000 (e) 300% (f) 22%
3. (a) 9 Btu/Wh (b) the mid-range model
(c) approximately 65% (d) approximately 16% (from 9.5 to 11)
5. (a) 45 (b) 172 (c) 50% (d) 258
7. (a) 2008; 800,000 (b) any two of these: 1996, 1998, 2001, 2002, 2003, 2005
(c) lowest: 1991, highest: 2005 (d) approximately 4,000,000
(e) approximately 82% (f) 41%
9. (a) tuition (b) lab fee (c) $850 (d) $540

B. 1.

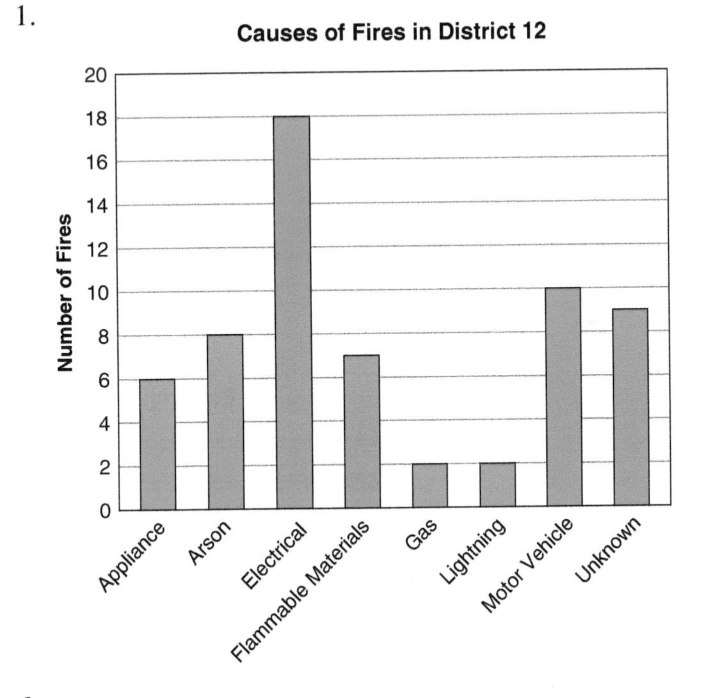

3.

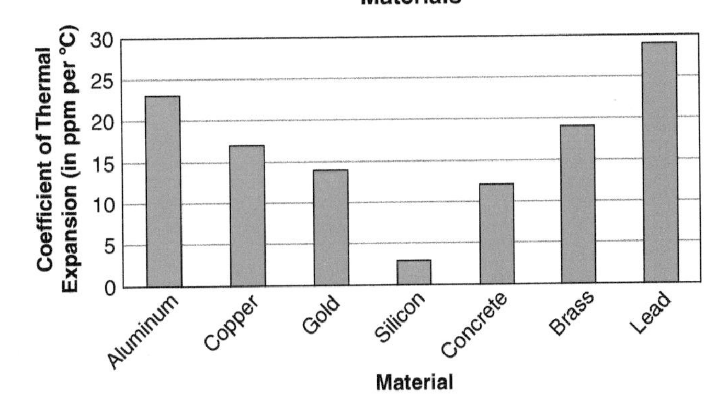

5.

Yearly Sales of Construction Material for
CASH IS US
Wood
Masonry
Amount (in Thousand Dollars)
$450
$400
$350
$300
$250
$200
$150
$100
$ 50
$ 0
2008
2009
2010
2011
2012
2013
Year

7.

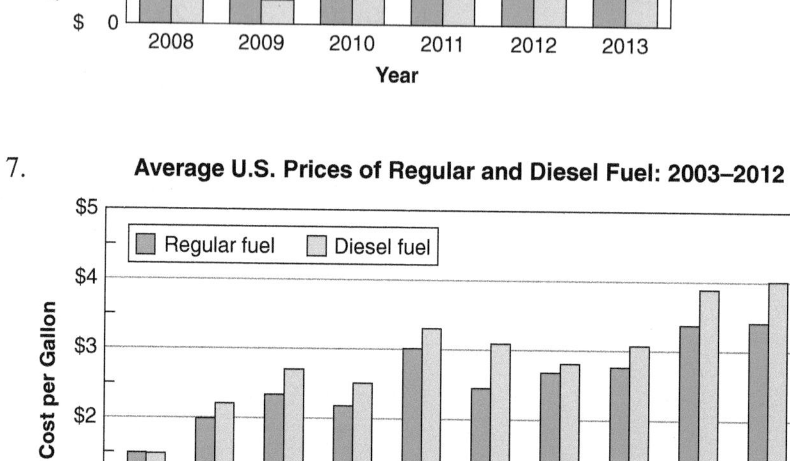
Average U.S. Prices of Regular and Diesel Fuel: 2003–2012
Regular fuel
Diesel fuel
Cost per Gallon
$5
$4
$3
$2
$1
$0
2003
2004
2005
2006
2007
2008
2009
2010
2011
2012
Year

9.

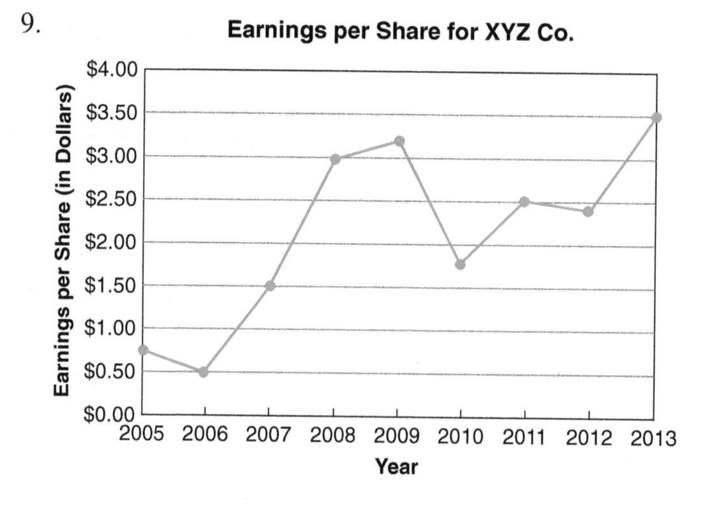
Earnings per Share for XYZ Co.
Earnings per Share (in Dollars)
$4.00
$3.50
$3.00
$2.50
$2.00
$1.50
$1.00
$0.50
$0.00
2005
2006
2007
2008
2009
2010
2011
2012
2013
Year

11.

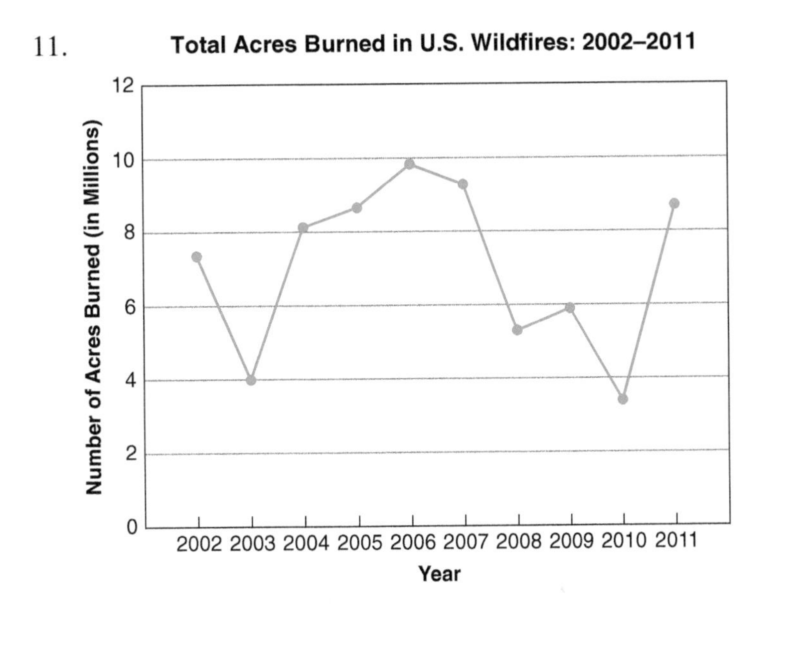
Total Acres Burned in U.S. Wildfires: 2002–2011
Number of Acres Burned (in Millions)
0
2
4
6
8
10
12
2002 2003 2004 2005 2006 2007 2008 2009 2010 2011
Year

13.

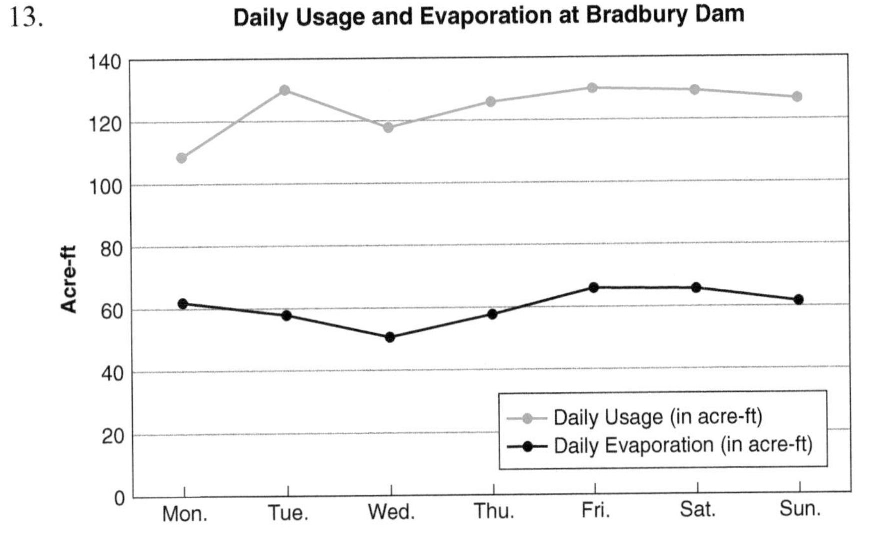
Daily Usage and Evaporation at Bradbury Dam
Acre-ft
0
20
40
60
80
100
120
140
Mon. Tue. Wed. Thu. Fri. Sat. Sun.
Daily Usage (in acre-ft)
Daily Evaporation (in acre-ft)

15.

California's In-State Sources of Electricity

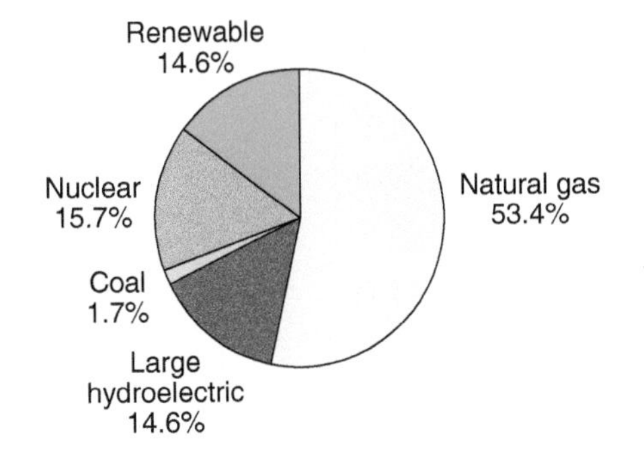
Renewable
14.6%
Nuclear
15.7%
Coal
1.7%
Large
hydroelectric
14.6%
Natural gas
53.4%

17.

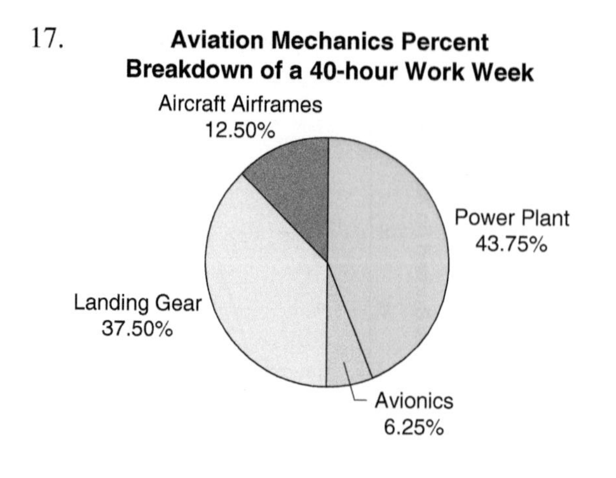
Aviation Mechanics Percent
Breakdown of a 40-hour Work Week
Aircraft Airframes
12.50%
Power Plant
43.75%
Landing Gear
37.50%
Avionics
6.25%

Answers to Selected Exercises

CHAPTER 1

Section 1.1

Check Point Exercises

1. Answers will vary; an example is $40 \times 40 = 1600$. **2. a.** Each number in the list is obtained by adding 6 to the previous number.; 33 **b.** Each number in the list is obtained by multiplying the previous number by 5.; 1250 **c.** To get the second number, multiply the previous number by 2. Then multiply by 3 and then by 4. Then multiply by 2, then by 3, and then by 4, repeatedly.; 3456 **d.** To get the second number, add 8 to the previous number. Then add 8 and then subtract 14. Then add 8, then add 8, and then subtract 14, repeatedly.; 7 **3. a.** Starting with the third number, each number is the sum of the previous two numbers.; 76 **b.** Starting with the second number, each number is one less than twice the previous number.; 257

4. The figures alternate between rectangles and triangles, and the number of appendages follows the pattern: one, two, three, one, two, three, etc.;

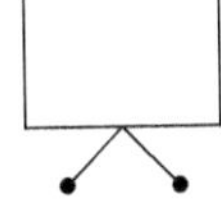

5. a. The result of the process is two times the original number selected.
b. Using n to represent the original number, we have

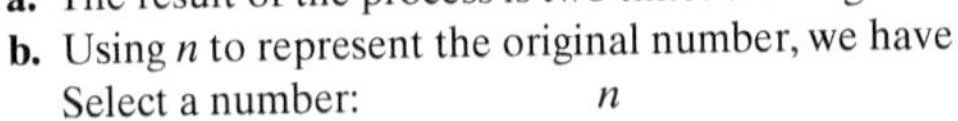

Select a number: n
Multiply the number by 4: $4n$
Add 6 to the product: $4n + 6$
Divide this sum by 2: $\frac{4n + 6}{2} = 2n + 3$
Subtract 3 from the quotient: $2n + 3 - 3 = 2n$.

Blitzer Bonus: Are You Smart Enough to Work at Google?

1. SSSS **2.** 3 1 2 2 1 1

Concept and Vocabulary Check

1. counterexample **2.** deductive **3.** inductive **4.** true

Exercise Set 1.1

1. Answers will vary; an example is: Barack Obama was younger than 65 at the time of his inauguration. **3.** Answers will vary; an example is: 3 multiplied by itself is 9, which is not even.
5. Answers will vary; an example is: Adding 1 to the numerator and denominator of $\frac{1}{2}$ results in $\frac{2}{3}$, which is not equal to $\frac{1}{2}$.
7. Answers will vary; an example is: When -1 is added to itself, the result is -2, which is less than -1. **9.** Each number in the list is obtained by adding 4 to the previous number.; 28 **11.** Each number in the list is obtained by subtracting 5 from the previous number.; 12 **13.** Each number in the list is obtained by multiplying the previous number by 3.; 729 **15.** Each number in the list is obtained by multiplying the previous number by 2.; 32 **17.** The numbers in the list alternate between 1 and numbers obtained by multiplying the number prior to the previous number by 2.; 32
19. Each number in the list is obtained by subtracting 2 from the previous number.; -6
21. Each number in the list is obtained by adding 4 to the denominator of the previous fraction.; $\frac{1}{22}$
23. Each number in the list is obtained by multiplying the previous number by $\frac{1}{3}$.; $\frac{1}{81}$
25. The second number is obtained by adding 4 to the first number. The third number is obtained by adding 5 to the second number. The number being added to the previous number increases by 1 each time.; 42 **27.** The second number is obtained by adding 3 to the first number. The third number is obtained by adding 5 to the second number. The number being added to the previous number increases by 2 each time.; 51 **29.** Starting with the third number, each number is the sum of the previous two numbers.; 71 **31.** To get the second number, add 5 to the previous number. Then add 5 and then subtract 7. Then add 5, then add 5, and then subtract 7, repeatedly.; 18 **33.** The second number is obtained by multiplying the first number by 2. The third number is obtained by subtracting 1 from the second number. Then multiply by 2 and then subtract 1, repeatedly.; 33
35. Each number in the list is obtained by multiplying the previous number by $-\frac{1}{4}$.; $\frac{1}{4}$
37. For each pair in the list, the second number is obtained by subtracting 4 from the first number.; -1
39. The pattern is: square, triangle, circle, square, triangle, circle, etc.;

41. Each figure contains the letter of the alphabet following the letter in the previous figure with one more occurrence than in the previous figure.;

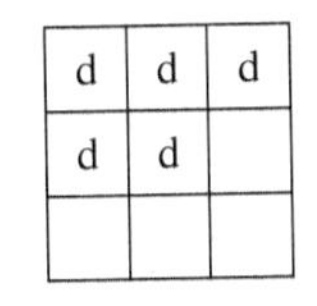

43. a. The result of the process is two times the original number selected.
b. Using n to represent the original number, we have
Select a number: n
Multiply the number by 4: $4n$
Add 8 to the product: $4n + 8$
Divide this sum by 2: $\frac{4n + 8}{2} = 2n + 4$
Subtract 4 from the quotient: $2n + 4 - 4 = 2n$.

45. a. The result of the process is 3.
b. Using n to represent the original number as we have
Select a number: n
Add 5: $n + 5$
Double the result: $2(n + 5) = 2n + 10$
Subtract 4: $2n + 10 - 4 = 2n + 6$
Divide by 2: $\frac{2n + 6}{2} = n + 3$
Subtract n: $n + 3 - n = 3$.